CURIOUS & CURIOUSER

Burping Cows, Bending Spoons, Beer Goggles
& other scintillating scientific stories...

Dr Karl Kruszelnicki

MACMILLAN

First published 2010 in Macmillan by Pan Macmillan Australia Pty Limited
1 Market Street, Sydney

National Library of Australia Cataloguing-in-Publication data:

Kruszelnicki, Karl, 1948–

Curious and curiouser / Karl Kruszelnicki.

9781405040020 (hbk.)

Science –Popular works.
Science – Miscellanea.

500

Designed and typeset in Adobe Caslon Pro by Xou Creative, www.xou.com.au
Internal illustrations by Douglas Holgate
Printed in Australia by McPherson's Printing Group

Papers used by Pan Macmillan Australia Pty Ltd are natural, recyclable products made from wood grown in sustainable forests. The manufacturing processes conform to the environmental regulations of the country of origin.

I dedicate this book to The Last Minute,
without which nothing would ever get done

CONTENTS

Scientific research is always pushing forward the frontiers of our knowledge. Sometimes this research deals with obscure stuff that probably won't help the human race for decades or centuries. But sometimes the research deals directly with stuff that's important to us, right now. And what could be more important, or immediately useful, than finding out whether drinking alcohol really does make people of the opposite sex appear more attractive?

Science of Attraction

Professor Barry T. Jones from the Department of Psychology at the University of Glasgow and his colleagues carried out a study on this very topic. They gave their paper the catchy title of "Alcohol consumption increases attractiveness ratings of opposite-sex faces: A possible third route to risky sex". (There's always a catch …)

The *"risky sex"* part of the title refers to indiscriminate and/or unprotected sex. This can lead to unplanned pregnancies and sexually transmitted infections (including HIV/AIDS).

But it's a medical paper. So they can't just cut to the chase and title their paper "risky sex". Nope, they have to add other distracting phrases like *"a possible third route to risky sex"*. Their proposed Third Theory tries to explain the link between *"alcohol consumption"* and *"risky sex"*.

This, of course, implies that there are already at *least* two other theories that try to explain this.

STRENGTH OF BEER

Low-alcohol beer contains around 1 to 2 per cent alcohol. On average, beer is about 5 per cent alcohol (the remaining 95 per cent is practically all water). It's not too difficult to get a few per cent higher more alcoholic. But at around 12 per cent, the alcohol actually kills the regular yeast that turns sugar into alcohol. However, brewers have been able to achieve 20 per cent alcohol content by using special champagne yeast. By using freeze-distillation, it is possible to get beers of around 40 per cent alcohol.

Theories of "Risky Sex" and Alcohol

The first theory is called "Alcohol Myopia". This theory claims that alcohol can temporarily blind your "logical" brain – but only in a few areas. In plain English, this theory claims that alcohol will make you pay attention only to "interesting" stuff like sexual arousal – and ignore other "stuff". This other "stuff" includes the potential negative results that might happen during or after drunken sex – premature ejaculation, poor performance, falling asleep on the job, pregnancy, disease, broken friendships, and so forth.

ANCIENT BEER AND BEERSTONE

We humans have been drinking beer for at least 5500 years. Virginia Badler, a graduate student at the University of Toronto, examined a crude antique jug from Godin Tepe in western Iran. The inside of this jug was crisscrossed with deep grooves. She found calcium oxalate in these grooves. This chemical is also called beerstone, because it precipitates out of beer. Even today, we still find beerstone in the bottoms of beer vats.

The second theory is the "Alcohol Expectancy" theory. It says that in our society we have learnt, either directly or indirectly, a whole bunch of things about alcohol consumption. And so, many of us might expect that if we have a lot of alcohol, our sexual experiences will be much better.

Professor Jones's paper investigated a third route that might link alcohol consumption to risky sex. It examined whether alcohol makes your potential sexual partner appear more attractive. From an evolutionary point of view, "attractiveness" suggests that you have good genes and a healthy body. And way back in 1966, Dr Walster had shown *that for both men and women the best predictor of satisfaction on a blind date is facial attractiveness*.

Maybe people shouldn't choose their sexual partners based on the way they look. However, most social interaction happens face to face, so if they look attractive to each other, then ...

ANCIENT MIXED DRINKS

Three thousand years ago, the Minoans from Crete and the Greeks on the nearby mainland drank crazy cocktails of beer, wine and mead.

Ancient pottery gave us the clue as to what they filled their raised glasses with. Scientists have analysed the dried-out remnants of various liquids that soaked into the tiny pores of their pottery. Tartaric acid is abundant in grapes, and so it appeared in the pores. Chemicals present in honey and beeswax tell us they drank mead. And beerstone tells us they drank beer.

But how do we know that they mixed their drinks together, as opposed to having the different drinks one after the other in the same cup? Because so many pottery cups have the same chemicals in the same ratio.

King Midas (the guy who loved gold) also loved a cocktail. Scientists think that they have found his tomb at Gordian in central Turkey. This tomb is the oldest known intact wooden structure in the world, some 2700 years old. A male body, some 60 to 65 years old, *"was laid out in state on a thick pile of dyed textiles in a unique log coffin"*. We think he was King Midas because of the enormous size of the earth mound that covered the tomb, the luxuriousness of the burial goods inside the tomb, and the Assyrian inscriptions. It also contained the most comprehensive Iron Age drinking set ever found

– consisting of over 100 bowls, and many bronze mixing and serving vessels.

And what did they mix? Wine, beer and mead.

Why did they do this? Beer is fairly low in alcohol, so adding wine would give it more kick. Wine back then was often very vinegary, so adding mead would make it sweeter.

Test "Risky Sex"

Professor Jones and his colleagues tested 40 male and 40 female university undergraduates. They chose them so that half the men and half the women had already consumed alcohol, and half had not. They found their volunteers not in a laboratory, but (surprise, surprise) in the quiet corners of bars and licensed eating areas on a university campus. The volunteers were told that they were doing market research to help identify different types of student faces.

Gay students had to be excluded because the study was specifically about opposite-sex faces. Other students were left out because they recognised some of the faces in the photographs, or because they had worked out what the experiment was really about.

All the volunteers were shown 118 faces (half male, half female) on a laptop computer.

VEGETARIAN BEER

Beer is made with cereal grain – usually barley, although wheat, maize and rice are also used. The cereal is used for its starch (which is just a bunch of different sugars joined together). This starch is fed to a fungus that eats it and makes alcohol as a by-product.

So how can beer be anything except 100 per cent vegetarian?

It turns out that a meat product is involved in purifying the beer. Beer is usually cloudy. A "clarifying agent" is added to the beer to precipitate out the solids, leaving the beer bright and clean. A common clarifying agent is "isinglass" which comes from the swim, or air, bladders of fish.

But it's possible to clarify beer with seaweed or artificial agents such as Polyclar. Such beer is labelled "suitable for vegans".

Results of "Risky Sex"

First, they asked the volunteers to rate the distinctiveness of opposite- and same-sex faces – how big was the nose, how sparkling were the eyes, and so on. In general, the volunteers were pretty good at picking big ears or small noses. Men and women were each pretty good at rating the distinctiveness of faces, regardless of whether they were completely sober or had drunk some alcohol.

Second, they asked the volunteers to rate the attractiveness of 114 wrist watches. This was the supposed control. Again, the volunteers were either completely sober, or a little drunk.

There was a slight tendency for the people who were drunk to rate watches as more attractive than when they were sober. Fair enough, we've all been there. Who hasn't woken up after a big night to find themselves with a completely unfamiliar watch on their wrist, and no memory of how it got there? Even worse, in the cold, sober light of day, you might not find its face particularly attractive anymore! Who knows where its hands have been?

But the real difference in results came with the third comparison – when the volunteers rated the attractiveness of opposite-sex faces. Both men and women, when they'd had a few drinkies, had a 25 per cent increase in how attractive they rated the face of a person of the opposite sex.

The authors soberly concluded that if alcohol consumption causes an increase in the attractiveness of opposite-sex faces, it could increase the desire for risky sex – and possibly even the likelihood of risky sex happening!

EXPLODING CHINESE BEER BOTTLES

In 1998, exploding beer bottles topped the list of consumer complaints – in China.

There is pressure inside a bottle of beer, because of the dissolved carbon dioxide. And some beer producers had been using soy sauce or vinegar bottles, which could not withstand the pressure.

So on 1 April 1999, the Chinese State Quality and Technical Supervision Administration brought in a new standard for beer bottles. Today, new beer bottles are distinguished by a special mark "B" for "beer".

Reward Centre

So where in the brain does the alcohol act to make the opposite sex appear more attractive? Anything to do with the brain is very complicated and tricky, and there is so much that we do not know. But there's a lot of evidence to suggest that the area of the brain known as the "Nucleus Accumbens" becomes particularly active after drinking alcohol, in both humans and animals. The Nucleus Accumbens is one of the main so-called "reward centres" in the brain.

In one famous experiment, rats had a wire inserted directly into their Nucleus Accumbens. When they pressed a switch, they received a pleasurable surge of electricity. In fact, the rats loved squirting their Nucleus Accumbens with electricity so much that they would ignore food and literally starve to death, rather than stop pressing the switch. So the Nucleus Accumbens is a very powerful reward centre in the brain.

And it appears that in humans, the reward centre seems to get triggered by alcohol – leading to potentially risky sexual behaviour.

We humans have been drinking beer for thousands of years – and having sex for even longer. What these scientists discovered about alcohol making the opposite sex a whole lot more attractive has long been known in Australian society as "Beer Goggles".

So maybe on your next big night out, your plan should be to pick your potential partner *before* you fit your beer goggles …

BEER PRIZE

An ancient Finnish legend deals with a wife-stealing gang. It led to a bizarre competition, still in practice today, in which a man has to carry a woman over a 250-yard obstacle course. It is carried out in the central Finnish village of Sonkajärvi, close to the Arctic Circle, and it attracts over 8000 people.

The Estonians devised the prize-winning tactic of the very effective "Estonian Carry". The woman hangs upside down on the man's back, while squeezing her thighs on the sides of his face. The prize is the woman's body weight in beer.

BEER AND BREAD

The fungus that makes beer is called *Saccharomyces cerevisiae*. It turns sugar into alcohol and carbon dioxide. In the word "Saccharomyces", "saccharo" means "sugar", while "myces" means "fungus". "Cerevisiae" is a Latin word relating to beer.

This fungus also makes bread for us. In this case, the alcohol evaporates in the heat of the oven, while the carbon dioxide makes the bread rise. Where would our modern civilisation be without beer and bread? What a useful fungus!

This fungus has given us a rather corny (or starchy?) joke:

Male bus conductor to female passenger running late for bus: *"Please hurry up, madam. If you had more yeast in you, you would rise earlier".*

Female passenger: *"Sir, if you had more yeast in you, you'd be better bred".*

People love their seafood. We humans have been eating mussels for thousands of years. Now, I once believed two things about mussels. First, you should eat them only during months that had the letter "R" in them. Second, you should throw away the mussels that don't open when you cook them. How easy it is to be wrong!

Mussel Myth – 1

The first Mussel Myth is simple to debunk.

The advice to eat mussels only in months with the letter "R" applies only to the northern hemisphere. The eight months of September through to April are when mussels are supposedly "in". The situation is different in the southern hemisphere because the seasons are different.

That will teach me to get my gastronomic advice from European books.

Mussel Myth – 2

The second myth takes a little more time to prove wrong, and then to correct.

Start off by looking at the influential cookery books of the mid-1900s, such as *Larousse Gastronomique* in 1961 and *Italian Food* by Elizabeth David in 1954. These books made absolutely no mention of discarding unopened mussels.

The myth was mentioned in Italian cookbooks dating back to 1915, and possibly earlier. But in the English language, it seems to have been popularised by the English food writer Jane Grigson in her 1973 publication *Fish Cookery*. The exact quote is, *"Throw away any mussels that refuse to open"*. This quote had absolutely no science behind it – it was just an opinion. This advice came at the end of a discussion on preparing and cooking mussels – but there was no clear reason given as to why the unopened mussels should be thrown away.

According to Nick Ruello, the mussel expert and fisheries biologist, over the years this incorrect advice has stuck as tightly as a barnacle. By the 1970s, some 13 per cent of cookbooks were agreeing with Jane Grigson, and by the 1980s, this had risen to 31 per cent. By the 1990s, there was almost universal agreement among cookbook writers. But not one of these cookbook writers had any expertise in marine biology – and hadn't bothered to check with a marine biologist.

Nick Ruello was curious about this, and personally contacted two prominent Australian cookbook writers and asked them why they advised readers to discard unopened mussels. They replied that the information, *"came from their young research assistants who did much of the work in preparing the latest book"*. It was as though once the advice had been written down, it kept on spreading because other writers quoted it, without checking if it was correct or not.

And the advice was not correct.

Culinary Science

Nick Ruello originally got involved in this Mussel Myth because he was commissioned to write a report for Seafood Services Australia on the rather specific topic of "adding value to mussels". And of course, along the way, he cooked and ate over 30 batches of mussels (of various sizes, ranging from 21 to 111 mussels).

The mussel has a shell with two halves. Thanks to how the elastic ligaments are joined on, these two halves have a "natural" tendency to be open. To keep them closed, mussels have muscles (try reading that sentence aloud). They use what are known as "adductor" muscles. When we cook mussels, the heat damages the adductor muscles. Sometimes, the heat of cooking is great enough to "denature" the proteins in the adductor muscles so that they simply disintegrate. But sometimes, the heat can make one, or both, ends of the adductor muscles come unstuck from the shell.

Nick Ruello found that 1.9 per cent of mussels opened early in the cooking process. These mussels opened before they had been cooked long enough to kill any potential pathogens in them. If you removed them from the stove once they opened and ate these mussels, you could get food poisoning. But you would be strongly warned away by the texture of the meat – it would be unappetising, jelly-like, uncoagulated, and stuck to the perimeter of the shell. So in this case the mussels were open – but unsafe to eat.

At the other extreme, he found that some 11.5 per cent of mussels remained closed after a so-called "normal" cooking time. When he forced them open with a knife, every single one was both adequately cooked and safe to eat. So, according to Nick Ruello, even if the adductor muscles refuse to bow to the heat, the meat is still safe to eat.

Even when he cooked the mussels for a further 90 seconds, about one-seventh of them still refused to open. And in the mussels that finally did open, thanks to the overcooking, the meat was now shrunken and tough.

The best way to check the safety of mussels is to examine them *before* you cook them. Mussels have such a small mass that if they are invaded by a pathogen or germ, they will be overwhelmed almost immediately and will smell bad.

The ultimate test is the taste test. Like all foods (meat, fruit and so forth), if it tastes bad, don't eat it.

If we take notice of the actual evidence and stop throwing out cooked mussels that stubbornly refuse to open, we will stop wasting each year some 370 tonnes of perfectly good seafood worth around $3 million.

So use a little brain muscle, and put the mussel where your mouth is.

MUSSELS – AN OPEN AND SHUT CASE

According to anarchists, "the job of a government is to take money from its citizens, and if they refuse to pay up, put them in jail". Queen Elizabeth I brought in a beard tax. Everybody with more than a fortnight's growth of beard was taxed. I wonder if Santa and mussels were exempt …

The year 1972 was a good one for something "new". In 1969, we had three amazing technological events – we walked on the Moon, the 747 Jumbo jet was introduced, as was the supersonic passenger jet, the Concorde. But on the social/human side, the Vietnam War, which had begun back in 1955, was going badly for the West (but not so badly for Vietnam).

So when the Israeli-born Uri Geller claimed that he could bend spoons, purely with the Power of his Mind – the Western World was ready to believe. He rocketed to fame.

Uri 101

Soon Uri's mental skills had expanded so much that he could project the Power of his Mind through the TV set (or so he claimed). While on live TV, he told the audience that he could make their broken machinery at home start working again. And sure enough, the TV switchboard would light up with the audience telling amazing stories of how old watches had started working again. So now his repertoire included both "watch starting" *and* "spoon bending".

Uri's abilities soon expanded even further. He claimed that he had solved the mystery of déjà vu. It was simply his mind sending telepathic waves ahead of him while he walked, so that he would "know" what was around the corner.

Then he got into "Map Divining". He received $350,000 from the Australian mining company Zanex for advising them where to find gold around the old gold-mining town of Maldon in Victoria, and in the Solomon Islands. We don't know what resulted from his Solomon Islands advice. But we do know that Mr Geller spoke with Alan Svansio, a Zanex geologist, about Maldon. Apparently, he didn't tell Zanex anything new, just the standard geological information for the area that they already knew. It would have been ridiculously easy (especially if you had a budget of $350,000) to find out what the geology reports for any area are.

FORK

The one true utensil

BEND,
DAMN YOU, BEND! OH
URI GELLER, WHY WON'T YOUR
RIDICULOUS URI GELLER
POWERS WORK?!

OR NOT ...

Uri Geller has lots of fans in the "psychic" community. One of them, Gary Wiseman, wrote in *People* magazine that Mr Geller had successfully found minerals for the mining company RTZ (Rio-Tinto Zinc Corporation). However, RTZ wrote to the Australian Skeptics society saying that they had never actually employed Mr Geller.

And after it was reported that a director of the mining company Zanex had employed Mr Geller, some of the larger shareholders sought to have two of the directors of Zanex replaced.

Mr Geller later wrote newspaper columns in which he got his readers to "improve" their lives with special "energised" orange paint or ink. More recently, he has moved into the lucrative motivational-improvement self-help personal-growth New Age industry. You can buy a Mind-Power Kit, which includes a crystal and a book which can help you develop your ability to perform dowsing, or Extra-Sensory Perception.

Curiously, Mr Geller still flies in aeroplanes and drives around in cars – rather than using teleportation.

The Secret

The well-known skeptic and magician James Randi, also known by the stage name of "The Amazing Randi", summarised the secret of bending a spoon in just seven words: "BEND IT WHEN NO ONE IS LOOKING".

PSYCHIC URI GELLER?

Uri Geller calls himself a psychic and claims that he has had visions for many years. He says that it's possible that his powers came from "extraterrestrials".

According to the *The Skeptic's Dictionary*, "*... he has sued people for millions of dollars for saying otherwise. His psychic powers were not sufficient to reveal to him, however, that he would lose all the lawsuits against his critics*".

In 2000, Mr Geller sued the Nintendo video game company for US$100 million for devising a character that he claimed was a theft of his identity. The case was thrown out of court.

Over the years, he has made many public predictions about sporting events. Over the years, the players and teams that he most often chooses to win will actually lose.

There is nothing paranormal or psychic about bending a spoon – it's just plain old Stage Magic (if you can ever call something as wonderful as "Magic" plain or old). More precisely, Spoon Bending is an example of "sleight-of-hand". "Sleight" means "the use of dexterity or cunning, especially with the aim of deception", and so "sleight-of-hand" means "manual dexterity, usually related to performing magic tricks". (The word "sleight" comes from the Old Norse word for "sly".)

Now here's a clue to what's going on. Please note that Uri Geller is a strong and fit man. But, even so, whenever he bends a spoon *only* with his mind, he has to hold that spoon with *two* hands. This is quite surprising, as I have seen people in their nineties who are strong enough to carry a spoon (sometimes even three!) in just one hand. But Mr Geller, who is much younger, needs two hands to hold a spoon. What is going on?

If Mr Geller really were using the power of his mind to bend the spoon, he wouldn't need to touch it. He could just place it on a table and use the supposed power of his mind. But, surprisingly, he uses his two hands to hold the spoon, and after some entertaining and distracting stage patter and a few hand movements, Bingo, another bent spoon ...

Leonardo da Vinci's paintings are more than just "paint on canvas", and a good magician's hand movements are more than just "hand movements". The skill of the execution of the hand movements is everything – and Uri Geller is reasonably skilled.

If you are a Card-Carrying Cutlery Mutilating Stage Magician, it's important that you distract your audience by standing up, sitting down, telling jokes – anything will do. While they are distracted, bend your spoon that you are holding with your two hands. Next, cover the bend with one hand and release the other hand and wave it around. Get a random innocent member of the audience to hold the other end of the spoon. Then, gradually transferring all the weight of the spoon to the volunteer, wave your free hand above the centre of spoon, and slowly uncover the bend that you added a few moments earlier. Voilà, instant psychic powers!

A nice variation to this trick is to take the spoon back and (when nobody is looking) bend it even more. Then, while you distract the audience again, dump the spoon on a bench. Casually tell the audience that often the spoon will keep on bending *after* your mind has given it the initial impulse. On cue, everybody turns to look at the spoon all by itself on a bench, and – gasp! – it has bent even more.

If you want to learn how to Bend a Spoon, check out "Spoon Bending" on Google and YouTube. You will find vast numbers of detailed instructions and movies showing exactly how to do it.

Neuroscience of Magic – 1

For thousands of years, magic has been one of the most popular types of performance art. It succeeds only when the magician can manipulate our attention (what we see, hear, smell and so on), our perception (what we actually notice), our trust and our awareness. And of course, magicians can get away with practically anything if they can get the audience laughing.

So magicians have some rather special insights into human consciousness. These powerful yet subtle insights are what some neuroscientists are now exploring by working with magicians.

SHAKE = BENT?

There is a well-known illusion called the "Dancing Bar" or "Rubber Tree". Hold a metal (or wooden) bar so that it points at the person you want to trick then wobble it rapidly up and down. Amazingly, the bar appears to bend in the middle, the closer end moving independently from the end that you are holding.

Welcome to the "Dancing Bar" illusion. recently, neuroscientists have worked out what's really going on.

In your brain there are regular motion-sensing neurons that specialise in looking at things that move. They spring into action as soon as you start moving the bar up and down. But there are also other cells in your brain called "End-Stopped Neurons". They look at things that move *and* they also perceive the boundaries of objects, such as corners and edges. The End-Stopped Neurons and the regular motion-sensing neurons respond differently to moving objects.

So two parts of your brain respond differently to the same moving object. This difference warps (or shifts) your estimation of where the edges of the moving bar really are.

And this makes your brain "see" the solid bar appear to flop like boiled spaghetti.

You might notice that about half of the proponents of the Bending Spoon will aim the spoon right at the camera and rapidly oscillate it up and down – and yes, it really does look like the head of the spoon is moving relative to the handle.

In general, most magic tricks use one or more of the five following "devices".

The first device is "Visual Illusion". An example of this is the after-image – the image left in your vision when there is a sudden change of brightness. A woman stands on stage wearing a skin-tight, form-fitting, white dress. The magician tells us that he will magically turn her dress red. The house lights dim and then he theatrically turns on a very bright red spotlight. The white dress, and the woman's face, turn red. He gets a weak laugh from the audience. The magician apologises. The timing of what happens next is critical. He turns off the very bright red spotlight (the house lights are already off). There will be total darkness for one-tenth of a second. Trap doors open around the woman. Hidden cables pull strongly on her white dress, which turns out to be held on with Velcro. The white dress vanishes through the trap doors, which immediately shut. During this time, thanks to the very bright red spotlight which is now switched off, an after-image of the woman has been "burnt" into the audience's vision. They "see" the woman, even though it's total darkness. After 1/10th of a second, the house lights snap on to full brightness. The woman is now seen to be wearing a bright red dress – which was hidden all the time under her white one.

The second device is "Optical Illusion". A few thousand years ago, the great Greek thinker Aristotle noticed that if he stared at the moving water in a river for a while and then looked at the rocks on the side of the river, something strange happened. He wrote, in his work the *Parva Naturalia,* that the rocks appeared to move in the opposite direction to the flow of the water.

This illusion is used when the magician gets the audience to stare at (for example) spinning discs that have concentric rings of slanted lines. Depending on how the lines are drawn, they might appear to simultaneously expand and contract.

HOLDING HANDS

If you go looking on the interweb for "how to bend spoons", you'll mostly find either skeptics or believers.

Surprisingly, most believers admit that they have to touch the spoon to make it bend. But they say that this is only to "channel" the energy. They also claim that while they do apply "some" force, this force isn't enough to bend the spoon. Mind you, they often insist that you shout loudly while touching the spoon, and/or do this with a group of people who are simultaneously shouting and "touching" their spoons ...

Neuroscience of Magic – 2

The third device is "Cognitive Illusion". This is where the magician aims to misdirect the attention of the audience. As a result, they don't notice that something has changed. This is called "Inattention Blindness".

A magician might move his hands slowly in a curve, or quickly in a straight line. Your eyes will accurately follow the slow-moving hand in a smooth pursuit. But when your eyes follow a fast-moving object, they don't move smoothly – instead, they jump from one location to the next. These sudden eye movements are called "saccades" – and during a saccade, you are effectively blind. You actually see "reality" only at the beginning and end of a saccade – and the stuff in between you "make up" and insert into "reality".

Another "neuroscientific" fact to add to the mix is that our brains treat curves differently from straight lines. Straight lines are fairly predictable – they just go straight. But curved lines (and corners as well) are less predictable. So our brains are "wired" to pay more attention to curved lines. And this is something a magician can do to get you to not notice something, or to redirect your attention.

Another way of getting the audience to not notice something is the famous "Gorilla Illusion", devised by the American Drs Simons and Chabris. Here, a person in a gorilla suit walks across a basketball court while the audience is trying to count how many times the basketball players pass the ball to each other. Just to make himself really obvious, the gorilla stops in the middle of the players, turns to fact the audience, crouches, beats his chest, straightens, turns again, and finishes his walk across the basketball court. Half the audience does not see the gorilla – regardless of their age, gender, level of education, nationality, religion and so on. Why? Two reasons – first, you see only a microscopic part of reality, and second, "attention".

The only "bit" of reality that you actually "see" in sharp, full colour is an area the size of your thumbnail when held at arm's length. It's tiny. The vast majority of what you see is just "virtual reality". When you enter a new location, your eyes quickly scan around and build up a fake virtual world. There are motion detectors to get you to respond to moving objects in your peripheral vision, and to shift your gaze and stare at them. But in general, all you really see and pay attention to is that tiny area the size of your thumbnail.

Also, your "rational" brain has been given the job of counting. So, for half the audience, this instruction overrides what passes right through their field of view.

The fourth device used by magicians is the field of "Special Effects". These include false gunshots, impressive explosions and so on.

The fifth device is the "Gimmick" – mechanical and secret devices such as a spoon made of a special metal alloy (for example, Nitinol) that can change shape at a certain temperature.

FOOLING THE BRAIN

Why is so easy to fool the "visual" parts of the brain?

In short, because there is too much "reality" for us to see. So our brain compresses "reality", alters "reality" to make it "reasonable", and takes shortcuts so that it can handle the massive torrents of data pouring in.

Suppose somebody walks towards you. As they get closer, their image fills more and more of your field of vision on your retina. But are they really getting bigger, or is their height stuck at 1.7 metres? Nope, they just stay the same height. So our brain has to do "something" so they "appear" the same size.

Is this what the hippies meant when they said, *"reality is for people who can't handle drugs"*?

What magic can do is expose the compressions of reality, and the shortcuts our brain takes, in order to try to make sense of the big crazy world around us.

To Catch a Thief ...

The right person to catch out a magician is another magician – not a scientist. A scientist is definitely the wrong person.

First, a scientist is expecting everything to be honest and above board – while a magician is aiming to trick you. So scientists are no different from the rest of us – they are easily tricked. Second, there's an old saying, *"You set a thief to catch a thief"*. Only a thief knows the tricks of a fellow professional thief. So, in trying to catch a fellow magician, only a professional magician would know what to look for, and where and when.

Back in 1973, when the TV host Johnny Carson invited Uri Geller onto his show to bend some spoons and other metal items, he also invited James Randi along. Johnny Carson had been an amateur stage magician earlier in his career. James Randi knew that it was easy to "prepare" and weaken a spoon: all you had to do was bend it back and forth many times until it got hot, and the force needed to bend the spoon suddenly decreased. Before Mr Geller went on air, Johnny changed all the spoons and other metal items that Mr Geller had planned to use. Mr Geller responded by saying that his "power" couldn't be turned on and off like a switch – and that he simply didn't feel strong enough to try.

And what about the broken watches spontaneously restarting at home for the TV audience when Mr Geller told them to? Actually, they didn't spontaneously restart – they were picked up and given a bit of a shake ... And for how long did they keep going – a few minutes, or the next 20 years?

Mr Geller started his climb to fame with the Bending Spoon trick in 1972. But in 1968, a conjuring magazine published in Israel gave *"the instructions for a spoon trick that was indistinguishable from the Geller demonstration"*.

Uri Geller is not a psychic with supernatural powers. He's just a skilled magician who turned a few basic magic tricks into a career. To quote *The Skeptic's Dictionary*, *"... Geller is a fraud, he has no psychic powers, and what Geller does amounts to no more than the parlour tricks of a conjurer".*

And as James Randi said, *"If Uri Geller bends spoons with divine powers, then he's doing it the hard way".*

CHOICE BLINDNESS

A surprising result came out of a simple card trick. The card trick was the Double-Card Ploy, where the magician uses skilful sleight-of-hand to switch cards from one hand to the other. The technical name for this sleight-of-hand is The Magic Palming Technique.

Dr Johansson and his colleagues set up an experiment. They had small cards, each of which had a markedly different face on it (for example glasses or no glasses, long or short hair and so on). Volunteers were asked to choose which of two faces they found more attractive. Then, after the volunteers had made their choice, the experimenters surreptitiously switched the two cards from one hand to the other.

Here comes the weird stuff.

First, only one-quarter of the volunteers noticed that the "more attractive" face was now in the experimenter's other hand.

Second, when the volunteers were asked why they liked their chosen face, they came up with a whole bunch of reasons. And they did this even when (as in three-quarters of the faces) they were referring to the face they had previously chosen as less attractive! The volunteers were now justifying a choice that was the exact opposite of what they originally made.

Why on earth do we humans do weird stuff like that? Why are we so irrational? Maybe this experiment will help the neuroscientists understand the human mind a little better – and possibly bring us close to World Peace. (Just kidding.)

One of the best-known rhymes in the English language is *"Twinkle twinkle little star, How I wonder what you are"*. The rhyme's author, Jane Taylor, first published it way back in 1806, in a book called *Rhymes for the Nursery*. She originally called the poem "The Star" for its first publication. And sure enough, if you look up at the night sky, the stars really *do* seem to twinkle.

But the reality is that stars don't twinkle.

Stars Are Not Constant Candles ...

The stars we see at night are huge objects, of the order of a million kilometres in diameter. All the stars that we can see with the naked eye are quite close to us, and well and truly inside our galaxy, the Milky Way.

For a star to actually "twinkle", it would have to get brighter and duller by a noticeable amount, and do this a few times per second.

Stars can in fact vary their brightness, but not a few times per second.

For example, our star, the sun, will change its brightness by 0.1 per cent (or one part in a thousand) over the Solar Cycle of about 11 years. We've been mapping this for about 400 years. Recent peaks were in 1991 and 2002, with the next one expected around 2013/2014, and so on.

There are some uncommon stars, called Variable Stars, that can vary in brightness not by one part per thousand, but up to 10,000 times. They can do this over periods from as short as a few hours to as long as a year.

Some stars will destroy themselves in a gigantic explosion called a supernova, becoming millions or billions of times brighter than normal. Of course, they can do that only once.

But no stars can vary their brightness as much and as quickly as the twinkling star in the nursery rhyme would have us believe.

... But That's Not Why They Twinkle

So what makes stars seem to twinkle, to the joy of stargazers, but to the intense annoyance of astronomers?

The answer is our atmosphere – that turbulent, fragile, translucent ocean of five trillion tonnes of air that is our window to the heavens.

Imagine that you are looking at the bottom of a shallow pond, with the surface of the water totally smooth. Everything on the bottom of the pond is easy to see. Suddenly, a wind springs up, rippling the surface of the water – and the floor of the pond now appears fuzzy. Then, to make matters worse, a stream of turbulent water suddenly begins to flow into the pond exactly where you are looking. Now it's impossible to pick out small details on the bottom. The "twinkling" water blurs all the details.

You can see another example of "twinkling" on a country road on a hot day – the shiny "lake" in the distance. The sun heats up the dark road, which heats up the air immediately above the road. The hot air next to the road bends the light more than the cooler air in the next layer higher up. The effect of all this "physics" is to make a virtual mirror out of this hot air. This "mirror" reflects the sky, and so you see a shiny patch on the road off in the distance. So that "water" in the road ahead is just the sky.

In the same way, our atmosphere can make the stars above appear to "twinkle".

In our atmosphere there are hot and cold areas. They appear as millions of columns or "bundles" of warmer or colder air, tens of centimetres across, and at an altitude of several kilometres. As the light from a star passes through these columns, on its journey down to the ground, it gets bent this way and that. The actual point size of the star is very small, but the turbulent air makes it look much bigger.

"I think I preferred you when you were a collapsing cloud of material composed primarily of hydrogen, along with helium and trace amounts of heavier elements," said the moon.

How to Fix Twinkling

The fact that air can bend light was first noted by the ancient Greek astronomer Cleomedes. In 1706, the great thinker Sir Isaac Newton in his work *Opticks* proposed that a solution to air turbulence interfering with telescope viewing might be found "*… in a most serene and quiet Air, such as may be found on the tops of the highest Mountains above the grosser Clouds*". Indeed, many of today's great telescopes are in such locations.

The whole point of the Hubble Space Telescope was to get a biggish telescope totally above the turbulent air. Indeed, the astronauts on the International Space Station get to see the stars without any added twinkling. The astronaut Jap Apt, who helped launch the Compton Gamma Ray Telescope said in 1991, "*for one thing, the stars don't twinkle because you're above the atmosphere*". And the astronaut Dr Edgar Mitchell, who went to the moon in Apollo 14, said, "*without the atmosphere to block, the stars don't twinkle*".

But there is a second way for astronomers to get around the twinkling of the stars. First, they use a laser to measure exactly how much the atmosphere is interfering with the incoming starlight. Second, they use this information to distort the mirror of the telescope, hundreds of times each second, to compensate for this interference. The US Air Force in 1982 first used this technology to peek at Soviet satellites. When the technology was declassified, the astronomers began using it. By 1990, it was built into the 3.6 metre telescope at La Silla, in Chile.

A third way for astronomers to get a clear image, unperturbed by twinkling, is to take a very short exposure, say one-hundredth of a second. But this will work only with very bright objects.

So the light from a distant star flies unperturbed for thousands of years, to get massively distorted only in its last dozens of microseconds of flight before it lands, as a twinkle, in our eyes.

TWINKLE LITTLE STAR

All the gold that you will ever touch in your life was "made" inside a star as it exploded. It was blasted into space, became part of our planet about four and a half billion years ago, was found and ended up in your hand.

SPONTANEOUS HUMAN COMBUSTION

One of the most bizarre, and still unexplained, things that happens to our human flesh is a phenomenon called "Spontaneous Human Combustion" (*if* it's real). Somehow, a human body bursts into flames – for no apparent reason. Let me emphasise that in true Spontaneous Human Combustion (*if* it really exists) the human body bursts into flames *without touching an external flame or source of heat*. Often the entire body is reduced to ashes.

Now I have to say, right at the very beginning, that I am still not convinced that Spontaneous Human Combustion actually exists. Part of the reason is that nobody has been obliging enough to burst into flames before an expert audience of forensic pathologists.

However, I reckon that it is well-proven that a human body can burn, via the "Wick Effect" (more below). But to start burning without any external source of heat? Not impossible, but definitely not proven.

History of Spontaneous Human Combustion

In the Old Testament of the Bible, Ezekiel 28:18 it is written:

> *"By your many sins and dishonest trade, you have desecrated your sanctuaries,*
> *So I made a fire come out from you, and it consumed you,*
> *And I reduced you to ashes on the ground in the sight of all who were watching."*

There have been about 200 reports of Spontaneous Human Combustion over the last 400 years. There is no obvious pattern. The cases are roughly equally divided between male and female. The victims can be any age between four months and 114 years. Some were drunkards, while others were teetotallers. Some had been underweight, while others had been overweight. There's just no simple pattern.

Charles Dickens included an instance of Spontaneous Human Combustion in chapter 32 of his 1853 novel, *Bleak House*, when he decided to get rid of one of his characters in the rather convenient way of having them burst into flames. He writes, describing the room after the paranoid and superstitious Krook has combusted, *"There is a little fire left in the grate, but there is a smouldering, suffocating vapour in the room, and a dark greasy coating on the walls and ceiling"*. Dickens was convinced that Spontaneous Human Combustion existed. In the preface to the second edition of *Bleak House* he describes how he studied the subject carefully and found about 30 cases of Spontaneous Human Combustion. So he decided to use it in his story. However, his description does not really count as "Spontaneous". Spontaneous means there is no possible external source of combustion – in *Bleak House* there was *"a little fire left in the grate"*.

A typical case of Spontaneous Human Combustion was that of Ann Martin in Philadelphia in 1957. It is said that only her feet and the top of her trunk remained intact, with everything in between reduced to ashes. Newspaper, just 60 centimetres away, was completely untouched.

In your average house fire, the extremities of the body (hands and feet, arms and legs) are burnt to ashes, while remains of the central trunk are always left behind. A forensic pathologist can examine the bones in the pelvis, and tell whether the person was a man or a woman, young or old. If they happened to be a woman, the pathologist can tell whether or not she'd borne children. Whichever the case, the central trunk is *always* left relatively intact in a house fire. But in Spontaneous Human Combustion (*if* it really exists), the central trunk is reduced to ashes, while the hands and feet are usually left untouched.

To burn a corpse in a crematorium, you need a *lot* of heat. They will typically burn the body at 1200 degrees Celsius for an hour and a half, and then at 1000 degrees Celsius for another hour and a half. Even then, they're not left with just dust and ashes but bone fragments – so they have to grind these down with a mortar and pestle. In even the worst house fire you won't get a temperature above 850 degrees Celsius – so where does the energy for this human fireball come from?

The Wick Effect (Totally Proven)

Dr J. D. DeHaan from the California Criminalistics Bureau carried out some rather convincing studies that showed that a pig body can actually burn. It's now popularly called the "Wick Effect".

He chose a pig carcass, because pigs are surprisingly similar to humans. Our diets and physiology are similar. In fact, we are so similar that a heart valve can be taken from a pig and successfully transplanted into a human heart, and work well for many years.

There is enough fat in a pig body (or a human body) to support combustion. Burning a gram of fat will release about 40 kilojoules of heat. If you set it up correctly, you can start a smouldering fire that is fuelled by the fat, and much of the central trunk can be consumed and turned into ashes. It's important that you burn the carcass only inside a room with a closed door. Air can get in, but not as quickly as it could through an open door or window. It turns out that for the Wick Effect to happen, you need to slightly limit the amount of air, so that you get a smouldering fire. The Wick Effect won't happen out in the open with ready access to air. For example, the clothing won't turn into a porous wick, but will burn totally into ash. No "wick" means no "Wick Effect".

First, he placed some clothing on a small pig (this would later act as a wick). Then he poured one litre of petrol on the clothing. Some soaked into the clothing, while some soaked into the carpet under the pig carcass. He lit the petrol. The petrol burnt strongly for about a minute, emitting about 60 kilowatts. Within that first minute, the top layer of the pig skin had dried, scorched and begun to split and curl. Liquid fat began to ooze out. The clothing had also scorched. It did not combust into powdery ash, but turned into a porous, stiff, blackened substance – in other words, a wick. It sat on top of the pork skin, soaking up the liquid fat.

Second, after about a minute, the petrol fire went out, but the carpet continued to burn. It burnt with about the same intensity as the petrol, but for about another 25 minutes, after which it extinguished. Like the petrol fire, the carpet fire emitted heat at about 60 kilowatts.

Third, within a minute of both the petrol extinguishing and the carpet beginning to burn, the pork fat began to burn. It was absolutely essential that a rigid, carbonaceous, char wick was present. The pork fat burnt where there was a "wick" (clothing), and did not burn where there was not a wick.

You can see this effect in a burning candle. A pool of molten oil surrounds the central burning wick. But the flame comes only from the wick. You can touch a burning flame (from a cigarette lighter or burning match) to the hot pool of molten oil – but it will not burn. (Apparently, the porous wick will *"increase the effective vapour pressure of the liquefied fat fuel."*) You can see the link to a human body burning on the trunk, but not the extremities – you need clothing, which can turn into a wick, to support the burning.

After about 10 minutes, the heat put out from the burning fat was great enough to keep itself burning. The pig carcass then burnt for about two hours, *" … small 4-6 cm flames were sustained continuously under (the left side) of the carcass"*. The pig carcass lost mass at about 1 to 2 grams per second. The heat output was about 35 to 40 kilowatts.

Dr DeHaan tested several pigs – some lean, some fat. As you would expect, the more fatty pig carcasses burnt for longer, generated more heat and consumed more of the carcass.

In the case of a large 95-kilogram pig, the carcass generated about 60 kilowatts, burnt for 6½ hours, had flames up to 30 centimetres high for most of that time, and lost 60 per cent of its initial weight.

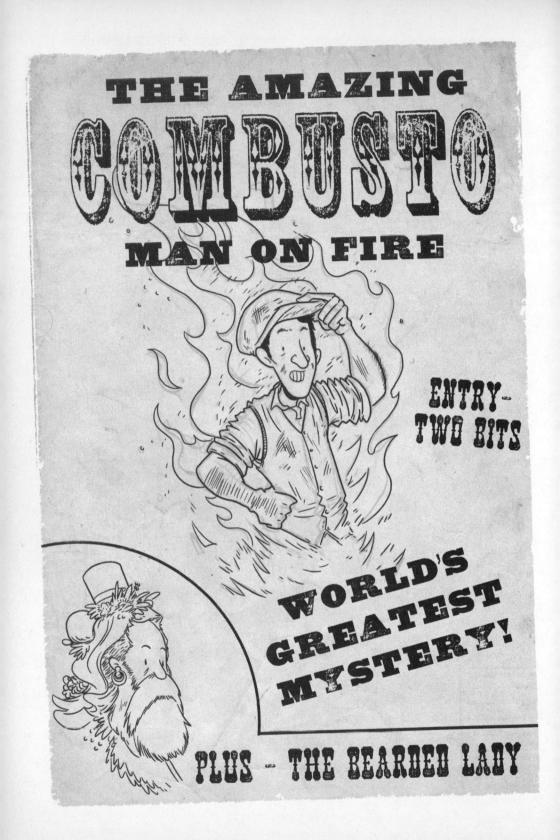

Brown Fat (Totally Unproven)

Okay, so a human body will burn, thanks to its fat. But you need an external source of heat to start it burning. Is it possible to generate lots of heat from a human body without a flame?

It's not impossible (but it's totally unproven, so far).

First, when we adults want to generate heat, we have to move *a* muscle or a *bunch* of muscles. Either we pump iron and get warm that way, or else we run around the block, if we are feeling athletic. If we are pretty lazy, we will just sit there and shiver. Either way, if we want to generate heat we have to move muscles.

But newborn babies in the first few months of their life cannot make their underdeveloped muscles shiver. Luckily, they have a unique trick for generating heat. They have a substance called "brown fat".

Brown fat is different from white fat. White fat takes in energy and turns it into more white fat. (It turns out that white fat does a lot of other stuff as well, and is quite an active organ, and even makes hormones – but I won't go into that now.) Brown fat goes the other way – it turns stored brown fat directly into heat. It bypasses the muscle-shivering method of making heat.

It was wrongly thought until very recently that adults don't have brown fat. However, radiologists have been seeing brown fat on their MRI scans for years. They simply hadn't bothered to tell the hormone doctors (endocrinologists) who were wrongly convinced that adults don't have brown fat.

Big Finish

Maybe, in Spontaneous Human Combustion (*if* it really does exist), a person has brown fat, and *then* has an abnormal runaway reaction that generates enough heat to set the body alight. (I have no idea of what this abnormal runaway reaction might be. Okay, I have a suspicion. Look up "decoupling of oxidative phosphorylation", if you have a spare hour or two.)

But in the early 21st century, we really don't know. The closest medical phenomenon to Spontaneous Human Combustion that we know of is Malignant Hyperthermia. In this rare (and often fatal) disorder, under the right circumstances a person's body temperature can get as high as 47 degrees Celsius. But that's a long way from burning a body.

I really didn't think that Spontaneous Human Combustion might be possible, until I read a report in *New Scientist*. It was by a retired Scenes of Crime Police Officer, John Heymer, from Gwent in the UK. He described something that seemed to be a classic case of Spontaneous Human Combustion, including the total absence of a source of flame or heat in the room. But at the time, he couldn't describe it as such in his official report, or else he would have been laughed out of the Police Force.

So as for me, I will just remain vaguely dubious, until a really well-documented case turns up.

After the common cold, head lice are probably the most common communicable disease in children. According to the Centre for Disease Control in Atlanta, Georgia, head lice infect between 6 and 12 million people each year. Lice have been our near (but not so dear) friends for a long time – we have found preserved head lice in the hair of 5000-year-old Egyptian mummies. And yet, it was only in the 21st century that we found out how lice can most effectively travel from person to person.

Head Lice – Social Costs

Professor Tina Coch, from Flinders University in South Australia, wrote a paper on the social implications of head lice. In her paper "Towards the eradication of head lice: literature review and research agenda", she wrote that with regard to head lice from a medical point of view, *the problem was trivialised, information sources were contradictory, and research was lacking*. She also wrote that, *it was usually mothers who spent hours each day tediously and meticulously combing the hair of their offspring and therefore it was seen as a feminist issue*.

Those two little words ("head" and "lice") can send an avalanche of panic through any family, kindergarten or school. They affect the sufferer physically with an itching scalp. The family itself can become deeply embarrassed, because of the common belief that head lice are associated with a "dirty" household. From a social point of view, the infested child may well be ostracised and teased.

On top of the social cost, there is an economic and environmental cost due to the shampoos and repeated laundry cycles of washing.

There is a minor worldwide epidemic of head lice among children. This is because of a move towards group learning (in any primary school you'll often see the kids crouched over the same table, with their heads touching), and the removal of the public health "nit nurses".

Head Louse 101

The head louse (*Pediculus capitis*) is a wingless, six-legged insect that cannot fly, swim or jump – instead, it swings like a tiny Tarzan through a forest of hair. Head lice live only on humans and depend on us totally for their existence. They have three stages in their life cycle – the mature adult louse, the egg laid by the adult nit, and the developing nymph which hatches from the egg.

The adult female louse is about 5 millimetres in length. In her 30-day life she can lay about 130 eggs. A single mating with a male is all that's needed for a lifetime of fertility, because she can store the sperm in a special compartment (called a spermatotheca). She spends practically all her time in the host's hair, not on the skin of the scalp. She comes down to the scalp about three times per day to feed on fresh blood – and each feeding session lasts about 15 minutes or less. This is why you're unlikely to find a loose louse on the skin of the scalp. It's hard to find them in the hair as well, because they'll zip away quickly at speeds up to 23 centimetres per minute (that's about 14 metres per hour, or 0.014 kilometres per hour). They can survive for an estimated maximum of about three days without blood. So if you leave your house for the three days of a long weekend, you can be pretty sure that you'll return to a lice-free house – apart from any eggs around the house, and what you carry on your scalp.

HEAD LICE STATS

Professor Rick Speare of the School of Public Health, Tropical Medicine and Rehabilitation Sciences at James Cook University in Townsville offers these interesting facts about head lice.

As you might expect, head lice are more common in long hair, which is why they are two to four times more common in girls.

Head lice are usually spread through head-to-head contact, which is why they spread so rapidly in schools, families and child care centres.

Head lice do not always make the scalp itchy – which is why you sometimes have to look closely.

Head lice do not survive very long away from the head – so concentrate your treatment on the hair, not the house.

Truth or Dare?

In general, head lice do not prefer dirty hair. They usually find it easier to get their thrice-daily drinks of blood from a clean, healthy scalp rather than a dirty, unwashed scalp.

Even though we have lived with the little critters for thousands of years, we didn't really understand how they best moved from person to person, and so myths grew up about the infectiousness of lice. Indeed, the dermatologists Burkhart and Burkhart wrote a paper in 1999 in the *Journal of Clinical Dermatology* called "Odds and ends of head lice: characteristics, risk of fomite transmission and treatment". That paper helped spread one major myth: that transmission of lice could take place head-to-head between humans *"by the slightest bodily contact"*.

Theory is a great start to knowledge, but it's the experiment that gets you even closer to the truth.

A good example of this occurred in early 2003, when Dr Deon Canyon's team at the School of Public Health and Tropical Medicine at James Cook University in Townsville decided to investigate this claim. They used 480 head lice, freshly plucked from local primary school children. Each louse was individually placed on a human hair (either stationary or mobile), which was then presented to an uninfested hair shaft (also either mobile or stationary) to see if the head louse would transfer across.

They found that, contrary to published wisdom, head lice would *not* transfer *"by the slightest bodily contact"*. Instead, they nipped across, but only in a mere 7.1 per cent of the trials. Indeed, they would usually transfer from one hair to another and only under quite specific conditions. The optimum conditions were when the recipient hair was moving at around 36 millimetres per second, when it was close to and parallel to the infested hair, and when it was moving in the direction from the louse's tail to its head. (It turns out that 36 millimetres per second is about 130 metres per hour, or 0.13 kilometres per hour.) The action of the louse was like jumping onto a moving tram. In every single case of a successful transfer, as the recipient hair came near, the louse would grab onto it with its free front leg. Once it had a firm grip, it would swing across to the new hair.

FART TO BE HATCHED

The egg is called a nit. A cement-like biological glue attaches it firmly to the hair shaft. It usually sits within one and a half centimetres of the scalp. The nit can survive for 10 days before it dies.

A nymph, the juvenile form of the louse, hatches the nit, helped by massive amounts of farting. While inside the egg case, the nymph sucks in huge amounts of air and expels it out through the alimentary canal, building up "fart pressure" behind its body. This pressure, helped by the cutting action of a special hatching organ at the upper end of the creature, will burst its way through the wall of the egg – and release the nymph.

The nymph will moult three times before it turns into an adult louse, which is then capable of either mating or laying eggs. The fastest lice of all are the nymphs in their third and last stage, where they can travel at 23 centimetres per minute.

LICE SAVED MOTHER RUSSIA

The invading army of Napoleon finally reached Moscow in 1812, only to find it abandoned. His army struggled back to France, losing men all the way. The Grande Armée had left France with more than 450,000 men – but fewer than 40,000 returned home. It is said that because the taller men enlisted in Napoleon's armies, the effect of his wars was to reduce the average height of Frenchmen by 10 centimetres.

Many causes have been put forth for the massive loss of life – the clever military tactics of the Russians of avoiding direct conflict and retreating, the unbelievable harshness of the Russian winter, the "scorched earth" tactics of the Russian Army, and so on.

Another cause could be lice. A team of scientists examined a mass grave of Napoleon's soldiers in Vilnius, in Lithuania, 800 kilometres west of Moscow. More than 30 per cent of the soldiers were killed by bacteria that, in turn, were carried by the lice. One bacterium was a rather nasty one – *Bartonella quintana*, known for causing "Trench Fever", a killer in the Western Front in World War I. Another bacterium found was just as nasty – *Rickettsia prowazekii*, known for causing the deadly disease typhus.

What Do We Do?

But Dr Canyon's paper also discussed a rather novel transfer method for head lice. If your hair is dry enough and if the humidity is low, a head louse can be ejected up to one metre from your hair by the static electricity created by combing! So avoid dry combing of lice-infested hair, because they can land on your hair.

Another reason to avoid combing dry hair is that head lice travel more quickly on dry hair than they do on wet hair. Wet hair slows them down, so that they are easier to see. So first lubricate the hair with lots of hair conditioner and then remove the lice with a fine-toothed comb.

Unfortunately, lice can be resistant to some of the insecticides that are supposed to kill them. A single chemical can kill either the eggs or the louse – but not both at the same time. In general, people do not like to use toxic chemicals in the hair of their children. So this all means that you need to spend a lot of time combing their hair with a fine-toothed comb to remove both the lice and the eggs – and you have to do this several times.

Beyond that, we're still scratching our heads for a solution …

Back in the early 1980s, there was an epidemic of "Repressed Memory" in the Land of Psychotherapy. Repressed Memory got a huge amount of publicity in the newspapers, and in talk and current affairs shows on radio and TV.

Therapists "uncovered" thousands of people whom, they claimed, had been sexually abused as children. In fact, the abuse had scarred these people so much that they had suppressed these terrible memories and forced them into their subconsciouses. Luckily, however, these "expert" therapists had been able to tease these repressed memories out of their patients' subconscious minds and back into their working memory. The therapists did this so that their "broken" patients could be "healed" – and could get on with their lives.

With the wisdom of hindsight, it now seems that this epidemic was closer to a Witch Hunt than to Real Science. Traumatic memories can indeed be repressed, but nowhere near as frequently as the therapists claimed.

It is surprisingly easy to implant false memories into around one-quarter of all people. And if you can be bothered to create a fake picture to go along with the memory, you can increase that fraction to two-thirds of us.

Memory 101

Memories make us who we are, they are part of our identity, and they are the link to the past that we share with friends and family.

But memories are not fixed – instead, they can be as fluid as water. The Uruguayan novelist Eduardo Galeano said, *"Memory is born every day, springing from the past, and set against it"*.

Sigmund Freud, the famous psychotherapist, believed that many of his troubled adult patients had actively suppressed some of their traumatic childhood memories. Freud believed that to truly understand, and fix, his patients' adult problems, he first had to understand their childhood problems. There is no doubt that repression is real – indeed, this is one of the cornerstones of psychotherapy.

But later in his career, Freud changed his opinion. He realised that in many cases he himself had accidentally suggested these memories to his patients, who then believed them.

So one way that false memories can evolve is when real memories are combined with external suggestions.

An example of this happened when the satanic horror movie *The Exorcist* was re-released in 2002. The countries in which it appeared all reported sudden and unexpected increases in the number of Satanic Events. In turn, this was followed by an increase in the numbers of "crack" exorcism teams to rescue people from, and neutralise, the surge of Satanic Events.

Memory is *not* like a videotape, a DVD or a memory stick that we can simply replay in its original form, whenever we wish. Instead, memory seems to be re-created each time we use it.

Unfortunately, every single time we rebuild and run that memory, there's an opportunity for extra information to be inserted into our memory banks. For example, say you have a fond and accurate memory of a recent birthday that happened to be on a day that was fine and free of clouds – all day long. But when you discuss your birthday with a friend, they wrongly say that the day was indeed free of clouds in the afternoon, but that it had started off cloudy with a hint of rain, before becoming fine. Furthermore, your friend is pretty definite about this. In this case, it's likely that you will insert this "false" memory into your "real" memory. In fact, you will probably "remember" the cloudy start to that particular birthday for the rest of your life.

This makes sense of the saying, *"The story got better with each retelling"*.

False Memory 101

It turns out that it is really easy to implant memories into people.

Elizabeth Loftus is both the Distinguished Professor of Law, Criminology, Psychology and Social Behavior at the University of California in Irvine, and Professor of Psychology and Law at the University of Washington in Seattle. In addition to her academic qualifications, she has wide and deep practical experience – she has spent over 30 years studying the fallibility of memory in some 200 studies involving over 20,000 people.

She calls the "fallibility of memory" the "Misinformation Effect".

In one study she showed advertisements to 167 people. These advertisements suggested that the people in her study had been to Disneyland and had shaken hands with Bugs Bunny. And, you guessed it, one-quarter of the people in her study said that this had *actually happened* to them. But of course this is totally impossible. It could not have happened, because Bugs Bunny is a Warner Brothers character, not a Disney character!

Over the decades, Professor Loftus has been able to consistently insert a memory into about one-quarter of people.

So roughly one-quarter of us can be led to believe the false memory that at the age of five we were separated from our parents in a shopping mall but luckily rescued by a kind elderly male. Or we can be made to "know" that at the age of five we accidentally spilt a bowl of punch at a wedding. Or we can be convinced that as a child we rather cheekily put green Slime in a teacher's desk.

Rather worryingly, it is easy to increase the percentage of us who insert a false memory into our brains. After all, what if you are a witness in court, and a fellow witness remembers an incident very differently from how you remember it?

If adults are shown a falsified photo, two-thirds of us will believe the false Slime incident (even if it never happened). In fact, most of us will then actually embellish our memory of it, by adding (without any prompting) extra details.

Numerous studies have looked at many different false memories that were successfully implanted. They include being rescued by a lifeguard from a swimming pool; having a nurse remove a skin sample from a finger; damaging a computer by pressing the wrong key; or being injured by an attacking animal. In each case, the volunteer with the implanted memory later embellished and "improved" the original false memory, getting more confident in its reality with each re-telling.

It doesn't matter how old or new the memory is – even fresh memories are as changeable as the weather.

THE TROUBLE WITH MEMORY

In 2010, a UK study from the University of Hull showed that some 20 per cent of students had fictional memories. These memories mostly dated back to when the students were between four and eight years old. For example, one student clearly remembered incidents while playing hockey – but they had never played hockey. Another remembered seeing dinosaurs walking – even though dinosaurs had died out (apart from the birds, which are indeed dinosaurs) about 65 million years ago.

Another study at the University of Sydney showed students two different versions of a three-minute crime movie. Then the students discussed the movie with another student who had seen the different version. They did not know that the two versions were slightly different. A week later the students were interviewed by Dr Helen Paterson, the lead researcher. Curiously, over 40 per cent of the students had *falsely* remembered seeing something that was not in the version they saw.

Dr Paterson noted, *"this suggests to us that people sometimes find it difficult, if not impossible, to distinguish between genuine memories and false memories of an event. This research has clear implications regarding the reliability of witness memory"*.

Agreeing with the study from the University of Hull, Dr Paterson said that about 20 per cent of Australians have clear, definite and vivid memories from their childhood of events that never happened.

Recent Repressed Memories

It's one thing to implant false memories in people in a laboratory experiment, purely as an academic exercise. But it's quite another when accused people wrongly end up in jail.

At the height of the 1980s Repressed Memory epidemic, therapists claimed to find repressed memories that supposedly "revealed" not just childhood sexual abuse (terrible as it is), but also Satanic Ritual Abuse carried out by vast, interconnected, underground cults.

These cults had apparently survived for centuries, killing babies as part of their rituals, and making young girls pregnant so as to have a constant supply of untraceable babies for these ritual killings. Some of the recovered "memories" were truly horrible. They included eating meat loaf made of human flesh, or people killing their own children.

The American legal system was unexpectedly hit with an entirely new type of case – people started suing their parents, teachers, relatives, doctors and neighbours after uncovering memories of past sexual abuse. Individual payouts of over US$10 million were made.

In 1991, George Franklin Sr, of San Mateo County in California, became the first person in the USA to be convicted of murder on the basis of a repressed memory. There was absolutely no other corroborating evidence. In this case, it was his daughter, Eileen, who provided the memory. (Just as an aside, all the information she gave to the police was freely available in newspaper reports of the murder. She gave no new information. In fact, she "remembered" some information about a ring that the newspapers wrongly reported – so the information that she supposedly "remembered" was false. George Franklin's conviction was overturned in 1996.)

But in 1991, repressed memories were breaking out all over the place. Both Roseanne Barr (the sitcom actor and producer) and Marilyn Van Derbur (a former Miss America) reported that they, under therapy, had uncovered repressed memories of childhood abuse.

The epidemic began to fade away in the mid-1990s. By 2002 in the USA, over 100 prisoners who had been convicted on the basis of what turned out to be false memories had been released on later-produced DNA evidence. Some of them had been in jail for over 20 years.

What Went Wrong?

In all these court cases, there was a Core Belief. The belief was made up of two parts.

The first part of the belief was that when people are repeatedly abused, they will *always* suppress any memory of the abuse deep into their subconscious. It was claimed that this memory will be so deeply hidden that the "victims" can live their lives for decades without it coming to the surface.

The second part was that this memory can be *reliably* retrieved by a therapist. The therapist would use devices such as hypnosis, dream interpretation, sodium amytal, age regression, guided visualisation and so on to retrieve the memory.

Well it won't come as much of a surprise that both parts of this Core Belief are wrong.

First, not all memories are suppressed. There have been many studies of children who had truly suffered very traumatic events (such as actually seeing their parents murdered). They found that the children did *not* suppress the terrible memory. Instead they dwelled on it, long and hard. Other studies of children caught up in the Nazi Holocaust and Serbian "ethnic cleansing" atrocities found that, again, the children did *not* repress the memory. Of course, there is the occasional (let me emphasise "occasional") real case where real memories of real traumatic events are repressed. But these cases are far less frequent than was claimed during the Repressed Memory epidemic of the 1980s.

Second, there was very little, if any, proof that suppressed memories of bad events could be reliably retrieved, or that they ever even existed.

The so-called therapists were asking their patients rather odd questions. In some cases, if the patient replied with a single "yes" to any of the questions about problems with eating or sleeping, this was apparently absolute and undeniable evidence that this patient had been sexually abused by their parents, and/or a local Satanic Cult!

But the remarkably low Threshold of Suspicion wasn't the

worst of it. Some of these so-called therapists were asking leading questions like, *"You sound to me like the sort of person who must have been sexually abused. Tell me what that bastard did to you"*.

Furthermore, many of the so-called therapists were dodgy, in terms of training, qualifications and being licensed to practise.

In one famous case, the late Cardinal Joseph Bernardin of Chicago was accused of sexual abuse that had supposedly happened some 17 years earlier. The accusation was based on a repressed memory found by a "therapist" with a Master's Degree, a certain Michele Moul. It turned out that the Master's Degree was awarded by a New Age Guru who was running an unaccredited school – not by a university. (By the way, the Guru believed that he was the embodiment of a divine spirit.) Furthermore, the therapist had completed only three of the 20 hours needed to pass the hypnosis section of his degree – which he earned over a few weekends. When it was revealed that the therapist was unqualified, untrained and unlicensed, the case against the Cardinal collapsed.

LEGAL MEMORY – 1

Professor Elizabeth Loftus, who was voted one of the top 100 psychologists of the 20th century by her peers, suggests a modification to our legal system. Perhaps witnesses should be asked in court, *"Do you swear to tell the truth, the whole truth, or whatever it is that you think you remember?"*

How Reliable is Memory?

At its height, the Repressed Memory epidemic was like the ancient Witch Hunts. In the original Witch Hunts of the 16th and 17th centuries, around half a million people across Europe were hunted down, accused of witchcraft to which they then confessed (under duress), and burned to death. The vast majority were women. Trevor-Roper wrote, *"The monks of the late Middle Ages sowed; the lawyers of the sixteenth century reaped; and what a harvest of witches they gathered in!"*

There are many cases of people being convicted on the basis of false memories and later being proved innocent by DNA testing.

In 1986, Ronald Cotton was convicted of raping a 22-year-old student, Jennifer Thompson, as a result of her sworn testimony. Eleven years later, not only did DNA evidence prove Cotton innocent, but another person, Bobby Poole, confessed to the crime.

Jacob Beard of West Virginia spent many years in jail for the murder of two women on the basis of false memory in sworn testimony. He was later acquitted, and successfully sued the police for nearly US$2 million.

In the sniper attacks of 2002 in Washington DC, the media reported that a white van had been seen leaving the area. This misinformation contaminated the testimonies of later witnesses, who also reported seeing the mysterious white van. In fact, the snipers were driving a blue car.

Today, knowledge of the Science of Memory is gradually spreading into the training of police, prosecutors and defence lawyers. For example, we now know one should ask open-ended questions, avoid leading questions, and not interrupt the responses of eyewitnesses. There is also a trend for law enforcement officials to ask potential witnesses to write down what they remember of the incident *before* they speak to anybody else.

Professor Loftus has said, *"… when these traumatic memories are accepted uncritically by therapists, social workers, police officers and attorneys in the absence of any corroborating evidence, the result is the wholesale destruction of families. The ultimate tragedy is that society will begin to disbelieve the cases of genuine abuse that need its vigilance."*

So it seems very strange in our modern age, that on the basis of something as fragile as a memory uncovered by a so-called therapist, and without any other corroborating evidence, many people were wrongly sent to jail.

LEGAL MEMORY - 2

I had a fascinating insight into the legal implications of "memory" from a man I once met at a conference.

A few decades earlier, he had begun work as a junior accountant in the centre of Sydney. A terrible accident happened with some scaffolding near his office, and people died. By an amazing coincidence, he was walking by and happened to be looking directly at the scaffolding as it collapsed. People rushed to help. He had no training in First Aid, so there was nothing he could do.

For some unknown reason, he went straight back to his office and spent the next three hours writing and rewriting in great detail everything he could remember actually seeing with his eyes. He deliberately did not talk to anybody else during this time.

During the court case, his evidence was very useful. The court case dragged on for many years, and this man was asked repeatedly to reappear. On each occasion, he was asked if he had anything new to offer. And on each occasion, he replied "no". He told the court that everything that he had to offer was in the document he typed up immediately after the accident.

But he told me that he had noticed something odd. Over the years in their repeated appearances, other witnesses would change their testimony – they would add to it, or leave parts out.

He and I then had a long conversation discussing about the reliability of eyewitnesses in court – and the fallibility of memory.

MEMORY AID
INSTITUTE

"I'd completely forgotten I was an 18th-century French dandy from the King's court." Rod - Plumber

"And then I remembered I was a Renaissance courtesan during the reign of the Medici's!" Carol - Not a courtesan

"As soon as I recalled my time as Robert Johnson, famous delta blues guitarist and devil dealer...my life just seemed to make sense!" Peter - Privileged white guy

THE MEMORY AID INSTITUTE - HELPING THE PEOPLE OF TODAY REMEMBER THEIR REPRESSED AND HIGHLY IMPROBABLE YESTERDAYS SINCE 1981.

Most parents have experienced the effects of the odd phenomenon called "teething". Teething is that slow process when a tooth slowly erupts out of the gum, to its final functional position. The kids are sometimes grumpy – and why not, when a perfectly fine gum is having a hole punched in it from underneath by the rising tip of a sharp tooth?

Parents and health professionals have been debating the effect of teething on infant health for over 5000 years. The ancient Sumerians believed that teething caused worms. On the other hand, ancient Hindu writings, as well as those of Homer, Aristotle and Celsus, claimed that there was a definite link between teething and serious infant illness.

As recently as 1839, 5016 infant deaths in Wales and England were blamed on teething. The truth was slow to emerge. On one hand, in 1975, the *British Medical Journal* wrote that, *"There can be no excuse for ascribing fever, fits, diarrhoea, bronchitis, or rashes to teething"*. But in 1979, both parents and physicians were still wrongly identifying teething as a cause of the symptoms of children being admitted to hospital.

Even today, most parents believe that teething causes major infant illness – but it's a myth.

Teething 101

Children start erupting their first tooth between 4 and 10 months of age – and usually have their full set of 20 "first teeth" by the age of 30 months. That works out to an average of almost one tooth eruption per month between 7 and 30 months of age. This period is also when infants have many rapid changes, and many minor illnesses.

So if the teeth are erupting, and if there are many minor illnesses, is there a relationship?

Practically all societies have a folk belief that says "yes" – teething causes problems.

Some 18 surveys covering Australia, Africa, Asia and the Americas found an almost-universal belief that teething causes diarrhoea. Other less serious symptoms were thought to include irritability, sleep disturbance, drooling, red cheeks, fever, nappy rash, "sooking", infections, pulling at ears, runny nose and smelly urine. Most parents manage teething in their infants with a combination of comfort, cuddles, something to chew on and teething gels. On average, about three-quarters of parents use some kind of medication.

The Science

Only recently have medical studies looked closely at the effects of teething.

One typical study by Dr Michael Macknin from the Cleveland Clinic Foundation in Ohio followed 125 well and healthy infants from 4 to 12 months of age. The parents were taught how to measure temperature with an ear thermometer, which they did twice each day. The parents also monitored the eruption of their children's teeth, and kept a daily log of 18 symptoms (for example, appetite for solids and liquids, sleep, stool looseness, irritability and so forth). They also recorded all illness, medications and vaccinations relevant to their children.

Overall, they followed 19,422 child-days and 475 tooth eruptions. Symptoms appeared about four days before the tooth emerged, and continued through the actual day of eruption to three days afterwards.

Dr Macknin found that teething was linked with daytime restlessness, increased biting, irritability, wakefulness, ear rubbing, decreased appetite for solid foods, thumb-sucking, gum-rubbing, slight facial rashes and drooling. There was also an association of teething with a slight increase in temperature. These all seem logically related to having something sharp attack your gum from the inside.

Interestingly, about one-third of kids had absolutely no symptoms related to teething.

There was no link between teething and stool looseness, stool frequency, sleep disturbance, decreased appetite for liquids, cough, vomiting or rashes other than facial rashes. There was also no link with a major rise in temperature or with major illnesses. He concluded that there was *no evidence that teething was associated with any severe, health-threatening conditions*.

Other studies have shown the same overall results.

Teething causes only minor illnesses. It does not cause major illness. This is good to know.

Smelly urine is a possible marker of a urinary tract infection, which is a serious condition. High fever can be a marker of a serious infection. If parents wrongly believe that smelly urine and high fever are part of the normal course of teething, they might ignore these markers of more serious illnesses.

The great paediatric teacher Illingworth was very close to the truth when he wrote that, *teething causes nothing but teeth*.

Part of being human is being irrational – and superstitions are a really good example of that. Most of us will have heard of the "Friday the 13th" superstition and how unlucky that day supposedly is.

Lots of Fridays the 13th

The UK independent research consultancy Populus interviewed 1011 adults by telephone a week before Friday the 13th back in 2004. They found that 86 per cent of adults treated Friday the 13th like any other day. A few people (5 per cent) impudently and deliberately became more adventurous to try to prove the Friday the 13th superstition wrong, while 4 per cent became more cautious. But 3 per cent believed so much in this superstition that they actually stayed at home to avoid any bad luck or danger.

Dr Donald Dossey, founder of the Stress Management Center and Phobia Institute in Asheville, North Carolina, estimates that in the USA, on any Friday the 13th, about *"$800 or $900 million is lost in business ... because people will not fly or do business they would normally do".*

This is unfortunate, because a quirk of our Gregorian calendar means that the 13th of the month is more likely (by a microscopic amount) to fall on a Friday than on any other day.

The Gregorian calendar runs on a 400-year cycle, in which each year is 365 days long, except for leap years, which are 366 days long. A leap year happens every fourth year, unless that year (for example, 1600, 2000) is exactly divisible by 400. Having 12 months in each year means that in 400 years, there is a total of 4800 months – so there are 4800 13ths of the month.

If the Gregorian calendar were totally random, the number of Fridays the 13th in a 400-year cycle would be 4800 divided by 7, which works out to 685.714285714285 ... But the Gregorian calendar is *not* totally random. Back in 1933, B. H. Brown reported in *American Mathematical Monthly* that in a 400-year Gregorian cycle, there are actually 688 Fridays the 13th. Sunday and Wednesday come in second at 687, Monday and Tuesday are third at 685, with Thursday and Saturday fourth at 684.

So how did Friday the 13th get its bad reputation? Well, it comes down to two things: the day "Friday" is considered unlucky – as is the number "13".

Unlucky Friday

In Western Christian society, Friday is unlucky for many reasons, not least because it was the day Jesus Christ was crucified. The Bible has been variously interpreted to assert that Friday also hosted the Great Flood, Adam and Eve doing some forbidden apple eating with the snake, the loss of speech of the builders of the Tower of Babel, the destruction of the Temple of Solomon and so on. But where did it all start?

By the late 14th century, Chaucer's *The Canterbury Tales* thought Fridays to be downright nasty, claiming, *"And on a Friday fell all this mischance"*. But it took until the mid-17th century for Friday's reputation to be thoroughly soured. Many popular writers of the time allude to Friday being a bad day to launch a ship, start a business/trip/letter/venture, receive medical treatment, harvest/ reap crops, get married/born, or even hear news. Fridays used to be reserved for hangings in the UK.

Unlucky 13

The number "13" has its own set of issues, as evidenced by the number of hotel floors and airline seat rows that skip from 12 directly to 14, avoiding that Unmentionably Evil Integer. In France, even the house numbers run 12, 12½, 14 and so on. But where did it all start?

Well, there is the oft-quoted Norse myth of 12 Norse Gods (Odin and 11 close god-friends) having an intimate dinner party at Valhalla. Loki, the god of mischief, gatecrashed the party, and convinced Hoder (or Hod), the blind god of darkness/winter, to attack Balder the Beautiful (or Good). Hoder killed Balder with an arrow tipped with mistletoe, several other gods died in the fighting, and the earth experienced darkness/winter for the first time. If it were me, I would think that the message from that Norse myth would be the entirely reasonable, *"Don't kill people, especially with mistletoe"*. But no, the Norse interpretation was the rather obscure, *"Don't have 13 people at dinner"*. A similar problem also plagued the Last Supper, with Judas turning up late, making the number present equal to "13".

The important thing is that as a result of these two stories, 13's reputation was on a downhill slide.

Another curious aspect to the number "13" is that the Babylonians (early mathematicians and astronomers) had "12", rather than "10", as the base of their numerical system. The number "10" is divisible only by "2" and "5", while "12" is divisible by "2", "3", "4" and "6". This is very handy. The Babylonians are also responsible for our 60 seconds in a minute, 60 minutes in an hour, and 24 hours in a day. But, while "12" is lovely and complete, "13" (which is just a little bit bigger than "12") is very difficult to work with. Maybe this helped make it "unlucky".

And while "12" is associated with the months in a year – the 12 signs of the Zodiac, the 12 gods of Olympus, the 12 tribes of Israel, the 12 apostles of Jesus and the 12 labours of Hercules – "13" is associated with that bewilderingly Lost Tribe of Israel.

If you're into feminism and conspiracy theories, then you'd probably know that the number "13" was linked to evil in an effort to disempower women, because women supposedly have 13 menstrual cycles each calendar year. Consider the 27,000-year-old carving of a female figure known as the "Earth Mother of Laussel". She holds a crescent-shaped horn with 13 notches (coincidence, I don't think so!).

Indeed, *fear* of the number "13" has its own special word,

It was to be the dinner party of the decade.
But nobody counted on...
THE 13TH GUEST
un film di DARIO ARGENTO
DAVID HEMMINGS · DARIA NICOLODI in THE 13TH GUEST con GABRIELE LAVIA
MACHA MERIL · EROS PAGNI · JUDAS ISCARIOT · e con la piccola NICOLETTA ELMI · e con GLAUCO MAURI
e con la partecipazione di CLARA CALAMAI
DARIO ARGENTO, BERNARDINO ZAPPONI
GIORGIO GASLINI
CLAUDIO ARGENTO
SEDA SPETTACOLI
regia di DARIO ARGENTO
CINERIZ

"triskaidekaphobia" (coined by Coriat in 1911 and first used popularly in the *New York Times* on 8 November 1953 in an article about the UN). The word comes from the Greek, with "tris" meaning "three", "kai" meaning "and", "deka" meaning "ten" and finally, "phobia" meaning "fear".

Unlucky Friday the 13th

Fear of Friday the 13th also has its own even more rarely used word, "paraskevidekatriaphobia".

But is Friday the 13th bad for your health?

By an amazing coincidence, this is the title of a paper in the *British Medical Journal*. It also seems to be the only "scientific" paper that analyses several common human statistics on a few sequential Fridays the 13th. The statistics the authors (Scanlon et al) chose were road traffic numbers, supermarket patronage and hospital Emergency Room admissions. They found that Friday the 13th is dangerous, and advised that, *"we may just have to accept that Friday the 13th is indeed unlucky for some and that it might be safer to stay at home"*.

However, non-medical readers of this paper would not notice the significance of the date of publication. The article appeared in the 18–25 December issue of the *British Medical Journal*. This is traditionally the comedy, end-of-year, anything-goes issue. When you actually read the paper and look at the numbers reported, you notice the authors had a lot of tongue-in-cheek fun simultaneously rejecting the numbers that did not fit their belief, while tirelessly torturing the remaining indifferent numbers into reluctant submission to "prove" their hypothesis.

There can be between one and three Friday the 13ths in a year. The next years that will have three Fridays the 13th are 2012 and 2015 – but I'm sure that the world's economics will survive the financial loss associated with those extra Fridays the 13th.

And if you waste your time worrying about any upcoming Friday the 13th, well I'm afraid that that's your bad luck.

It's easy to fight those infectious diseases that are caused by germs, such as viruses and bacteria. Just wash your hands after going to the toilet, and before touching food (and some people wash their hands *before* going to the toilet). That way, the germs won't get into your mouth.

Washing your hands is a simple yet effective thing to do. And it seems so easy to get it right – grab some soap, get it wet and start washing. So how come it was only very recently that we worked out the correct temperature for the water that we use to wash our hands?

On my 2009 Triumphal Spoken Word Tour of Taiwan, I was surprised to find that many of the elevator buttons were covered with cling wrap, and that an employee would wipe them clean with alcohol every hour. The locals were worried about the spread of H1N1 flu virus – as they'd already experienced the deaths associated with SARS when it broke out in that part of the world. So the use of cling wrap was easy to understand.

But the locals also insisted on washing their hands with soap, and the hottest water they could stand. Surprisingly, they could have cleaned their hands just as well with tepid water.

FLOATING SOAP - 1

During the American Civil War (1861–1865), the Procter family's soap-and-candle company supplied soap to the Union Army. In 1878, Harley Procter asked his cousin, James Gamble, to make a brand-new soap. He wanted it to be both nicely scented and pure white. They were good at their chemistry, and so their new White Soap frothed up a generous lather, even in cold water.

Part of the soap's production involved chemicals being mixed. One day, one of the workers forgot to switch off the mixing machine when he went to lunch. As a result, too much air became blended into the soapy solution. The worker didn't want to be wasteful and throw the frothy solution away, so he let it get fully processed into soap.

Some bars of this soap, "contaminated" with huge numbers of tiny bubbles, were delivered to a few shops. To everybody's surprise, favourable letters poured in from delighted customers. They loved this soap that simply would not vanish in the bath water – instead it forgivingly bobbed to the surface.

But "White Soap" was far too prosaic a name for such a wonderful product as floating soap. What would Harley Procter call it? He worried about a new name long and hard. One Sunday morning in church, his Pastor happened to read the 45th Psalm. *"All thy garments smell of myrrh, and alloes, and cassia, out of the ivory palaces, whereby they have made thee glad."*

So that's how Ivory Soap came into existence, and got its name.

Chemistry of Soap 101

Water is fine for removing some types of "mess" from your hands or clothes. If the mess dissolves in water, then the water will "pick up" or dissolve it and your hands or clothes are left clean.

But if the messy stuff is made from fat and grease, it will not dissolve in water. Now you have a problem – a mess that water cannot shift – and you are left with dirty hands or clothes.

Soap is the magic stuff that can shift greasy dirt. That's because it is made up from rather special molecules (a molecule is just a bunch of atoms joined together). Each one of these molecules has two ends that are very different. One end "loves" water, will dissolve in water, and will "stick" to water molecules. This end is called the "hydrophilic" end. The other end "loves" fats and grease, will dissolve them, but "hates" water. This end is called the "hydrophobic" end.

Using the fat-loving end, these molecules grab onto the grease, dissolve it and remove it from your skin or clothes. The other end of the molecule, the water-loving end, ensures that these molecules (still hanging onto their load of grease or fat) dissolve in the water.

So thanks to the "special" molecules in soap, the greasy dirty fat has left your skin or clothes, and is now floating in the water. And if you wash the soapy "rinse" water down the sink, your hands or clothes will be left clean.

FLOATING SOAP - 2

Two inventions hit the American market in October 1879 – Procter and Gamble's Ivory Soap, and Thomas Edison's incandescent light bulb.

Harley Procter's company made both soap and candles. He was smart enough to realise that this new-fangled "incandescent light bulb" would kill the market for candles. So he wound down the candle side of the business, and threw all his energy into advertising his miraculous floating soap.

His first stroke of advertising genius came when he looked at the chemical analysis reports of his Ivory floating soap. One chemical laboratory found his soap had impurities at a level of only *"56/100 of 1%"*. He turned this around into the statement that, *"Ivory Soap is 99 and 44/100% pure"*.

His second stroke of advertising genius was to emphasise the "mildness and purity" of Ivory Soap – it couldn't hurt the delicate skin of a baby. Harley Procter gave shopkeepers full-size cardboard display posters of a baby – the "Ivory Baby".

Even today, marketing courses quote his concepts as one of the most effective advertising campaigns ever.

Chemistry of Soap 202

Soap is the congealed slippery gloop that is left behind after you boil together just two substances – a fat and an alkali. It was probably invented by accident. Sometime in the distant past, somebody tried to remove some animal fat from their clothes by rubbing it with water and the ashes from a fire.

If you burn plants, the remaining ash is rich in potassium carbonate – which is an alkali. Some 4000 years ago, the Hittites of Asia Minor added the ash of the soapwort plant to water, and washed their hands with it. Around the same time, the Samarians of Ur used alkali solutions for the same purpose.

Today we make soaps in three stages.

Stage one is "saponification". You simply boil together a fat and an alkali. A fat can be vegetable fats (olive oil, coconut oil, etc) or animal fats (beef tallow, goat fat, etc). Alkalis can be potassium salts, sodium salts, and so on, and one type is easily found in the ashes of plants (potassium carbonate). (Another name for an "alkali" is a "base" or "lye".)

Stage two is drying. A slippery solid is left after the water has been boiled and evaporated away.

Stage three is milling (fine grinding). This stage ensures that any over-dried lumps of soap get ground so finely that they no longer feel gritty. For extra "fineness" or smoothness in the soap, there can be up to three millings.

This process will give you a basic soap.

Chemistry of Soap 303

You can "tailor-make" many different types of soap by adding various substances.

If you use potassium rather than sodium for your alkali, you will get a "soft" soap that is more soluble in water than a sodium-based soap. If you use fats like tallow or palm oil, you will get a slow-lathering soap that is gentle to the skin and that will cleanse well.

If you use coconut oil, you will get a quick-lathering soap that will work with sea water (a so-called "marine" soap). If you use olive or peanut oil, you will get a soap of a lovely soft feel – but it may change colour or become rancid.

Finally, if you add abrasives such as chalk or talc, you will get a good work soap suitable for a tradesperson.

WHITER AND BRIGHTER

You might have seen or heard the phrase *"whiter than white"* associated with washing detergents. Strange but true, this common advertising phrase is not a lie.

Way back in 1929, the German chemist Hans Krais first thought of adding microscopic amounts of "ultraviolet fluorescent chemicals" to washing powders. These ultraviolet fluorescent chemicals were formulated so that they would stick to the fibres of your clothes, and never come free.

The way they work is all to do with sunlight.

The "light" from the sun has various components. There's the "visible light" that our eyes are sensitive to, and that we use for vision. This visible light lands on our white clothing, and is reflected into our eyeballs – so our brains see our clothing as being " white".

There's also the invisible "infra-red" light that we cannot see with our eyes. However, we *sense* infra-red with our skin as "heat".

And there's also the invisible "ultraviolet" light that none of our senses can detect. When it hits our skin, it helps make useful vitamin D. And we all know how ultraviolet light is implicated in causing various types of skin cancers.

But when this invisible ultraviolet light hits the "ultraviolet fluorescent chemicals" in our clothes, it excites them. These chemicals take in the invisible ultraviolet light and "squirt" out visible light. So suddenly, there is an extra amount of white light being emitted from your white shirt. Yes, your white shirt is now truly "whiter than white".

But there is an extra advantage. This new and extra white light is not pure white – it's a little bluish. This bluish tinge helps counteract any yellowing that might have happened over time to your white shirt.

History of Soap

Something similar to soap was made in ancient Babylon around 2800 BC, and in Egypt around 1550 BC. Around 600 BC, the seagoing Phoenicians made a soap similar to the soaps we have today. They added the ash of plants (rich in potassium) and the fat of goats to water – and boiled it. After evaporating the water and letting the residue cool, they were left with a waxy solid – soap. The Phoenicians were great traders, and sold it to the Greeks and Romans for cleansing purposes, and to the Gauls as a laxative (according to the Roman writer Pliny the Elder, who was a little critical of the Gauls).

The ancient Celts of Britannia also made soap from the ashes of plants and the fat of animals. They called it "saipo", which gives us the modern word "soap".

By 300 AD Zosimos of Panopolis in Egypt, a chemist, was skilled in soap-making, and wrote about it. There was a soap-makers' guild in Naples in the sixth century, and in Spain in the eighth century. Also in the eighth century, the Arab intellectual Jabir ibn Hayyan wrote about using soap for washing the body.

The production of soap waxed and waned, depending upon the knowledge and beliefs of the day. For a while in the 11th century, Venice was a major production centre for soap (after Marseilles had had its turn, and then Genoa). The first English soap-makers set up shop in Bristol around the end of the 12th century.

In the Middle Ages, the Church loudly warned against exposing the flesh, and soap production virtually ceased. But when medical scientists realised that bacteria caused disease, soap production increased.

Queen Elizabeth I (1533–1603) is claimed to have boasted that she had enough soap to have a bath once every three months – whether she needed it or not. In 1549, soap was so uncommon in some parts of Europe it was considered remarkable that a box of soap had been given to the Duchess of Juelich. And in 1672, when Lady von Schleinitz was sent some soap, it had to be accompanied by specific instructions on how to use it.

In the 19th century, the German chemist Baron Justus von Liebig claimed that the more soap a nation used, the more civilised it was. In the late 1860s, French perfumers introduced the first scented soaps.

Types of Skin Bacteria

There are roughly 100,000 bacteria living on each square centimetre of our skin. These bacteria fall into two main classes – the "resident bacteria" that live there all the time, and the "transient bacteria" that drop in from time to time.

The resident bacteria have evolved and adapted to survive on the skin. In general, they don't cause disease – in fact, by living on your skin, they stop the nasty bacteria from getting a foothold. They like to live in little "caves" in the skin, such as hair follicles, nail folds, and the sebum-producing sebaceous glands. Usually, hand-washing removes only half of the resident bacteria.

However, if you do continually expose your skin to the nasty transient bacteria, they may become permanent residents, especially if you have skin damage. Luckily, hand-washing removes practically all of the transient bacteria. In most cases, the transient bacteria are easy to wash off from the skin. First, they usually don't have the "adhesion characteristics" needed to stick onto the skin. Second, they are usually somewhat suppressed by the skin's resident bacteria.

These transient bacteria can include nasty disease-delivering pathogens, or harmless species that happen to live in the local environment, or bacteria from the spoilage of foods and the like.

THE PERFECT SOAP

The ideal soap will wet your skin and temporarily neutralise its slightly acidic barrier. Then, with a bit of mechanical agitation, the soap should remove the stuck-on fatty mixture of bacteria, grease, dirt and debris from the skin. Finally, the soap should be able to hold the fatty mixture suspended in the water. Once it's floating in water, it's easy for clean water to rinse away the dirt.

The soap should also not damage the skin.

It would be nice if the soap's appearance was simple and elegant, and if it felt velvety in your hand.

Some people like a lather that is rich and long-lasting – maybe so thick that you could use it as a shaving cream. But a lather like this could dry your skin too much.

BACTERIA LIVE ON SOAP?

Is it true that bacteria live on soap and can be transmitted from person to person?

Most bacteria die fairly quickly when they come into contact with soap, but they vary considerably in their susceptibility. Some will die within 10 seconds, while others take 20 minutes. We still don't fully understand how soaps destroy the bacteria (maybe it has something to do with the fatty cell wall of bacteria?). However, soaps are not totally successful in destroying all bacteria, because you can always find bacteria living on soap.

When you compare "regular" soaps with "antibacterial" soaps, you find no real difference in the populations of bacteria living on the soap. So you can't really trust all the advertising claims that are made about "antibacterial" soap. One claim is that they can reduce body odour by killing the bacteria that "eat" our sweat and other secretions.

In fact, it is thought that antibacterial soaps could lead to bacteria developing unwanted resistance to antibiotics. So you should probably avoid using so-called antibacterial soaps.

There's another complication regarding soap harbouring bacteria.

When you test soaps for bacterial populations over a period of time, you find that different populations of bacteria sporadically appear and disappear. So it's better to store your bath soap in a way that lets it dry out – because the drying out tends to reduce the bacterial count. You also find that over a week, the total bacterial count does not increase, even though the bacteria are continually multiplying. Somehow, their numbers are being kept constant. Perhaps they are being mechanically washed off when a person uses that soap to wash their hands, or perhaps they are being killed by some unknown action of the soap, or ...

But the bottom line is straightforward. In general, the risk of bacteria being carried from one person to another via the soap is so small as to be microscopic.

Types of Infection

You can classify infections into two main classes – those that you get from the community around you, and those that are associated with you receiving some health care or assistance, such as from a hospital or at childcare.

First, let's consider community-based infections.

Suppose you compare school kids who wash their hands four times each day with kids who don't wash their hands at all. The hand-washers have 24 per cent fewer sick days due to respiratory infections, and 51 per cent fewer days off due to tummy problems.

In fact, proper hand-washing could eliminate about half of all cases of food poisoning, also known as "foodborne illness". Food handlers who carry a nasty germ but who do not have any symptoms are responsible for about *one-third* of all outbreaks of food poisoning. Those outbreaks wouldn't have happened if those food handlers had had good hand-washing habits. Every hour, 800 Australians come down with food poisoning.

A study which looked at foodborne illness outbreaks in the USA between 1973 and 1997 found that poor personal hygiene caused about 30 per cent of these outbreaks.

Second, let's take health care–linked infections.

Each year, hundreds of millions of patients around the world suffer a health care-associated infection. These infections prolong hospital stays, cause serious illnesses, lead to long-term disability and can sometimes kill. From a financial standpoint, they inflict massive costs on the patient and on the health-care system. The annual costs are estimated to be about $6 billion in the USA, and about £1 billion in the UK.

In the USA, one out of every 136 hospital patients gets seriously ill from picking up an infection in a hospital, which works out to two million cases each year – and out of those, about 80,000 people die. That's over 220 deaths every day of the year. In the UK, infections associated with health care infect more than 320,000 people each year, of whom about 5000 die. The figures are far worse in poor countries than in wealthy countries.

Hand-washing makes so much financial sense. One study in the Russian Federation looked at the cost of one single health care–associated infection in a neonatal intensive care unit. The cost of that single infection (about US$1100) would cover the cost of 3265 days of using hand antiseptic.

One World Health Organisation study looked at 55 hospitals in 14 countries scattered across South East Asia, Europe, the Eastern Mediterranean and the Western Pacific. In this study, about 9 per cent of all hospital patients picked up an infection. At any given moment, about 1.4 million people in the world are suffering from the complications of an infection associated with health care.

Spread of Infection

In the hospital system, if just one person in a large department does not wash their hands, disastrous results can occur.

The mathematics of it is that medical staff who treated all the patients (even if only briefly) were much more efficient at spreading germs than staff who saw only a few patients (even if they spent most of the shift with them). Take the example of a department with a total of 22 staff. Suppose that one of those 22 staff saw all patients – and never washed their own hands. That one person caused more infections by themselves, than if the entire staff of 22 did not wash their hands one-quarter of the time.

You've probably heard of the rather nasty bacterium called "Golden Staph" – its scientific name is *Staphylococcus aureus*. It does bad things to people, but the good news is that it can be stopped with antibiotics. The bad news is that after 75 years of using antibiotics, a few strains of the Golden Staph have developed resistance.

So bad things have happened.

In a nursery with 45 health-care workers, one person who was a carrier of antibiotic-resistant Golden Staph did not wash his or her hands – set off an epidemic. In another hospital, a single respiratory therapist had chronic sinusitis with (again) antibiotic-resistant Golden Staph – and again, they did not wash their own hands, and set off a hospital-wide epidemic that infected 32 people.

According to the US Center for Disease Control and Prevention, *"hand washing is the single most important means of preventing the spread of infection"*.

SOAP – THE GOOD, THE BAD AND THE UGLY

Soap is terrific for washing your hands and getting the dirt off, and it's also very useful for washing your bottom. But it is probably not the best substance for washing the rest of you.

If you have dry skin and your ancestors come from northern climes, and you have red hair and pale skin and pale eyes, then soap is definitely not for you. This is because soap removes fat from your skin.

There are two types of fat mixed together on your skin – one comes from dead skin cells, and another (called sebum) comes from the sebaceous glands. All soaps, even the so-called "medicated" soaps, wash these natural fats from your skin. Your body tries to make more fats to protect your skin. It can't make your skin cells die any faster, but it can crank up the production of sebum. So once you start washing with soap, you change the natural balance of your skin fat to have too much sebum. This sebum-rich fat gets colonised by bacteria. They eat it, and leave behind "free fatty acids", which can be as corrosive as hydrochloric acid. The free fatty acids can attack the skin, and set off acne.

When I was working as a doctor in the Dermatology Clinic at the Children's Hospital in Sydney, I saw red-headed kids whose arms looked like they had been scalded with boiling water, or painted with red paint. But once we took them off soap and put them on sorbolene, the majority healed up as if by magic.

We used "sorbolene with 10 per cent glycerine" – the glycerine is what makes it more manageable. I was so impressed with it that I immediately gave up soap (apart from on the hands and groin). I always use sorbolene with 10 per cent glycerine now. The last time I used soap on my body (apart from my hands and bottom) was 1984.

I use it by standing under the warm shower and getting all of my skin wet. Then I get a glob of sorbolene, about half the size of my little finger, and rub it between my hands, as though I'm trying to get a lather. (If you like a good lather, you're out of luck – you can't get a lather with sorbolene.)

Then I rub this white stuff on my face. Then I get another glob, and rub it on one arm and my first hairy bit, my armpit. I repeat this for the other arm. And then I repeat this process for my chest, and my back, and work my way down my body until I get to my feet. Then I wash it all off my body.

I then turn off the water, and pat myself dry with a towel, leaving my skin just a tiny bit moist. Then I get another glob, and rub it over my whole body, especially my face and neck, feet, and the backs of my hands. Finally, I walk around for a minute until the water evaporates off my skin, and I'm done.

Surgical Scrub

In general, soap does not kill bacteria upon immediate contact. Instead, soap dissolves (or emulsifies) the mixture of dead skin cells, dried sweat, dust, oils and yes, bacteria, into a sloppy emulsion, and then the water washes it away. This mixture is rather "fatty", so you need soap, rather than plain water, to successfully remove it.

As a medical student, I learnt how to scrub up (to clean my hands) for operating theatre. It was nothing like the way that I had previously washed my hands.

I'd apply enough soap to cover the entire surface of my hands. Then I'd vigorously rub my hands together under running water – palm to palm flat, palm to palm with fingers interlaced, palm to back of other hand, backs of fingers to opposing palms, rotational rubbing of one thumb in clenched palm of other hand and so forth. I would finish off with a single-use towel to remove the water (and any germs it might contain). Studies show that some areas of the hand (such as the fingers and the web between the thumb and the first finger) are not as thoroughly washed as other areas.

The "drying towel" is an important part of the hand-washing process. There are still lots of germs in the thin layer of water remaining on your skin – and the towel removes these. We would use our elbows to turn off the water.

A full "surgical" scrub would take up to six minutes.

TOO HOT

A temperature of 45 degrees Celsius is near the human discomfort threshold – indeed, second- and third-degree burns have been observed at not much over 43 degrees Celsius in the elderly.

More specifically, third-degree burns have resulted from a two-second exposure to 66 degrees Celsius water, a six-second exposure to 60 degrees Celsius water, and a thirty-second exposure to water at 54.4 degrees Celsius.

When I was a junior doctor I would see 20 to 40 patients in a morning. I did *not* wear a tie, because that could brush over one patient and carry their germs to the next patient. But I did wash my hands between each patient – originally with tepid water, and later with alcohol-based hand wash.

How Hot Should the Water Be?

It's definitely good to remove germs from your hands, in terms of general hygiene. It's especially important if you work in food service.

Over the years, many studies have looked at issues such as the type of soap (plain or antibacterial, liquid or bar), the quantity of soap used, nail brush or not, drying technique (paper versus cloth towels, air-drying versus towels) and the use of instant hand-sanitising liquids.

But very few studies have looked at the effect of water temperature on hand-cleaning. This all changed in 2000 at the US Conference for Food Protection, when this topic was very intensely discussed.

In 1938, Dr P. B. Price published his summary of 80 studies that he carried out over a nine-year period. He had experimented with water at temperatures from 24 degrees Celsius up to 56 degrees Celsius. He found that the temperature made no real difference in how well the hands were cleansed of germs. The most significant factor in removing germs was the vigorousness of scrubbing the hands.

In a 2002 study by Dr Barry Michaels, hands were soiled with ground beef contaminated with *E. coli* bacteria, and then washed with soap and water at five different temperatures ranging from 4.4 degrees Celsius to 48.9 degrees Celsius. After the hand-washings at different temperatures, there was no real difference in the number of bacteria left on the skin – either permanent resident bacteria, or transient immigrant bacteria. The only real difference was that the more vigorous the scrubbing, the more bacteria were removed. The friction of rubbing is more effective at removing transient bacteria (which are more likely to be nasty) than resident bacteria.

On one hand, you might think that hot water would provide more energy to both make a lather and provide the energy needed to melt and/or dissolve fats and oils on the skin. But if the warm/hot water is flowing over your hands, it will very rapidly cool to skin temperature. However, water will tend to keep its temperature if it's in a bowl.

So hot water does not have any advantage in removing germs, but it can make some soaps more irritating to the skin, and cause contact dermatitis. One study noted, "*… temperature of water used for hand washing should not be guided by antibacterial effects but comfort, which is in the tepid to warm temperature range. The usage of tepid water instead of hot water also has economic benefits*".

People find it easier to wash their hands more frequently if the water temperature is less hot.

In the USA, the 2001 Food Code lowered the recommended hand-washing water temperature to 37.8 degrees Celsius. The majority of soaps are designed to lather most effectively at around 35 degrees Celsius.

Anyhow, it's impossible to kill the bacteria on your skin via the temperature of the water you use to wash your hands. The temperature needed to kill bacteria is over 80 degrees Celsius. If water is hot enough to kill bacteria, it will definitely scald you.

So how did this myth that hot water was necessary for effective hand- washing arise? Probably it is much easier to measure and regulate water temperature than it is to regulate how effectively you scrub, rub and dry your hands.

Hospital laundries did away with hot-water washes of clothes and sheets years ago. And health-care staff can go ahead and wash their hands with tepid water between each patient – and their hands will be just as clean, and less likely to be damaged. Which is a handy hint …

Grab some soap, get it wet and start washing!

SORBOLENE

If you like a good lather,
you're out of luck.

Dr Karl brand guarantee

HOW MUCH WATER?

How much water should you run over your hands each minute so that the bacteria, dirt and debris will be reliably carried away? Some people quote 9 litres per minute. Perhaps a well-designed nozzle could spray less water over the hands and still be effective.

Professor Fred Hollows (the eye doctor who did wonderful work in delivering cheap and high-quality eye care to poor and underprivileged peoples) once told me that the average person needs 100 litres of water per day to stay healthy. Less than 5 per cent of that water goes directly into our mouth – most is used for other purposes.

He said that nomadic peoples would spend most of the day walking, and so every day they would walk away from their wastes, dirt and debris. Nomads didn't need a lot of water. (In the case of our family on the "El Camino" pilgrimage in Spain, we found it easy to walk eight hours every day.) But now that most of us are no longer nomadic, and spend most of the day sitting, every day we need 100 litres of water to wash away our wastes, dirt and debris.

NO SOAP FOR KIDS?

According to leading dermatologist Dr Peter Foley in Victoria, one-third of the kids aged five and under he studied had dermatitis. The ratio of one-third of a population of kids having dermatitis is one of the highest such ratios ever found.

"Derm" means "skin", while "itis" means "inflammation of". In this study, the most common site was the skin creases (front of elbow, behind knee), followed by the face, trunk and limbs. One-third of the parents did not know that their child had dermatitis.

Dr Foley and his fellow dermatologists examined 1116 kids at centres for childcare, maternal health and child health. About one-third were badly affected, but two-thirds had mild or moderate cases. Of all the kids who had dermatitis, about one-quarter had no family history of asthma, dermatitis, or hay fever – but three-quarters did. The highest incidence happened around when they were one year old – 40 per cent of all one year olds in this Victorian study had dermatitis. The most common stereotype was the child of an Asian-born mother, living during winter, in an urban area.

Dr Foley advised that young kids shouldn't be washed with soap. He said that soap dried the skin and aggravated dermatitis, *"Most dermatologists in Australia would say to parents that in the first few years of life, kids don't need soap"*. Referring to preschool kids, he said *"it's a bit hard to just justify soap on the skin of any child"*.

Humans have been domesticating cats for at least 10,000 years. They are often admired for their lovely coats. While most of today's 600 million domesticated cats have a dark coat, about 5 per cent of them have a white coat. It's often thought that all white cats are deaf. But the truth about white cats being deaf is this: some white cats are deaf and some are not, depending on their eye colour (and other stuff we don't understand yet).

But to uncover this simple truth, we had to learn much about genetics and biochemistry.

History of White Cats

Back in 1859, Charles Darwin wrote his revolutionary *Origin of Species*. Most people think that this was his final and definitive work on evolution.

But no.

This Modest Tome was just the Short Version, the Reader's Digest-type summary. Darwin spent several more years expanding his ideas and in 1868 released his two-volume Big Version, called *The Variation Of Animals And Plants Under Domestication*. (What a title!) In this Bigger Book he wrote, in Volume II, pages 329 to 330 that, *"white cats, if they have blue eyes, are almost always deaf"*. He reiterates this on page 354, *"So it is with the organs of sight and hearing; for instance, white cats with blue eyes are almost always deaf"*.

Over the years, various scientists have tried to understand why white cats with blue eyes are usually deaf.

By 1934, some very interesting studies had looked at white cats that had different coloured eyes. They found that these cats were usually deaf on the side with the blue eye, and usually had normal hearing on the side with the yellow-green eye.

What was going on? Why should white fur and a blue eye sometimes lead to deafness?

To understand, we need a little biochemistry.

COLOURS OF IRIS

The iris of the eye can have many different colours – blue, light green, dark green, brown and so on. Surprisingly, the different colours in the iris do not come from many different-coloured dyes.

No, there is only one coloured dye in the iris – melanin.

If you have lots of melanin particles your iris is dark; fewer melanin particles give a green tinge; while very little melanin gives blue eyes.

My Favourite Amino Acid

Back in medical school, my favourite amino acid was tyrosine. In the plant world, tyrosine is involved in the chemicals that make photosynthesis possible, and in the manufacture of the painkiller opium.

Like the other 19 amino acids, tyrosine is used by the body as a building block to make general proteins. But the body also has a special use for tyrosine. It modifies tyrosine to make some wonderful and special chemicals. These include adrenaline, thyroid hormones, brain neurotransmitters such as DOPA, and the amazing and still-mysterious melanin.

There are at least three different varieties of melanin. It can be black, dark brown or dark red. It turns out that melanin gives your skin and hair its colour, but it does other stuff as well. Melanin in the ear drum helps dampen unwanted acoustic waves to improve

your hearing, while melanin in the skin protects you from skin cancer due to ultraviolet light.

And of course, melanin is also a colouring dye. If there's no melanin in a cat's fur, it will have a white coat. And if there's very little melanin in the iris of its eyes, it will have blue eyes.

So we know that white cats with blue eyes are like this because of low melanin levels in parts of their bodies – but how is this related to deafness?

Embryology

The answer lies in embryology.

At conception, an egg meets up with a sperm. Shortly afterwards, the fertilised egg splits and splits again, and soon develops three separate sets of stem cells.

One, the endoderm, eventually turns into your gut (and other tissues). Another, the mesoderm, eventually turns into your skeletal muscle (and other tissues). But the third one, the ectoderm, turns into the central nervous system (which includes your hearing and your sight) and (wait for it) pigment cells. That common origin is the connection between "hearing" and "pigments" (and why "deafness" can happen in "white" cats).

It seems that in our deaf, blue-eyed, white-furred feline friends, there is a developmental fault in the ectoderm. This unknown fault is the link between the white coat and blue eyes (low melanin from pigment cells) and deafness (melanin acting "somewhere" in the central nervous system, or at least the part relating to "hearing"). However, because there are many genes involved, not *all* white, blue-eyed cats are deaf. About 30 per cent of white cats have blue eyes, and about 70 per cent of these are deaf. Of the white cats that do not have blue eyes, about 15 per cent are deaf.

So there you have it. Abnormalities with the chemical melanin are the reason why white cats with blue eyes are quite likely to be deaf, but not always. And next time you say, "Here here, kitty kitty", don't be disappointed if it blanks (blancs) you ...

CAT HEARING

A cat with normal hearing can hear frequencies as shrill as 65 kilohertz. This is far beyond our pathetic human 20 kilohertz.

The Job Description of Santa Claus – that rosy-cheeked, rotund, bearded, elderly white Caucasian male – is to give gifts to good children and coal to bad children at Christmas time. But in keeping with modern norms, along with the Job Description, Santa has had a scientific Time-And-Motion Job Evaluation of his work. It turns out that he has to visit 1000 houses each second and travel between them at about 1000 kilometres per second!

The Original St Nicholas

The legend of Santa Claus begins with Nicholas, a Turkish man who was born somewhere around the middle of the third century AD (245 AD or 280 AD, depending on the sources), in the town of Patara, in the coastal region of Lycia, in south-eastern Turkey. As a child Nicholas was already very holy, and would fast twice a week – every Wednesday and Friday. When his parents died, he entered the priesthood and began a career of performing miracles and good works. In one instance, on a boat journey to Palestine,

Nicholas was able to calm the violent ocean by spreading his arms. As a result, he became the patron saint of sailors. On another occasion, he brought back to life three children whom a butcher had chopped up and dumped into a tub of salt water. (I hope that this didn't happen on Christmas Eve.)

While he was still quite young, Nicholas was made the Bishop of Myra. He made the ruling Roman officials very angry because of his generosity to the poor, and because he converted many people to Christianity. Once, he gave three bags of gold to three sisters who would have otherwise been forced into a life of prostitution. And every December 6, he would deliver small gifts to children.

Nicholas was eventually imprisoned during the reign of the cruel Roman Emperor Gaius Diocletianus. Surprisingly, the Emperor gave up all his power at the age of 60 after a reign of despotism and terror to live on a farm and grow cabbages. He was replaced by the Emperor Constantine, who freed Nicholas, and later converted to Christianity. In 325 AD, Nicholas attended the first Church Council at Nicaea, which was convened by Constantine.

Nicholas is said to have died on 6 December 342 AD. He was buried at Myra, in Turkey, but in 1087, his remains were transported to Bari in Italy, where they today reside in the basilica of San Nicola.

SANTA WAS STOLEN

Around the turn of the first millennium, the pilgrimage industry was very profitable. But in Italy, the town of Bari was getting none of the action.

The town elders decided to mount an expedition to sail to Turkey to *steal* the remains of St Nicholas. They also paid for a basilica in which to display them. It turned out to be a good investment. The town of Bari became such a popular pilgrimage site that the revenue from the pilgrims easily covered the cost of the expedition and the basilica.

The Myth Begins

From a Christian point of view, St Nicholas was a good thing. He replaced a few pagan figureheads who also gave gifts. These included Berchta and Knecht Ruprecht from Germany, and Befana from the Roman Empire.

By the Middle Ages, much of Europe honoured St Nicholas as a good man. He was the patron saint of Greece, Sicily and Russia, of guilds and charitable fraternities, and also of children, merchants, pawnbrokers and unmarried girls. Christians would give each other presents on 6 December, which is the feast day of St Nicholas. (Greek folklore has a very similar tale about Basil of Caesarea who, like St Nicholas, gave presents. Basil's feast day is 1 January, so this is when the Greeks exchange gifts.)

ENCOUNTER WITH REALITY

How do kids deal with the "reality" of Santa Claus – in other words, that he really isn't real?

In 1994, Drs Anderson and Prentice interviewed 52 kids who no longer believed in Santa Claus. About half of the kids had worked out the truth by themselves, and about a third had been told by their parents.

They had worked this out at an average age of 7.2 years. Surprisingly, kids back in 1896 had made this discovery at roughly the same age.

Overall, the parents were keen for their kids to believe in Santa. The kids were usually positive about realising the truth. But the parents were generally sad about their kids' discovery.

But the veneration of St Nicholas lessened during the Protestant Reformation of the 16th century, when he was "expelled" from most European countries. In fact, there was a big swing against even celebrating Christmas. In 1740 in New England, the Puritans treated Christmas as just another working day. Even as late as the 1860s, Christmas Day was just a regular work and school day in Massachusetts.

Back in Europe, however, the Dutch kept the tradition of St Nicholas alive, and shifted it from 6 December to 25 December. Children prepared for the annual nocturnal arrival of St Nicholas by placing two wooden clogs by the fireplace. They would each be filled with straw – a snack for St Nicholas's donkey (note, a donkey, not a reindeer). As a reciprocal act of generosity, St Nicholas would take a small gift from the back of the donkey and place one in each clog.

Because he was the patron saint of sailors, a likeness of St Nicholas was carved into the prow of the very first Dutch ship that sailed to America. In fact, the very first church that was built in the city of New Amsterdam (later rechristened New York) was named after St Nicholas. In Holland, the Dutch spelled Saint Nicholas as "Sint Nikolass". But when they were in America, this changed to "Sinter Klass". When the English took control of New Amsterdam from the Dutch, they turned "Sinter Klass" to "Santa Claus".

BELIEFS IN SANTA – GOOD OR BAD?

Back in 1966, Dr B. C. Nelms, the editor of the *Journal of Paediatric Healthcare*, spoke about Santa to a parent. The parent said that *"she would never lie to her children and that parents who support a belief in Santa are wrong, and that their children will have trouble trusting their parents in the future"*.

Certainly, back in 1951, Dr Sereno discovered that *"when children are involved in the Santa belief against their will, they will feel their parents lied to them"*. Other negative aspects of the Santa belief are its overcommercialisation, and the use of Santa as a bribe for good behaviour.

But on the positive side, the kids believe that there's somebody besides their parents who cares for them. And for children fantasies, such as Santa, can help them deal with the real world. Santa is a symbol for altruism and the spirit of giving – and surely that's not a bad thing.

Santa Gets Reindeers

The next stage in the evolution of Santa Claus occurred in 1809. The popular author Washington Irving, writing under the pseudonym of Diedrich Knickerbocker, wrote a book called *History Of New York From The Beginning Of The World To The End Of Dutch Dynasty*. It was actually published on St Nicholas Day, 6 December. Irving wrote about a small, elfin, pipe-smoking St Nicholas, who would plunge down chimneys to deliver gifts to children.

The next major addition to the Santa Claus legend came in 1823, when Clement Clarke Moore wrote a poem called *A Visit From Saint Nicholas* that began with the words, *"Twas the night before Christmas"*. This poem was the first reference to Santa flying through the sky, and the first time that Santa was linked to *"eight tiny reindeer"*. They were originally named Dasher, Dancer, Prancer, Vixen, Comet, Cupid, Dunder and Blixem. The last two names were later changed to Donner and Blitzen.

Moore did not compose this poem to make money – he did it just so that he could read it privately to his children on Christmas Eve. But one of Moore's friends, without asking him, mailed a copy of the enchanting poem to a newspaper – the *Sentinel*, in Troy, New York – where it was first published on 23 December 1923. Something about the poem caught the popular imagination, and it spread like wildfire. But because Professor Moore was a classical scholar, he was at first ashamed to admit that he had written a children's poem. By the time he finally admitted authorship in 1838, almost every American child knew the poem by heart.

WHY FLYING REINDEER?

We don't really know where the idea of flying reindeer came from. But one theory explains it by the hallucinogenic fungus, the fly agaric mushroom.

Clement Clarke Moore wrote the famous poem, *A Visit from Saint Nicholas*, but his day job was as a Professor of Oriental Languages and Theology. As such, he was familiar with the religious rituals of the Siberian people.

In north-west Siberia, the Koryak, Kamchadal and Chukchi people all worshipped the "Great Reindeer Spirit". The tribal witch doctor, or Shaman, is the only person in the tribe who can talk with this spirit. To do this, the shaman first eats the fly agaric hallucinogenic mushroom. He then flies through the smoke hole in the roof of the hut to the spirit world to collect various software – songs, stories, dances and messages – and brings them back as presents for the tribe.

Perhaps this is why Moore added flying reindeers to the Santa legend.

Santa Gets Fat

Back in the 1800s St Nicholas, or Santa Claus, was a tall, slim, elegant person, rather than a jolly fat man. A cartoonist called Thomas Nast evolved Santa to the next stage. Nast had a big influence on today's culture via his cartoons. He invented the symbols of the elephant for the Republican Party in America and of the donkey for the Democrats.

He also gave us the roly-poly Santa Claus with the big belly and rosy cheeks. Nast did a series of Christmas drawings from 1863 until 1886 for *Harper's Weekly*. Over those 20 or so years, Santa gradually changed from the tiny elf that Professor Moore wrote about to the bearded, slightly overweight, bell-ringing Santa that we know today. Nast was the first to tell us of Santa's workshop at the North Pole and how he had a list of good and bad children.

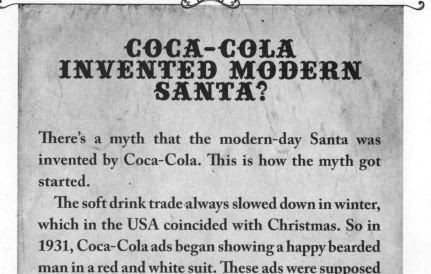

COCA-COLA INVENTED MODERN SANTA?

There's a myth that the modern-day Santa was invented by Coca-Cola. This is how the myth got started.

The soft drink trade always slowed down in winter, which in the USA coincided with Christmas. So in 1931, Coca-Cola ads began showing a happy bearded man in a red and white suit. These ads were supposed to kick along sales during the colder months. Coca-Cola commissioned the illustrator, Haddon Sundblom, who used his next-door neighbour, Lou Prentice, as a model for the new Santa.

The Coca-Cola version of Santa became very popular – jolly, a white beard, red coat with white collar and cuffs, and black leather boots and belt. It was convenient that the corporate colours of Coca-Cola were also red and white …

The Santa image appeared everywhere, including on the back cover of the Christmas issue of *National Geographic* magazine for 27 of the next 30 years. These ads led to the myth that the modern image of Santa Claus was created by Coca-Cola, and invented to sell soft drinks.

However, Santa's image had already been around for over half a century. In 1927, the *New York Times* noted that, already *"a standardised Santa Claus appears to New York children. Height, weight, stature are almost exactly standardised, as are the red garments, the hood and the white whiskers. The pack full of toys, ruddy cheeks and nose, bushy eyebrows and a jolly, paunchy effect are also inevitable parts of the requisite make up"*.

Indeed, another soft drink company had already used Santa to sell its products. In 1915, White Rock Beverages used his image to sell mineral water, and in 1923, followed up with ginger ale. So Coca-Cola did not invent modern Santa.

The final stage in the evolution of Santa Claus occurred in 1939 when "Rudolph" popped into existence. The Montgomery Ward department store in Chicago wanted something new and jazzy that Santa Claus could give out to parents and children. Robert May, who wrote advertisements for Montgomery Ward, suggested that they hand out an illustrated poem. He came up with the idea of the reindeer with the red nose.

May was pretty keen on alliteration, and needed a reindeer name that began with the letter "R". Not everybody liked the names "Rollo" or "Reginald", but his four-year-old daughter's suggestion of "Rudolph" was very well received. So at Christmas 1939, 2.4 million copies of a poem called "Rudolph The Red Nosed Reindeer" were given away at Montgomery Ward stores across the USA.

In 1947 Johnny Marks, a friend of Robert's, decided to turn the poem into a song. But nobody would sing it for him until 1949 when Gene Autry recorded it. Until the 1980s the original version of the "Rudolph The Red Nosed Reindeer" was the second bestselling record of all time after Bing Crosby's "White Christmas". More than 80 million records have been sold in over 300 different versions.

MILITARY RADAR AND SANTA

Back in 1955, the Sears Roebuck store in Colorado Springs, Colorado, invited children to phone Santa and talk to him. The phone number given in the advertisement was ME 2-6681. Unfortunately, that was the unlisted phone number of CONAD (Continental Air Defence Command). CONAD was responsible for finding and tracking any possible aerial threats to the USA – and it was located in Colorado Springs.

The first phone call for Santa went straight to the Director of Operations, Colonel Harry Shoup. He immediately worked out what happened, and told the child that yes indeed, he could see on the radar that Santa was heading to Colorado Springs from the North Pole. There were many more such phone calls that night.

In 1958, CONAD was upgraded to NORAD (North American Air Defence Command). Ever since then, NORAD has tracked Santa's annual southward Christmas Eve journey on the radar – and shared his progress with the rest of the world.

Time and Motion – At Each House

But what about the maths and physics of Santa Claus and his enormous task of delivering presents to kids? Roger Highfield discusses this in his book *Can Reindeer Fly? The Science Of Christmas*. He reckons that this time-and-motion study first appeared in *Spy Magazine*. Our basic analysis begins with a few numbers.

LEGAL DISCLAIMER

Let me emphasise right now that the following are what physicists call "back-of-envelope" calculations. They are not exact, but are close enough, or "in the ball park". So long as the answers are somewhere between ten times too big, and ten times too small, that's okay. Physicists call this as "being within one magnitude of the right answer", where a "magnitude" is a "factor of 10".

Here's an example of "back-of-envelope" calculations:

We humans are about a metre high (thereabouts). Mount Everest is about 8800 metres high (close enough to 10,000 metres). So there are four magnitudes of size between us and Mount Everest.

The distance from the earth to the sun is about 150,000,000 kilometres, or 150,000,000,000 metres. That's 150 followed by nine zeros, or 1.5 followed by 11 zeros. So there are 11 magnitudes of size between "us" and "the distance between the earth and the sun".

The entire universe covers about 41 magnitudes.

So if you start with a tiny proton, and then multiply its size by 10, and you do this 41 times, you will end up at the diameter of the universe.

In mid-2010 there were about 6.875 billion humans on the planet. But only about 2 billion of them were children under the age of 18. This would make for a huge delivery task for Santa. But luckily, only about one-quarter of these children are Christian. So "officially", Santa has to visit only 500 million children. (However, I'm sure that Santa would visit any child of any religion who wanted a visit – off the record.)

On average there are 3.5 children living in each household, so Santa has to visit about 140 million separate homes.

Santa doesn't have a lot of time to deliver the presents – just the six-hour window between midnight and dawn. Fortunately, the earth rotates. Suppose Santa travels from east to west, and starts off at the "leading edge" of midnight, and then gradually allows the "trailing edge" of dawn to catch up with him. In this case, Santa's Christmas Night lasts for 30 hours (30 = 24 + 6). There are 108,000 seconds in this 30-hour day. That works out roughly to 1000 visits per second to each household!

According to the legend, bad children miss out – but let's assume that for our calculations of Santa's Delivery Schedule, all the children have been good.

So in a whole thousandth of a second, Santa has to park the reindeer and the sleigh, slip nimbly down the chimney, fill the stockings, neatly scatter his presents under the tree, eat the lollies that have been left out for him, and scramble back up the chimney into the sleigh and then to the next house. That's a lot of stuff to do in just one-thousandth of a second.

BIG NUMBERS – 1

Santa's sleigh has to travel at 1000 kilometres per second. One thousand kilometres per second is enormously fast. Even the asteroid that wiped out the dinosaurs 65 million years ago smashed into us at only about 30 to 50 kilometres per second.

Time and Motion – Between Each House

But there's another factor. Santa has to travel very quickly *between* the chimneys.

Let's assume that these 140 million Christian households are evenly scattered across the earth. There are about 150 million square kilometres of land on our planet. That means that the households are about one kilometre apart.

To make things simple, let's ignore the famous Travelling Salesman Problem, where the salesman has to travel between the cities by the shortest route, without retracing his steps. Let's just assume that Santa can easily bounce from one house to the next, and the next, and so on. He has to travel 150 million kilometres (by a coincidence, roughly the distance from the earth to the sun). Unfortunately, this means that his average speed is around 1000 kilometres per second, or roughly 3000 times the speed of sound. (It's closer to 1400 kilometres per second, but remember, this is just a back-of-envelope calculation.)

So not only does Santa have a very short delivery time *at* each house (one-thousandth of a second), he has to travel very rapidly *between* each house – about 1000 kilometres per second.

But then it gets worse.

Santa has to accelerate and decelerate from zero to 1000 kilometres per second, and back again – and do this 1000 times each second. The size of the acceleration and deceleration is the killer.

Down here on earth, we experience one "g" of acceleration standing still due to gravity – this is the norm. An average person might weigh 70 kilograms. If you are subject to 5 g of acceleration, you will "weigh" 350 kilograms. If the average person is subjected to 5 g of acceleration for five seconds, they will become unconscious. Fighter pilots have to wear special G-suits, which pump blood to their head, so they can remain conscious.

But Santa would have to tolerate accelerations/decelerations of 400 million g – so his 100-kilogram body would "weigh" 40 billion kilograms, or 40,000,000 tonnes! The human body cannot even begin to support this kind of weight. According to Professor Lawrence Krauss, Santa would turn into *chunky salsa*.

But if the speed of Santa's sleigh is one problem, so is his payload.

SOLUTION TO THE SANTA PROBLEM – TOYS

Half-a-million tonnes amounts to a lot of toys. But there is a solution – "nanotechnology".

Nanotechnology refers to technology of an incredibly small size. Larry Silverberg is a Professor of Mechanical and Aerospace Engineering at North Carolina State University. He suggests Santa carries on his sleigh a nanotechnology mobile manufacturing system.

As it flew from one house to the next, it would capture oxygen, nitrogen, dirt, snow and soot from the air that it flew through. It could then use this as raw materials to build the kids' toys.

Santa's Payload

Suppose each of the 500 million children receives one kilogram of presents. That will mean the sleigh has to carry around 500,000,000 kilograms (or 500,000 tonnes) of goodies. A reindeer can pull a maximum of about 150 kilograms. So Santa needs around 3,333,000 reindeer (that's 500,000,000 kilograms divided by 150 kilograms).

A smallish and cute reindeer weighs about 100 kilograms, or a tenth of a tonne. All the reindeer would weigh another 333,000 tonnes, giving us a total mass of 830,000 tonnes. Let's be conservative, and approximate this down (very roughly) half a million tonnes.

If you have half a million tonnes travelling at about 1000

kilometres per second, you've got enormous wind resistance. Think of a spacecraft re-entering the earth's atmosphere at 5 to 7 kilometres per second – but much much bigger, and much much faster.

Each second, the lead pair of reindeer would have to dissipate about 15 quintillion joules of energy. That's 15 million million million watts of power. In comparison, the power consumption of the entire human race in 2008 was about 15 million million watts – a million times less.

Because of their enormous speed through the atmosphere, the lead reindeer on Santa's sleigh would have to dissipate *on their bodies* one million times more power than the whole human race dissipates over *the entire planet*.

No wonder Rudolph is called the *red*-nosed reindeer!

BIG NUMBERS – 2

The amount of solar power that the sun sends to the earth is about 174 thousand million million watts. About 90 thousand million million watts are absorbed by the surface. This is about 6000 times more power than the human race used in 2008 (15 million million watts). There are 8760 hours in a year.

So in one and a half hours, our planet gets more energy from the sun than the human race uses in a whole year.

This enormous amount of power would make the lead reindeer burst into flames immediately, as well as vaporise the entire reindeer team and the half-million-tonne sleigh with Santa and the presents within a few thousandths of a second. And of course it would create sonic booms that would deafen everyone within hundreds, if not thousands, of kilometres, and enormous shock waves that would flatten every tree and building within hundreds, if not thousands, of kilometres.

But on the other hand, it wouldn't really matter, because Santa would be decelerated by the wind resistance from 1000 kilometres per second to a dead stop in about a thousandth of a second, so our jolly 100-kilogram Santa would be thrown forward onto the vaporised reindeer with the equivalent weight of some 10 million tonnes, turning him into a thin red layer of protoplasm that would be destroyed by the expanding shock wave.

It seems that what Santa really needs is some decent Occupational

Health and Safety Legislation – because the Time-and-Motion studies aren't doing him any favours.

Luckily, Santa has lots of Little Franchisee Helpers (called parents) all around the world who turn his Vision Statement into World's Best Practice. Otherwise Santa Claus would be a very Splattered – oops! – a very Sad Cause.

SOLUTIONS TO THE SANTA PROBLEM – QUANTUM STUFF

In quantum mechanics, an electron can simultaneously be orbiting the nucleus of an atom *and* be everywhere else in the universe. Also in quantum mechanics, the mere act of observing an event can change that event, and make it vanish.

Perhaps Santa Claus is a quantum entity – so he can easily be everywhere at the same time, and can deliver all his presents simultaneously. This means he doesn't have to rush from one house to the next – because he's already there.

But if Santa Claus *is* a quantum entity, then the act of a child observing Santa delivering presents could make the Wave Equation (that is, the quantum Santa) collapse into nothingness. This naughty act would disrupt Christmas and cause untold chaos. Perhaps this is the real reason that Santa does not visit naughty children.

SANTA - LEGALS

From the point of view of the Sydney law firm Toomey Pegg Drevikovsky, Santa is a *"fly-by-night, offshore outfit with no address in Australia"*.

It's possible, they say, that Santa, *"as a manufacturer·extra, importer and supplier of goods"* could be committing several breaches of the *Trade Practices Act*.

In their 1998 newsletter, they wrote *"... Santa disappears on December 24, the day before the goods he supplies are opened by his customers"*. How can disappointed children possibly return the boring presents that they don't want? To whom can the children make enquiries about the exciting toys for which they asked, but did not get? And what about the legal ramifications of the deception that tricked the kids into being good, on the promise that they would get the presents they desired for Christmas? The law firm asks, *"if Santa does not come up to expectations, has he engaged in misleading and deceptive conduct in breach of section 52?"*

Furthermore, they enquire, referring to the claim that Santa's toys are made at the North Pole, *"what about section 53(h) which prohibits making a false or misleading presentation about the place of origin of goods?"*

THE CHRISTMAS SPIRIT

The Christmas spirit is a poorly defined mixture of altruism, kindness, compassion and feelings of goodwill toward your fellow human being.

World War I began in 1914. Around 25 December 1914, some soldiers stopped trying to kill each other and carried out what is now known as the "Christmas Truce". They spontaneously began singing carols and then, *"put down their guns and walked across a blasted field toward their enemies on Christmas Day 1914"*.

A British soldier described it in a letter: *"Just before dinner I had the pleasure of shaking hands with several Germans. A party of them came halfway over to us so several of us went out to them. I exchanged one of my balaclavas for a hat. I've also got a button off one of their tunics. We also exchanged smokes etc., and had a decent chat. We can hardly believe that we would have been firing at them for the last week or two — it all seems so strange"*.

It didn't take long for the soldiers to get back to "normal". By the end of World War I, 10 million soldiers and 10 million civilians had died.

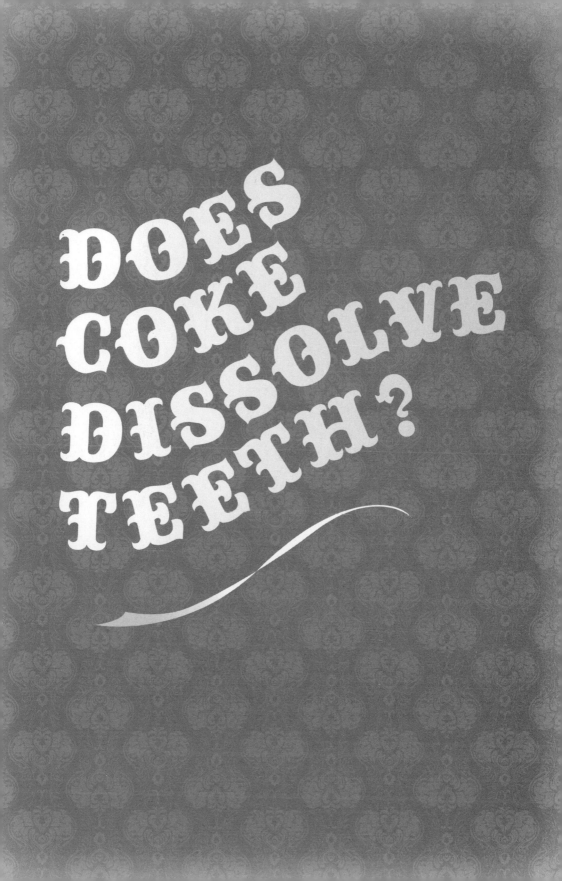

ohn S. Pemberton, a pharmacist in Atlanta, Georgia, invented Coca-Cola in 1886. Back then, it contained tiny amounts of cocaine (from the coca leaf) and moderate amounts of caffeine (from the cola nut). He sold his business to Asa Griggs Candler for US$2300 in 1891, who incorporated it as the Coca-Cola Company in 1892. Candler then sold the Coca-Cola Company in 1919 to a consortium for an astonishing US$25,000,000.

Cocaine in Coke?

Back in 1880s, cocaine was seen as a remedy for a number of ills and it was incorporated into several "tonics".

So yes, way back then, there was some cocaine in Coca-Cola. But the cocaine levels were never high. Around 1890, a slowly growing public concern began over "the cocaine habit", or "cocainism" as it was sometimes called back then. This led to a problem.

Asa Candler thought that it would be wrong to call his product Coca-Cola if there were absolutely no cocaine in it. So he had to keep at least a tiny amount of cocaine in his product. Part of his reasoning was related to protecting the brand name, and the registered trademark. So by 1902, the cocaine levels were dropped to a microscopic 1/400th of a grain of cocaine per ounce of concentrated syrup, or about five parts per million. By 1929, when the cocaine was finally removed entirely, it had dropped even further to one part per 50 million.

Conspiracy Theories

The Coca-Cola brand is huge, and the income is huge – and so are the number of rumours and conspiracy theories associated with it. They cover health and hygiene tips, handy household advice, political conspiracy theories and so on.

These items of "Cokelore" include that it is an effective spermicide (partly true); that drinking a mix of Coke and aspirin will get you high (false); that Coca-Cola invented the modern image of Santa Claus (false); that American Highway Police officers carry a few gallons of Coke in the boot to wash blood from the road at major accidents (false); that the company once refused to do business in Israel (true); and that the formula is so secret that only two executives in Coca-Cola each know only half the formula and have to meet physically to make the secret syrup (false). The final piece of "Cokelore" is that Coke is so acidic that it will dissolve a steak, and even a tooth placed in it and left overnight.

The rumour about Coke's acidity was discussed by Frederick Allen in his book on Coca-Cola, *Secret Formula*. The rumour began in 1950 when Professor Clive M. McCay from Cornell University testified before a select committee in the US House of Representatives that the high levels of sugar in Coke caused cavities in teeth. Indeed, he claimed, the phosphoric acid in Coke was so dangerous that it would dissolve a tooth after just two days' continuous contact.

Real Health Issues

First, Coke *does* contain very high levels of sugar – as do most fizzy sweet soft drinks. There is no doubt that the high sugar levels are a good food supply for many of the bacteria that cause tooth decay. This type of decay starts in the areas where bacteria accumulate – such as in the grooves on the teeth, and between the teeth. When dentists see "multiple interproximal decay", they know the culprit is almost certainly the sugar in fizzy drinks.

Second, Coke *is* very acidic. It *does* contain 0.055 per cent of phosphoric acid – but orange juice has twice as much. It also contains small amounts of citric acid, from the orange, lemon and lime oils needed to make it. The citric acid levels are (again) lower than those in orange juice.

Even so, the acid in Coke is strong enough to erode the tooth surface. This first appears as the destruction of the cusp tips of the

"We prefer the uncompromising refreshment of Sweet Cola, because it sits right with our beautiful lifestyle."

It's a handsome world and it's true that 3 in 4 beautiful people with terrible teeth prefer the uncompromising refreshment of Sweet Cola to other inferior less sweet cola drinks. A modern trend that you too can be a part of, every time you pour a frosty cold glass of Sweet Cola.

- Refreshment for a handsome world.

Each bottle sealed with the Sweet Tooth League Foundation's approval

lower molars, and the removal of normal irregularities on the upper incisors.

There is an unfortunate tendency for some people to shun plain water because it is tasteless. Instead, they will sip an acidic soft drink all day. Under these circumstances, the teeth don't get a chance to be "healed" by the saliva, as they are being constantly bathed in an acid.

Big Finish

But, even if you did soak a tooth in Coke overnight, it would not dissolve. And a steak will just get soggy.

But there is another use for Coke. Show-business people talk about "Coking the stage". They wash the stage with Coca-Cola before a show, and the high sugar content makes it so sticky that the performers won't slip.

Warts are those small, hard and usually harmless growths on the skin. Thousands of years ago, the doctors among the ancient Greeks and Romans knew about warts and had various treatments – mostly unsuccessful. More recently, in 1951, the dermatologist W. W. Lempiere wrote, " ... *of all the disorders of the skin, it would be hard to find any that are regarded with greater contempt by the lay public, and yet capable of resisting a greater variety of treatments, than ... warts*". So it's not surprising that over thousands of years, a broad mythology has sprung up around warts, including the story that touching a frog (or toad) will give you warts.

Now not only is this wrong, but the truth actually runs a bit the other way.

History of Warts

Warts are often seen, but are not usually mentioned in polite company. We have the phrase, "warts and all", meaning the whole truth and nothing but the truth (including those details that are not necessarily flattering, or in fact quite ugly). Warts pop up in many of Shakespeare's plays, such as *The Merry Wives of Windsor, Hamlet* and *King Henry IV*. Huckleberry Finn and Tom Sawyer discuss cures for warts in *The Adventures of Tom Sawyer*, and warts afflict a main character, Juni Cortez, in the movie *Spy Kids*. And where does the young wizard Harry Potter go to school? Hogwarts, of course.

Indeed, the belief that touching a frog (or toad) or its urine will give you warts is part of the folklore of many countries, especially the USA, the UK and Japan. William Faulkner, in his book *The Sound and The Fury*, has his character, Versh, agree with this belief.

Over the last two millennia people have suggested all sorts of different causes for warts. These have included coming into contact with the foam on the seashore, repeated and frequent washing of one's hands, contact with chickens or cows, masturbation and, of course, cuddling up to frogs and toads.

It took a long time to work out what actually caused warts.

"Go on then...give us a cuddle!" said the terribly ugly toad.

Science of Warts

The earliest Real Science on warts appeared in 1823, when an English physician, Sir Astley Cooper, observed that warts could in fact be passed from one person to another. He wrote, *"I must observe, that they frequently secrete a matter which is able to produce a similar disease in others".*

In 1907, the Italian physician, Dr G. Ciuffo deliberately gave himself warts. He extracted a fluid from warts and then passed it through very fine filters. The holes in these filters were small enough to stop bacteria and parasites. He then infected himself with this filtered fluid and, hey presto, he got warts. So whatever the infectious agent might be, it had to be *smaller* than bacteria and parasites. But nobody knew what it was. It took until 1931, and the invention of the electron microscope, before we had our first images of a virus.

Finally, in 1949, the American dermatologist Dr Maurice J. Strauss used an electron microscope to photograph this mysterious infectious agent that caused warts. It turned out to be a virus. Today, we call this virus HPV (Human Papilloma Virus).

So warts on humans are caused by a human virus, not a frog virus.

In fact, it turns out that there are more than 120 different sub-types of HPV. They can cause lots of problems on the surface of the human body, and about 30 of these sub-types attack the area around the groin.

These 30 sub-types are associated with genital and anal warts, and even cervical cancer. The two sub-types associated with cervical cancer are HPV-16 and HPV-18. These 30 sub-types are usually spread by sexual contact, and the incubation period is about three months. They tend to stick to their local area. So you can be pretty sure that a wart on your thumb usually won't transfer across to your genitals.

Frogs Can Heal

So, what about frogs? Does the skin of the frog carry HPV? Nope.

In fact, it's kind of the opposite.

In 1986 an American biologist, Dr Michael Zasloff, was idly staring at a frog that he had just done an operation on, noting how well the wound was healing. The water in the tank was not particularly clean. He suddenly realised that in the many years that he had operated on frogs, he had *never* seen a wound become infected. How could this be? After months of research examining frog skins, he found they contained previously undiscovered chemicals that actually kill bacteria, fungi and parasites. Unfortunately, none of them could kill viruses (like HPV).

So first, frogs don't give you warts, and second, antibiotics based on chemicals naturally present in the skin of the frog can actually heal you, instead of infecting you.

So all the princesses can relax, and get back to kissing frogs …

A few decades ago, crop circles hit the headlines in a really big way, and ever since then they've become more ornate and complex. But some simple circles, in the guise of "fairy rings", have been enchanting us for centuries.

Shakespeare knew about fairy rings. Prospero exclaims in *The Tempest* (Act V, Scene I):

> *you demi-puppets that*
> *By moonshine do the green sour ringlets make,*
> *Whereof the ewe not bites, and you whose pastime*
> *Is to make midnight mushrooms ...*

Shakespeare wrote that the "ringlets" are "green" in colour and "sour". The "green" describes the grass in the circle which is a luxuriant green colour. The "sour" refers to the unpleasant taste of the grass, which stops the livestock (cattle and sheep) from eating it. And also, Shakespeare linked fairy rings and mushrooms.

Fairy rings are circles of mushrooms in the grass. Often, the mushrooms are present only for a short time before dying. Near the mushrooms, the grass is often darker and grows very plushy. In spring and autumn, the mushrooms on the perimeter often grow vigorously, while the grass might die in the centre of the ring.

Sometimes the "fairy circles" are only parts of a circle, with irregular shapes. Fairy rings can be hundreds of metres across, and centuries old. Some of the fairy rings in existence today started growing before Shakespeare was born. There are fairy rings in the United Kingdom's Lake District that are more than 600 years old. One ring in France is over 600 metres around, and is thought to be over 700 years old! Fairy rings have been measured as expanding at speeds between 7.6 and 49.5 centimetres a year.

Non-Scientific Theories

Some people thought that the fairy ring could be a gateway into the fairy kingdom. If you were foolish enough to enter the fairy ring, you might never return. You might become invisible to those on the outside. You might be forced to dance until you died from exhaustion. Perhaps you would be enchanted by the fairies' music, and become their eternal servant. Or in the unlikely event that you did return, you might find that 20 years had passed, and/or crumble to dust as the sunlight hit you, or moulder away as you ate your first food from the outside world ...

Many people really believed that they saw fairies. In 1663 the antiquarian John Aubrey wrote of an experience that his curate, Mr Hart, had one night. Mr Hart was walking over the downs near a local fairy ring. He was astonished to see *a quantity of pygmies, or very small people, dancing round and round, and singing and making all manner of small odd noises*. Mr Hart claimed that he became paralysed as the little people pushed him to the ground and swarmed all over him. He lost consciousness and awoke at sunrise to find himself in the middle of a fairy ring.

With stories as detailed as this, why wouldn't you believe in the Little Folk?

Centuries ago, people didn't really have good explanations for fairy rings – apart from the standard one about the fairies dancing around and wearing out a circle in the grass. Or there was the one about the fairies who sat on the actual mushrooms, sipping tea and chatting with each other. Another version had the fairies using the mushrooms as umbrellas or parasols to protect themselves from the rain or bright sunlight. In Devonshire in England, it was thought that the fairies would catch horses and spend the night riding them around in tight circles.

Other people blamed love-crazed hedgehogs chasing each other around. An odd variation on this, rather popular in the 1700s, laid the blame on underground moles running in their circular tunnels.

Their faeces, rich in nitrogen, supposedly made the grass above ground grow thickly.

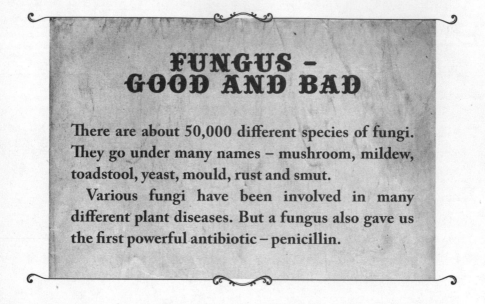

FUNGUS – GOOD AND BAD

There are about 50,000 different species of fungi. They go under many names – mushroom, mildew, toadstool, yeast, mould, rust and smut.

Various fungi have been involved in many different plant diseases. But a fungus also gave us the first powerful antibiotic – penicillin.

Other explanations for fairy circles included starlings flying close to the ground in large circuits, or horses or other farm animals tied to a central stake and moving around it.

Yet another explanation was related to cow pats. In wintertime a farmer would dump a bale of hay on the ground. The cattle would rush in to feed, and they would naturally arrange their bodies like the spokes of a bicycle wheel – with their heads at the centre feeding on the hay bale, with their rear ends pointing out. The rather potent poo dumped onto the soil enriched it and made the grass grow more exuberantly.

A Dutch legend claimed that the Devil spent the night stealing milk from cows. He supposedly stored the milk in an enormous metal churn, which He carried with Him. Of course, the churn was heated by the Infernal Fires Of Hell. So, whenever He placed his churn on the ground, it left behind a characteristic circular burn mark – the fairy ring. (Mind you, He does seem a rather tame Lord of the Underworld if all He does at night is run around stealing milk. Perhaps He really really liked hot milk for his bedtime toddy.)

More recently, fairy rings have been explained away as UFO landing sites.

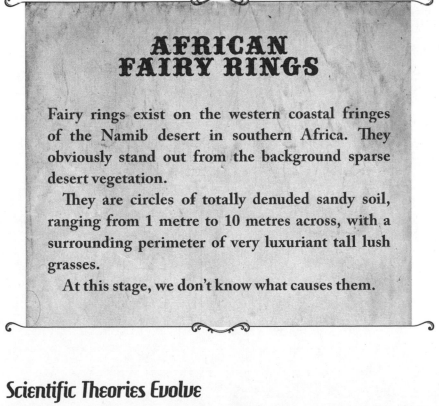

AFRICAN FAIRY RINGS

Fairy rings exist on the western coastal fringes of the Namib desert in southern Africa. They obviously stand out from the background sparse desert vegetation.

They are circles of totally denuded sandy soil, ranging from 1 metre to 10 metres across, with a surrounding perimeter of very luxuriant tall lush grasses.

At this stage, we don't know what causes them.

Scientific Theories Evolve

Hundreds of years ago, people didn't have the benefit of the Scientific Knowledge or the Scientific Method that we have today. Today we can bring the clarifying Power of Scientific Knowledge and the Scientific Method to answer the perennial question of what is actually going on in a fairy ring. We can use the power of Science to answer why the grass in the centre of the ring was usually of poor quality, why the mushrooms were usually confined to the periphery, and why the ring kept enlarging. And what about the conundrum that sometimes the grass near the ring of mushrooms could be deep green in colour, and richly luxuriant?

Henry More wrote his *Antidote To Atheism* in 1653 that he simply wasn't sure whether fairy rings were made by "*witches*", or by "*those little puppet sprites which they call elves or fairies*".

But soon after, in 1675, the first scientific paper on fairy rings appeared in the journal *Philosophical Transactions*, published by the newly born Royal Society.

Dr Robert Plot continued the scientific tradition with his research, which he wrote up in 1686 in his *Natural History of Staffordshire*. He dug up the soil and compared the dirt inside and on the boundary of a fairy ring to the surrounding dirt. He thought that the rings were made by witches or elves, or by deer having sex, or possibly by an infection from a fungus. But his favourite explanation was that hollow tubes of lightning had struck the ground, somehow causing the rings.

In 1790, Erasmus Darwin also thought that fairy rings could possibly be the product of natural lightning strikes – he was wrong. This was the "Electrical Origin" theory.

But it was William Withering, a doctor from Shropshire in England, who came up with the correct answer in 1792. (Just as an aside, he was the guy who gave the West its very first heart drug, Digitalis, from the plant called the Golden Fox Glove.) William Withering dug into the soil of many fairy rings and consistently found a white mass of intermingled threads. He recognised this to be the underground root-like bodies of mushrooms. He soon realised that as the underground cottonwool-like fungal mass spread outwards, mushrooms appeared on the surface. The mushrooms on the surface were not separate, but instead were all part of the same organism.

This finding was incorporated into the "Chemical Causes" theory, put forth by Dr Wollaston in 1807 and also by Professor Way in 1846.

In 1874, samples of soil were analysed from a fairy ring for nitrogen levels. Nitrogen is essential for the growth of plants. The lowest levels of nitrogen were found inside the fairy ring, higher levels directly underneath the mushrooms of the actual fairy ring, and the highest levels of all outside the ring where the mushrooms had not yet reached. This implied that as the fungus grew, it consumed the nitrogen in the soil.

Today we know that there are about 60 or so different species of mushrooms that make fairy rings. One mushroom commonly found in fairy rings is *Marasmius oreades* – small and pale with cream-coloured gills, and quite deliciously edible.

FUNGUS AND STRADIVARIUS VIOLIN

Fungi and bacteria are nature's most important "detritivores" – eaters of rubbish. They are the perfect recycling machines and decompose dead organic matter and turn it into humus, the organic component of soil.

When you walk through a forest, the reason that you don't see lots of dead branches is because they have been eaten by a fungus. But now it seems that one fungus can gently attack wood to make the world's best violin. The fungus is the common split gill mushroom, *Schizophyllum commuod*. The Empa scientist Francis Schwarze let this fungus attack some wood for nine months. It changed the structure of the cells in the wood, simultaneously making it less dense and more homogenous (the same throughout). The wood was then used to make a violin.

In 2009, this "biotech violin" was judged to be superior to a Stradivarius violin. Antonio Stradivari (1644 to 1737) made about 1200 violins. Only about 600 still survive, and they are valued at around $5 million each! We do not know why a Stradivarius violin sounds so good. It might be the chemicals used in the varnish, or the chemical treatment used to protect the wood from attack by worms.

But we do know that letting a fungus attack wood can give you the sound of a Stradivarius violin.

Lord of The Ring

Plants have seeds, but in the fungus world the equivalent of a seed is a spore. A spore can lie dormant in the soil for years, until the conditions (for example, enough fertiliser, proper moisture and so forth) are right for its particular needs.

When the conditions are right, the spore will grow and turn into a cottonwool-like mass of fine filaments called a "mycelium". The part of the fungus that you see above the ground is just the "fruiting body" – the part that spreads the spores. The underground fungal threads of the mycelium make up most of the fungus. As the mycelium grows, it consumes the nitrogen in the soil. This means that the inner central part of the fairy ring will die when it runs out of food. But if the fungus expands outwards, it can find soil that is rich in the nutrients that it needs.

A fungus eats very differently from how animals eat.

We humans eat food with our mouths and then we digest or break down the food with chemicals inside our gut.

But fungi do it in the opposite order.

First, they dump their digestive chemicals into the ground around them to break down the food. Effectively, they pre-digest their meal, and then they suck it up via the mycelium threads.

But if they don't eat all of the pre-digested food – they are rather messy eaters – the leftovers can then stimulate the grass to grow. This is one explanation for getting a fairy ring with luxuriant growth.

Types of Rings

There are three different types of fairy rings, classified by how they look.

You can't actually see the first type of fairy ring until the fruiting bodies pop up and make a temporary circle of mushrooms.

In the second type of fairy ring, there is a rather vigorous growth of the grass just inside the mushroom ring. In this case, the dying mycelium has released plant nutrients into the soil. But in some cases the fungi release "gibberellins", which are a kind of plant growth hormone.

The third type of fairy ring shows the opposite – bare or damaged patches of grass which are also called "necrotic zones". (Yes, you can think of mushrooms as the vampires of the soil, sucking out its lifeblood.)

Sometimes, the underground mass of fungus is so dense that it actually stops the nutrients from getting to the roots of the grass. Sometimes, it releases chemicals into the soil that make it "hydrophobic", so the water cannot penetrate the soil. And sometimes, the mycelium has already depleted the soil of the nutrients that the grass needs.

With This Ring, I Thee Divorce ...

It's actually quite difficult to get rid of fairy rings from your lawn.

Some people say the easiest thing is just to accept it – harvest frequently and make a soup out of the fairy ring mushrooms. *Marasmius oreades* have a definite and somewhat sweet flavour.

Some companies sell various chemicals which they claim will kill only the mushrooms of the fairy ring. But to make sure that the chemicals can penetrate deeply, you might have to use a garden fork to punch holes all across the infected area. Unfortunately, these poisons sometimes kill the good fungi in your lawn.

Other people rely on the fact that when two fairy rings meet, they'll attack each other, and they'll each die (technically called "fungistasis"). This method is for the very patient gardener who believes in serendipity in the form of another fairy ring just happening along – and who has a lot of time ...

But in some cases, you just have to remove all the soil to a depth of 30 centimetres, throw in a few tonnes of new soil, and start again.

So, as we see, since the time of Shakespeare, Science has been leading us on a merry dance to explain Fairy Rings – but hey, what's wrong with being off with the fairies ...

PHOTOSYNTHESIS

The big difference between "plants" and "fungi" is that plants can do "photosynthesis", but fungi cannot.

It was way back in 1771 when the English chemist Joseph Priestly did the first experiments with photosynthesis. This was even before oxygen had been discovered. Priestly burned a candle inside a closed jar. Sure enough, once the oxygen inside the jar had been consumed, the flame went out. He then inserted a sprig of mint into the narrow mouth of the jar. After a few days, the sprig of mint had made enough oxygen to again support a flame.

Photosynthesis is the process where a plant captures the energy of sunlight. It uses this energy to turn water and carbon dioxide into carbohydrates (simple sugars) and oxygen.

Speaking of "carbon", all life on our planet is based on the element carbon. This element is present in practically every chemical in our body. (But not in water, which is made only from the elements "hydrogen" and "oxygen".)

More than 2.7 billion years ago, there was no photosynthesis. But then a type of bacterium called "cyanobacteria" evolved photosynthesis. The cyanobacteria were able to grab carbon dioxide from the air around them and split it into carbon and oxygen. They kept the carbon for themselves to incorporate into their body. The oxygen was released into the atmosphere. Plants evolved from the early cyanobacteria. And this is how we got oxygen.

But fungi are different from plants, even though they grow in the same soil. They can't do photosynthesis. So the only way they can get carbon is by "eating" some organic chemicals in the soil and breaking them down. These organic chemicals can come from rotting wood and leaves, animal droppings and compost.

odern-day parents miss out on so many of the old-fashioned **M** ways to impress the kids. They can't hunt down a 2-tonne diprotodon to feed the family, and they can't enthral an entire village with their storytelling skills. But at least they can still show the kids the right way to skip a flat stone across a pond.

However, science has shown us that the time-honoured way is actually not the best way.

Skipping Stones — History

The great Charles Darwin referred to throwing stones when he wrote in the *Descent of Man*, "*hands and arms could hardly have become perfect enough to have hurled stones and spears with true aim, as long as they were used for supporting the body*". In other words, as long as we stayed on all fours, we could not develop our hand-and-arm skills well enough to successfully throw stones as weapons.

The "sport" of skipping stones across water goes back to the ancient Greeks. The Oxford English Dictionary mentions skipping stones with regard to the phrase "Ducks and Drakes", which first appeared in 1583. Back in the 16th century, somebody had decided that the first, third, fifth and so forth skips would be the "ducks", while the even-numbered skips would be the "drakes". The moral intent of this phrase is that in the same way that the stone ultimately vanishes in the water, the spendthrift squanders everything in "playing ducks and drakes" with his or her money.

Skipping stones were the inspiration for the "Bouncing Bombs" invented by Sir Barnes Wallis in World War II. They hit the water, skipped several times, struck the dam wall, sank and then exploded while hard up against the dam wall, destroying it and flooding the valley below.

Skipping Stones – Science

The first scientific analysis of skipping stones was done in 1968 by a chemistry student named Kirston Koths at Amherst College, Massachusetts. Kirston discovered that successful skipping stones first hit the water with their trailing edge at an angle of at about 20 to 30 degrees. They then built up a moving "wedge" of water in front of this edge, and when the hill of water became big enough, slide over it to do the next skip. Each "skip" or "impact" would last about one hundredth of a second. Of course, the energy to make this mini-hill of water comes from the moving stone, which, after a number of skips, loses all its energy and sinks.

In 2003, Lydéric Bocquet, a physicist from the Claude Bernard University in Lyon, France, derived a mathematical formula. It accurately described the number of bounces of the stone in terms of its mass, angle with respect to the water, launch speed and spin rate. His formula was so accurate that it even described the increasingly shorter skips of the stone at the end of its run, known to "Stone Skipping" experts as the "Pitty Pat". Bocquet's Personal Best is 15 skips, corresponding to an initial launch spin rate of nine spins per second.

But Jerdone Coleman McGhee, a travelling oil field engineer, used his journeys to find "good" stones, and his intuition to win the Guinness World Record for stone skipping in 1992. He achieved an astonishing 32 bounces on the Blanco River in Texas. Bocquet's formula tells us that McGhee must have launched the stone at around 43 kilometres per hour, with an initial spin rate of about 14 times per second. McGhee reveals his secrets in his book, *The Secrets of Stone Skipping*.

The current Guinness World Record holder is Russell Byars, who skipped his stone 51 times back in back 2007.

DCCLXXVI BC
OLYMPIAD

1st. Skipping Stone World Record Holder
Flamenco Twistonicus

How to Do it

Now the important part, the technique.

First, the stone should sit comfortably in the hand, and be reasonably flat. And yes, it should be thrown parallel to the ground with as much spin and speed as you can impart. But you should *not* bend down and start with your arm close to the ground. This is where I, and presumably many others, made our first mistake that held us back from Skipping Stone greatness.

Instead, you should (according to the World Record Holders, and other expert Stone Skippers) start with your throwing hand curved and high above your head (flamenco dancer position) and fill your lungs with air. Then, in a carefully choreographed ballet, you simultaneously expel the air, zip your non-throwing arm across your body, twist your shoulders 180 degrees, shift your weight onto your leading foot, forcefully bring your throwing arm down and forward and then launch the stone with as much spin as possible. The angle that you would like to achieve between the spinning stone and the water should be about 20 degrees.

Indeed, when the Space Shuttle returns to Earth, it does a little "skipping" off the dense atmosphere in its descent.

The latest proposed use for this Skipping Technology is in the HyperSoar plane. It would rocket up to an altitude of 40 kilometres, glide down until it hit the denser air and bounce/skip off it and back up again, while simultaneously firing the engines. Eighteen skips and 72 minutes would get you from Chicago to Rome.

But the rest of us can use the Hand-Above-The-Head launch position to really impress the kids with an enormous number of skips.

BOUNCING BOMB
= DAM BUSTERS

During World War II, an English scientist, engineer and inventor practised skipping marbles over the surface of the water in his bathtub because he wanted to blow up dams and ships.

His name was Barnes Wallis. One very specific target was the German battleship *Tirpitz*, which was a threat to Allied ships in the North Atlantic. This 52,600 tonne ship would safely moor in a Norwegian fjord, where it was heavily protected by the steep sides of the fjord. Conventional bombers could not get close enough. His other target was a series of German hydroelectric dams in the heavily industrialised Ruhr Valley. These dams supplied electricity and water to heavy industry and cities. Again, these dams were heavily protected.

The only way to explode an enormous and solid concrete dam wall was by detonating large amounts of high explosive, directly against it. But how could he get a bomb directly against the concrete wall? The Germans had hung heavy torpedo nets in the water, which would stop any torpedos. And it was technically very difficult (that is, almost impossible) to drop a bomb from a bomber so that it would come to rest immediately next to a dam's concrete wall.

After playing in the bathtub with spinning marbles, he eventually came up with the concept of drum-shaped Bouncing Bombs. They would be dropped some distance from the dam wall, and then "skip" across the water until they hit the dam wall, and sank. Skipping meant that they would avoid being snagged by the heavy torpedo nets. He came up with two similar bombs, of different sizes. The larger one, "Upkeep", was to be used against dams, while the smaller one, "Highball", was to be used against ships.

He soon realised it was essential that the bombs be given some "back-spin" at 500 revolutions per minute (RPM), to stabilise them as they bounced across the water. And once they hit, the spin would also make the bombs "run" downwards along the dam wall or side of a ship, until they reached the correct depth for exploding. It was also essential that the bombs be dropped from the very specific height of 60 feet (18 metres). The barometers of the day were not accurate enough to measure this height. He came up with an ingenious, yet simple, way to measure this height from a speeding plane, flying at 390 kilometres per hour above the featureless surface of the calm water of a dam or fjord. Each plane had two spotlights on the bottom, aimed slightly inward. The spotlights were calibrated to meet in a single spot, only when the bomb was exactly 60 feet above the surface.

Each bomb weighed about 4196 kilograms, of which 2994 kilograms was a high explosive called "Torpex". Once the bomb had slammed into the dam or ship wall, hopefully without destroying itself, it would sink and hydrostatic sensors would detonate the Torpex at a depth of 9 metres. The reason for not exploding the bomb on the surface was that underwater explosions have a phenomenon called "bubble pulse", which enhances their effectiveness.

On 16 to 17 May 1943, 19 RAF planes from 617 Squadron (later known as the Dambusters) attacked dams in Germany's Ruhr Valley, in Operation Chastise. Some of the *bombs bounced seven times over some 800 yards (730 metres), sank, and detonated*. Two of the dams (Mohne and Eder) were successfully breached, causing loss of life, damage and flooding. More than half of the 1700 or so lives lost belonged to the RAF pilots, allied Prisoners of War, and Forced Labourers held captive at their locations. Eight of the 19 planes did not return. The story is told in the 1955 movie *The Dam Busters*.

The remaining "Upkeep" bombs were not used against other dams, while the "Highball" bombs were never used against enemy ships.

After someone has had a near-death experience, or survived an unusual accident, well-wishers will often say, *"Don't worry. After all, lightning never strikes the same place twice"*. In fact, if you look at how and where lightning strikes occur, you'll find the exact opposite is true.

Lightning 101

Lightning is one of the most beautiful and most destructive of all natural phenomena. On average, each year it kills more people than practically any other natural disaster, such as earthquakes, cyclones, floods, tsunamis and bushfires.

At any given moment there are 1800 thunderstorms blasting away around the planet, usually in the late afternoon and early evening, when the land temperatures are at their highest. Most thunderstorms happen between 50°N and 50°S - about 80 per cent over land and 20 per cent over the oceans. They generate about 100 lightning strikes each second. About 80 per cent of these lightning strikes happen inside the cloud, or from one cloud to another – fewer than 20 per cent run between the cloud and the ground.

Our understanding of lightning began in 600 BC, when the Greek philosopher, Thales, (who was also the first person to predict eclipses) rubbed a rod of amber with a dry cloth. The rod of amber then attracted feathers. The amber was an excellent insulator, and once it had attracted some electrons from the dry cloth by mechanical friction, it hung onto them. In the 1500s William Gilbert, scientist and physician to Queen Elizabeth I, repeated Thales's experiment. He called the strange phenomenon "electrica", because the Greek word for amber is "elektron".

We're not exactly sure how, but some kind of rubbing or collision causes electrons to be stripped from their atoms in a thundercloud. It's probably associated with collisions between small ice particles – because a thundercloud without ice tends to contain very little lightning. A typical thundercloud has an excess of electrons on its underside, making it negatively charged. Once you get enough of them, these electrons then repel other electrons in the ground below, say half-a-kilometre below. The ground electrons then leave the area, resulting in the ground becoming positively charged.

Once the attraction between the negatively charged bottom of the cloud and the positively charged ground becomes great enough, small, skinny, mini-bolts of lightning called "step leaders" stutter their way towards the ground, zigzagging this way and that, at about 150 kilometres per second. The path is thought to stutter because of random dust particles, random variations in the electric fields, and perhaps even random cosmic rays. The important fact is that these step leaders create a conductive pathway through the air, which is normally an insulator. When the step leader gets close enough to the ground, the circuit is finally completed and suddenly huge amounts of electricity rush through this conductive pathway in the air – 30,000 amperes at one million volts.

Lightning and People

The purpose of a "lightning rod" is to provide a safe pathway for electricity to the ground, bypassing people and structures such as buildings. One of the first lightning rods was invented by Benjamin Franklin, that great American all-rounder, vegetarian and expert swimmer. But the British Admiralty wouldn't use something invented by their "rebel colonists", so over 220 of their tall ships were damaged by lightning in the Napoleonic Wars before they finally swallowed their pride and began fitting them with lightning rods.

In the old days, churchgoers had to ring the bells during thunderstorms, supposedly to pacify the anger of God. But over a 33-year period in the 1700s, some 100 French bell ringers died from lightning, which struck the tall pointy bell tower and then ran down the wet rope. So the French parliament had to make a law forbidding the ringing of bells during thunderstorms.

Safety really is paramount when you think about lightning.

In the USA alone, lightning kills about 100 people each year, with another 500 to 1000 people injured. Three-quarters of the survivors are left with some permanent disability.

According to the *Guinness Book of World Records*, Roy C. Sullivan, a park ranger from Virginia, holds the world record for being struck the most times by lightning – seven. He was known as the "Human Lightning Rod". In 1942, he lost a toenail with his first lightning strike, and in 1969, he lost both eyebrows in a second strike. He was then hit by lightning again in 1970, 1972, 1973, 1976 and 1979. Unfortunately, he committed suicide in 1983, apparently as a result of being rejected in love.

Lightning Strikes Twice?

So why would lightning be likely to strike twice?

Well, if the local geography of a landscape funnels thunderstorms down a particular pathway, and you happen to work in that pathway (say, as a park ranger), then you are more likely to be hit by lightning, which is what happened to Roy C. Sullivan.

For example, on 31 July 1988, in Massachusetts, lightning struck the movable drawbridge between Vineyard Haven and Oak Bluffs, leaving the bridge stuck in the closed position for three days. Three weeks earlier, a previous lightning strike had closed the bridge for 24 hours.

The Empire State Building in New York and the Sears Tower in Chicago are each struck thousands of times per year by lightning bolts – as the buildings are still intact, the lightning rods are clearly doing their job.

So it's totally and completely wrong to say, *"lightning never strikes the same place twice"*. In fact, the opposite is true – lightning is more likely to strike the same place twice, given that the same weather patterns are likely to repeat themselves in the same geographical landscape. But don't worry too much – in the USA, your odds of being hit by lightning over an 80-year life span are roughly one in 3000.

THE LIGHTNING CAPITAL

Darwin is the "Lightning Capital of Australia", and attracts many visiting lightning scientists.

A recent summer thunderstorm in Darwin generated an amazing 1634 lightning bolts in just a few hours – which is roughly the number of bolts Perth receives in an entire year.

Darwin is in the tropics and so it gets a lot of heat energy from the sun, which then heats up the land. This makes the air rise. But this air is moist, because Darwin is on the coast. The rising moist air cools into ice crystals, which collide with each other and help set up the separation of the positive and negative charges. Once the voltage between the positive and negative charges gets big enough, the negative charges head for the nearest positive charges and voilà – you have a lightning strike.

If this lightning strike heads for the ground, it will usually head for the same high point that it hit last time there was a thunderstorm in that area. In Darwin, many of the tall structures and power poles have been hit by lightning more than once, and have the burn marks to prove it.

I've always had doubts about those warm air hand dryers often found in public toilets. They used to have a sticker on them, warning us of the *"dangers of disease that may be transmitted by cloth towels or paper towel litter"*. More recently, another sticker told us that it was more hygienic to dry your hands by blowing warm air over them than any other method.

But it seems that the opposite is true – that using warm air hand dryers in a public toilet can actually *increase* the numbers of bacteria on your hands.

On the other hand, the bacteria you'll pick up are almost certainly not dangerous.

Hand-Washing and Drying

In Australian society, the worst offenders when it comes to not washing their hands are males in two age groups – young boys and teenagers, and mature men over the age of 55.

But unfortunately, most people are terrible at hand hygiene. One in five of us does not wash their hands before preparing food at home, or after going to the toilet. One in six just quickly wave their hands under cold running water, while only one in ten actually washes for the necessary 30 seconds. And of every five people who *do* wash their hands, one will not dry them properly, leaving a nice moist environment for the remaining bacteria to go forth and multiply. One US survey found that on average, American males in public toilets kept their hands under a warm air dryer for 17 seconds, while American females kept their hands under for only 13 seconds.

In the olden days, people used paper or cloth towels to dry their hands. This changed after 1953, when Dr Paul E. Walker, the Director of Medical Services at the Public Health Service Hospital in Seattle, Washington, looked at drying hands with warm air. Dr Walker made two conclusions.

First, he found that there was *"a probably significant reduction of* cross contamination of the hands when a mechanical air dryer was used". Let me make one thing perfectly clear – "*a probably significant reduction*" is, in fact, not significant at all.

Second, he found that, "*the mechanical air drying technique is less expensive than the towel-drying technique*".

This might be the real reason why you see so many warm air dryers today – they're cheaper than cloth or paper towels!

Testing Warm Air Dryers

In 1998, Keith Redway and Brian Knights of the Applied Ecology Rescarch School at the University of Westminster wrote a paper entitled, "Hand Drying: Studies of the Hygiene and Efficiency of Different Hand Drying Methods". They were funded by paper towel manufacturers, however they agreed to do the research only if they "*retained the rights to the experimental results, and were free to use them as they saw fit regardless of whether they provided the results the sponsor was looking for, or not*".

They examined how people dried their hands (whether they used individual disposable paper towels, continuous-loop cotton towels, or warm air dryers), and how many bacteria remained on their hands afterwards. They specifically did *not* do this in a nice clean laboratory. Instead, they used toilets and washrooms in Real World Situations. These included restaurants and other eating places, railway stations, public houses, shops and sports clubs.

They found that people would spend about 20–25 seconds using a warm air dryer (as compared to 8–12 seconds with other methods). This was shorter than the average dryer cycle time (30 seconds), and about half the time needed to get their hands to a level of 95 per cent dryness. So even though the warm air dryer users spent twice as long trying to dry their hands – they failed. As a result, approximately 60 per cent of people walked out with wet hands, while 40 per cent dried their hands on their clothes or hair!

It is curious that when people in public toilets are given a choice,

69 per cent use paper towels, 18 per cent use warm air dryers, and 13 per cent ignore them both and prefer to wipe their hands dry on their clothing (or elsewhere).

Bacterial Count – Dryer or Towel?

The researchers got a real surprise when they counted the bacteria left on the fingertips after using one of these drying methods. Washing their hands and then using paper towels or continuous-loop cotton towels reduced the bacterial count by 45–60 per cent. But using a warm air dryer actually *increased* the bacterial count by an average of 255 per cent.

How could drying your hands increase the number of bacteria on your skin?

When they went looking further, the researchers found their answer. It turned out the bacteria were already *inside* the warm air dryers, thanks to the warm moist environment. Every single warm air dryer had high bacterial counts on the air inlet, while 97 per cent had them on the outlet nozzle surface, too.

These were the figures for warm air dryers in public toilets. Of course, if you choose to do your measurements in a clean laboratory, you would find lower bacterial counts.

Just visualise warm air blowing over poorly-washed moist bacteria-laden (usually nasty gram-negative bacteria) fingers in a grimy public toilet. It's an ideal way to spread bacteria and other germs through the air in an aerosol of tiny droplets.

Happily, in most cases, our immune systems are resilient enough to keep these bacteria at bay, where they belong. Furthermore, the overwhelming majority of these bugs are fairly harmless. They don't usually include the real nasties like Salmonella, Shigella, Campylobacter, Hepatitis A or B, the SARS Coronavirus, or the virus that causes meningococcal disease.

In The Real World

One reason that you want to dry your hands is to remove the bacteria that are floating in the thin layer of water. After all, if you just let your hands dry slowly in the air, the bacteria will still be sitting pretty on your skin.

With a towel (paper or cloth) it's possible to apply some decent mechanical friction to your hands. This is an important part of the hand-cleaning process. A towel soaks up the water and the bacteria end up in the bin. You can dry 90 per cent of the surface area of your hands within 10 seconds with a towel. If the towel is in one place in the washroom and the bin is in another, you can dry 90 per cent of your hands while you walk from one place to the next, before you walk out. This suits most people just fine – after all, public toilets and washrooms are not the kind of places where you want to spend your holiday.

That said, I did once meet a couple who spent their entire honeymoon in a public washroom. They had gone to Fiji and immediately after they arrived, a tropical cyclone changed course and destroyed all the accommodation in the resort. The roads were blocked, too. Luckily, the resort's tennis courts had a strong concrete shower block. Unfortunately, the cyclone ripped off its roof. Fortunately, the couple managed to find two mattresses. They spent three days huddled in the shower block, lying on one mattress, with the other mattress on top of them to protect from the regular impacts of flying branches, coconuts and sea creatures. They laughed about it – afterwards.

A warm air dryer cannot dry your hands in 10 seconds. Part of the reason for this is that the wind blast is so pathetically gutless. On average, a warm air dryer takes 60 seconds to dry 90 per cent of your hands. This is really inconvenient, especially when other people are queuing up to dry their hands. Warm air dryers are also great at spreading bacteria – but, as we saw above, in the vast majority of cases, these bacteria are not really a health risk.

Jet Air Dryers have come on the market in the last few years.

They blast air at enormous speed (they claim over 600 kilometres per hour, which I find hard to believe) and with enormous noise. If you can apply some mechanical friction and rub your hands together, it's possible to dry 90 per cent of your hands within 10 seconds. This is good.

On one hand, because the air does move faster, the jet air dryer can blow bacteria some two metres, rather than the half-metre or so of a gutless warm air dryer. (But on the other hand, the overwhelming majority of these bacteria are not dangerous.)

Big Finish

The most important lesson to take from all this is to get into the regular habit of washing and drying your hands! Drying your hands on your jeans is better than not drying them at all.

And don't believe that warm air dryers were installed to improve hygiene – they're there to save money.

Back when I was a hippie living in the city, I visited one of my hippie mates living in the bush. He told me that if I was unlucky enough to be chased by a snake, I should run straight up the nearest steep hill. Snakes, he said, can't go straight up a hill, so they have to weave back and forth, which makes them a lot slower.

Snakes 101

Snakes have been wriggling around for about 80 million years. They have survived remarkably well, considering that they have no ears, no legs, no arms, no voice, no eyelids and only one lung. They also have a bad reputation, beginning with that unfortunate episode with those two naked people back in the Garden of Eden.

Now snakes don't regularly hunt people, and almost always attack only in response to perceived human aggression. There must be a lot of scared or aggressive people out there, because, according to the World Health Organisation, snakes still bite about five million people each year worldwide, killing some 100,000 of those. The bites usually happen not at the end of a long chase, but in that first moment of a surprise encounter.

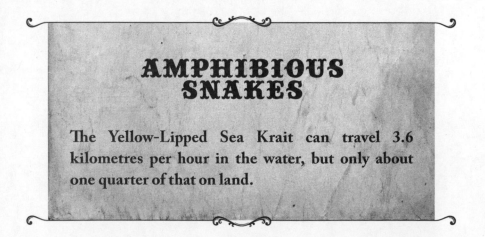

AMPHIBIOUS SNAKES

The Yellow-Lipped Sea Krait can travel 3.6 kilometres per hour in the water, but only about one quarter of that on land.

Snake Motion

Most snakes get around by "serpentine" locomotion. They send S-shaped horizontal waves down their body. Each time a loop pushes backwards against anything in their environment, they move forward. The African Black Mamba uses this method, and it is usually quoted as the world's fastest snake, able to reach 20 kilometres per hour for brief bursts. But like most snakes, the African Black Mamba uses its speed to escape predators, not to hunt prey (more sinned against, than a sinner). Some tree snakes use a second method known as "concertina" locomotion, where they alternately compress and expand their body, like the closing and opening of a concertina (like in a piano accordion). A third method used by some heavy-bodied snakes is "caterpillar" or "rectilinear" motion, which, thanks to muscle contractions along the body, looks remarkably like the motion of a caterpillar.

The fourth method is called "sidewinding", and is used by snakes that live where the ground offers little resistance, such as desert sands. Here the snake alternately lifts the front and rear parts of its body, placing them down to one side of where they originally were.

A surprising new form of snake motion has been recently investigated – flying. The Paradise Tree Snake of South East Asia is a glider. Typically, it will launch itself from a tree by forming itself into a loop, then rapidly straightening its spine and letting go of the tree. It will first fall rapidly at an angle greater than 45 degrees (to build up speed and generate lift). At the same time, it will send distinctive S-shaped waves down its spine to its tail.

Once it has enough airspeed, it will then flare out its ribs to double the width of its body. It does this by changing its shape from a cylinder to having a slightly concave belly. It then forms a flying "wing" that constantly changes its shape – with waves running along its body both left-to-right and up-and-down. No wing that we humans have yet made can do this. (Some aerodynamicists claim that it probably has the favourable characteristics of a "highly slotted wing".) In this second phase of its flight, the serpent then glides at an angle as shallow as 13 degrees. The snake shows great control over the direction and duration of the flight. It can swing between trees, chase prey and avoid predators.

While flying, the Paradise Tree Snake has been clocked at a horizontal speed of 29 kilometres per hour, and an airspeed of 36 kilometres per hour. This is the kind of speed only an Olympic sprinter can reach.

It's All Good

Getting back to my bush hippie mate – he was wrong! Snakes do not have to weave left and right to make their way up a hill. They just send S-shaped waves along their body as they normally do, and go straight up the hill, albeit a little more slowly, because they have to do more work. Second, in general, the faster snakes tend to be longer and thinner. For example, the Australian Black Whip Snake is almost as fast as the African Black Mamba, and travels at around 19 kilometres per hour. Most unfit human adults could not maintain the 20 kilometres per hour needed to get away from the faster snakes – so head for the nearest low-friction surface, like a convenient ice sheet (which will have the added advantage of slowing down the snake's metabolism), or a bitumen road. And don't even think of trying to outrun a flying Paradise Tree Snake, unless you are an Olympic-grade sprinter.

But if you ever do step on a hungry and angry snake, you'll need all the speed you can get. Remember this – the snake is just running for their dinner, but you are running for your life. (Mind you, very few snakes can actually eat us – our wide shoulders are apparently a problem.)

VARIABLE SNAKES

Snakes are extraordinarily flexible in all kinds of ways. They seem to be able to switch instantaneously between different modes of locomotion, depending on factors such as the availability of rough spots for getting a grip (or "purchase", as they call it in the trade).

The slope of the land is critical – Professor Rick Shine from the University of Sydney told me that, *"many snakes have eluded my despairing grasp by launching themselves straight down a steep slope like an arrow, relying on gravity to get to the bottom of the slope far quicker than I could scramble down. On the flat, I would back myself against most but not all Aussie snakes – a Black Whip Snake in the Northern Territory made a fool of me not too long ago".*

Atmospheric scientists tell us that we humans have affected our planet's atmosphere in two major ways. First, we have "punched a hole in the ozone layer", and second, we have set off "global warming" by dumping so-called greenhouse gases into the atmosphere. Most of us know that the most villainous of these gases is carbon dioxide. Many of us know that methane from cattle and sheep is another significant greenhouse gas. But practically all of us wrongly believe that this methane comes from the back end of the animals. And very few of us know that methane is 22-or-so times nastier than carbon dioxide.

Gas and Gut

Once again, let me say it – *"everything is made from atoms"*. Carbon dioxide is made from one atom of carbon and two atoms of oxygen. Methane is a bigger molecule – it's made from one atom of carbon, but four atoms of hydrogen.

Livestock (of which cattle are a significant proportion) produce about 20 per cent of the world's methane. The rest comes from rice paddies, coal mining, landfill sites and so on.

There are 1.3 to 1.5 billion cattle on Earth today. India has about 30 per cent, Brazil about 20 per cent, the USA about 10 per cent and Australia just 3 per cent.

The methane that comes from cows is not made directly by the cows themselves. No, it's made by tiny bacteria and bacteria-like critters that live in the cows' guts. These critters have a happy symbiotic relationship with the cattle – the cattle give the critters a safe home, and the critters turn grass into food for the cattle.

More specifically, these critters "eat" cellulose. Cellulose is a big molecule that makes grasses stiff and tough enough to stand upright. We humans would starve to death if we tried to eat grass as we'd be unable to turn it into energy.

SAME SAME BUT DIFFERENT

When cattle are born, the babies of both genders are called "calves" until they are weaned. Then they are called "weaners". In the USA, an orphaned calf is called a "dogie". So you now know what they mean in the song, "Rawhide", when they sing the line "... *keep them dogies moving* ...".

A female who has not had a calf is called a "heifer". Females who are bred for milk production are called "milking" or "dairy cattle". A female who is born as the twin of a male is usually infertile, has non-working ovaries, and "masculine" behaviour – and is called a "freemartin". A female who has had a calf is called a "cow".

An intact (that is, not castrated) adult male is called a "bull". If he is castrated, he's a "steer". A "steer" that's used as a draft animal is called an "ox". Oxen can pull a bigger load than horses, can work for longer, and are less prone to injury.

If cattle have been raised to be eaten, the correct term is "beef cattle".

The word "cattle" is never singular – you can have "three cattle" or "two cattle", but you can never have "one cattle". Surprisingly, with such a plethora of different words for animals of the bovine persuasion, there is no non gender-specific word for a single bovine animal.

However, you can usually get away with the word "cow". After all, on average most of the adult cattle that you'll see will be female. However, every now and then, you might end up saying "*that cow over there is a bull*".

AUSTRALIA'S GREENHOUSE EMISSIONS

In 2003, 48 per cent of Australia's greenhouse emissions came from the production of energy (mostly coal). About 18 per cent came from agriculture (plants, animals and so on), 8 per cent from cars, 4.5 per cent from trucks and other transport, with 21.5 per cent coming from "other" (mining, construction).

Ruminant Gut

Cattle can eat grass and grow big and healthy because the critters in their gut can digest the cellulose.

The average rumen (see "Ruminant" over page) can hold around 160 litres, which is two to four times the volume of your car's petrol tank. Tiny creatures (bacteria, fungi, protists and viruses, and bacteria-like critters called "archaea") live in the rumen and help digest the cellulose. Some of these archaea can actually eat the cellulose, as well as the by-products of the other microbes living in the rumen.

These archaea are messy eaters, and "waste" about 6 to 10 per cent of what they eat. The waste comes out as methane. If this potential source of energy were not wasted, it could be used to bulk up the cow. On the other hand, the strange combination of cow-and-archaea does have a marvellous, very special and very rare skill – so surely we can forgive their slight inefficiency? Their special skill is to turn non-protein into protein, or grass into cattle. I have always been amazed that a cow can get so huge and meaty while eating such a low-energy food as grass. It's all because of the archaea in their gut. We humans do not have critters in our gut that can do that for us – so we have to eat protein.

RUMINANT

Cows are called "ruminants". Other ruminant animals besides cows are sheep, goats, deer, giraffes and moose.

They're not called "ruminants" because there is lots of "room in it". No, the word "rumen" comes from the Latin for "gullet" or "throat". Ruminants partially digest the food in the rumen, and then vomit it back up into the mouth to chew it some more. A more polite word for "vomit" is "regurgitate".

A "ruminant" is also a person who "ruminates" – they think deeply on matters, they contemplate and they meditate. They "chew over" ideas and concepts, in the same way that cattle "chew over" their food. The word "ruminant" comes from the Latin word *ruminat* meaning "chewed over" – and it's closely related to the word "rumen".

Cattle have four compartments at the top end of their gut. The "rumen" is the largest. The next one, the "reticulum", is the smallest. This is where metal objects accidentally eaten (barbed wire fragments and so forth) usually end up. The next compartment is the "omasum" – it absorbs nutrients and water. Finally, the "abomasum" is similar to our human stomach, which is why it's called the "true stomach".

Methane, Methane, Methane

Cattle produce around 280 litres of methane per day, while sheep (far smaller) produce only 25 litres.

In terms of volume, methane is the number two greenhouse gas after carbon dioxide. We humans (and the livestock and agriculture that we manage) dump a lot less methane into the atmosphere than we do carbon dioxide – but methane is about 22-or-so times more potent as a global warming gas than carbon dioxide. So one tonne of methane has the same "Carbon Dioxide Equivalent" as 22 tonnes of carbon dioxide. If you take account of this extra "potency", in the USA, methane is responsible for 2 per cent of their greenhouse gas damage.

Different countries have different proportions of heavy industry and primary industry, or of "smoking chimneys" and "bucolic pastures". In the USA, there are fewer cattle than people – about two head of cattle for every five people.

There are only four million New Zealanders on their two islands. But they share their home with 45 million sheep, 10 million cattle and over one million farmed deer. Because New Zealand has so little heavy industry, *over 50 per cent of its greenhouse gas emissions arise from methane from enteric fermentation (the guts of livestock)*", according to Katherine Hayhoe, an atmospheric scientist at the University of Illinois. So about 50 per cent of the greenhouse gases that New Zealand emits is methane – and this methane is about 22 times more potent than carbon dioxide.

In Australia, sheep and cattle produce 14 per cent of our total greenhouse gases. (This figure is measured in "Carbon Dioxide Equivalents". In other words, the actual volume of methane is less than 1 per cent, but because of methane's potency, it comes out equivalent to 14 per cent of greenhouse gas damage.) Most of Australia's methane comes from the agriculture sector. Our tens of millions of cattle and sheep produce 90 per cent of this methane, about 3 million tonnes per year.

RICE MAKES METHANE

During photosynthesis, plants pull carbon dioxide from the atmosphere and turn it into sugars that are sent to the roots. Depending on the plant, about 40 to 90 per cent of the sugars get into the soil. In wetland soils that are low in oxygen, such as rice paddies, much of the carbon in the sugars gets turned into methane.

The critters that do this were only recently discovered, and given the name of "Rice Cluster I Archaea".

First, the Knowledge

Methane from cattle is a significant worry, so various bodies around the world have researched this.

The first thing is to work out from which end of the cattle the methane comes. (At last, we get to the Answer.) The New South Wales Department of Agriculture in Armidale has been using a "reverse aqualung" combined with a small vacuum pump in their research. Instead of delivering gas into the lungs, it samples what comes out. It turns out that the vast majority of the methane (around 95 per cent) comes out the cow's mouth.

In plain words, most livestock-related methane comes from burping (or "eructation" if you want to be polite), not from farting (or "the other end" if you want to be polite).

In the USA, Rep. Henry Bonilla wrote an editorial in the

Serenity Farms Organic Dairy Milk

Milk so fresh it's like digesting the cellulose.

Pecos Enterprise, a newspaper in Reeves County in Texas. He claimed that by funding research on cow belching, the Environmental Protection Agency was taking things too far. In effect, he was saying that we should *not* know, and should not find out, what the situation really is.

In Australia, the CSIRO has taken the opposite approach. It has produced a colour-coded map of methane emissions, covering all of Australia.

NOT BACTERIA!

The little critters in the gut of the cattle that make methane are not actually bacteria. Their technical and official name is "methanogenic archaea" (fancy words for "bacteria-like critters that make methane"). They are very ancient organisms. So if they're not bacteria, what are they? Are they animal or vegetable or mineral? And if they have only a single cell, why *aren't* they bacteria?

It was easier back in the 18th century, when Carolus Linnaeus split living creatures into either "Animal" or "Vegetable" Kingdoms. He also had a third Kingdom for "Minerals".

But about a century earlier, Antonie van Leewenhoek, one of the first people to use a microscope, realised that there were tiny single-celled critters that he could see through a microscope. These were neither Animal nor Vegetable. So in 1886, Ernst Haeckel added unicellular organisms (Protista) as his third Kingdom.

Since then, many people have proposed many classification systems for this strange thing that we call Life. A recent 21st century classification has one Domain for "Bacteria" (which are single-celled creatures), a second Domain for Archaea (which are very different single-celled creatures, some of whom live in the gut of cattle) and a third Domain for Eukarya (which is everything else such as slime moulds, animals, fungi, plants, algae and so on.) It's all very confusing.

But the important thing to know is that some critters that live in the gut of cattle and make methane are not really bacteria – they are Archaea.

Then, the Treatment

Research has shown that we can reduce methane emissions from livestock.

First, adding urea to the diet of livestock reduces the amount of methane emitted.

Second, New Zealand scientists found that if the livestock ate plants rich in condensed tannins, they would produce up to 16 per cent less methane. The catch is that these plants are more expensive than the livestock's regular feed.

Third, we can breed cattle that process what they eat more efficiently. According to Andrew Alford, a livestock researcher with the New South Wales Department of Primary Industries, in the next quarter century this could reduce methane emissions from livestock by 3 per cent – and at the same time result in bulkier cattle.

Fourth, antibiotics given to cattle can attack the critters that produce the methane, and so reduce the methane output. However, we need to consider the issue of critters becoming resistant to these antibiotics, and passing on this resistance to the critters that attack humans.

A fifth approach is being taken by CSIRO Livestock Industries – they've come up with a vaccine to slow down these methane-producing bacteria. The vaccine lowers methane production by 20 per cent. Because there's a greater efficiency of processing food in the animal's gut, there's also a mild increase in weight, and possibly wool production for sheep.

Sixth, what about cutting back on how much meat we eat?

And so on.

The point of all of this is that the vast majority of methane comes out of the mouth of the cattle, not the back end. I guess this shows a lot of us can't tell one end of a cow from another.

COW INTO KANGAROO?

Kangaroos and other plant-eating animals such as camels are not ruminants, but they have a gut that is quite similar. The big difference is that while cattle burp hundreds of litres of methane every day, kangaroos release virtually none.

A cow's foregut can hold over 100 kilograms of grass. Fermentation releases hydrogen, which the methanogenic archaea combine with carbon to make methane. Cattle are known as "foregut fermenters", because that's where most of the fermentation happens. Kangaroos are also foregut fermenters. But instead of using the methanogenic archaea to get rid of hydrogen, they have different critters that make vinegar (acetic acid). (We humans are "hindgut fermenters", so we mostly release gas from "the other end".)

Here's the controversial part.

Is it possible to do some fancy genetic engineering or transplantation? What if you could modify the gut of a cow to have the appropriate environment, so that different kangaroo-type microbes could make a new home there – would cattle then burp with vinegar instead of methane?

Have you ever worried or wondered about the Secret Tracer Chemical in swimming pools – the one that supposedly turns bright raspberry red when you do a wee? Orson Welles (the original voice of the *War of the Worlds* radio broadcast, and the *Citizen Kane* guy) reckoned that he had some of this chemical in his pool. According to Orson, only *"the nicest, cleanest, most respectable people"* would wee in the water.

But as you might have guessed, there is no such chemical. Even so, pool supply companies are regularly approached for the magical "urine-indicator dye".

CHLORINE SMELL

Your home bleach contains about 2 per cent chlorine – and yes, it does have the distinctive smell of chlorine. The level of chlorine in your backyard pool should be about 10,000 times less.

So do this experiment. Dilute some bleach 10 times – and keep on doing this until you get to a 10,000 times dilution. At each stage, sniff gently (not deeply) to see when and if the chlorine smell vanishes …

Chemistry of Pools

Swimming pools have been around since the times of the ancient Greeks and Romans. In the 1st century BC, the Japanese ran swimming races in pools. In the same century, the Roman, Gaius Maecenas (patron of the poets Virgil and Horace), was supposed to have built the first heated swimming pool.

In nature, clean pools of water seem to exist without any effort at all. But for us humans to achieve a swimming pool with water that is clean, clear, pleasant and free of germs takes a lot of science. Professor Ben Sellinger devotes a whole chapter to the topic of chlorine and swimming pools in his book, *Chemistry in the Marketplace.*

Our human swimming pools rely mostly on chlorine to keep them clean. (There are other chemicals such as ozone, and other processes involving ultraviolet light – but I won't deal with any of that in this story.) Chlorine is a cheap and effective chemical that kills various nasties in your swimming pool. Once in the water, it immediately splits into "hypochlorous acid" (very quick at killing bacteria) and "hypochlorite ions" (very slow at killing bacteria). Unfortunately, the hypochlorite ions quickly fade your swimming cossie, so you should rinse it immediately after getting out of the water.

Heavy Chemistry (Sorry)

Some Swimming Pool Science is exactly the opposite of what you would expect. For example, people often sniff the air at their local pool and then confidently proclaim, *"There's too much chlorine in the water, I can smell it"*. The truth is the exact opposite – there's not enough chlorine!

The chemistry runs like this. In the water there is organic nitrogen, which comes from urine, sweat, dead insects, bacteria and so forth. This organic nitrogen has used up all the hypochlorous acid and hypochlorite ions, and so there's none left. Indeed, the chlorine (in the hypochlorous acid and the hypochlorite ions) and the nitrogen have combined together to make a different class of chemicals called "chloramines" – which is what you are smelling. The cure is simply to add more chlorine and after a while, the smell goes away. I know this sounds weird – you have a "chlorine-like" smell in your pool, so the cure is to add more chlorine!

Let me explain how it works.

Chlorine goes through a few chemical stages in destroying (or getting rid of) the nasty organics. It first forms monochloramine, then dichloramine, then trichloramine and runs through a few more steps before ending up at nitrogen gas, or nitrates. It's the volatile trichloramine (in the middle of these chemical reactions) that gives off the supposed "chlorine" smell.

If there's not enough chlorine, the reaction gets stuck at one of the chloramine steps, such as the trichloramine one. So when you add more chlorine, you push the reaction along out of the trichloramine stage – and the smell goes away.

Urine-Indicator Chemical?

So, is there a chemical that can be added to swimming pools to change the colour of the water and mark out and embarrass naughty people who have done a wee? According to Professor Selinger, almost certainly not.

Urine is made from water, inorganic salts, urea, creatinine, ammonia, catecholamines, allantoin and the breakdown products of red blood cells, which give it its yellowish colour. There are also many many other chemicals. These chemicals, and their ratios, vary enormously with age, race, gender, hormonal levels, health and so on.

Which one of these many chemicals will you choose to react with?

If a "marker" chemical can react to your urine, it might also react to your sweat. This is such a difficult problem that it seems that nobody has tried to solve it. And if such a chemical did really exist, surely cheeky kids would wee while swimming past other kids, to put the blame onto them.

Maybe the only foolproof cure for the urine-in-the-pool problem is that used by the Preppy Pup Country Club in New Jersey. It's a day care centre that caters exclusively for dogs. The rule is plainly posted, for all dogs to read: *"Welcome to our ool. Notice that there's no P in it. Please keep it that way."*

WELCOME TO OUR OOL.

NOTICE THAT
THERE'S NO P IN IT.

PLEASE KEEP IT THAT WAY.

TOO MUCH CHLORINE

The pH balance in the average swimming pool should be between 7.2 and 7.8. By the way, pH is how you measure how acid or alkaline something is – pH 1 is very acid, pH 14 is very alkaline, and pH 7 is right in the middle and dead neutral. But the pH in a swimming pool, even though it's not absolutely neutral, is close enough to neutral not to bother most people.

This situation changed dramatically in Charlottesville, Virginia, back in 1982 when the town dentists noticed a sudden appearance of massive generalised erosion of the enamel of some people's teeth. It was so severe that it could only have been caused by a very strong acid. Some simple detective work revealed that all the affected people had one thing in common – they all belonged to the same local swimming club.

It turned out the pool's water was way out of specification. Instead of being very mildly alkaline, it was blisteringly acid. The pH was 2.7 – 100,000 times more "acid" than it should have been – acid enough to eat the metal fittings and even the concrete in the walls!

We humans think of cleanliness in two distinct ways. First we think of it *physically* in terms of personal hygiene, and second we think of it *morally* in terms of feeling virtuous. Surprisingly, it turns out that there is a link between washing your hands and feeling virtuous.

Historical Hand-Washing

Many religions, including Christianity, Islam, Shinto, Hinduism, Judaism and Bahai, speak of the ritual washing of hands.

Matthew writes in his Gospel, 27:24, *"When Pilate saw that he could prevail nothing, but that rather a tumult was made, he took water, and washed his hands before the multitude, saying, 'I am innocent of the blood of this just person: see ye to it'."* So Pontius Pilate symbolically washed his hands in front of the crowd baying for the death of Jesus, to show that he had no part in it. And Christians follow the advice given in Acts 22:16, *"Arise and be baptized, and wash away your sins".*

So there is some kind of link between the symbolic physical cleansing of the flesh and the spiritual cleansing of the soul.

In the English language, the phrase, *"to wash your hands of it"* means that you are not involved in, nor take responsibility for, an event. In Mandarin Chinese, the phrase *"a pair of dirty hands"* means a thief.

In Shakespeare's play *Macbeth*, Lady Macbeth helps murder King Duncan, her then lawful king, so that she and her husband can rule the land. But later, Lady Macbeth sleepwalks the castle corridors at night, compulsively rubbing her dry hands together in a washing motion, all the time crying, *"Out, damn spot! Out, I say".*

Many psychological studies have shown that if you think or feel that you have done something bad, you will often have an increased desire to wash your hands. And then, after doing so, you magically don't feel so bad. Strangely, this happens even if you didn't intend to wash your hands.

Linking Mind and Matter

How can this be? How can the mere physical act of washing your hands ease your mind, and even make you happier with a choice or decision that you have made?

We'll see in minute, using CDs and jam, but first …

If we look for an emotion that we can experience both *physically* and *morally*, "disgust" springs to mind. Physically, disgust evolved so that we could turn away from and avoid eating potentially dangerous food – and if needs be, vomit it back up. Over time, as we evolved to live together in tribes and societies, the emotion of disgust expanded to include both moral and social wrongs.

Today, we humans show considerable overlap between our *physical* and *emotional* responses to disgust. We show the same reaction on our faces and our bodies exhibit the same physiological reaction. For example, if you *see* something disgusting, or *eat* something disgusting, you still have the same physiological reaction – you vomit. In fact, in reaction to both *physical* and *emotional* disgust, the same parts of our brains will become active – mainly the frontal and temporal lobes.

So it is quite reasonable that a physical cleansing act that will relieve or reduce physical disgust might also relieve or reduce social, emotional or moral disgust.

In fact, lots of psychological studies have shown this to be true.

"Cleaning" the Mind

One study asked volunteers to recall in detail an event from their past – something either evil or good. They were given a list of incomplete words – words with only their first and last letters provided. Those who recalled an evil deed from their past were more likely to next choose words related to cleanliness, such as "wash" rather than "wish", or "soap" rather than "step". And, when they were offered a gift, they were more likely to choose something related to getting clean – an antiseptic hand wipe for example, instead of a pencil.

In a follow-up study, some of the volunteers who recalled an evil deed from their past were offered an antiseptic hand wipe to wash their hands, while others were not. Those who washed their hands felt less guilty, and were less likely to volunteer to do good works. (Presumably they were less likely to volunteer for good works because they now felt less remorse after washing their hands.)

Another study asked volunteers to rate how disgusting certain acts were. These acts included not eating your own dog after it had died *or* eating it; or keeping money from a wallet that you found in the street instead of handing it in; or switching the path of a train to kill only one worker instead of the five workers on the track; or after a plane crash, killing a terminally-ill fellow survivor so that you would avoid starvation, and so on. The volunteers who washed their hands rated these acts as less disgusting than volunteers who did not wash their hands.

In other words, the moral judgments of those who washed their hands, before making a judgment, were less severe.

Yet another study showed that washing your hands can help you live with a difficult decision. Volunteers were asked to rank how they liked 10 CDs. Then some of these volunteers were asked to rate how they liked washing their hands with a special soap, while others did not wash their hands. It was actually a trick – the researchers wanted some of the volunteers to wash their hands, without then realising that it was all part of the study. Then all of the volunteers were offered the choice of taking home one of the CDs that they did not rank very highly. The volunteers who did not wash their hands were not very happy with the CD they took home. But the volunteers who did wash their hands really liked their CDs.

So washing your hands can cleanse your mind from traces of past decisions – as Pontius Pilate showed in the Gospels.

The same thing happened when the volunteers rated various fruit jams, and could take home one of the jams that they did not rate highly. Again, washing their hands made them like the jam they were given more.

So with regard to morality, purity is not just a metaphor – washing your hands really can alter your moral values.

And do clean hands really make a pure heart? We don't know that, but at least clean hands can give you a clear conscience after you have sinned.

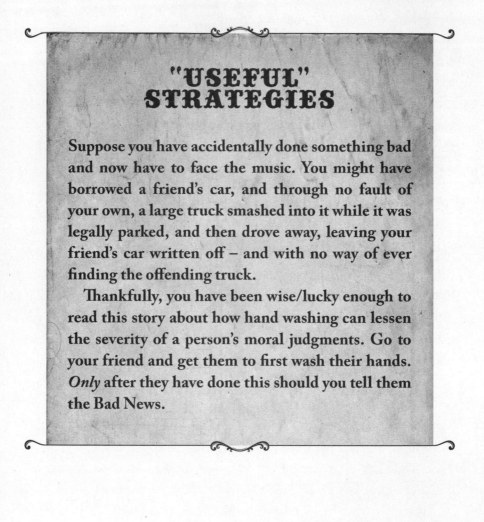

"USEFUL" STRATEGIES

Suppose you have accidentally done something bad and now have to face the music. You might have borrowed a friend's car, and through no fault of your own, a large truck smashed into it while it was legally parked, and then drove away, leaving your friend's car written off – and with no way of ever finding the offending truck.

Thankfully, you have been wise/lucky enough to read this story about how hand washing can lessen the severity of a person's moral judgments. Go to your friend and get them to first wash their hands. *Only* after they have done this should you tell them the Bad News.

Our world is full of rhythms. Birds flock and fly together, and glide and dart across the sky. Schools of fish, thousands thick, turn seemingly as one. Asian fireflies flash together in bursts of light that can be seen a kilometre away. In your heart, millions of minute muscle cells draw together in a beautifully-timed expanding wave of contraction that squirts out around 80 millilitres of blood on each beat.

The mathematicians call these curious systems "Globally Coupled Oscillators". And if you've spent a lot of time as a part of an audience, you'll almost certainly have heard humans turning themselves into a "globally coupled oscillator" and indulging in what's known as "Synchronised Clapping".

Hand Clapping 101

This is what happened one night at a performance of the play *The Bald Singer* at a theatre in the little Romanian town of Cluj-Napoca. In the audience that night was a man named Zoltan Néda, who just happened to be a Professor of Theoretical Physics at Babes-Bolyai University in Romania. As he and other members of the audience showed their appreciation, *"a beautiful rhythmic applause appeared"*.

This is what he heard.

Immediately after the performance ended, there was loud and raucous applause, as people in the audience clapped their hands randomly. The average time between claps was about 0.4 seconds.

After about 10 seconds, the random clapping flipped into synchronised clapping. Now, all of the hands in the audience suddenly hit together in pairs at the same time. But it's hard to keep synchronised while clapping rapidly. So, without really thinking about it, to help them transition from "random" to "synchronised", the members of the audience dropped every second clap. Now the average time between claps was about 0.8 seconds. The audience was again synchronised, but at about half its previous frequency. Because there were fewer claps overall, it also got quieter.

This lasted for another 10 to 15 seconds, while the audience showed their collective single-minded appreciation by clapping in unison. Then it disintegrated back into louder random racket, with the quicker hand clapping.

Zoltan heard this strange social self-organised spontaneity coming and going several times. And as the applause rippled on, the synchronisation disappeared (becoming louder) and reappeared (becoming softer) some half-dozen times.

Our hand clapping is the human equivalent of the synchronised flashing Asian fireflies.

If You Can't Measure It, You Don't Know It

What was going on? Well, an essential part of any scientific experiment is to take some measurements.

So Zoltan teamed up with Albert-Laszlo Barabasi, an associate professor of physics at the University of Notre Dame in Indiana. They and their colleagues recorded several opera and theatre performances in Romania and Hungary. At the end of each performance, they analysed the audience applause for loudness, "order parameter", average noise intensity, and the average interval between clapping. They also analysed the clapping of single volunteers in their laboratory.

They found that during thunderously loud, and random, applause, people clap, on average, every 0.4 seconds. But the "scatter" (the difference between the "fast" and "slow" clappers) is quite wide. Some people clap every 0.3 of a second and some clap every 0.5 of a second.

But then there's a brief transition period of a few seconds, where people omit every second clap. This period between clapping doubles to 0.8 of a second and, almost magically, you then have synchronised clapping. People are clapping in unison, but half as frequently. Now here's an odd mathematical observation. In synchronised clapping, where the time between claps has stretched out to 0.8 seconds, the scatter is much less. Practically everybody is clapping quite close to that 0.8 seconds. So it "sounds" like one giant pair of hands, clapping in a single beat.

If you analyse the maths of "globally coupled oscillators", it turns out that one of the essential conditions is that there is very little scatter in the period of each of the individual oscillators – and that's what the physicists found when people clap in synchrony.

Social Science of Clapping

But why do we drift in and out of synchronised clapping?

The scientists theorised that we humans, when we're part of an audience, harbour two conflicting desires.

One desire is to stay synchronised with our fellow humans with whom we have just shared a marvellous experience. This explains the synchronisation.

The other desire is to increase, or at least maintain, the average noise intensity. This is to show respect to the performers, by being as loud as possible. Unfortunately, when we synchronise, we clap half as frequently and generate half as much noise. (But at some of the gigs that I've been to, some people compensate for the reduced noise by stamping their feet.)

We can't have both "synchronisation" and "loudness" at the same time, so we resolve this frustration by having one after the other. That's why we drift in and out of synchrony.

We're still not sure whether synchronised clapping is initiated by stretching out the time between claps, or by human herd instinct.

Either way, there is one kind of synchronised applause *all* performers hope to avoid – and that's the slow handclap.

CULTURAL DIFFERENCES IN HAND CLAPPING

Now one very curious thing about this synchronised clapping is that it's different in different cultures.

It's very common in the audiences of Eastern Europe, but very rare in the USA.

Scientists are not sure why, but they think that it might be something to do with the American desire to be a rugged individual – an independent maverick, a solitary non-conformist, the lone cowboy working the cattle. In general, the members of an American audience will just get in there and clap rapidly by themselves, ignoring what their fellow Americans might do.

THE APPLAUSE
"Brilliant, synchronised performances..." - Martin Scorsese
"No Slow handclaps here..." - Gregor Jordan
"Globally Coupled Oscillators... audience pleaser." - Steven Spielberg
COMING 2010

ACKNOWLEDGEMENTS

This book is based on the Odd Stuff that scientists have discovered.

Other Real Scientists and Doctors have advised me, including Professors Ross Bradbury, Rick Shine, Mary-Louise McLaw, Frank Nicholas, Ben Selinger, as well as Dr Ben Phillips and Nick Ruello.

Once again, Dan Driscoll and my wife, Mary Dobbie, were essential in whipping these stories into shape.

Caroline Pegram was invaluable in getting the concepts turned into reality. I would like to thank my agent Sophie Hamley from Camerons Management, the photographer Mel Koutchavlis, and Jon MacDonald, David Henley, Lucy Schuman and Hannah Robinson from Xou Creative, as well as the wonderful people from Pan Macmillan including Rod Morrison, Emma Rafferty's-Rules, Louise Cornegé, Jane Hayes and Jessica Weir.

Douglas Holgate did the lovely illustrations.

Max and Carmel Dobbie helped proof the galleys, as did Caroline Pegram and my little son, Little Karl.

And let me thank the Australian Skeptics for all the good work they've done.

REFERENCES

BEER GOGGLES

Coghlan, A, "Pint pots designed to banishing bitterness", *New Scientist*, 21 November 1992, p 8.

Jones, BT et al, "Alcohol consumption increases attractiveness ratings of opposite–sex faces: a possible third route to risky sex", *Addiction*, August 2003, pp 1069–1075.

Leslie, M, "Uncorking ancient vintages", in *Science (NetWatch)*, 11 July 2003, p 147.

McGovern, PE et al, "A Funerary Feast Fit For King Midas", *Nature*, 23/30 December 1999, pp 863–864.

Pain, S, "Grog of the Greeks", *New Scientist*, 27 November 1999, pp 54–57.

MUSSELS – AN OPEN AND SHUT CASE?

Marino, M, "Blue Mussels: An Open And Shut Case", *Fish*, Vol 15 (2), 2007, pp 4–5.

"Mollusk", *Encyclopaedia Britannica* – Ultimate Reference Suite DVD, 2008, United States of America.

"Mussel", *Encyclopaedia Britannica* – Ultimate Reference Suite DVD, 2008, United States of America.

Ruello, NV, "Improving Post Harvest Handling To Add Value To Farmed Mussels", *Report for Seafood Services Australia*, January 2004, pp 1–57.

BENDING SPOONS FOR FUN & PROFIT

Adams, C, "How did Uri Geller bend spoons?", *The Straight Dope*, 26 August 1988.

Carey, B, "While a magician works, the mind does the rest", *The New York Times*, 11 August 2008.

Carroll, R, "Uri Geller", *The Skeptic's Dictionary*, 1994–2009 (Skepdic.com)

Martinez-Conde, S et al, "Attention and Awareness in Stage magic: turning tricks into research", *Nature Reviews* (Neuroscience), November 2008, pp 871–879.

Martinez-Conde & Macknik, SL, "Magic and the Brain", *Scientific American*, December 2008, pp 44–51.

Morris, D, "Bob Steiner Visits Uri", *The Skeptic*, September 1984, p 18.

Randi, J, "Geller, Uri", *An Encyclopaedia of Claims, Frauds, and Hoaxes of the Occult and Supernatural*, James Randi Educational Foundation, 2007.

"Zanex Pays Geller Over $350,000", *The Skeptic*, June 1986, pp 2–3.

TWINKLING STARS

Chaple, G, "Clearing the air about seeing vs. transparency", *Astronomy*, November 2008, p 75.

Comins, NF, *Heavenly Errors – Misconceptions About The Real Nature Of The Universe*, 2001, Columbia University Press, United States of America, pp 5–6, 46, 89–90.

Hardy, JW, *Adaptive Optics for Astronomical Telescopes*, Oxford University Press Inc, 1998, New York, pp 3–31.

Opie, Iona & Peter (ed), *The Oxford Dictionary of Nursery Rhymes*, Oxford University Press, 1951, Great Britain, pp 397–398.

Plait, P, "Twinkle Twinkle Little Star", *Bad Astronomy* (online), 23 August 1999.

Plait, P, "Taking out the Twinkle", *Bad Astronomy* (online), 30 August 1999.

Platt, BC & Shack, R, "History and Principles of Shack-Hartmann Wavefront Sensing", *Journal of Refractive Surgery*, Vol 17, Sept/Oct 2001, pp S573–S577.

SPONTANEOUS HUMAN COMBUSTION

Benecke, M, "Spontaneous Human Combustion. Thoughts of a Forensic Biologist", *Skeptical Inquirer*, 22 (2), 1998, pp 47–51.

Dawkins, MJR & Hull, D, "The Production of Heat by Fat", *Scientific American*, August 1965, Vol 21 (2), pp 62–67.

DeHaan, JD, "Combustion of animal fat and its implications for the consumption of human bodies in fires", *Science & Justice*, Vol 39 (1), 1999, pp 27–38.

DeHaan, JD & Burbakhsh, S, "Sustained combustion of an animal carcass and its implications for the consumption of human bodies in fires", *Journal of Forensic Science*, Vol 46 (5), September 2001, pp 1076–81.

Heymer, J, "A burnt-out case?", *New Scientist*, 19 May 1988, pp 68–69.

Heymer, J, "A case of spontaneous human combustion?", *New Scientist*, 15 May 1986, pp 70–71.

Mathai, ML et al, "Regulation of body temperature in response to heat", *Chemistry in Australia*, July 2005, pp 11–13, 22.

Merz, B, "Malignant hyperthermia: nightmare for anesthesiologists – and patients", *JAMA*, Vol 255 (6), 14 February 1986, pp 709–715.

"Mysteries of the unexplained", *Reader's Digest*, 1986, United States of America, pp 80–93.

Nickell, J & Fischer, JF, "Incredible Cremations: Investigating Spontaneous Combustion Deaths", *The Skeptical Inquirer*, Vol 11, summer 1987, pp 352–357.

Palmiere, C et al, "Ignition of a human body by a modest external source: A case report", *Forensic Science International*, Vol 188, May 2009, pp 17–19.

The Skeptic's Dictionary (online) – http://skepdic.com/shc.html

http://en.wikeipedia.org/wiki/Spontaneous_human_combustion

LICE LICE BABY

Bakalar, N, "Childhood: Combing Through Wet Hair May Be Best Way To Find Lice", *The New York Times*, 24 March 2009, p D6.

Canyon, DV et al, "Spatial and Kinetic Factors for the Transfer of Head Lice (*Pediculus capitis)* Between Hairs", *The Journal of Investigative Dermatology*, Vol 119 (3), September 2002, pp 629–631.

Downs, AMR et al, "Widespread insecticide resistance in head lice to the over-the-counter pediculocides in England, and the emergence of carbaryl resistance", *British Journal of Dermatology*, Vol 146, January 2002, pp 88–93.

Jenkins, R, "Head Lice Warning", *Australian Doctor*, 17 February 2006, p 18.

Robotham, J, "It's onc small step for head lice, but on giant leap for mankind", *The Sydney Morning Herald*, 26 May 2004, p 3.

Speare, Prof R, "Do head lice only like clean hair?", *ABC Health & Wellbeing* (online), June 2008.

"Wouldn't it be lice? How bugs bested Napoleon", *The Sydney Morning Herald*, 5 January 2006, p 9.

REPRESSED MEMORY

Braun, K, Ellis, R, Loftus, EF, "Make My Memory: How advertising can change our memories of the past", *Psychology & Marketing*, Vol 19 (1), January 2002, pp 1–23.

"Experts can't tell the difference between false and true accounts of children, Cornell study shows", *Science Daily* (online), 19 September 1997.

Gardner, M, *Are Universes thicker than blackberries?*, W.W. Norton & Company, 2003, USA, pp 215–224.

Loftus, E, "Creating False Memories", *Scientific American*, Vol 277(3), September 1997, pp 70–75.

Loftus, E, "Our changeable memories: legal and practical implications", *Nature Reviews*, March 2003, pp 231–234.

Loftus, E & Ketcham, K, *The Myth of Repressed Memory: False Memories and Allegations of Sexual Abuse*, St Martin's Press, 1994, New York.

Squires, R, "The trouble with memory", *Sunday Telegraph*, 8 August 2010, p 26.

"Tufts University Psychology Research Tackles Problem Of 'False Memories'; Study Is First To Examine Impact

Of 'Generative Learning' On Flawed Retention", *Science Daily* (online), 29 July 2003.

TEETHING BABIES AND ILLNESS
Macknin, ML et al, "Symptoms Associated With Infant Teething: A Prospective Study", *Pediatrics*, Vol 105 (4), April 2000, pp 747–752.

Wake, M et al, "Parents beliefs about infant teething: A survey of Australian parents", *Journal of Paediatrics and Child Health*, October 1999, Vol 35 (5), pp 446–449.

Wake, M et al, "Teething and Tooth Eruption in Infants: A Cohort Study", *Pediatrics*, Vol 106 (6), December, pp 1374–1379.

Wake, M & Hesketh, K, "Teething symptoms: cross sectional survey of five groups of child health professionals", *British Medical Journal*, Vol 325, 12 October 2002, pp 814.

FRIDAY THE 13TH
Brasch, R, *How Did It Begin?*, Longmans, Green & Co., 1965, pp 3, 296.

Brewer's Dictionary of Phrase and Fable, Cassell Publishers, 1990, London, pp 110, 411, 1018.

Panati, C, *Extraordinary Origins Of Everyday Things*, Harper and Row, 1987, New York, pp 11–13.

Scanlon, TJ, "Is Friday the 13th bad for your health?", *British Medical Journal*, 18–25 December 1993, pp 1584–1586.

HAND-WASHING – HOT & BOTHERED

"Beware Dirty Docs", *New Scientist*, 24 October 2009, pp 6–7.

Carter, H, "Kids Don't Need Soap", *Medical Observer*, 30 March 2001, p 5.

McBride, M, "Microbial Flora Of In-Use Soap Products", *Applied And Environmental Microbiology*, August 1984, pp 338–341.

Michaels, B et al, "Water Temperature As A Factor In Hand Washing Efficacy", *Food Service Technology*, Vol 2, September 2002, pp 139–149.

Panati, C, *Extraordinary Origins Of Everyday Things*, Harper and Row, 1987, New York, pp 152–155, 217–220.

Price, PB, "The Bacteriology Of Normal Skin: A New Quantitative Test Applied To A Study Of The Bacterial Flora And The Disinfectant Action Of Mechanical Cleansing", *Journal of Infectious Disease*, Vol 63, November–December 1938, pp 301–318.

Temime, L et al, "Peripatetic Health Care Workers As Potential Superspreaders", *PNAS*, 27 October 2009, pp 18,420–28.

"WHO Guidelines On Hand Hygiene In Health Care (Advanced Draft): A Summary", 2005, (WHO/EIP/SPO/QPS/0 5.2).

Wilson Sir G & Miles Sir A, *Principles Of Bacteriology, Virology And Immunity*, Edward Arnold, 1975, London, pp 161–163.

ARE ALL WHITE CATS DEAF?

Geigy, C et al, "Does a pleiotropic gene explain deafness and blue irises in white cats?", *The Veterinary Journal*, Vol 173, May 2007, pp 548–553.

Heid, S et al, "A model for prelingual deafness, the congenitally deaf white cat – population statistics and degenerative changes", *Hearing Research*, Vol 115, January 1998, pp 101–112.

Nicolaus, BJR, "A critical review of the function of neuromelanin and an attempt to provide a unified theory", *Medical Hypotheses*, Vol 65, 2005, pp 791–796.

Penderis, J, "Common cranial nerve disorders in dogs and cats", *In Practice*, June 2003, pp 342–349.

Ryugo, DK et al, "Separate forms of pathology in the cochlea of congenitally deaf white cats", *Hearing Research*, Vol 181, July 2003, pp 73–84.

SANTA'S FRANTIC RIDE

Anderson, CJ & Prentice, NM, "Encounter with reality – children's reactions on discovering the Santa Claus myth", *Child Psychiatry and Human Development*, Vol 25 (2), winter 1996, pp 67–84.

"Book Of Facts", *Reader's Digest*, 1994, Australia, pp 138–139.

"Christmas 2007: peace, goodwill and the power to move us from the trenches of our hearts", *Washington Post*, 25 December 2007.

"Did you know?", *Reader's Digest*, 1990, London, p 91.

"Fat but a fast mover", *Focus*, January 1999, pp 22–23.

Highfield, R, *Can Reindeer Fly? The Science Of Christmas*, 1998, Metro Publishing Ltd, Great Britain.

Nelms, BC, "Santa Claus: good or bad for children?" *Journal Of Paediatric Health Care*, Vol 10 (6), Nov–Dec 1996, pp 243–244.

Panati, C, *Panati's Extraordinary Origins Of Everyday Things*, Harper and Row, 1987, New York, pp 72–75.

Patterson, O, "A holiday for us all", *The New York Times* (Opinion), 23 December 2006.

Porter, D, "Santa dynamics", *New Scientist*, 6 February 1999, p 55.

"Santa's fly-by-night antics breaches Act", *Australian Financial Review* (Rear Window), 22 December 1998.

DOES COKE DISSOLVE TEETH?

Levine, RS, "Fruit juice erosion – an increasing danger?", *Journal of Dentistry*, Vol 2 (2), 1973, pp 61–75.

Mikkelson, B, "Tooth in Advertising", *Snopes.com*, http://www.snopes.com/cokelore/tooth.asp

FROGS AND WARTS

Brinton, DG, "Reminiscences of Pennsylvania Folk-Lore", *The Journal of American Folklore*, Vol 5 (18), July–September 1892, pp 177–185.

Brodell, RT & Johnson, SM, *WARTS – Diagnosis and Management An Evidence-Based Approach*, Martin Dunitz, 2003, London, pp 3–7.

Hausen (zur), H, *Infections Causing Human Cancer*, Wiley-VCH, Weinheim, 2006, pp 1–16 (Historical Review).

Hughes-Simon, G, "Some Japanese Beliefs and Home Remedies", *The Journal of American Folklore*, Vol 65 (257), July–September 1952, pp 281–293.

Peavy, CD, "Faulkner's Use of Folklore in The Sound and the Fury", *The Journal of American Folklore*, Vol 79 (313), July–September 1966, pp 437–447.

Tomasek, TM et al, "What's Slithering Around on Your School Grounds?", *The American Biology Teacher*, September 2005, Vol 67 (7), pp 419–425.

FAIRY RINGS

Coghlan, A, "Blame Them On The Fairies", *New Scientist*, April 2004, p 12.

Evershed, H, "Fairy Rings", *Nature*, 21 February 1884, pp 384–385.

Faust, JL, "A Season for Toadstools, by Whatever Name", *The New York Times*, 4 August 1996.

"Fungus-Treated Violin Outdoes Stradivarius", *Science Daily*, 14 September 2009.

Rutter, G, "Away with the Fairies", *Fortean Times*, Vol 141, December 2000, pp 34–38.

Sergeant, J, "Fairy rings", *Nature*, 17 November 1887, pp 61–63.

SKIPPING STONES

Bocquet, L, "The physics of stone skipping", *American Journal of Physics*, February 2002, Vol 71 (2), pp 150–155.

Bocquet, L et al, "Secrets of successful stone-skipping", *Nature*, Vol 427, 1 January 2004, p 29.

Sweetman, J, "Barnes Wallis's Other Bouncing Bomb", *The Royal Airforce – Airpower Review*, Vol 5(2), 2002, pp 104–122.

Walker, C, "Walking on Water", *Discover*, August 2003, pp 22–23.

http://en.wikeipedia.org/wiki/Bouncing_bombs

http://en.wikeipedia.org/wiki/Operation_Chastise

LIGHTNING NEVER STRIKES TWICE?

Cooper, MA, "Lightning Injury Facts", (Adapted from) *Seminars in Neurology*, Vol 15(4), December 1995.

Torok, S, *Wow! Amazing science facts and trivia*, ABC Books, 1999, Australia, p 74.

Woodford, J, "Lightning doesn't strike twice; it's more like 1000 times", *The Sydney Morning Herald*, 2 June 2006, p 8.

A LOAD OF HOT AIR

Adams, C, "What 'dangers of disease' do hot-air hand dryers prevent?", *The Straight Dope*, 3 July 1981.

Coward, M, "Now wash your hands", *Fortean Times*, March 2005, p 15.

Lee, M, "Paper and cloth towels found to be more hygienic than air dryers", *Health Facility Management*, August 1994, Vol 7 (8), pp 114–116.

Redway, K & Knights, B, "Hand Drying: Studies of the hygiene and efficiency of different hand drying methods", study by University of Westminster, Applied Ecology Research Group, 1998.

"The hygiene of hand drying", *The Health Report* (Transcript), ABC Radio National, 19 July 2010.

FAST SNAKES

Hu, DL et al, "The Mechanics of slithering locomotion", PNAS, 23 June 2009, Vol 106 (25), pp 10,081–85.

"Snake", *Encyclopaedia Britannica* – Ultimate Reference Suite DVD, 2007, United States of America.

Shine, R & Shetty, S, "Moving in two worlds: aquatic and terrestrial locomotion in sea snakes (*Laticauda colubrina*, Laticudidae), *Journal of Evolutionary Biology*, Vol 14, 2001, pp 338–346.

Socha, JJ, "Becoming airborne without legs: the kinematics of take-off in a flying snake, *Chrysopelea paradisi*", *The Journal of Experimental Biology*, September 2006, pp 3358–3369.

Socha, JJ, "Gliding flight in paradise tree snake", *Nature*, 8 August 2002, pp 603–604.

Socha, JJ et al, "A 3-D kinematic analysis of gliding in a flying snake, *Chrysopelea paradisi*", *The Journal of Experimental Biology*, May 2005, pp 1817–1833.

Socha & LaBarbera, "Effects of size and behaviour on aerial performance of two species of flying snakes (*Chrysopelea)*", *The Journal of Experimental Biology*, May 2005, pp 1835–1847.

COWS – BUM OR BURP?

Adams, C, "Do Cow And Termite Flatulence Threaten The Earth's Atmosphere", *The Straight Dope*, 24 March 1989.

"Graziers Flock To Block Burps", CSIRO Media Release, Ref 2001/136, 6 June 2001.

Jay, C, "Science Takes On The Ruminant With A Phew", *Australian Financial Review*, 26 March 2004, p 70.

"Livestock Purpose Mapped In Greenhouse Check", CSIRO Media Release, Ref 2000/191, 21 July 2000.

Onishi, N, "Trying To Stop Cattle Burps From Heating Up The Planet", *The New York Times*, 13 July 2010.

Roach, J, "New Zealand Tries To Cap Gaseous Sheep Burps", *National Geographic News*, 13 May 2002.

Watson, P, "New Zealand Aims For Greener Pastures", *Los Angeles Times*, 8 June 2008.

PEE IN THE POOL!

Mikkelson, B, "Piscine of the Crime", *Snopes.com*, http://www.snopes.com/science/poolpiss.htm

Quindelen, A, "The Magnificent Orsons", *The New York Times* (online), 15 September 1985.

Sellinger, B, *Chemistry In the Marketplace*, Harcourt Brace Jovanovich, 1998, Sydney, pp 201–212.

HAND-WASHING – CLEAN CONSCIENCE

Lee, SW & Schwarz, N, "Washing Away Postdecisional Dissonance", *Science*, 7 May 2010, p 709.

Schnall, S et al, "With A Clean Conscience: Cleanliness Reduces The Severity Of Moral Judgments", *Psychological Science*, Vol 19, December 2008, pp 1219–1222.

Zhong, CB et al, "Washing Away Your Sins: Threatened Morality And Physical Cleansing", *Science*, 8 September 2006, pp 1451–1452.

A ROUND OF APPLAUSE!

Gura, T, "Rhythm Of Life", *New Scientist*, 4 August 2001, pp 32–35.

"Quiet Enthusiasm", *New Scientist*, 26 February 2000, p 23.

Vicsek, T et al, "Physics Of The Rhythmic Applause", *Physical Review* (E), Vol 61 (6), June 2000, pp 6987–6992.

Vicsek, T et al, "The sound of many hands clapping", *Nature*, Vol 403, 24 February 2000, pp 849–850.

dr Karl

Dinosaurs are^{n't} dead

Dr Karl Kruszelnicki

Illustrated by Douglas Holgate

PAN
Pan Macmillan Australia

AVAILABLE NOW

ISBN: 9780330425797

Praise for *Pray for the World*

"Prayer is the fuel of global missions. No book, ministry or resource has done more to mobilize God's people to pray than *Operation World*. And so, it is with great delight that I recommend *Pray for the World*. This new tool will mobilize immeasurably more prayer, bringing the latest research from the Operation World team to a broader audience. What a service they've performed for the global church and for the least-reached peoples. Take up, and read . . . and pray!"
Michael Oh, executive director and CEO of the Lausanne Movement

"The advancement of the gospel is always to be coupled by desperate prayer. Whether we are told to pray for laborers, for open doors for ministry or that the Word would spread rapidly and be honored, the Bible is clear: when it comes to kingdom expansion, prayer is crucial. *Pray for the World* is a valuable tool to assist us in global disciple making. Incredibly informative, well-written, easy to understand and to the point, this book is a helpful guide as we work to carry out the Great Commission. Read it, keep it close by, and pray, pray, pray!"
J. D. Payne, pastor of church multiplication, The Church at Brook Hills, Birmingham, Alabama

"For those like me who will quietly confess that *Operation World* was a little overwhelming in terms of information, meet the more concise and user-friendly *Pray for the World*. I will use this personally— especially the calendar that helps me pray for all of the countries of the world in one year. I will use it in mobilizing local churches to greater global understanding and intercession, and I will use it in the classroom to introduce students to global realities. My Bible tells me what God wants to do in the world; *Pray for the World* directs me on how to pray."
Paul Borthwick, senior consultant, Development Associates International, author of *Western Christians in Global Mission*

Praise for *Operation World*, 7th Edition

"This is probably one of the most important missionary tools in the entire history of missions."
George Verwer, founder, Operation Mobilization

"Outside of the Bible, no book has had a greater practical impact on my personal prayer life than *Operation World*. God has used this book to open my eyes and the eyes of the church I pastor to the needs of the world and the greatness of the God who desires to make his glory known in the world. I eagerly welcome this new edition and wholeheartedly recommend it."
David Platt, president, International Mission Board, author of *Radical*

"An invaluable source of background information on every country we work in. . . . It has provided an objective platform of information that combines well with our own experiential perceptions in the task of strategic planning."
Christopher J. H. Wright, international director, Langham Partnership International, author of *The Mission of God*

"For years I have used *Operation W___ __ __* pray for people in every tongue, tribe and nation. *Operation World* is a time-honored and well-tes..:d global manual of prayer that will provide you with everything you need to bring the nations of the world before the throne of God. It will expand your heart, vision and passion for the peoples of the world and God's deep desire to reach those in the darkest corners with his help and hope."

Joni Eareckson Tada, founder, Joni and Friends International

"*Operation World* is one of the most important Christian books in the world because it mobilizes the church to reliably informed intercession. As a long-haired student I kept a previous edition by my bedside and prayed through almost every nation. Today, I recommend *Operation World* wherever I go."

Pete Greig, international director, 24-7 Prayer

"Next to your Bible, *Operation World* will be the most important book you will own. Go nowhere without it. Pray daily sharing the burden of our Lord."

Dr. K. P. Yohannan, international director, Gospel for Asia

"The day after I became a Christian in the 1980s, the friend who led me to Christ took me to a bookstore and bought two books for me – The Bible and *Operation World*. The Scriptures helped me gain God's heart for the nations, and *Operation World* helped focus my life on where and how I could strategically serve Him."

Paul Hattaway, author of *The Heavenly Man* and director, Asia Harvest

"*Operation World* has remained a veritable source of mission information about the status of the remaining task and a tool that brings together in one volume detailed update that inspires passion for the unreached and stirs up hearts to intercede."

Reuben Ezemadu, international director, Christian Missionary Foundation

"*Operation World*, since its inception, has been a great gift to God's global church. It offers a clear concise update on the state of each country in the world with some helpful prayer points. It is a wonderful resource which has been widely used among university students around the world and has been a great means of increasing their global awareness."

Lindsay Brown, international director, Lausanne Committee for World Evangelization

"Few documents combine the awesome effect of touching individuals, movements and nations. *Operation World* has also changed the way the Church in Africa, especially IFES students, prays for the world and its people. By facilitating global intercession *Operation World* has contributed immensely in provoking a global vision for the world-wide Church."

Rev. Gideon Para-Mallam, regional secretary for English and Portuguese-speaking Africa, International Fellowship of Evangelical Students

"I personally welcome the 2010 edition of *Operation World*. Since the time the first edition of this book was printed, the world has been different, because it was possible for us to know where the need for the gospel was and gave us a detailed picture of unreached nations and peoples."

David Ruiz, associate director, World Evangelical Alliance Mission Commission

Pray

for the

World

Abridged from *Operation World,* 7th edition,
by Jason Mandryk
Advising editor: Molly Wall

OPERATION
WORLD
family of resources

IVP Books
An imprint of InterVarsity Press
Downers Grove, Illinois

WEC International

InterVarsity Press
P.O. Box 1400, Downers Grove, IL 60515-1426
ivpress.com
email@ivpress.com

InterVarsity Press® is the book-publishing division of InterVarsity Christian Fellowship/USA®, a movement of students and faculty active on campus at hundreds of universities, colleges and schools of nursing in the United States of America, and a member movement of the International Fellowship of Evangelical Students. For information about local and regional activities, visit intervarsity.org.

Scripture quotations, unless otherwise noted, are from The Holy Bible, English Standard Version, copyright ©2001 by Crossway Bibles, a division of Good News Publishers. Used by permission. All rights reserved.

Cover design concept: www.projectluz.com
Interior design: Beth McGill, Maureen Tobey
Image: © Orla/iStockphoto

ISBN 978-0-8308-3686-4 (print)
ISBN 978-0-8308-9695-0 (digital)

Printed in the United States of America ∞

g green press INITIATIVE *As a member of the Green Press Initiative, InterVarsity Press is committed to protecting the environment and to the responsible use of natural resources. To learn more, visit greenpressinitiative.org.*

Library of Congress Cataloging-in-Publication Data
A catalog record for this book is available from the Library of Congress.

P	21	20	19	18	17	16	15	14	13	12	11	10	9	8	7	6	5	4	3	2	1
Y	33	32	31	30	29	28	27	26	25	24	23	22	21	20	19	18	17	16	15		

CONTENTS

130180

INDEX OF COUNTRIES

Notes:

1. Territories without permanent inhabitants have not been listed, including Antarctica.

2. States under the occupation or jurisdiction of other states are included under the latter. For instance, the Western Sahara is under **Morocco**; Tibet is under **China**; Kosovo is under **Serbia**. This is to represent the *de facto* situation, and is not an expression of a political opinion.

A NOTE FROM PATRICK JOHNSTONE

It was 50 years ago in 1964 that I wrote the first edition of *Operation World*. That first edition was followed by six subsequent editions. The 2010 edition was the first one after the hand-over to my successors. The first edition was just 30 pages long, but each edition has grown in the quantity of information provided. By the 2010 edition, *Operation World* was almost 1,000 pages long and no longer a handbook! Molly Wall and team have courageously tackled the task of preparing a paraphrased edition. We believe this will enable many more to obtain a copy and for this edition to be translated into other languages. The aim is to multiply passionate, informed prayer for the evangelization of our needy world, and for the readying of the Church, the Bride of Christ, for the soon return of our King Jesus.

I look back over these 50 years with awe and astonishment at all God has done through the prayers of His people. When I went out to Africa in 1962, evangelical Christians were a marginalized minority in the worldwide Church. There had been 50 years of sowing the gospel seed in times of war and difficulty, but the global harvest had not really begun to be reaped. Then followed a further 50 years of astonishing growth. It began first in Africa during the 1960s, then in Latin America in the 1970s, East Asia in the 1990s, and in recent years came the first significant people movements to Christ in parts of the Muslim world. Few realize that this was a global awakening of staggering size and extent because it was also a time of stagnation and decline especially in Europe and also in the wider Western world. I believe the massive increase in intercession for the world from Africa, Asia and Latin America is a major factor in this Awakening. Evangelical Christianity has moved to centre stage in the world of the 21st century.

Yet how needed such a book as this is today! There is still much to be done if we are to see the fulfilment of the words of the Lord Jesus that this gospel of the Kingdom will be preached throughout the whole world to all nations so that He may return with the global Church complete with people from every race, tribe, people, and tongue who will worship Him. We will never reach every part of humankind unless there is passionate, urgent, Satan-binding prayer to raise up, sustain, and enable harvesters to have the right strategies and close walk with Jesus to bring in the lost. This book gives a picture of every country of the world and the state of the Church and the lost. May it stimulate much-informed prayer that receives answers!

Patrick Johnstone
12 June 2014

PREFACE

Even before the latest edition of *Operation World* was sent out the door to the printer, author Jason Mandryk had a growing vision to see this information placed in the hands of the rapidly expanding Church around the world.

He knew that throughout its 50 years God had used *Operation World* (OW) to transform the prayer lives of people, families, and churches. Many were called to a lifetime of ministry and mission as they prayed through its pages. Earlier editions of OW played a significant role in the formation and growth of Protestant mission-sending movements in countries like Brazil and South Korea.

Could this prayer handbook have a similar impact, on an even wider scale, if more people had access to it in their own country or even language? Would we dare to believe God might use it to fuel the fires of intercession around the globe, and even to give rise to a new wave of global mission?

Jason's vision for *Pray for the World* took hold within the Operation World team. We imagined a prayer handbook – a paraphrased or abridged version of the 2010 edition of *Operation World*. The shorter length, written with simpler English, would be designed specifically for non-native English speakers and for translation. As a publishing project, OW is large, complex, technical, and costly. *Pray for the World* could allow publishing houses to handle the printing, distribution, and sales within their own markets.

I write this, now about to send *Pray for the World* out the door to the printer. We rejoice that God has once again sustained our ministry and team, and provided for our needs as we prepared this latest addition to the Operation World family of resources. We pray with expectation that God will use this new version of *Operation World* to inform and inspire prayer for millions, to mobilize His Church to complete the Great Commission, and to prepare it for the return of the Lord Jesus!

Molly Wall
Bulstrode
United Kingdom
January 2015

EDITOR'S ACKNOWLEDGEMENTS

Such a work cannot be produced by one person alone, and this book builds on 50 years of previous *Operation World* resources (over 2 million copies in all 7 editions, translated into 12 languages, and the family of related products, including children's editions, electronic resources, maps, and more). We will always be grateful for the vision and dedicated labour of Patrick Johnstone, for his decades of contribution to world evangelization through founding and developing Operation World. His ongoing availability for consultation and guidance are irreplaceable!

Pray for the World came together through the editorial work of myself, Jason Mandryk, and a handful of contributing editors: Michael Jaffarian, J. Robert Parks, Glenn Myers, Chris Maynard, and Bryan Nicholson. The task of abridging 1,000 pages to around 300 was not easy, and each person brought prayerful discernment, thoughtfulness, and skill to their work. We are also thankful to Sandy Waldron, Pamela Shaw, and the editorial team at IVP, who carefully reviewed the entire manuscript, making numerous suggestions and improvements throughout. Margaret Bardsley brought years of experience with Operation World to her proofreading and work preparing the country fact boxes.

We could not have seen the project through without support from others actively involved or associated with the Operation World ministry during this season, including Bethany Campbell, Linda Sullivan, Jeremy and Kate Ellis, John Bardsley, Shin-seon Jeong, Paul Dzubinski, Tony Woodward, David Phillips, and several others who kindly served OW in a variety of ways. We extend ongoing appreciation to the Bulstrode community and to our colleagues at WEC International, who continue to provide fellowship, spiritual covering, encouragement, and support.

We again thank the team at Global Mapping International for their excellent work on the maps for *Operation World*, 7th edition, which we have largely adapted for use in *Pray for the World*. Special thanks go to Bryan Nicholson (of cartoMission) for his expertise with recolouring, adjustments, and creation of the few new maps and charts as well. Thanks go also to Chris Maynard for his skillful contribution to adjusted religious figures for Sudan and South Sudan.

We thank Pieter Kwant (of the Piquant Agency), our literary agent and much more, for his excellent work, friendship, encouragement to persevere, and enthusiasm to share the glory of God among the nations! We feel equal gratitude to Jeff Crosby, Al Hsu, Andy Le Peau, and the rest of the team at InterVarsity Press, as we find it a joy to work alongside a publisher whose staff shows such kindness, dedication, and excellence in their work with authors and booksellers.

Thanks be to God for drawing so many uniquely gifted individuals into His service! He has allowed our paths to cross for this season, enabled us to sharpen and strengthen one another in the journey, and we trust He will use our combined effort to build up the wider body of Christ (Ephesians 4:11-12).

INTRODUCTION

In the early Church, the apostle Paul and his small team shared the news and needs of the churches as they travelled from place to place. Believers could rejoice and thank God together for answers to prayer, and also share in the burdens and challenges faced by their brothers and sisters in Christ throughout the region. This continues today as the global body of believers rejoices together, and shares their burdens in prayer. Just as in the early Church, this prayer leads to action and practical help.

Millions of Christians, particularly from the Churches of Latin America, Africa, and Asia, gather regularly at the local level to pray. Today we can also connect through the Internet to prayer gatherings around the world. And we can pray with greater unity, as technology allows us to connect and share information in ways we did not imagine even 10 or 20 years ago! Tens of thousands of people now follow the Operation World (OW) prayer calendar, which means that each day a wave of focused and unified prayer is lifted – from around the globe – for a specific nation.

Prayer gatherings often bring together followers of Christ from diverse denominations within a city or nation. Where divisions once existed, Christians often find God builds unity and trust among them as they pray, whether for the suffering believers of the persecuted Church around the world, for a nation in a time of need, or for God to reveal Christ's love and care for people.

We must not underestimate the unifying and even reconciling work of prayer gatherings!

Some of the largest prayer meetings in history have been in Nigeria, in our day. Networks in Indonesia and India work hard to establish prayer groups in every village of a state, or across the whole nation. Prayer networks, especially among women, are the backbone and strength of a vibrant Brazilian Church. The 24/7 prayer movement (prayer chains or rooms dedicated to round-the-clock prayer) has spread to many major world cities, with prayer houses on university campuses, churches, or other creative locations. And people continue the centuries-old traditions of gathering for all-night prayer vigils, or concerts of prayer – now often in large numbers – to focus prayer on geographical areas or special issues.

The book in your hands weighs less than one kilogram, yet if all the desires, requests, and goals expressed in it were implemented, it would radically change the nations of this world! God is calling you and me into the ministry of prayer for the nations. The following pages give some of the challenges of our needy, sin-sick world. The enemy will try to frighten us with these, and to distract us from the vision of a heavenly, eternal Kingdom filled with people from every race, tribe, people, and language (Revelation 7:9-12). At times, we may look up to Jesus in agony, but we must see our true position – we are looking down with Him, praying with the authority He has given to every Christian.

We do not merely pray *about* the many points in this book, we pray *toward* something – the fulfilment of the Father's purposes, and His Kingdom come. May we become intercessors with a world vision that prays Satan-defeating, Kingdom-taking, people-reaching, captive-releasing, revival-giving, Christ-glorifying prayers!

THE ETHOS OF OPERATION WORLD

Our goal is to help believers come before God in prayer, to see His Kingdom advance in every country of the world. Operation World exists for 2 main purposes:

- *To inform for prayer.* This prayer handbook was developed as a prayer diary, with praise points and prayer requests assigned for each day of the year.

- *To mobilize for ministry.* We provide information and relevant statistics that we hope will encourage ministry among the least-reached and neediest areas and peoples of our world.

For many Christians, *Operation World* is their only source of global prayer information, and earlier editions became an essential resource for the growing mission movements around the world (in particular the non-English editions).

The people directly involved in preparation of *Operation World*, 7th edition (the basis for *Pray for the World*) represented over 10 nationalities, 3 generations, and 20 denominations. Even that is only a tiny proportion of the vast diversity in the body of Christ. Our own perspectives naturally influence the material selected and opinions expressed. We trust that we have been sensitive to other points of view beyond our own. We value constructive advice for future revisions, and always try to engage in fruitful discussion with our critics. Many of these have eventually become helpful contacts!

We made the following guiding decisions as we prepared this work:

Readership. We write for committed Christians who want to obey the instructions of Jesus by evangelizing the world and completing the Great Commission. Many of these people will be evangelicals (see definition, p. 305). But many who identify themselves differently will also use this handbook. We hope that we are sensitive to you, and to the diversity in the family of God.

Theology. Operation World takes a broadly evangelical position, an outlook closely associated with that of the Lausanne Covenant. On secondary theological issues that divide evangelicals (such as church government, baptism, the sovereignty of God, the gifts and work of the Holy Spirit), we attempt to write in a way that accepts diverse interpretations.

Politics. Even while our team has diversity, most of us are still Westerners. We know that our views are affected by our cultures and our backgrounds. We aim for balance and fairness, even when writing about what we see wrong with the world. But sometimes we might not achieve the result we hoped for, and people may interpret our words as judgemental.

Research. Careful observation and fact-finding, when they are done with discernment and trust in God, have a basis in Scripture. Some people wrongly associate statistical research with God's judgement of King David's census in 2 Samuel 24. But God also allowed, and even commanded, the use of statistics by Moses, Joshua, the Chronicler, Ezra, Ezekiel, Luke, John, and others in Scripture.

Time validity. The statistics for this book, like any statistics used in publications, are out of date before they ever make it to print. The world constantly changes. *Pray for the World* was abridged from *Operation World*, 7th edition (2010), and almost all statistics and prayer points come from that work. We focus the prayer points on long-term, strategic issues. These do not change overnight! Sometimes they require decades of sustained intercession. Changes will come for every country (elections, natural disasters, wars, and more). But most of these prayer points will require our labour in prayer for years to come.

Emphasis on the Church. We centre our information around the Church in each country. However, other Christian organizations are often the best source of information, which explains their mention in the text as well. The hundreds of people we correspond with, and who provide us with information for each country, generally represent a good mixture of church and mission leaders, and an effective balance of national Christian leaders and foreign Christian workers.

Resources. *Pray for the World* is an act of faith. None of the team receive a salary from the Operation World ministry. Our equipment is not expensive, and our office space is generously offered courtesy of WEC International. Royalties from all of our resources go into a fund that pays for ministry and production expenses for future Operation World projects. This is one of several reasons why neither *Pray for the World* nor *Operation World* is made available in full, for free, on the Internet.

The burden for prayer. Our resources are tools for prayer, more than anything else. Everything else about our work is secondary to this. In keeping with all we see of God's character, we long for poverty to end, for justice to flow, for the blind to see and the lame to walk, for widows and orphans to be looked after, for those in chains to be freed, for the earth to be rightly stewarded, for wars to cease, for enemies to be reconciled, and for those who are lost to be found by Jesus and the salvation He brings. Many believers (and many who are not) work faithfully to see these things happen.

Our mandate is to see churches multiplying among every people, according to the Lord's command. This is the preparation of the Bride, ready for the Bridegroom. But our supreme, overarching goal is still higher: the glory of God. A longing for God's glory and for the return of Jesus as King drives our prayers. We resonate with the words of Revelation 22:17-20, "The Spirit and the Bride say, 'Come'. And let the one who hears say, 'Come'. . . . Amen! Come, Lord Jesus".

HOW TO USE *PRAY FOR THE WORLD*

Pray for the World is a book to be used, not to be filed away on a bookshelf. Keep referring to it. Use it with those you lead or spend time with. You can encourage and inspire others with what God is doing around the world.

FOR USE IN YOUR HOME

Pray for the World *gives so many encouragements, and tells of areas where the Church has grown incredibly. These can give us hope in our own situations.*

 Pray through the world in a year! The Prayer Calendar (see p. 310) gives you a country to pray for every day of the year. When you turn up a country, you can know that you are joining with a large chorus of prayer around the world for that specific country. Perhaps focus on *only one or two items* that the Holy Spirit lays on your heart. Why not mark items covered in prayer, and later you can make note of God's answers?

 Keep the book near your television, radio, newspaper, or computer. When news comes of major events in a far-off land, find out the spiritual situation. Turn secular news into informed spiritual prayer!

 Use it together with missionary prayer letters, or mission agency magazines and websites. This book will give a wider context and perspective to the stories and updates shared in these valuable resources.

 Read a small section at family time (devotions, meals, while you travel), and pray for the country of the day.

 Use the book as a source of fun, informative quiz games. This is a favourite activity of the OW team!

FOR USE IN YOUR CHURCH

Missions and prayer for the world should be at the heart of every fellowship. Use Pray for the World *with all ages, in large and small groups, as often as possible.*

 In a small group, or at a prayer meeting. Read the information on one country ahead of time, and choose just a few pieces of information to share with the others. For example, you might share the population, the largest religion, the number of Christians, and one key prayer point.

 During a worship service. When we pray with others, agreement is powerful! Encourage everyone to appreciate the high value of prayer. It is not a dry duty, but an awesome privilege. As children of the living God, we can come before Him on behalf of the nations of the world, and we can expect to see Him act! Give a little background information to set the context, then focus on one key area for prayer.

3 **In church bulletins and magazines.** Use quotes from relevant sections of the book in your church publications to gain interest and stimulate prayer. Please quote the source! Make use of maps, pictures, videos, and presentation materials that relate to the country.

For Use in Prayer Days, Conferences, Concerts of Prayer, Prayer Journeys, and Other Prayer Venues

The original purpose of Operation World *was to provide information for prayer conferences that focused on the world. Below are a few guidelines for prayer-session leaders.*

1 **Be brief.** Remember that people are gathered to pray. The aim is not to impress others with information, or to share so much that they feel confused about how to pray.

2 **Be personal.** We do not mention individuals for prayer in the book, but rather give the overall situation in a country. Personal information on individual workers you know or support, and specific situations connected to your prayer group, should be used together with *Pray for the World* prayer points.

3 **Be selective.** Too many facts will be hard to remember. Carefully select just a few items for prayer that will stay with believers long after the meeting.

4 **Be careful with statistics.** Too many figures make any report very dull! This is why the statistical sections are in a smaller type. Choose the statistics that specifically apply to the prayer items you mention.

5 **Be dependent on the Holy Spirit.** The burdens imparted by the Holy Spirit inspire others to pray in the Spirit, and move them into God's will for their lives. This could mean commitment to intercession, financial giving, or going to a particular area or people for which prayer has been made. The Holy Spirit has guided many Christians into specific missionary service as a result of prayer with *Operation World*.

For the Glory of God

"Here lies the supreme missionary motivation. It is neither obedience to the Great Commission, nor compassion for the lost, nor excitement over the gospel, but zeal (even 'jealousy') for the honour of Christ's name. . . . No incentive is stronger than the longing that Christ should be given the honour that is due to His Name" (John Stott).

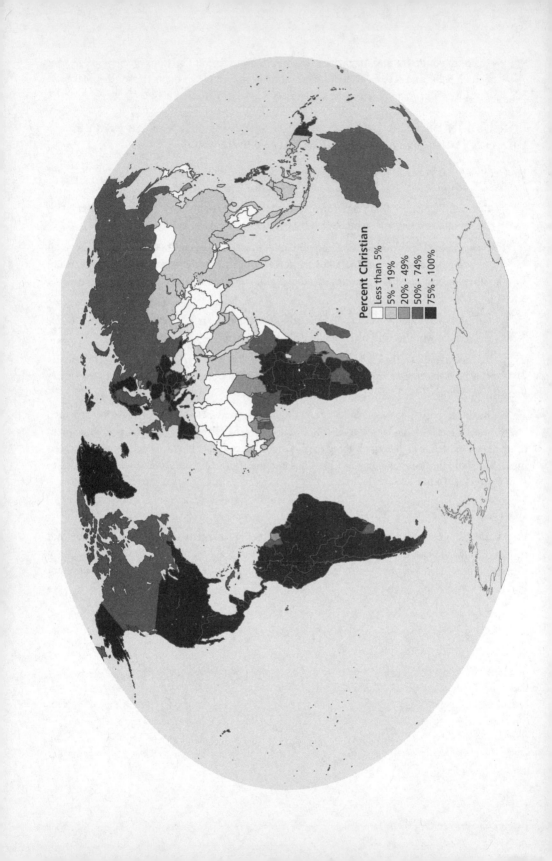

Percent Christian

Less than 5%
5% – 19%
20% – 49%
50% – 74%
75% – 100%

THE WORLD

Pop 6.9 billion.
Christians 2.2 billion. *Evangelical Christians* 545.9 million.
Largest Religion Christian.
Fastest Growing Religion Muslim.

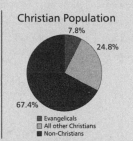

Christian Population
7.8%
24.8%
67.4%
■ Evangelicals
□ All other Christians
■ Non-Christians

487 of the world's cities have over 1 million inhabitants, and 21 cities have over 10 million. The urban population reached over 50% for the first time in history in 2009.

Peoples The Joshua Project lists 16,350 distinct peoples. The World Christian Database lists 13,674 peoples. Both base their figures on an ethno-linguistic basis, with peoples counted multiple times across the various countries where they live.

Languages The world's largest languages (by number of first-language speakers) are Chinese (1.2 billion), Spanish (329 mill), English (328 mill), Arabic (221 mill), Hindi (182 mill), Bengali (181 mill), Portuguese (178 mill), Russian (144 mill), Japanese (122 mill), and German (90 mill).

All Languages The numbers vary by definition of language and dialect. The Ethnologue (2009) counts 6,909 languages. The World Christian Encyclopedia counts 13,511 with 30,000 dialects. The Global Recordings Network estimates over 10,000 spoken languages and dialects.

Languages with Scriptures Wycliffe Bible Translators list 6,909 languages, out of which only 662 have adequate Scriptures. 2,582 languages have some Scripture (457 have Bibles, 1,202 have New Testaments, and 953 have portions of the Old or New Testament). They list 2,252 languages that may still need Scripture translation (and 1,363 projects are underway). The population of people groups with no Scripture, who still wait for work to begin, is 200 million.

God remains sovereign in our world today, now as much as ever. Yet prayer can be a difficult act for believers. God makes many promises to His people, but the world, the flesh, and the devil cause us to doubt. News reports focus on wars, disasters, famines, scandals, tragedies, and every form of evil. The beautiful, wholesome, and good things – like the works of God and His servants – often go unreported or even unnoticed. Our spiritual vision is not perfectly clear. Here on earth, we see through a glass darkly (1 Corinthians 13:12).

Like the disciples on the road to Emmaus (Luke 24), we need Jesus to open our eyes to the hidden truth. God is answering prayers, and doing wonderful things in the world! This has been a remarkable generation in church history. Who among us, 30 years ago, could have imagined more than 100 million Chinese Christians, or massive people movements to Christ in Iran and Algeria, or breakthrough in Cambodia and Nepal? Only God! So we begin here with answers to prayer, with all gratitude and praise to our Lord. And we persist in prayer for the things that to our eyes seem impossible, because nothing is impossible with God.

1 **The amazing harvest of new believers continues** across Africa, Asia, and Latin America. By contrast, the Church grows very slowly or even declines in the rest of the world. Although sometimes small in number, or away from public view, Christians now live and fellowship inside every country. World mission, migration, and globalization all spread the Church. It is not a European "white man's religion", but a global faith for all peoples. The majority of Christians today are Africans, Asians, and Latin Americans.

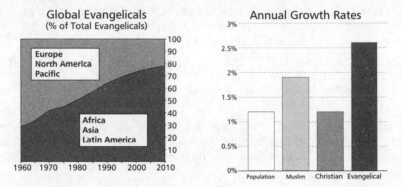

Global Evangelicals (% of Total Evangelicals) — Europe, North America, Pacific; Africa, Asia, Latin America. Annual Growth Rates — Population, Muslim, Christian, Evangelical.

2 **Evangelical Christianity grew faster than any other world religion or global religious movement.** Most of this growth happened through local movements, in places where the evangelical church was new. Evangelicals numbered 89 million (2.9% of the world's population) in 1960, but by 2010 they were 546 million (7.9%)! Much of this growth was by conversion, not just by birth rates. The Church grows in lands where past or present persecution of Christians is quite strong. But as population growth continues to slow down, evangelical growth will slow down as well.

3 **Pentecostals and other charismatic movements grew beyond expectation.** The Pentecostal movement began over 100 years ago. Charismatic renewal began mostly in mainline denominations in the 1950s and 1960s, and then a Third Wave came at the end of the 20th century. The charismatic renewal movement has touched many parts of the Church, in thousands of denominations, in nearly every country! Every movement has human flaws, but charismatic renewal has revived or renewed the faith of almost half a billion people.

4 **Many of the world's least-reached peoples received the good news!** In many cases, peoples with no known believers 10 or 20 years ago now have churches that grow and thrive! Research work in the 1990s helped the global Church pray for, adopt, and focus missionary efforts on unreached peoples. Today we have an even greater understanding of the need, yet much pioneer mission work remains. But praise God that doors opened and people responded to the gospel within hundreds of people groups – even some groups once considered impossible to reach!

5 **God's people joined together to pray** in greater numbers, and with greater focus, than ever before! Grassroots movements on the local, national, and international levels pray for their communities, for countries and people groups, and for important global issues (like the persecuted Church, children at risk, victims of human trafficking, others). Go and connect with others around the world to pray for the country, region, or issue you are passionate about!

6 **Aid, development, and charity work increased around the globe** through the 1980s and 1990s, and into this decade. Praise God that, more than ever before, people reach out to address the needs of the world's most vulnerable and needy. Ministry that cares for the needy, and that brings justice for the oppressed, reflects both the heart of God and the commands of Scripture. It also opens many doors to the gospel message. Christians can enter countries, regions, and communities through practical service, where traditional missionaries cannot reach.

7 **The globalization of the Great Commission movement** changed the face of missions. Many nations in Asia, Africa, and Latin America have mission-sending movements (like Ethiopia, Nigeria, Brazil, Philippines, South Korea). The Majority World nations together already send more missionaries than Western countries. This exciting 21st-century reality also introduces unique challenges. New missions movements will still make old mistakes, and workers from the Global North will now work alongside or even serve under the leadership of those from the Global South. International agencies see more recruits from the Majority World. Praise God for a global mission force that is more multi-cultural and multi-national than ever before!

8 **The Church must find new ways of training, sending, and supporting missionaries,** especially non-Western workers. Traditional Protestant mission agencies will continue to serve the global movement, but changes in global politics and economics require new models and patterns of mission work.

- *Mission agencies increasingly work through partner networks,* based on specific unreached areas or people groups. The networks share resources or even workers, and collaborate on initiatives.
- *Mission-minded Christians serve overseas in a variety of vocations,* whether relief and development, business, education, sports, the arts, or others. Some serve through agencies, but others go on their own, or hold looser connections with a mission fellowship.
- *Groups that migrated all over the world* (like Filipinos, Chinese, Koreans, Nigerians) have become stronger forces for mission as they see opportunities for Kingdom service abroad.

9 **Areas that appear in the news because of tragedies or conflict** often become the focus of intense prayer and related mission efforts. In the past 20 years, more Muslims than ever before came to Christ, and more workers serve in Muslim heartlands. As the world became more aware of the size, complexity, and challenges of the Muslim world, many believers developed a burden to share Jesus with Muslims. Political crises in Buddhist strongholds (Tibet, Thailand, Cambodia) raised a similar interest in the Buddhist world, and the difficult situation of the Dalits/Untouchables (India, Nepal) attracted prayer and ministry from around the world.

10 **Global movements shaped the course of world mission** in the last generation. The Lausanne Movement, the World Evangelical Alliance, the Global Day of Prayer, and AD2000 & Beyond, all helped mobilize different parts of the global Church for outreach.

11 **God uses many tools** to minister to both believers and non-believers (personal witness, literature, Scripture translation, Christian audio resources, TV, the Internet, and so many more). Pray that the new combined ministry efforts in Bible translation (Vision 2025), audio resources (The 10K Challenge), Christian radio (World by Radio), and others, might greatly increase the opportunity for non-Christians to hear the gospel and respond! Yet, even with all this activity, probably 24-27% of the world's population have not had the good news presented to them in a way they could understand and receive.

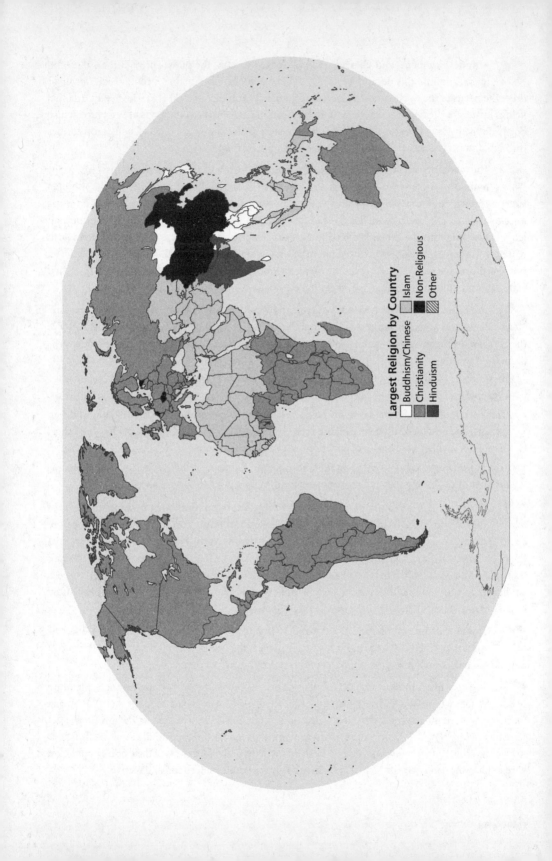

Largest Religion by Country

Buddhism/Chinese
Christianity
Hinduism
Islam
Non-Religious
Other

Jesus founded the first missionary team: the apostles. The New Testament Church was the result. The global Church should function as a missionary agency, and be involved in this Great Commission that Jesus gave to us all. Much missionary progress has been made in the last 50 years, but around 25% of the world have still never heard the good news! Pray for a united Church to reach the world for Christ.

THE UNFINISHED TASK (THE WORLD'S RELIGIOUS SYSTEMS)

1 **World religion in the 21st century.** Religion plays a foundational role in most societies, and many people turn to religion or spirituality as a reaction against changes in the world around them.

* *The world has become more religious in this century, not less*—across every region and in almost every religion! Many thought the 20th century would be a time of triumph for secularism, yet religion is very much alive in the 21st century.

* *Fundamentalist groups increased within most every religion.* Some act with aggression and even violence against people of other faiths, or sometimes against those within their own faith.

2 **The future of global faith** will likely be dominated by Christianity, Islam, and the non-religious, when considering birth rates, evangelistic activity, and cultural influence. Other religions mostly stay within one region of the world, or within specific ethnic groups. Islam has the highest birth rate, but fewer conversions. Although many people "convert" to non-religion, the birth rates of that group are very low. From 1900 to 2010, Christianity went from 34.5% of the world population to 32.3%, only a small change. Christian growth in Africa and Asia offset the decline in Europe.

3 **Christianity** is the most global religion. Every country has a Christian witness or a fellowship of believers. But only a minority of the world's Christians actively practise their faith. Many have a Christian heritage, but personally know very little about Jesus. In some cases, people groups received Christianity, but mixed it with their traditional religious practices and folk superstitions. Cults such as Mormons, Jehovah's Witnesses, and others call themselves Christian, but also hold un-biblical beliefs, values, or practices. Millions who go by the label of "Christian" are not saved, and still need to hear the true gospel.

4 **Islam** dominates a territory that stretches from West Africa, through the Middle East and Central Asia, down to Indonesia. Islam grew quickly, from 12.3% of humanity (1900) to 22.9% (2010). Most Muslim growth comes through high birth rates, but conversion plays a big part in West Africa, Indonesia, and the USA. But Islam faces significant internal crises. The violence and terror tactics of radical Islamists horrify the world, including many of the peace-loving Muslims who make up the majority of Islam. More Muslims than ever have turned to Jesus, but many Muslims decide to abandon religion altogether. Muslims have become a large minority inside many Western countries, but communities struggle with the social and spiritual effects of secular culture on their faith, especially among young people. Pray for the small streams of Muslims who come to Christ to become rushing rivers all over the world!

5 **The bloc or group of people who claim no religion** had the most massive growth of the last century. This group was just 0.2% of the world's population in 1900, but 13.6% in 2010. The majority are Chinese or European. As Communism declined in Europe and now declines elsewhere, many religions see new growth. But all over the world, people continue to leave their religious traditions. So far, Christianity has not effectively communicated the gospel to secular, postmodern cultures. Churches struggle against the spread of secular thought and values, and many leave the faith, especially the younger generation.

6 **Hinduism** remains strongly centred in India (90% of the world's Hindus live there). But Hindu ideas became more popular across the world, through New Age thinking, yoga, transcendental meditation, the Hare Krishna sect, and popular Indian *gurus* (spiritual guides). Like Islam, Hinduism also has a violent side. Extremist Hindu groups actively persecute Christians and followers of other faiths in India and Nepal. The Indian sub-continent has the world's highest concentration of unreached peoples. While the Church continues to grow rapidly among the poorest and the lowest castes, the main body of caste Hindus remains largely isolated from the gospel.

7 **Buddhism** is the state religion of 4 nations in Asia, of the majority in another 3, and of a significant minority in 9 others. In most places, followers actually mix Buddhism with Chinese religions, Daoism, Confucianism, and Shinto. After Communism lost strong influence in Asia, Buddhism began to grow again. The Dalai Lama of Tibet has made Buddhism more popular in Western countries. Only a small minority from Buddhist backgrounds have come to Jesus. The worldviews of Buddhists and Christians have great differences, and many Buddhists struggle to understand the gospel message in the ways Christians have tried to communicate it. Pray for a breakthrough.

8 **Ethnic religions and animism** now grow again in some parts of the world. In many cases, when people accepted other religions (Islam, Buddhism, Hinduism, even Christianity), they actually added a thin layer on top of deeply held ethnic religious beliefs and practices. Traditional religions still greatly influence people's lives, communities, and whole cultures. Even in the secular West, people have a fascination with New Age or other alternative spiritual practices, mysticism, or the occult. This reveals that humans are truly spiritual creatures! And that we are in a spiritual war.

9 **Several other religions** exist in smaller numbers and fewer locations. Sikhs, Jains, Parsees all live mostly in South Asia, while the Baha'i have spread around the world.

10 **The number of Jews** decreases in most countries from a combination of low birth rates, secular influences, conversions to Christianity, and migration to Israel. (Nearly 37% of all Jews now live in Israel.) Of the world's 14.8 million Jews, perhaps around 150,000 follow Jesus. Pray for the Jewish people to find salvation in *Yeshua*, their Messiah.

THE UNFINISHED TASK (THE WORLD'S PEOPLES)

It was nearly 2,000 years ago that Jesus commanded His followers to make disciples of all peoples. But it was only in the last 20 years that we gained a clear picture of the world's peoples and languages! In the Joshua Project list, 6,645 out of the world's 16,350 peoples remain in the unreached/least-reached category. That's 41% of all peoples! The total population is 2.8 billion individuals. (Keep in mind that Christian individuals can be part of an unreached people group, just as unreached individuals can be part of a reached people.)

1 **Churches around the world must gain a vision for unreached peoples.** "Peoples"—or *ethne* in New Testament Greek—are the basic units in God's plan to redeem all humanity. When we read the Old Testament, the Gospels, and Revelation, we see that disciples will come from among every people on earth. Pray that the Church might passionately pursue this end! Christian missions will have many strategies, approaches, and trends, but the concept of *ethne* always needs to be part of how the Church understands the Great Commission.

2 **Most of today's least-reached peoples** have not heard the gospel because it remains so difficult to reach them! Many barriers (geography, language, culture, religion, politics, economics, spiritual darkness) leave them hidden or overlooked. These unreached groups generally will not hear the good news until someone reaches across the barriers to share and demonstrate the love of Christ, until a Church grows among them. Pioneer mission work is hard, expensive, and takes time. It requires great cultural understanding, commitment, and spiritual warfare through prayer. Many unreached peoples have small populations, and Christians know very little about them because they are so isolated, or because they appear to blend in with larger groups. Ask God to reveal Jesus to these smaller, more vulnerable groups.

When Jesus commissions the Church, He assures the believers of God's power and authority, and the presence of the Holy Spirit. The work before us is great, but not so vast as the greatness of God, who promises to go with us and empower us.

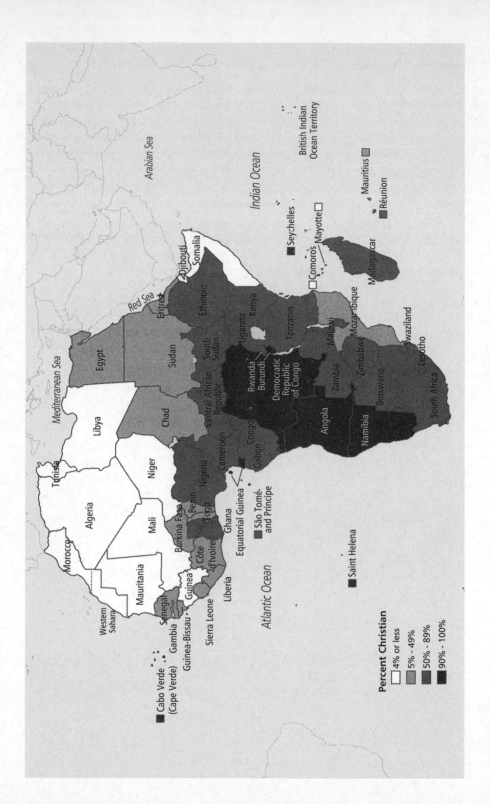

Percent Christian

4% or less
5% - 49%
50% - 89%
90% - 100%

AFRICA

Pop 1 billion.
Christians 503.7 million. *Evangelical Christians* 182.4 mill.
Largest Religion Christian.
Fastest Growing Religion Non-religious.
The 57 countries of Africa contain 15% of the world's population, and its population grows at nearly double the world's average. 32 of the 33 least-developed countries in the world are in Africa.

All Languages 2,110. **Languages with Scriptures** 173 Bibles, 335 New Testaments, 223 Old or New Testament portions (figures from the United Bible Society). Work is underway on 693 language projects. At least 225 languages (and possibly as many as 925!) still need the Scriptures. Africa remains among the greatest challenges for Bible translation!

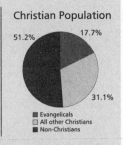

Christian Population

51.2%   17.7%

31.1%

■ Evangelicals
☐ All other Christians
■ Non-Christians

Almost all countries in Africa became independent only since 1957. Democracy and true multiparty politics have begun to take hold across the continent, but slowly. Not all Africans believe that Western-style politics works best in the African context. Many leaders cause greater poverty and upheaval through corruption, tribal favouritism, poor economic policies, and a refusal to give up their power. Some have built billion-dollar personal fortunes through corruption and theft.

Africa is the continent with the greatest human needs and the most widespread poverty. Yet decades of aid and development have achieved too little progress. Many argue that less aid and more global free trade will better assist Africa.

The national boundaries drawn 100 years ago by Western colonial powers still cause problems today, and lead to violence and even war in over a dozen countries. Violent Islamist movements generate terror and war in several hot spots along the great fault line between Muslim and Christian majorities that runs west to east across the whole continent.

Algeria

Pop 35.4 million. **Capital** Algiers (2.8 mill).
Christians 99,000. *Evangelical Christians* 84,000.
Largest Religion Muslim.
Fastest Growing Religion Non-religious.
Largest Ethnic Groups Maghreb Arabs (69.9%), Berber (22.8%), Bedouin (6%), Other Arabs (1%).
Official Languages Arabic, Berber. French and English used widely. 25% speak one of the Berber languages.
All Languages 22.

Economy Fast-growing due to oil and gas reserves and nationalization of related industries. Most oil wealth does not reach the general population, and unemployment is high.

Politics French colony for 132 years. Independent in 1962 after a bitter war. A 1-party socialist regime held power for 25 years. Islamists won the 1992 election, but the army intervened. This led to a civil war with over 100,000 deaths. The current president (1999-present) worked to achieve peace and harmony. The violence decreased, though attacks by Islamist militants increased again from 2006.

---

1 **The growth of the Algerian Church over the past decade is an answer to prayer!** Many years of hard work by missionaries and praying people produced beautiful fruit. Most believers come from a Kabyle Berber background, but faith grows among Arabs and most other people groups as well. The Christian community enjoys a spirit of unity, which stands out from the long history of conflict among ethnic groups. Some received supernatural visions of Jesus, but most came to Him through personal evangelism. New fellowships began throughout Algeria, partly because Berber believers moved into unreached Arab areas in order to share the good news. Pray for continued growth of this people movement to Christ!

2 **Algeria suffered deeply** in the past. First it was from French colonial oppression, then the war of liberation that ended in 1962, and most recently the brutal civil war that began in 1992. The constitution promises democracy, but people have limited freedom. Violations of human rights continue. Islamists, who want *shari'a* law to rule, fight against the state, media, foreigners, and any imams who oppose them. Pray that God will use this situation to draw many more to Christ. Pray for powerful conversions to Jesus among Islamic leaders in Algeria.

3 **The Algerian Church faces persecution** and other challenges. It grew through bold witness and evangelism, but religious and political leaders reacted strongly against this new movement. Believers face threats from family, friends, Muslim extremists, and employers. Unemployment among believers from a Muslim background is as high as 90%. They face new restrictions from the government on evangelism and gathering for worship. The government also banned the import of Bibles, which hinders discipleship. Many still need access to Scripture. Pray that the Algerian Church will respond to these pressures with faith and perseverance.

4 **The Church has a very indigenous, truly Algerian way of expressing faith.** Scriptures and study materials, worship styles, and even training and leadership reflect Algerian culture well. Algeria needs more workers to help strengthen the local church and to bring the gospel to the unreached millions. Several agencies reach out to Algerians through radio, literature, satellite TV, portable media, and Bible correspondence courses. Praise God for the increase of these resources, and pray for wider distribution!

5 **Pray especially for these less-reached groups:**

- *Over 4 million Algerians live in Europe,* many illegally. They have more access to the gospel in Europe, but also to Islamic teaching. Pray for the network of agencies and churches who reach out to them. Pray for discipleship, for churches planted among the Berber and Arabic language groups, and for God to raise up many Algerian believers as missionaries to their own people.

- *Young people* often try to move to Europe in search of more freedom and a better life. 65-70% of the population in Algeria is under age 30. In school, students receive much teaching from the Qur'an. No ministry specifically reaches children.

- *The Berber peoples* of the Atlas Mountains (23% of the population) seek a return to their cultural roots after centuries of domination by Arabs. Their ancestors were Christian, and many have turned to Christ among the Kabyle. But the other 13 Berber groups are among Africa's least evangelized. Pray for Christian witness among each of these groups!

Angola   *Africa*

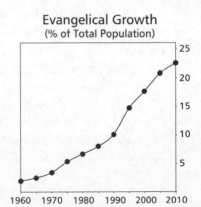

Pop 19 million. **Capital** Luanda (4.8 mill).
Christians 17.9 mill. *Evangelical Christians* 4.3 mill.
Largest Religion Christian.
Fastest Growing Religion Muslim.

Largest Ethnic Groups Ovimbundu (25.5%), Mbundu (22.9%), Kongo (12.9%), Luvale (8.1%), Chokwe (5.0%), Mixed race (1.2%), Khoisan (0.6%).
Official Language Portuguese. **All Languages** 41.

Economy Some of the world's richest natural resources (oil, diamonds, minerals, farmland), but widespread poverty. Infrastructure devastated by war, but now rebuilding.
Politics Former Portuguese colony (450 years). A Marxist coup ended colonial rule (1975). Civil war displaced millions. 900,000 died. Peace deal in 1990, but fighting 1998-2002. Parliamentary elections (which determined president) held in 2008. Some separatist fighting continues in Cabinda.

---

1 **Forty years of almost constant war** (1962-2002) devastated Angola. Innocent civilians suffered most. Fighting destroyed roads, schools, hospitals, homes, and churches. Millions fled their homes. Land mines crippled over 80,000 people. 70-90% of the population live in poverty. Deep psychological, social, and spiritual wounds will require years to overcome. Praise God for peace, and the return of many to their homes. The Church helps lead the way to reconciliation as the country works to rebuild.

2 **Biblical Christianity grew,** even amidst war and poverty! The first president, a Marxist, vowed to eradicate Christianity in 20 years. He failed! The number of evangelicals grew 4 times larger from 1990 to 2010. The Church needs much prayer to overcome the wounds of conflict. Pray for forgiveness and love in action. Only a few

Evangelical Growth
(% of Total Population)

congregations have trained pastors. False beliefs, ignorance of the Bible, witchcraft, and animistic practices pollute many lives and churches. Islam grows with its simple message and foreign financial support. Pray for Christian unity, holy living, and biblical faith.

3 **Young people and children.** Marxism and war left a scarred generation, deprived of educational opportunity and physical security. This generation is the first in decades to know peace. Most of Angola's Christians are under age 25. Pray for primary and secondary schools to be rebuilt, staffed, and full.

4 **The foreign missionary presence** was a good testimony during years of suffering. Ministries should now shift from aid/relief to development, and from evangelism to discipleship and training. Most missions work holistically, and minister to both physical and spiritual needs. Pray for ministries such as World Vision International, Samaritan's Purse, and others, as they focus on primary health care, education, vocational training, and disease prevention.

Benin *Africa*

Pop 9.2 million. **Capital** Porto-Novo (287,000).
Christians 3.7 mill. *Evangelical Christians* 768,000.
Largest Religion Christian.
Fastest Growing Religion Muslim.

Largest Ethnic Groups Over 60 ethnic groups, mostly in the south. Guinean (59.5%), Gur (17.4%), Yoruba (13.1%), Fulani (4.8%).
Official Language French. Trade languages: Fon (south), Dendi (north). **All Languages** 56.
Economy Built on agriculture, with cotton the largest product. Strong trade links with Nigeria, but remains one of world's poorest countries.
Politics Independence from France (1960). After 7 coups and 1 Marxist regime, a democracy was formed in 1991. Stable government.

1 **Benin remains one of the world's least-developed countries.** Efforts to help the economy often fail because of corruption. Almost 75% of economic activity is "underground" or illegal, with ties to Nigerian interests. Some suspect that criminals smuggle tens of thousands of children out of Benin each year to sell them as child labourers. Pray for justice and righteousness to grow in Benin, and for Nigeria's influence to be more positive and godly.

2 **Benin has the highest percentage in Africa of people who follow traditional ethnic religions.** Many Christians mix their faith with animism. They go to the church on Sunday, but consult the witch doctor during the week. Pray for revival that makes the Church pure. Pray also for many witch doctors to experience the power of Jesus and turn to Him! Voodoo developed from Fon animism, and it touches the lives of all Fon (the largest people group), even the Christians.

3 **Church growth continues across the whole country,** but especially in the African-originated denominations. All churches feel a desperate need for discipleship and for trained leaders. Almost half of Benin's languages still need a Bible or even a New Testament. Some evangelicals have a goal to plant 20,000 congregations by 2020! Pray for the endurance to reach every region of Benin, and to plant churches among every people. Village health ministries and holistic rural development bring good responses from both animists and Muslims.

4 **Most peoples in Benin remain unreached.** Only a few smaller groups have a Christian majority. It is one of the few countries where almost equal numbers of Muslims, Christians, and animists live side by side. Christians have freedom to minister and evangelize, but Benin is probably the least-evangelized non-Muslim country in Africa! Pray for churches and missions to send more workers, especially to the central and northern regions. Very few evangelical believers live among the Muslim peoples of the far north.

Botswana   *Africa*

Pop 2 million. **Capital** Gaborone (201,000).
Christians 1.3 mill. *Evangelical Christians* 160,000.
Largest Religion Christian.
Fastest Growing Religion Christian.
Largest Ethnic Groups Tswana (69.1%), Kalanga (10.1%), Ndebele (3.3%), San (Bushmen) (2.8%), Shona (2.4%), Kgalagadi (2.3%), Herero (1.2%), Mbukushu (1.1%), Yeyi (1.1%).
Official Languages English, Setswana. **All Languages** 40.
Economy Rapid development since independence (1966) through export of diamonds, copper, nickel, gold, and beef. Tourism now part of economy. Revenue used wisely to develop the country. The most stable, sustained growth in Africa (1990-2010).
Politics Independent from Britain in 1966. Stable, multiparty democracy (rare in Africa).

1 **Praise God for political stability, economic growth, and lower corruption in Botswana.** Religious freedom allows agencies to evangelize and plant churches. The government set new goals for health, economy, and society (Vision 2016), which fit well with biblical principles.

2 **The Tswana responded to the gospel first out of all the Bantu people in Africa.** Several tribes found God in the 19th century through the London Missionary Society. Today many Tswana families break apart, and people struggle with sexual sins and drunkenness. Pray for moral and spiritual renewal among the Tswana.

3 **Botswana has the world's second-highest AIDS rate.** Life expectancy has dropped by 28 years, and over 100,000 orphans need care. Pray that those who suffer receive the drugs they need, and that the government acts wisely. AIDS now touches every congregation. Pray that ministries and churches show Christian love to victims and orphans, and work together to prevent spread.

4 **The Church.** Western missionaries planted mainline Protestant churches, but most of these now lose members and need revival. Pentecostal churches grew rapidly at first, and many of these churches truly help people change their lives. African Indigenous Churches (AIC) are the largest religious group in Botswana. Most AICs focus on God's healing power, but some mix biblical teaching with harmful traditions. Pastors need good Bible training. Pray that each of these churches uses its strengths to reach others with the gospel of Jesus. Praise God for the unity and cooperation among them!

Many peoples still need the gospel.

• *The Kalanga* live under the stronger Tswana culture. AIC and Pentecostals work among them, and the Bible is now available in Kalanga (mother tongue).

• *The San* were nomads, but now live in poverty near towns. Modern development destroyed their land and lifestyle. Pray for them to adjust to their new life, and to find true identity in Christ. The San have several thousand believers among them.

Burkina Faso
Africa

Pop 16.3 million. **Capital** Ouagadougou (1.9 mill).
Christians 3.4 mill. *Evangelical Christians* 1.4 mill.
Largest Religion Muslim.
Fastest Growing Religions Muslim, Christian.

Largest Ethnic Groups Over 78 distinct people groups. Gur (77%, 45 peoples), Fulani (7.8%, 4 peoples), Mande (5.7%), Malinke-Jula (4.6%), Malinke (2.5%), Other African (2.1%).
Official Language French, but spoken by a minority. Trade languages: Moore, Jula (south, west). **All Languages** 70.

Economy One of world's poorest countries. 90% rely on agriculture, so the country is hard hit in times of drought. Cotton is main cash crop, but some potential for gold and other mineral resources. Low levels of education (especially for girls).

Politics Independence from France in 1960. 6 coups since 1966. Leader from last coup (1987) was later elected 4 times by a large majority, and has now introduced multiparty democracy.

---

1 **Burkina Faso struggles with poverty.** Immediate change does not seem likely. Pray for aid, development, and small loans for business projects that will lift people out of poverty. Pray against corruption in the government and the aid industry that takes resources away from the people who most need them.

2 **Christianity increased steadily** across recent decades. Evangelicals grew from 10,000 in 1960 to 1.44 million in 2010! The Church now faces a leadership crisis, as many new believers need discipleship. Pray for the Bible schools. Pray for godly wives for the pastors and evangelists who struggle to find a helpmate. Present and future Bible translators need prayer to complete their enormous task (28 active translation projects, with 12 more needed).

3 **The power of the spirit world has not been broken.** Some people say that the population is "50% Muslim, 20% Christian, and 100% animist"! Idols, charms, and secret societies have more control in Burkina Faso than in most West African countries. The occult shows its power even in some churches. The strongest animist groups live in the west and southwest. Pray for the risen Christ to demonstrate His power and set many free.

4 **More than 25 unreached peoples do not have an effective witness.** Churches and missions that work in their areas often minister to the more responsive groups, or to peoples more similar to themselves.

• *Muslims.* Islam now grows within almost every ethnic group. Praise God the Fulbe have begun to respond to the gospel through the witness of several groups! Up to 70% of Burkinabé who work abroad convert to Islam while away. Churches send pastors and missionaries to reach them, but need more workers.

- *Urban areas.* Traditional rural life can no longer support families or occupy young people, and many migrate to cities. Rural churches set up branches in the capital to keep contact with their students and educated members. This also strengthens the church at home.

Religions
(% of Total Population)

5 **Missionaries and Christian aid/relief workers** play a vital role in this land of physical and spiritual needs. Missionaries are welcome, but the work is hard. Pray for their protection and encouragement. The Church does not have a strong missions vision, with the exception of VIMAB (the Burkinabé Assemblies of God). This successful indigenous mission has 150 couples who serve as missionaries at home and abroad!

Burundi

Africa

Pop 8.5 million. **Capital** Bujumbura (480,000).
Christians 7.7 mill. *Evangelical Christians* 2.3 mill.
Largest Religion Christian.
Fastest Growing Religion Muslim.
Largest Ethnic Groups Hutu (83.6%), Tutsi (13.6%), Congolese/Lingala (1.5%), Twa Pygmies (1%, neglected by other groups), South Asian, European, Arab (0.2%).
Official Languages Kirundi, French. English use widespread. **All Languages** 4.
Economy Recent economic stability, but high debt and dependent on outside aid. Tea and coffee are exported, but mineral resources mostly untouched. One of world's poorest nations with 70-80% in poverty.

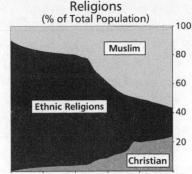

Politics Tutsi lordship over the Hutu majority for 400 years. Independent from Belgium (1962), followed by Tutsi-dominated governments and military regimes. Poor human rights record against Hutus. A peace accord in 2000, followed by democratic elections in 2005 and 2010, brought stability and more representation for the Hutus.

1 **Praise God for stability** after all rebel groups signed a peace accord. Pray next for people to hand in their weapons and pursue peace, not lawlessness. An elected government now includes both major ethnic groups (Hutu and Tutsi). Pray for genuine respect and cooperation as these two peoples build Burundi's future together. The president professes Christ, and seeks the counsel of church leaders on some issues. Corruption seems to get worse, not better. Pray for change that lasts, which only the gospel can bring.

2 **Praise God for evangelical growth.** Nearly all Protestant and Anglican churches saw growth, even during periods of war. Revival in the 1950s brought blessing and great church growth, but a generation later the land was physically, morally, and spiritually devastated. Most Burundians recognize the Church as the only institution that can bring true reconciliation and peace. Pray that spirits of enmity and revenge may be bound by the power of Christ. Violence caused Bible schools to close. Pray for re-opened schools and programmes to meet the urgent need for Christian leaders.

 Peoples and groups of greater spiritual need:

- *The Burundian refugee population* was Africa's largest in the 1990s. In 1972 about 200,000 fled to Tanzania. That number more than doubled in 1994. In the camps, people struggle with disease, abuse, and resentment. Ministry is difficult but vital.

- *Over 450,000 refugees and displaced peoples* have returned home. Many face serious problems due to a shortage of land, and they lack even basic services in health, education, and shelter.

- *The Muslim community* increased dramatically in recent years. Pray that Christians would gain a heart for their Muslim neighbours and countrymen.

Young people and children suffered the worst of the violence and poverty. 45% of children under 5 are undernourished, and many thousands suffer from malaria and AIDS. Pray for the ministries and NGOs that care for children. Pray for Homes of Hope, where orphans from different ethnic groups grow up together in a Christian setting.

Burundi needs expatriate Christian workers. Between 1970 and 1985, nearly all missionaries were expelled. Now Burundi needs workers to assist national Christians in discipleship, theological education, trauma counselling, literacy and education, and holistic development. Pray especially for workers to live and work in neglected rural areas. Pray also for millions more Bibles and Christian books in the Kirundi language.

Cameroon
Africa

Pop 20 million. **Capital** Yaounde (1.8 mill).
Christians 10.7 mill. *Evangelical Christians* 1.8 mill.
Largest Religion Christian.
Fastest Growing Religion Muslim.
Largest Ethnic Groups One of Africa's most ethnically and linguistically complex countries (over 286 peoples, with sub-groups and dialects). Grassfields Bantu (26.5%), Northwest Bantu (24.7%), Chadic (9.7%), Fulani (9.4%), Other Benue-Congo (8.7%), Cameroonian Creole (5.8%), detribalized Cameroonian (5.7%), Adamawa-Ubangi (5.5%), Hausa (1.4%).
Official Languages French, English. **All Languages** 279.

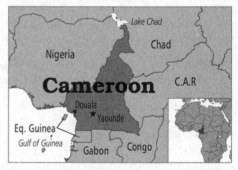

Economy Based on agriculture and oil exports. Potential for development with good rainfall and mineral resources. One of Africa's highest literacy rates, and one of world's highest corruption rates.
Politics German colony (1884-1919), then divided between Britain and France. Independent from France in 1960, and united with English-speaking West Cameroon (1961) as a bilingual, one-party republic. Multiparty elections since 1992, but international and opposition groups claim government suppression of opposition. Member of British Commonwealth and *La Francophonie*, with tensions between English-speaking and French-speaking regions.

God has blessed Cameroon with material resources, relative stability, and a diversity of peoples. Many significant leaders (professional, military, police, political) now follow Christ! This gives hope for change in a society infamous for corruption. Pray that those who steal from the nation would be caught and stopped, and that the people will no longer tolerate corruption.

2 **Deep divisions** of language, faith, and politics lead to tension and violence. Cameroon divides between French and English regions. It also divides between Christian, Muslim, and traditional religions, and between those who hold political power and the opposition. Pray for God to raise up reconcilers and peacemakers in this divided land.

3 **Cameroon has a serious problem with weak Christianity**. The lack of indigenous, heart-language Scriptures is one of the reasons for spiritual poverty in the churches. Bible translation for Cameroon's 278 languages is an overwhelming task, and only 10 languages have a complete Bible. Tribalism, pagan practices, alcoholism, and low moral standards all infect the churches. Most have little concern for the unreached peoples in the north. Pray for deep repentance, deliverance, and true revival. Ask God to restore Bible reading, preaching, and holiness among Christians.

4 **Evangelicals, especially Pentecostals, grew rapidly** in the last 20 years, even after opposition from the older denominations. Nigerian evangelists started many of these newer groups. Pray for the formation of an evangelical association of churches. This will help address the challenge of discipleship for both immature and new believers. Pray that evangelicals would get involved in politics, justice, and education, in order to positively impact the nation.

5 **Less-reached peoples.** This complex nation urgently needs a national survey. Cameroon needs missionaries for Bible translation ministry, and to reach the Muslim and northern animist peoples. Pray for God to call more workers for translation, literacy, and support work. Pray especially for:

- *Muslims,* a majority in 59 people groups. Few Christians come from the Hausa, Kanuri, Kotoko, and Fali peoples. The nomadic Shuwa Arabs have only 1 or 2 known believers among them (1 agency works to plant churches). The Fulbe had 10 known Christians in 1991, with more believers now, but still very few (several agencies seek to reach them).
- *The many peoples of the Mandara Mountains.* 30% Muslim, but most practise animism. Some church-planting agencies see signs of breakthrough!
- *The northern plains peoples.* Mainly animist, but Islam grows in influence. Several missionaries and churches work among them.
- *The Baka/Pygmies* (southeastern forests). Both Baka and cross-cultural workers serve here after long years of neglect. Spiritual warfare in prayer is a key to breakthrough among this highly animist and spiritual people.

Central African Republic
Africa

Pop 4.5 million. **Capital** Bangui (718,000).
Christians 3.4 mill. *Evangelical Christians* 1.5 mill.
Largest Religion Christian.
Fastest Growing Religion Muslim.

Largest Ethnic Groups About 80 ethnic groups. Adamawa-Ubangi (78.7%), Sudanic (6.2%), Sara-Bagirmi (4.9%), Fulbe (3.6%), Bantu (3.0%), Arab (2.8%), Pygmy (0.3%).
Official Languages French, Sango (trade language). **All Languages** 82.

Economy Rich in natural and mineral resources. Diamonds are 55% of exports. Conflict has crippled

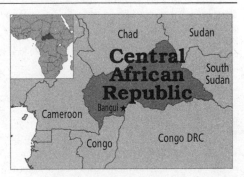

potential development. A large economic difference between the rich capital city and poor outer regions.
Politics Independent since 1960, but not fully free. A long history where periods of democracy are interspersed with military regimes. The ongoing rebellions and military coups slow progress. Conflict between the Christian majority and Muslim minority has intensified amid the chaos since the 2013 coup.

1   **The Central African Republic (CAR) faces immense physical human needs.** The long series of coups and counter-coups devastated the economy and infrastructure. The most recent coup caused a breakdown in law and order. Rebels executed opponents and looted homes. Community conflict now occurs along religious lines between Muslims and Christians. Hundreds of thousands have fled their homes. Pray for an end to the chaos, abuses, and destruction of this humanitarian crisis. Pray for God to establish peace throughout the country.

2   **Education, healthcare, and other vital services have almost stopped** in this country. Many already suffer from malnourishment, a lack of clean water, AIDS and other diseases, and extreme poverty. Mission agencies play an important role in health, in education, and with children at risk, but also in church planting and Bible translation. Most workers evacuated during the 2013 crisis.

3   **Widespread evangelism brought massive numbers of converts to Christianity** in the 1960s and 1970s, but smaller numbers truly live as disciples of Jesus. Many Christians do not affiliate with a church, and many church members do not understand or apply the truths of Scripture to their lives. The terrible acts committed by apparent Christians during the conflict shows a national lack of discipleship and Christian leadership. Only 2 indigenous languages have a fully translated Bible, with translation in progress for 7 more. Pray for Christians, especially spiritual leaders, to model godliness, trust, and forgiveness.

4   **The country has potential for massive church growth.** The number of national missionaries and agencies increased, and new indigenous-led ministries emerged in recent years. After decades of neglect, a few groups now equip and send more women into ministry. Several new Christian radio stations help broadcast the gospel every week to millions of potential listeners. The Bangui Evangelical Graduate School of Theology (FATEB) was the first evangelical theological seminary for French-speaking Africa. Pray for its spiritual impact throughout the continent. Many are eager to study at this and other schools, but the lack of funds for students and staff holds back education.

5   **The CAR was one of the world's most evangelized nations,** but the upheavals here and in nearby Chad and Sudan mean the progress in some regions has reversed. Pray for all CAR denominations to send students for missionary training. Pray that those with training would resist the draw to serve as a city pastor and instead go to the unreached. Pray especially for the northern region, for the Runga (90% Muslim), the Sara Kaba (50% Animist), and the Gula/Kara (65% Muslim). Muslims grew rapidly in influence, especially in the cities. Few Christians feel equipped to reach out to them.

Chad

Pop 11.5 million. **Capital** N'Djamena (829,000).
Christians 4.4 mill. *Evangelical Christians* 1.2 mill.
Largest Religion Muslim.
Fastest Growing Religion Muslim.

Largest Ethnic Groups A complex mix of 150 or more peoples. Sara-Bagirmi (23.8%, 17 peoples), Chadic (17.9%, 51 peoples), Arab (14.5%, 6 peoples, mostly nomadic), Kanuri-Saharan (14.1%, 8 peoples), Ouaddai-Fur (12.7%, 21 peoples), Adamawa-Ubangi (7.3%, 21 peoples), Guera-Naba (4.4%, 6 peoples), Fulbe (2.9%), Other Sub-Saharan African (2.4%).
Official Languages French, Arabic. **All Languages** 133.

Economy An agricultural economy (80% farm or raise livestock). Economic growth hindered by lack of rainfall, severe drought, civil wars, distance from the sea, and poor infrastructure. Recent development of mineral and oil deposits helped growth, but corruption may cancel the benefits. 80% live below the poverty line.
Politics A history of violence, coups, and rebel activity since independence from France in 1960. The Zaghawa tribe dominate the government, though set up as a democracy. The conflict in Darfur (Sudan) forced up to 400,000 refugees into eastern Chad, but brought aid money as well.

---

1 **Chad needs a stable and just government.** The current regime struggles with violence and corruption. Some consider Chad the world's most corrupt nation. Tribal rivalries and conflict between the north (Muslim) and south (Christian) create an unstable situation. Bandits and rebels from inside Chad and from Darfur disrupt economic progress and Christian ministry. Pray for a government that represents both north and south fairly, and that governs with honesty and commitment to all people in Chad.

2 **We must lift up the Church in prayer.** Resentment between tribes prevents Christian witness and burdens many congregations. Most Protestant and Independent groups are evangelical, but they struggle to find unity. Christians disagree over questions about tribal initiation rites. African traditional religions regain influence as people return to African spiritual roots. Sects and secret societies lead believers into false teaching. Poverty, instability, violence, and lack of funds all hinder training of pastors and evangelists. Pray for freedom from all bondages by a work of the Holy Spirit in every congregation!

3 **Many Muslims have heard the good news!** New groups of believers from Muslim backgrounds have emerged. Bible storytelling and Chadian Arabic Christian radio help spread the gospel in culturally relevant ways. Violence in nearby Darfur at the hands of other Muslims caused some to question Islam, and left them open to the loving ministry and witness of Christians. Still, Islam grows in numbers, and in financial and social influence. Pray that Christians will learn to reach out to the Muslims around them.

4 **Chad has more unreached peoples than any other African country,** and very few Muslim-majority countries offer Christian workers such openness. There is great need in church planting, evangelism, Bible teaching, leadership development, and holistic ministry. Workers must prioritize Bible translation. Only 12 (out of over 120) language groups have the whole Bible translated. Radio ministry reaches many. Pray for programmes in the languages of the unreached. Pray especially for:

- **The Saharan peoples** (Sunni Muslims), who dominate politics. They live mostly in the north and in larger towns. These groups are among Africa's least evangelized, with only a few Christians among them.
- **The Ouaddai-Fur peoples** (Muslim), who live in the eastern provinces near Sudan. Little evangelism happens here because of harsh living conditions, violence, language barriers, and lack of roads.
- **The Shuwa Arabs,** who have influence in Chad. Their language is the main language of communication. Missionaries have made little outreach to them.
- **N'Djamena,** the only large city in the country. Most ethnic groups live here. This is a great outreach opportunity for the Church, but most congregations focus on their own ethnic group. Pray for the thousands of Christians in N'Djamena to become effective witnesses.

Comoros

Africa

Pop 691,000. **Capital** Moroni (49,800).
Christians 6,400. *Evangelical Christians* 1,300.
Largest Religion Muslim.
Fastest Growing Religion Muslim.

Largest Ethnic Groups Comorian (97%, mixed Arab, African, and Malagasy ancestry), Minority groups (2.4%, Makua, Malagasy, Réunionese, French, Arab).
Official Languages Arabic, French, Comorian (a mix of Swahili and Arabic). **All Languages** 7.

Economy One of Africa's poorest countries. Overpopulated. Perfumes, spices are main exports. Dependent on food aid, rice imports, and remittances from Comorians abroad.

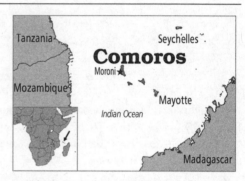

Politics One-party state until 1990, followed by multiparty democracy. Over 20 coups or attempted coups since independence (1975). A 2001 constitution granted greater self-rule to 2 smaller islands that seek independence, but turmoil continues.

1 **Almost all the people of Comoros (99%) follow Islam,** with fundamentalism on the rise. But under the surface most people engage with the occult through witchcraft, curses, and spirit possession. Young people feel discontent with society, and seek comfort in drugs, sex, or an opportunity to leave the island. Pray that Comorians may have opportunities to hear the gospel of life that offers hope to all!

2 **The Church slowly grows in number amidst opposition.** The government forbids evangelism, and most new Christians endure opposition from their communities and families. The quiet witness of Christian medical and veterinary workers here and in Mayotte has won public honour, and has brought opportunities to share about Jesus with the people. The majority of new believers are Réunionese, Malagasy, and French, but not Comorian. Pray for leaders for these new fellowship groups, and for their training. Pray for more opportunities for witness that will bear much fruit.

Congo-DRC

Democratic Republic of Congo. Also known as DR Congo, DRC, Congo, Congo-Kinshasa.

Pop 67.8 million. **Capital** Kinshasa (8.8 mill).
Christians 62.5 mill. *Evangelical Christians* 12.7 mill.
Largest Religion Christian.
Fastest Growing Religion Muslim.

Largest Ethnic Groups Nearly 250 ethno-linguistic groups and numerous sub-groups. Bantu (80.2%), Sudanic (9.8%), Adamawa-Ubangi (4.3%), Nilotic (1.5%), Pygmy (1.5%).

Official Language French. **Trade languages** Lingala/Bangala (north, northwest), Swahili (east, south), Tshiluba (centre), Kikongo/Tuba (west). **All Languages** 217.

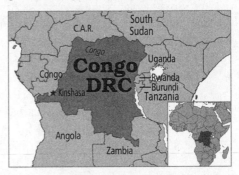

Economy Enormous potential from diamonds, minerals, agriculture, and hydro-electric power. Wars, damaged infrastructure, and corruption hinder progress, and make the nation one of the world's poorest. Agricultural land has reverted to forest, transport systems hardly function, and most people live without electricity, plumbing, education, or medical services.

Politics For centuries Congo suffered exploitation by Arab slave-traders, Western interests, and later by other Africans. Independence from Belgium (1960) was followed by violence, chaos, a corrupt dictatorship (1965-1997), and autocratic rule (1997-2006). Further war from invasion by Uganda and Rwanda required foreign intervention. By 2003 most forces withdrew. Free elections in 2006, but conflicts continue.

---

1 **Congo must overcome the evils of its tragic history** through repentance and reconciliation. 19th-century Arabs raided the country for slaves. The horrific colonial rule of Belgium's King Leopold II led to the deaths of 10 million people in the 30 years before 1908. Belgian control and international mining companies exploited Congo's resources, but oppressed the people. Western countries then supported the corrupt regime of the dictator Mobutu, which caused much of the current chaos. Inter-ethnic hostility in the 1990s led to warfare and killings. Many people fled for their lives. These past evils must be confessed, repented of, and put right, in order for the Congo to have a workable future. Christian groups in Belgium expressed repentance for past evils their country committed, and this was a positive start.

2 **Conflict in the Congo** has produced more deaths than any war since WWII. The Second Congo War involved military forces of 7 nations, and provoked the rise of local, inter-ethnic conflicts. Most foreign forces withdrew by 2006, but many militias continued to operate. Many groups used rape, violence, and torture as weapons of fear. Pray for warlords and war criminals to face justice. Pray also for the peaceful return of 1.7 million displaced people to their homes. Those who lived in refugee camps faced militia attacks, disease, sexual abuse, and live with very few resources for life beyond survival. Pray for peace and justice that will last, and for God to restore all that was destroyed or damaged.

3 **The powerful spiritual evil** that influences much of this land shows itself in deeper ways than wars, killings, greed, and corruption. Wicked men committed widespread rape, unspeakable brutality, cannibalism, and witchcraft against adults and children. How could these horrors spread throughout a land with over 90% who profess Christianity? This moves our hearts, and calls us to spiritual warfare. Cry out for God to deliver this land, and to bind the spirits that have such power over a suffering people.

4 The Democratic Republic of Congo faces every form of human and spiritual need. The lands under this name have little central government, no connection between the many regions, and no single language or culture to unite its diverse people. More than 5 million people died through war, violence, starvation, and disease. A constant state of humanitarian crisis exists. How to rebuild such a broken land? Pray for an effective national government that will rule with honesty, justice, and concern for the people. Pray that Congo's neighbours and the global community may act with righteousness and mercy towards this nation.

5 Massive numbers turned to Christ in the 20th century (from 1.4% Christian in 1900 to over 90% in 2010)! Many call themselves Christian, but do not practise their faith. There have been revivals in some areas before and after independence. Praise God for faithful believers who paid the price for this harvest. The Simba Rebellion of 1964 made martyrs of thousands of Christians, and hundreds of Catholic and Protestant missionaries. Many Christians died in the conflicts from 1991 until today, some as martyrs. Their example gives strength to others, and their sacrifice lays the foundation for a future harvest.

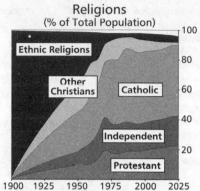

Religions
(% of Total Population)

6 The Church is the only national social structure to endure and work for the people. When countless public, church and ministry buildings were destroyed, the Church stepped in to care for the many needs in this broken land where other institutions failed. Many hospitals, clinics, and schools operate with Christian initiative. Thank God for the educational ministries of the Catholic Church and some Protestant churches. Without them, an entire generation may have gone without education. Pray for God to raise up Christian leaders of spiritual maturity and moral integrity to serve the Church and society. Many leaders compromised their standards under the dictatorship of Mobutu and the conflict that followed.

7 The DRC needs a complete re-evangelization. In some areas the work of the Holy Spirit led to increased love for God's Word, prayer movements, mobilization of youth, and new indigenous songs and hymns! Other areas have no evangelical witness and little outreach. An uncountable number of refugees have moved between the DRC, Rwanda, Burundi, Uganda, Sudan, and Tanzania in the last 20 years. After all the destruction and displacement, Congo needs a nationwide survey to reveal the state of the Church and the needs of the nation. Pray for a team of researchers, supported by the national Churches, to undertake this large task.

8 The DRC has more opportunities for expatriate Christian workers than any other African nation. Needs exist in church planting, discipleship, development, Bible teaching, leadership training, and specialized areas such as media, translation, and medical work. The destruction of roads and railways increases the strategic importance of the 7 Christian agencies with aviation programmes. Missionary involvement decreased radically due to war, instability, and the breakdown of government. Pray for a new wave of workers from around the world to live out the gospel in the DRC, and to meet the many needs of the people. Even hundreds of workers will not be enough! Bible translation remains an unfinished task. 94 languages need Bible translation, and 29 more have works in progress. Most Congolese have never owned a Bible.

Congo

Republic of Congo. Also known as ROC, Congo, Congo-Brazzaville.

Pop 3.8 million. **Capital** Brazzaville (1.3 mill).
Christians 3.4 mill. *Evangelical Christians* 598,000.
Largest Religion Christian.
Fastest Growing Religion Non-religious.
Largest Ethnic Groups Kituba (18.8%), Kongo (16.7%), Teke (12.7%), Yombe (11.5%), Adamawa-Ubangi (6.5%), Pygmy (1.3%).
Official Language French. **Trade languages** Lingala, Munukutuba (Kongo Creole). **All Languages** 66.
Economy Huge potential hindered by limited transportation. Rich oil and mineral deposits, rainforests, and agricultural potential. Slow and difficult transition away from socialist structures due to corruption, civil unrest, war, and other problems. About 50% of the people live below the poverty line.
Politics Independent from France in 1960. Communist government until 1992, then civil conflict and war until 1999. Now a constitutional republic, but with same leader in power.

---

1   **The Congo has past troubles, but future potential.** After two decades of Communism, the past dictator eventually became president of the new democracy. But in the years between he provoked a civil war that devastated the land, killed thousands, and displaced over 300,000 people. Pray for good government, for wise economic policies, for good stewardship of natural resources, and for justice to rule in society.

2   **The Church needs revival and restoration.** Congo was Christianized, but never truly converted. The majority of the population are Christian, but some sources claim up to 50% actually live as animists. Pray for a new move of the Spirit, even greater than the revival that swept the region over 50 years ago. Churches must be cleansed of false beliefs, filled with the Spirit's power, and led by biblical truth.

3   **Training for Christian leaders** causes concern. Poverty and instability led many Christian leaders to leave for other lands. Congo needs more Bible colleges, TEE, and other training programmes. The government prevented ministry to young people during the Marxist years, and still prohibits religious meetings on university campuses. As a result, few churches developed ministries to children or youth, but 41% of the population are under age 15. Pray for many new youth and children's programmes in this nation.

4   **Mission work** thrived until 1968, when the government expelled nearly all expatriates. Some returned in the 1990s, but the civil war complicated their work. Workers now have opportunities to help churches restart abandoned ministries, to address poverty, to help with health and education, and to evangelize the nation. The great harvest of the 1920s-1960s did not reach all areas.

Côte d'Ivoire

Africa

Pop 21.6 million. **Capital** Yamoussoukro (885,000).
Christians 7.3 mill. *Evangelical Christians* 2.3 mill.
Largest Religion Muslim.
Fastest Growing Religion Muslim.

Largest Ethnic Groups Guinean/Akan (31.7%, 21 groups), Gur (24.6%, 21 groups), Malinke (18.7%, 11 groups), Mande (10%, 11 groups), Kru (9.1%, 28 groups), Other Africans (4.9%). Large, undocumented population of migrants from nearby countries.
Official Language French. **All Languages** 93.

Economy Major world producer of cocoa, coffee, and palm oil. 70% of population depend on agriculture. Oil and gas production now earn more than cocoa. Post-independence growth attracted massive immigration of job seekers. Political conflicts and a coup drove down the economy.
Politics Independent from France in 1960. 1-party presidential government until 1993, followed by military overthrow, rebellion, and unjust elections. Conflict rose to deadly levels at points, and tension continues.

---

1 **Praise God that stability returned** after the violence of the 2000s, even though troubles are not yet fully resolved. People feel the sad effects of a near civil war, and have less confidence in national unity. Côte d'Ivoire currently divides mostly along ethnic and religious lines. The Muslims (north), and the Christians and animists (south), all seek political power. Pray for leaders to be free of corruption, and to work for unity and nation building.

2 **Millions of immigrants** from nearby countries present a challenge for society, but also an opportunity for the Church. Around 70% of the foreign population is Muslim. All the people groups of Côte d'Ivoire, Mali, and Burkina Faso have a significant community in Abidjan, but most churches overlook them. Christians start new congregations every month, but these focus on already-Christian peoples and fail to reach out to their Muslim neighbours.

3 **The number of animists decreased,** and more evangelical congregations now exist here than sacred "fetish groves" (shrines for spirit worship). But spirit power remains strong, and many Christians and Muslims still use charms and ancestor worship. Pray for Jesus to set free all those still stuck in their traditional religions. Pray that believers might stand against temptation to go back to old ways.

4 **Pray for the Church** of Côte d'Ivoire. The Catholic Church and Methodist Church have the most followers, and while some of them do not practise their faith, each contains many committed believers and a lively charismatic movement. Evangelical churches grew in the 1990s and even during the conflicts (2002-2007). Abidjan alone probably has over 3,000 churches now, mostly newer and independent. Nearly every main denomination has at least 1 Bible training institute, and theological education grows. But many Christians do not know or understand the Bible, and churches pursue prosperity teaching, or focus on miracles and healings more than on Christ.

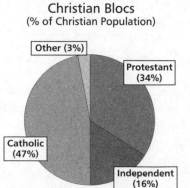

Christian Blocs
(% of Christian Population)

Other (3%)
Protestant (34%)
Catholic (47%)
Independent (16%)

5   **Evangelical mission agencies** had a late, slow start here compared with other West African nations. Early groups arrived around the 1930s to work in the centre and south of the country. The Assemblies of God came in the 1950s, and now have churches all over the country. Many missionaries left after the violence in 2002, and only some returned later. This put greater responsibility on the indigenous Church, but foreign missionaries can still serve in evangelism, church planting, Bible translation, and other ways.

6   **Several African mission agencies** now send workers mainly within Côte d'Ivoire, but also to unreached peoples in West Africa and beyond. CAPRO opened the first missions training institute for French-speaking Africa in Abidjan. Pray that this and other training programmes would produce excellent Ivoirian missionaries for the harvest field! Many indigenous missionaries live by faith with very little income. Pray that God might supply all their needs, and that their churches might support them in every possible way. Many Christian resources for French-speaking Africa come from Côte d'Ivoire, and media development work happens here. Christian music and television programmes produced here influence all of West Africa.

7   **The unevangelized peoples** live mostly in the north or concentrated in cities. Some people consider Côte d'Ivoire a "reached" nation when they see Christianity and many missionaries in the south, but millions in the north live without the gospel. The Movement for African National Initiatives (MANI) and CAPRO research the nation's people groups in order to help churches with mission and church planting. Pray especially for:

- *The Mande and Malinke people groups* of the northwest. None of these larger groups is more than 1% evangelical.
- *The Gur* peoples of the north and northeast. Most practise African traditional religions, and the Lobi, Koulango/Bouna, Senoufo, Nafanra, Khisa, and Karaboro all are 1% evangelical or less.

8   **Islam grew rapidly in the 20th century,** and up to 42% of the population follow this faith. Tribal groups in the north and around the country continue to convert to Islam. Over 2.5 million people in Abidjan (half the city) follow Islam. The overlap of the Muslim/Christian divide with the painful north/south political divide hurts Christian witness to Muslims. Pray for believers to overcome this barrier through humility and love for Muslims.

Djibouti   *Africa*

Pop 879,000. **Capital** Djibouti (577,000).
Christians 15,000. *Evangelical Christians* 1,200.
Largest Religion Muslim.
Fastest Growing Religions Muslim, Non-religious.

Largest Ethnic Groups Somali (61%, 3 major clans in southern half of country), Afar/Danakil (28%, in northern half of country), Arab (8%). [Breakdown is only an estimate, and does not account for Ethiopian and Eritrean refugees and the fluctuating Somali population, including refugee camp population.]
Official Languages French, Arabic. **All Languages** 10.

Economy Lacks water, arable land, and natural resources. Dependent on French aid and military bases. The best assets are its strategic location, and the deep-water

ports and railway (a trade link for Ethiopia). 50-80% unemployment and high levels of *qat* (drug) consumption burden the potential workforce.

Politics French control from 1884, though the boundaries covered a centuries-old conflict zone between Afars and Somalis. Independent from France since 1977 as a multiparty republic. Civil war in the early 1990s. In 2002 *shari'a* law was replaced by a Family Court.

---

 1 **Djibouti enjoys peace, but suffers under serious social and economic problems.** Western military presence helps create an atmosphere of calm and safety. Pray that the Islamist voice that seeks to make Djibouti conform to its own values will not destroy current freedoms. Serious national problems include widespread famine, extreme unemployment, human trafficking, prostitution, and drug abuse.

2 **The government recognizes only 3 Christian Churches:** the French Protestant Church, the Roman Catholic Church, and the Ethiopian Orthodox Church. But a few other Christian groups exist. Missionaries find work here a challenge with the hot, dry climate and desperate poverty. Physical and spiritual oppression, ethnic tensions, and so few believers, all lead to discouragement among workers. Many leave the field. Pray for the work in education, public health, literature, Bible translation, literacy, and youth ministry. Pray for God to send long-term workers, especially from nearby countries and people groups. Pray for the spiritual breakthrough that is long awaited but still unseen!

3 **The few Somali and Afar believers** often suffer many pressures from relatives who may reject, beat, or even kill them for leaving Islam. Tribal loyalty and jealousy can create division among the believers, and they resist meeting together. Pray for a new bond of unity! Several evangelical fellowships exist among recent immigrant groups from Ethiopia, Madagascar, Congo-DRC, the Philippines, Eritrea, and elsewhere. Many of these congregations share a strong spiritual burden to reach the Somali and Afar peoples. Pray for unity in Christ among them all, as a witness to the divided and hostile peoples of Djibouti.

4 **Pray for the peoples of Djibouti:**
- *The Afar* live mostly in Ethiopia and Eritrea, where there is little witness to them, and there is no known church among them in Djibouti.
- *The Somalis* in Djibouti, although smaller in number, can be a key for evangelization of their kinsmen across the border.
- *Local Arabs and Yemeni Arabs* need a specific approach for their spiritual needs. There is no work among them, although believers can interact more freely here than in Yemen.

Egypt

Africa

Pop 84.5 million. **Capital** Cairo (11 mill).
Christians 10.8 mill. *Evangelical Christians* 3.3 mill.
Largest Religion Muslim.
Fastest Growing Religion Muslim.

Largest Ethnic Groups Egyptian Arab (84.3%), Sudanese Arab (5.4%), Berber (2%, mostly Arabic speaking), Dom Gypsy (1.4%), Bedouin Arab (1.2%), Nubians (1.1%). Refugees (2.4%, including Ethiopians, Palestinians, Eritreans, Somalis, others, and black Sudanese may number 2 mill).
Official Language Arabic. **All Languages** 27.

Economy Wealth from agriculture. Other income from natural gas, some oil, textiles, tourism, and Suez Canal fees. Recent economic growth came through putting some business/industry under private control or ownership. Many Egyptians still live in poverty.

Politics Largest Arab country, a republic. Stability and economic progress under long rule of President Mubarak, but with repression. Massive protests ended his rule (2011), which ushered in political turmoil. A transitional government was sworn in (2013) after the army removed the Islamist president elected in 2012.

---

1 **Political turmoil in Egypt continues.** People rejoiced and hoped for justice, economic growth, and less corruption after the popular uprising in 2011. The head of the Muslim Brotherhood movement (Morsi) won the 2012 election with help from many liberal, secular, and even Christian voters who did not want his opponent to win. But he quickly moved to extend his own power, and began the process to impose Islamic law on all citizens. Mass protests followed. The army removed Morsi, and Muslim Brotherhood supporters protested. Violent military intervention followed, and a ban on the Muslim Brotherhood. Egyptians voted on a new constitution and president in 2014. Pray for a just constitution, for good laws, and for wise rulers who treat all Egyptians fairly. These years of upheaval made serious levels of poverty and unemployment even worse.

2 **For over 1,000 years, Egypt was a majority-Christian country,** even after the Arab Muslim conquest in AD 640. The Church has endured centuries of prejudice and persecution, yet it remains spiritually strong and full of life. The Coptic Church is the largest body of Christians in the Middle East. Pray for Church leaders, especially the new Coptic Pope chosen in 2012. Many Copts do not actively practise their faith. A renewal movement that emphasizes Bible study and personal faith began in the Coptic Church in the 1930s. Many Copts continue as faithful witnesses for the Lord!

3 **Persecution of Christians increased across the last 25 years,** mostly from Islamic extremists, although local police and the army often looked the other way. Pray for Christians to stand firm in their faith, and to live godly lives for their oppressors to see. Some die or suffer torture in prison. Others move to Western countries. Occasionally some Coptic youths behave in ways that do not honour Christ, which makes things more difficult for other Christians. The recent upheaval resulted in several beautiful displays of unity between Muslims and Christians. Each group helped to protect the other during times of worship or prayer as the unrest increased.

4 **The Protestant churches grew out of the Orthodox Church,** but remained small until a prayer and renewal movement in 1973 brought unity, spiritual excitement, and a vision for outreach in Egypt and beyond. Some Pentecostal and evangelical churches now see the most growth. Many churches have wide-ranging social and medical programmes to help the very poor and the disabled. Pray for theological training. Many evangelical congregations have no trained pastor.

5 **Muslim-background believers continue to grow in number,** and include some well-known former Muslim religious leaders. The number may be so high that it is unsafe to publish. Conversion is not illegal, but some Muslims who convert end up in prison under false charges. Others flee for their lives.

6 **Unreached peoples.** Most Muslims have never heard a Christian personally share the gospel. Pray for:

- *The urban population.* One thousand people a day migrate to Cairo, often peasants who end up in the slums. Drug addicts number around 500,000.
- *The Nubians of Upper Egypt,* who remained Christian for centuries but finally converted to Islam in the 17th century. Today only a few Christians remain.

- *The Bedouin,* proud desert nomads. Poverty and unemployment threaten their traditional tribal way of life, and very few Christians live among them.
- *The Berbers and the Beja.* These non-Arab peoples practise Islam, but mix their faith with folk magic and a fear of *djinn* (powerful demonic spirits).

7 **Millions of Sudanese and Southern Sudanese** fled to Egypt to escape the long civil war in Sudan. Many are Christians, and most live in poverty. Officials used violence to force them from their temporary homes, and in the process killed some. A few Christian agencies minister help to these refugees. Pray for more workers, and for the spiritual health of these Christians who suffer without a home.

8 **A vision for mission grows from ancient roots of the Egyptian Church.** The Copts have a long legacy of workers sent out. As Arabs, Egyptian Christian workers today have many advantages in the Muslim world. Pray that the millions of Egyptian Christians both inside and outside Egypt may catch the vision for evangelism and mission across the whole Arab world! Strategic media ministries (television, radio, websites, Scripture distribution) touch the lives of tens of millions of people in Egypt and across the Arab world.

Equatorial Guinea   *Africa*

Pop 693,000. **Capital** Malabo (131,000).
Christians 624,000. *Evangelical Christians* 30,000.
Largest Religion Christian.
Fastest Growing Religion Muslim.
Largest Ethnic Groups Mainland Fang (57.2%), Islands Bubi (10.3%), Yoruba (8.3%), Igbo (4.2%), Spanish (3%), Eurafrican (2.5%), Hausa (2.1%).
Official Languages Spanish, French. **All Languages** 14.
Economy Prosperous until independence (1968), then mismanagement brought economic ruin by 1979. Offshore petroleum deposits discovered in 1995 transformed the economy. One of the world's highest

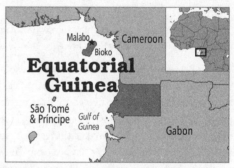

per capita incomes. A small minority hold wealth, but most continue in poverty. Corruption is a problem.
Politics Independent from Spain in 1968. The subsequent atheist regime turned the country into a virtual slave-labour camp, one of the worst human rights abusers in Africa. A multiparty government system formed in 1991, but greater freedoms for opposition parties still needed.

1 **Equatorial Guinea faces an unusual political and economic situation.** Large oil reserves make a small minority very rich. Western oil companies work with a regime whose human rights record is poor, in order to increase profits. Corruption means that most of the people do not benefit from such wealth. Pray for economic justice and wise stewardship. The oil boom brings in foreigners, both Christian and Muslim. Pray that expat believers might engage with the spiritual and physical needs of the nation. Pray that foreign companies might do business in ways that benefit the local people.

2 **Religious freedom increased** since the brutal persecution of the 1970s. Equatorial Guinea has the highest percentage of Roman Catholics of any African nation. But beneath the surface, most people never abandoned their animistic beliefs and practices. Pray that the 85% who claim Christianity might hear and respond to the true gospel of Jesus Christ. Several newer Pentecostal, charismatic, and evangelical denominations grow well. Pray for purity of life and commitment to evangelism, even in times of poverty, corruption, and despair. The government actually now sees a positive role for the Church and missions in society!

Eritrea

Pop 5.2 million. **Capital** Asmara (683,000).
Christians 2.5 mill. *Evangelical Christians* 111,000.
Largest Religion Muslim.
Fastest Growing Religion Christian.

Largest Ethnic Groups Semitic (72.5%, Tigrinya, Tigre, Belin), Afar (9.2%), Other Horn of Africa Peoples (5.4%, Beja, Somali), Arab (7.8%, 5 groups), Nilotic (5.1%).

Official Language Tigrinya. Tigre, Arabic, English also widely used. **All Languages** 18.

Economy Traditional agriculture hindered by war, drought, and land destruction. Cannot feed the population, and over half live in extreme poverty. Most highly educated and skilled professionals left the country.

Politics Former Italian colony (1890-1941). Later affiliated with Ethiopia until Independence in 1993 after decades of guerrilla warfare. A Marxist president since 1993 restricts freedoms of the population. Intense religious persecution since 2002.

---

1   **Eritrea longs for peace and national stability.** Conflict with neighbouring countries continues, especially along the border with Ethiopia. War and drought left millions dependent on food aid from abroad. Many face extreme poverty with no relief ahead. Mandatory military service limits the size of the workforce. Many people flee the country to escape the military, and the money sent home by those who live abroad now provides a vital source of income for the country.

2   **Religious freedom remains a major issue.** A law in 2002 officially recognized only 4 religions (Sunni Islam, Eritrean Orthodox, Catholic, and Lutheran), and banned all other groups from meeting or practising their faith. This affected all Eritreans, but especially Christians from non-approved groups. Pray for government acceptance of religious groups, and for restoration of basic human rights and religious freedom to all Eritreans.

3   **The Christian Church faces terrible persecution.** Some estimate over 3,000 leaders and church members suffer in prison, with others under house arrest. Prison beatings and torture cripple many, and some die. Pray that Christians may remain fervent for Jesus amidst hardship. The burdens of war, drought, and government oppression draw together Christians of all denominations in fellowship and renewed commitment. The intense suffering of the Church in Eritrea is an untold story of the past decade. Pray for this tragedy to produce great spiritual fruit for the nation and beyond.

4   **Evangelicals grew rapidly despite severe persecution!** The Church grows most rapidly among those who flee the country, those who live in camps in Ethiopia and elsewhere, and those in prison. Banned evangelical groups must now operate in underground networks based in homes (at least 20 exist, perhaps more). So many pastors, leaders, and evangelists now live outside the country or in prison that the Church must find and train new leaders. Young men or new believers who found Jesus in prison often step forward to lead. Pray for them to be full of God's wisdom as they grow and learn to lead.

Eritrea   29

5 Pray for continued commitment of the believers to preach Christ, whatever the cost and without compromise. Witnessing Christians are spread far and wide, despite opposition from authorities. Still, many villages and towns remain unreached. From 2002 onwards, the government forced almost all foreign aid workers (Christian and non-Christian) to leave. Pray for open doors for a return to Eritrea. Pray especially for the less-reached Tigre people (mostly Muslim) and the Jabarti people (a Muslim minority among the Tigrinya). The Afar and related Saho peoples live mostly as nomadic pastoralists, with few Christians. The Beja and Nara peoples of the northwest have no known witness among them.

Ethiopia
Africa

Pop 85 million. **Capital** Addis Ababa (2.9 mill).
Christians 51.6 mill. *Evangelical Christians* 16.7 mill.
Largest Religion Christian.
Fastest Growing Religion Non-religious.

Largest Ethnic Groups Semitic/Ethiopian (41.5%, 18 peoples, including Amhara, Tigrinya), Cushitic peoples (41.6%, includes Oromo, Somali, Afar), Omotic (14.7%, 49 peoples in south, southwest), Nilotic (1%, 19 peoples).
Official Language Amharic (spoken by majority). English widely taught, and regional languages important. **All Languages** 88.

Economy Based on agriculture, with coffee as main export (believed to originate in Ethiopia). War and famine hindered development, and millions suffer malnutrition. Dependence on foreign aid and food negatively impacts the local agriculture and workforce.
Politics One of the world's oldest-known nations, with a long-written history. Revolution in 1974 overthrew Emperor Haile Selassie and imposed Marxism, which collapsed in 1991. Democratic government since then. Border war with Eritrea and civil strife in nearby Somalia drain resources.

---

1 The nation struggles through social, political, and economic crises. The war with Eritrea (1998-2000) cost Ethiopia much money and many lives, and brought little gain. The major ethnic groups (Amhara, Tigrinya, Oromo, Somali, Afar) divide themselves largely by geographic region, which gives each more independence at the expense of national unity. Corruption increased with economic growth, and a wide gap now exists between the few who are rich and the many who are poor. Ethiopia depends on hundreds of thousands of tonnes of food aid every year, but tens of thousands of people still die from malnutrition. Pray for improved harvests, wise economic policies, and better use of outside aid.

2 The Ethiopian Orthodox Church was a Christian "island" in a "sea of Islam" for many centuries. This isolation led to its unique culture, theology, and tradition. 40% of the population are Orthodox, though millions do not practise their faith in daily life, and mix it with local superstitions. Others left Orthodoxy for newer Protestant churches. However, others stayed and helped develop strong evangelical and charismatic networks within the Orthodox Church! Pray for a deep work of the Holy Spirit to revitalize this large ancient Church, its biblical heritage and its spiritual legacy.

3 Praise God for massive growth of evangelicals, especially in Protestant and Independent churches. The Church suffered persecution both during the Italian occupation (1936-1941) and under the Marxist regime (1974-1990), when Western mission agencies withdrew. Many became martyrs, but millions turned to follow Christ. The greatest growth came in the last 20 years. Ethiopian Christian unity and missions vision grew through suffering. The Church has an outward vision and continues to evangelize, so expect its growth to continue! Pray for a recent strategy to evangelize Ethiopia that includes intercession, a focus on unevangelized peoples, and plans to engage local churches in mission work. Cross-cultural workers will be sent out to plant churches in all the regions of Ethiopia, and from the Horn of Africa to South Asia.

4 **Pray about the challenges faced by the Ethiopian Church.**

- *Church leaders* typically have 1 year or less of training. Who will lead and disciple so many new believers?

- *Young people* form the majority of Ethiopia's population (70% under the age of 30), and too little ministry focuses on them.

- *Kingdom workers* need support. The Church must minister as the poor to the poor. Pray for programmes that serve the poor, and good ways to generate income that can fund the workers.

- *Bible translation* remains a huge task. Almost all congregations use local languages. Agencies have 35 translation projects in progress. Another 17 languages have translation needs but no workers.

5 **The less evangelized.** Ethiopia remains a stronghold for Christianity across many centuries, despite Islamic advances. But Muslims now target this nation for converts. Violent reaction against evangelical outreach creates fear and religious tension, but also causes some Muslims to consider Jesus. 10 years ago only a few hundred believers came from a Muslim background, but now tens of thousands follow Christ! Pray especially for:

- *The Somali, Harari, and Afar regions* (east). Most are Muslim. Ethiopian Somalis number 4.5 million and are one of Africa's least-reached peoples. The number of Christians grows, but ministry among these peoples comes with great risk and high personal cost.

- *Many sections of Oromia* (especially east and south). Most are Muslim, and some feel hostile towards Christians. Warfare among Oromi tribes gets in the way of outreach, but provides opportunity for Christians to show compassion and care.

- *The many peoples of the southwest* (near the South Sudan border). Most of these small groups live in isolation. Some live a nomadic lifestyle. Pray for healthy churches among each people group.

Gabon

Africa

Pop 1.5 million. **Capital** Libreville (633,000).
Christians 1.2 mill. *Evangelical Christians* 191,000.
Largest Religion Christian.
Fastest Growing Religions Muslim, Non-religious.

Largest Ethnic Groups Central-Congo Bantu (51.5%), Northwest Bantu (41.8%), Other African (5.2%, Baka/Pygmy, native people and immigrants from neighbouring countries and West Africa).
Official Language French. **All Languages** 43.

Economy One of Africa's wealthier countries, but the majority does not benefit from the wealth. Rich in natural resources (oil, wood, minerals), but must import food.

Politics Stable multiparty democracy. Gabon's president was the world's longest-ruling politician (4 decades) prior to his death in 2009.

1 **Spiritist beliefs and practices** lie beneath the surfaces of Catholicism, other Christian groups, and Islam. Many Gabonese still use charms, hallucinogenic drugs, and ancestral spirits, and go to medicine men. Some leaders of the government, the police, and the army participate in nighttime rituals that use witchcraft and black magic. Christians who do not participate can be refused academic or professional opportunities.

2 **Muslim numbers grow** by immigration, and by conversions among Gabonese men. The former president and his successor converted to Islam. West African immigrants in the merchant class, and Arab influence in the oil industry, both shape the country. The Church wants to reach out to Muslims with the gospel, but has not yet effectively started.

3 **Traditional denominations** decreased in size and influence. The Catholic Church was strong in the colonial era. Most Gabonese received Catholic baptism, but a large number still follow old animist ways. Other Catholics left to follow Islam, other Christian groups, or sects. The first major Protestant denomination came to Gabon through French missionary work. This Church later grew liberal, and the leaders focus on social issues without evangelism. Now it does not grow. Ask God's Spirit to revive these older Churches. Pray that the many Christians may see and embrace the pure gospel.

4 **Evangelical Church growth in Gabon continues.** Through the Christian and Missionary Alliance (C&MA), the Pentecostals, and newer indigenous African churches, evangelicals increased from 2.3% in 1960 to 12.7% in 2010. The Church also grew in maturity, with commitment to yearlong prayer chains, all-night prayer gatherings, weekend prayer retreats, and more. Gabonese evangelicals have a vision for their country to be 20% evangelical by 2025, and for every Gabonese person to hear the gospel. The C&MA-planted churches have a World Missions Centre and a Prayer Chapel for the nations, and now they and Bethany churches both send workers to other nations.

5 **Least-reached peoples.** Gabon's east was closed to evangelicals, and the northeast was the least evangelized and least developed. Few born-again Christians come from these areas. Praise God that they have opened up, with churches planted and people reached! Much work remains. The Baka/Babinga people (often called Pygmies) are Gabon's earliest inhabitants. They live in the undeveloped forest, where other peoples exploit and mistreat their unique culture and gentle nature. The C&MA and Deeper Life reached out to them, and the Baka now have 10 congregations. Some Baka also joined churches of other ethnic groups.

The Gambia *Africa*

Pop 1.8 million. **Capital** Banjul (455,000).
Christians 78,000. *Evangelical Christians* 13,400.
Largest Religion Muslim.
Fastest Growing Religion Christian.
Largest Ethnic Groups Malinke (42.5%), Fulani/Fula (17.3%),
Wolof (12.6%), Soninke/Serahule (9.9%), Atlantic (5.9%),
Jola (4.7%), Other sub-Saharan African (10.1%).
Official Language English. Trade languages: Mandinka,
Wolof. **All Languages** 23.
Economy Agriculture, tourism, foreign aid. Possible oil
and gas reserves.
Politics Independent from Britain in 1965. Now an
elected government after several coups and military rule. Tight state controls over political and media activity.

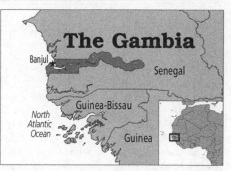

 Thank God for the mostly friendly relationships between Muslims and Christians in Gambia. Christians have more religious freedom here than in most Muslim countries. But most Christian work has been in the Greater Banjul area (coast). Few reach out to the Muslim majority, especially those who live upriver in the less-developed inland area. Pastors who serve inland struggle to maintain financial support. Pray for continued religious freedom and peace. Pray for Gambians to have a vision to reach their own nation, and for creative ways to support those who move into more isolated areas.

2 The small Gambian evangelical Church has few committed believers and many who do not practise their faith. Pray for immature Christians to grow deeper in their faith. The active Christians cannot meet all the ministry needs, and many feel overburdened. Churches need discipleship and leadership training.

3 Pray for unreached peoples in the Gambia. The Christian population receives more spiritual attention from missionaries and ministries than the unreached Muslim majority.

- *Mandinkas* (95% Muslim), who practise a mix of Islam and traditional customs. Few leave Islam because the community and family view those who leave as traitors.

- *Fulani,* who consider themselves the guardians of Islam in West Africa. Gambian Fulani have settled more than the nomadic Fulani in other countries, but remain unreached.

- *Jola.* Most revere spirit powers. Some now follow Islam, and a few follow Christianity. Pray for more Jolas to find freedom in Christ, and pray for the medical, translation, and church-planting work in their area.

- *Wolof, Serahule, and Serer.* Fewer than 10 known Christians come from the 180,000 Serahule of Gambia. Medical work opens doors to the gospel in some villages.

Ghana

Pop 24.3 million. **Capital** Accra (2.3 mill).
Christians 15.4 mill. *Evangelical Christians* 5.9 mill.
Largest Religion Christian.
Fastest Growing Religion Muslim.

Largest Ethnic Groups About 100 ethnic groups. Guinean/
Kwa (69.2%, includes Akan, Ewe, Ga-Adangme, Guang),
Gur (25.6%, 29 peoples), Yoruba (1.6%).
Official Language English. **All Languages** 84.

Economy Based on cocoa, timber, gold, and tourism.
New lake and hydro-electric project in development.
Rich natural resources, but Ghana struggles with
poverty. Forests were over-logged and soil depleted.
Lack of rainfall brought poverty to northern farmers, who often migrate south.

Politics Independent from Britain (1957). First regime was a disaster, followed by 5 military regimes. But
stable multiparty democracy since 1992. Ghana has a positive role in diplomacy and peacekeeping in the
region and continent.

---

1 **Ghana has multiple ethnic groups and faiths, but it remains largely peaceful.** Praise God!
The education system and constitution brought together all ethnicities, and helped build a
stable democracy. Almost half of Ghana's college-educated citizens live abroad. This slows development and prosperity at home. Pray that government leaders might seek guidance from God, and
not from human philosophies or the spirits.

2 **Ghana enjoys a rich Christian tradition!** Many newer churches emerged, and many traditional denominations have a vibrant spiritual life. When churches multiply quickly, doctrines
can become confused. Ghana has the blessing of many training institutions. Pray for mature leaders
for the Church. 63% of Ghanaians call themselves Christian, but only about 10% attend church regularly. Traditional African practices present the greatest challenge to Christians. Pray for a clear break
from all bondage to charms and the occult, and pray for true liberty in Jesus.

3 **Pray for a Christian vision for the nation.** Indigenous churches took up the challenge of the
unevangelized in their own country. More and more southern Christians now reach out to the
northerners. But thousands of villages in Ghana still have no church at all. Ghanaian and expat
workers must labour together for the harvest. Pray especially for the Gur peoples (mostly in the north),
and the Guinean/Kwa peoples (mostly in northern or Volta regions).

4 **Islam has set out to conquer Ghana,** and has made progress. Muslim numbers grow through
births, immigration, and conversions (especially non-Muslim women who marry Muslim
men). Most Muslims now live in the southern, traditionally non-Muslim, areas. Praise God that some
Muslims, even some *imams* (religious leaders), find Christ. Pray for loving witness by believers. Pray
especially for the Hausa, whose culture influences Islam in all of West Africa. Pray for the Holy Spirit
to win many more Muslims to Jesus.

5 **Less-evangelized parts of society:**
• *The cities* grew when many ethnic groups migrated there. Northerners in southern cities
(over 1 million) easily turn to Islam. Pray for cross-cultural workers to increase the northern-
language congregations in the southern cities.

- *Trokosi* (girls in servitude to fetish priests) number up to 20,000. Ministries like Every Child and International Needs offer them freedom in Christ. Ghana made this practice illegal in 1998, but priests hold significant spiritual power, and people need courage and faith to openly oppose them.

- *Street children* number over 30,000. Several ministries work with these needy orphans and abandoned children.

- *Young people* hold the key to revival in Ghana. Over 40% of the population are under age 15, and many feel open to spiritual matters. Current outreach to them does not meet the need. Islam and African traditional religions have the most influence in the villages.

Guinea $\quad$ *Africa*

Pop 10.3 million. **Capital** Conakry (1.7 mill).
Christians 461,000. *Evangelical Christians* 75,000.
Largest Religion Muslim.
Fastest Growing Religion Christian.

Largest Ethnic Groups West Atlantic (45.8%), Mande (42.7%), Mande-Fu (9.2%).
Official Language French. Major local languages: Fulbe, Malinke, Susu, Kissi, Guerze, Tome. **All Languages** 38.
Economy Huge potential from mineral deposits, fertile land, and good water supply. But corruption and mismanagement have led to poverty, riots, and demonstrations.
Politics Independent from France in 1958. Marxist regime from 1984, then one president for 24 years. Eventual transition to a civilian government with democratic elections since 2010.

1 Praise God for Guinea's long but peaceful transition to democracy from 1984. It remained more stable than nearby countries, and served as a refuge for those who flee war and violence. Freedom exists for Christian witness and missionary activity. Repression under the Marxist regime made Muslims more receptive to Christianity, although intolerance recently increased in certain areas.

2 Christians make up a small minority of the population. Most live in Conakry and the southeast forests. The Church declined around 15 years ago. Evangelism and church planting slowed down, and less-committed Christians left the faith. Guinea has 3 Bible schools and 6 leadership training schools, but still lacks Christian leaders. 43% of the population are under age 15. Pray for believers who will persevere, and pray against the enemy who seeks to destroy young or weak Christians before they can grow.

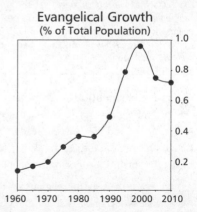

Evangelical Growth
(% of Total Population)

3 Missions vision. More than 20 evangelical missions serve the unreached with wonderful unity and coordination. A small, young, indigenous mission movement serves the nation as well. Out of more than 40 people groups, only a few have no church-planting work among them! Work among

Muslim peoples increased. Guinea still needs pioneer missionaries because it is a difficult field. Pray for strength, health, and perseverance for those brave enough to answer God's call. Pray for more missionaries, especially to the Muslim groups.

 Guinea remains largely unreached, and requires much prayer for a major breakthrough.

- *Malinke.* SIM International helped create worship music composed and recorded by Malinkes. Radio ministry now needs to be revived. A few Malinke churches exist, with Malinke leaders.

- *Fulbe, or Futa Jalon.* This people serve as guardians of Islam across West Africa. A small number of believers grows through efforts of mission agencies who work together. New believers struggle to break free from the social and spiritual bonds of Islam.

- *Susu.* 3 small Susu churches operate in or near Conakry, and a few believers live in the southern interior near the Guinea-Bissau border. Workers just finished the New Testament translation and recorded audio Scriptures. Pray for many to receive and hear the Word of God!

- *The forest region.* It received many thousands of refugees from Liberia and Sierra Leone, and needs special prayer. Some ex-rebels in the area promote an aggressive form of Islam, which creates tension with the native Kpelle people (which includes many Christians).

Guinea-Bissau   *Africa*

Pop 1.6 million. **Capital** Bissau (309,000).
Christians 180,000. *Evangelical Christians 27,000.*
Largest Religion Muslim.
Fastest Growing Religion Non-religious.
Largest Ethnic Groups Atlantic (53.5%, 17 groups), Fulbe (21.7%, 2 groups), Malinke (11.9%, 5 groups), Crioulo (11.9%).
Official Language Portuguese. National language: Portuguese Creole, spoken by at least half the population. **All Languages** 25.

Economy One of the world's poorest countries. Relies on cashew nuts, fish, hardwood, other agricultural products. Massive foreign debt. Trans-shipment point for cocaine from South America to Europe.
Politics Independent from Portugal in 1974, followed by one-party revolutionary government until 1994. 1998 uprising led to civil war until 2000. Series of elections, coups followed. Since independence no leader has served a full term in office.

---

1 **Poverty, political unrest, and violent conflict** combine to burden the population. Opportunity for progress and development seems distant. The influence of drug shipments leads to corrupt police, army, and government leaders, and can trap already poor people in destruction. Guinea-Bissau's history of political unrest reveals a need for stability and forgiveness. Pray that God would raise up righteous leaders for the people.

2 **Praise the Lord for religious freedom in Guinea-Bissau.** Evangelicals assisted with humanitarian needs during the civil war, and worked together with Catholics and Muslims in political reconciliation efforts. This brought respect and freedoms for the Evangelical Church of Guinea-Bissau. Pray that the Church might continue to show practical love and compassion, and to work for peace and reconciliation.

3 The Evangelical Church of Guinea-Bissau has mature, indigenous leadership. But the poorer, rural congregations suffer neglect, since pastors prefer not to serve there. Those who minister rurally must care for several congregations at once. Pray for trained, passionate national workers to go to the remote and unreached parts of Guinea-Bissau and the entire region.

4 Pray for the less-reached groups. Missionaries still come to Guinea-Bissau, mostly Latin Americans and Asians. Most do not stay long-term. Some set up new denominations near existing churches rather than going to needy and unreached areas. Pray for missionaries to work together well with one another and with the national Church. Pray also for a greater focus on reaching the unevangelized. The Muslim Fula/Fulbe and Mandinka brought Islam to Guinea-Bissau. Pray that they may also become responsible for spreading the good news of Jesus! Very little to no work exists for the Biafada, Nalu, Soninke, and other peoples with mixed Muslim and animist beliefs.

Kenya

Africa

Pop 40.9 million. **Capital** Nairobi (3.5 mill).
Christians 33.8 mill. *Evangelical Christians* 20 mill.
Largest Religion Christian.
Fastest Growing Religion Muslim.
Largest Ethnic Groups Bantu peoples (66%), Nilotic (29.8%), Cushitic (2.7%), Swahili (0.6%), South Asian (0.3%), Arab (0.2%), British (0.2%), Khoisan (0.1%).
Official Languages English, Swahili. **All Languages** 74.
Economy Based on agriculture, light industries, and tourism. Good growth 1963-1976, but then decline due to debt, recession, and mismanagement. Kenya is well-known for widespread corruption. Droughts, floods, and famines affect large areas, raise food prices, and cause loss of livestock.
Politics Independent from Britain in 1963. Years of mainly stable government favoured one ethnic group and suppressed opposition. Now a multiparty state. Violence and ethnic conflict followed the 2007 elections, and brought a coalition government. Kenyans approved a new constitution in 2010.

1 Kenya is stable at this time, but faces many threats. Droughts in the north resulted in the death of 80% of livestock, and decreased pastureland. Ethnic groups clash violently over limited resources. The fragile environment, the need for land reform, a wide gap between rich and poor, scarce water, and urban slums that quickly spread all create tension in Kenyan society. Many of these fed the ethnic and political violence of 2007-2008. Pray for peace, for wise governance, and for practical solutions.

2 Kenya has a massive evangelical presence. Nearly 50% of the population identify themselves as evangelicals, from Protestant, Independent, Anglican, and Catholic backgrounds! Pentecostals especially experienced rapid growth. Overall, 82% of Kenyans call themselves "Christian". Why then does Kenya have so much poverty, and such corruption? With so much corruption, terrorists and international drug traffickers use Kenya as a base. Pray for Christians to unite to oppose wrong-doing, and to promote policies that honour God. Kenya needs a just and honest government that will uplift the poor and punish the wicked.

3 Praise God for waves of church growth and renewal! The East African Revival (1948-1960) deeply impacted the Anglican, Presbyterian, and Methodist Churches. More recent charismatic renewal impacted millions of Catholics and Anglicans. Rapid growth brings challenges that need prayer. Less than 10% of Christians attend church regularly. Independent churches multiply quickly, but may lack accountability. Some mix Christian teachings with unbiblical beliefs and practices. Kenya has over 80,000 congregations, and they need trained leaders. 70 institutions train Christian workers for ministry, but even these cannot address such a large need. Pray for new, appropriate, affordable solutions.

4 Many Kenyans now serve cross-culturally within Kenya or abroad. The Finish the Task movement mobilizes the Church to reach every unreached people in the nation. Kenya sends many missionaries, but could send many more, especially to the needy Horn of Africa region. Pray for churches, denominations, Bible schools, and seminaries to emphasize the Great Commission. Nairobi serves as a strategic hub for ministry in Africa and beyond. Many international Christian organizations have continental offices here.

5 Major sectors of the population need specialized ministry:

- *Young people.* The majority of Kenyans are children and youth, and the Church must prioritize ministry to them. City slum dwellers include over 100,000 street children. Pray for ways to minister to all aspects of these young people's lives.

- *HIV/AIDS sufferers.* About 500 people pass away every day due to AIDS, even though the infection rate decreased. Previously some Christians shunned those with HIV, but the Anglican Church recently apologized to AIDS victims for this mistreatment. Pray that Christians may lead in ministry to the sick, and to the hundreds of thousands of AIDS orphans.

- *Muslims.* For centuries they have lived on the coast and in the northwest as a minority group. As Islam grows and changes, Christian-Muslim tensions increase. Violent outbreaks increase. Pray for peace between communities. Other Muslim groups live in the northeast (Oromo-related peoples), in the coastal hills (among the Mijikenda peoples), and along the coast (Swahili and Arab populations). Pray for Truth seekers to find the Saviour.

- *The Somali,* who live in the northeast and in the cities. Trouble in Somalia drove tens of thousands into Kenya where they can encounter the gospel more easily than in their homeland. Some Christian workers reach out to them through holistic ministry, and perhaps a few hundred now follow Christ.

- *The Asian community* made up of Muslims, Hindus, Jains, Parsees, Sikhs, and Christians. They work in trade and private industry, but face insecurity as Kenya's economy struggles. Asian-African Concern Kenya brings together Asian, African, and international ministries who seek to reach all of East Africa's Asian population. Pray for African churches to also pick up the challenge to reach Asians in Kenya.

Lesotho
Africa

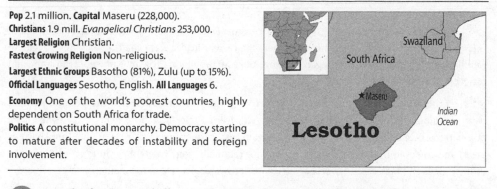

Pop 2.1 million. **Capital** Maseru (228,000).
Christians 1.9 mill. *Evangelical Christians* 253,000.
Largest Religion Christian.
Fastest Growing Religion Non-religious.

Largest Ethnic Groups Basotho (81%), Zulu (up to 15%).
Official Languages Sesotho, English. **All Languages** 6.

Economy One of the world's poorest countries, highly dependent on South Africa for trade.
Politics A constitutional monarchy. Democracy starting to mature after decades of instability and foreign involvement.

1   **Lesotho faces great challenges.** The HIV infection rate is among the highest in the world (23.2%). Family breakdown, poverty, unemployment, and limited access to water frustrate daily life. The people and the government struggle to cope with these burdens. Pray for wise leadership and creative ways to improve quality of life. Mission Aviation Fellowship planes transport medical supplies and Christian workers in this mountainous country with few roads. The mountain peoples are much less reached because of their isolated location. Christian radio reaches many in the lowlands, even non-churchgoers. Scripture Union shares God's Word with young people through school groups. Pray for fruitful ministry in this needy land.

2   **Pre-Christian traditional practices and beliefs are common in long-established churches.** Early missionaries Christianized the Basotho, but most did not fully convert. Practices like ancestor worship, curses and charms, and secret societies that use magic, all offend God's holiness and the purity of the gospel. Pray for the Holy Spirit to cleanse and bring new life. Newer evangelical groups continue to plant churches that grow! Pray for new growth, and a spirit of humility and cooperation among them.

Liberia
Africa

Pop 4.1 million. **Capital** Monrovia (827,000).
Christians 1.7 mill. *Evangelical Christians* 601,000.
Largest Religion Ethnic religions.
Fastest Growing Religion Muslim.

Largest Ethnic Groups Mande/Malinke (48.7%, 9 groups), Kru (35.1%, 19 groups), Atlantic/Guinean (10%), Americo-Liberian (2.5%, returned American blacks), Kongo (2.5%, returned Caribbean freed slaves).
Official Language English. **All Languages** 31.

Economy Many natural resources (water, rubber, iron, diamonds, other). Maritime registry of ships is 2nd-largest revenue source. But devastated by years of corruption (until 1980), then civil wars and chaos (1989-2003). Foreign aid and investment now help rebuild, but poverty affects many, and unemployment is high (up to 75%).
Politics Black Africa's first independent state (1847), created as a colony for freed American slaves. A coup in 1980 ended Liberian-American dominance. Massive corruption and repression resulted in rebellion (1989),

then a period of turmoil (2 civil wars) overwhelmed the country until peaceful elections in 2005. Liberia elected Africa's first female leader, Ellen Johnson Sirleaf.

---

1 **Praise God for peace and stability of recent years.** Hundreds of thousands of refugees returned, a new president came to power (the former leader was exiled), the country began to rebuild, and Christian ministry began to thrive once again. Liberia has an atmosphere of hope and progress, despite the obvious challenges.

2 **Liberia's recent civil wars devastated the country and traumatized the people.** Around 250,000 people died, including 50,000 children. Thousands more fled. Almost the entire population either suffered as victims or committed the harsh crimes. War rose out of ethnic hatreds, greed and corruption, and lust for power. Pray for reconciliation among the ethnic groups involved in the crimes and massacres. Several agencies work towards peace and reconciliation.

3 **The Church compromised its testimony,** and must now regain it. Most Christian groups tolerated African traditional beliefs, tribal secret societies, magic and charms, and Freemasonry, and the enemy gained influence within the Church. Believers lost their compassion, and failed to care for the most vulnerable people. Many church buildings, schools, Bible colleges, and hospitals closed or need repair. Trained spiritual leaders fled or lost their lives. But God has begun to change the Church into an instrument for healing and restoration. Some refugees studied theology while out of the country, and recently returned to serve. Pray for the Holy Spirit to purify, renew, and build up the body of Christ.

4 **Family life must be restored.** The war traumatized a whole generation of young people. Trauma counselling must now be part of training for Christian leaders and pastors, together with Bible teaching. Cry out to God for:

- *Former child soldiers.* The 15,000 who survived now live with memories of all they saw and did. Over 30% already attempted suicide at least one time. The prejudice and rejection they face since the war only wounds them again in the present.
- *Thousands of children who will never know their father.* Most of these are children of rape, who live with poverty and shame. Their fathers were rebels or soldiers, or West African peace-keeping forces.
- *Victims of sexual abuse.* Military troops and rebels took thousands of girls during the war to serve as maids, porters, and usually as sexual slaves. Even now girls face abuse from some peacekeepers, aid workers, teachers, and others in positions of power.

5 **Less-reached peoples:**

- *Muslims* in Liberia respond to the gospel when they see others demonstrate it through Community Health Evangelism and similar holistic programmes. Today foreign Muslim groups give money to restore mosques (the war also destroyed thousands of mosques), and spread Islamic teachings.
- *Peoples who follow animism* (traditional African religions) live in the forests of the interior. All have a Christian minority, but the power of magic and charms is strong. Spiritual warfare and breakthrough must come and then continue for the Church to remain free from the clutches of the enemy.

Libya

Pop 6.5 million. **Capital** Tripoli (1.1 mill).
Christians 173,000. *Evangelical Christians* 19,700.
Largest Religion Muslim.
Fastest Growing Religion Christian.

Largest Ethnic Groups Population data remains a difficult issue, due to undocumented foreign migrants and more recent immigration. Arab (76.4%), Bedouin (13.7%), Berber (5.8%), Other (4.1%, includes labourers such as Punjabi, Italian, Serbian, Gypsy, Croatian, and Sinhalese). Also many thousands of undocumented Sub-Saharan Africans in transit to Europe.
Official Language Arabic. **All Languages** 32.

Economy Discovery of oil in 1959 transformed the economy. Oil generates 95% of export income, but little of the wealth reaches the masses. UN voted to lift sanctions against Libya (2003), and the economy progressed.
Politics Ruled by Italy (1911-1943). Full independence as a monarchy in 1951. Military coup (1969) led to an Islamic revolutionary republic under Muammar Qaddafi, whose 42-year rule ended in violence with the 2011 uprising. First free elections in 6 decades held in 2012 to elect a General National Congress, with promise to transition to democracy and the rule of law. Destabilized by activities of many armed groups.

---

1 **The era of Qaddafi and sanctions is over.** Potential for increased foreign investment and trade both exist. The post-Qaddafi government promised an open and democratic state that would be fair to all citizens. This has not happened. Dozens of independent, armed militia groups continue to cause trouble for many, including for Christians. Pray for a future of peace, stability, religious freedom, and most of all for a future of peace with God.

2 **The spiritual climate in Libya changed significantly** in the years before the uprising. God has done a new work in this Muslim land, perhaps in answer to many prayers! Many people feel spiritually hungry, but those who seek Bibles often struggle to find them. Materials exist in standard Arabic, but no Scriptures and almost no audio or video resources exist in Libyan Arabic. More Libyans come to Christ each year, although it remains only a small few. Praise God for these changes, and pray that they would accelerate. Pray for further opportunities to connect Libyans to the wider Christian world!

3 **Large numbers of migrants come into Libya.** Most come from Sub-Saharan Africa, but some come from North Africa and even parts of Asia. A few find work in Libya, but more cross the dangerous deserts and seas in search of a new life in Europe. The current chaos in Libya gives freedom for traffickers to exploit these vulnerable people. Pray that these tens or even hundreds of thousands would find salvation, and not just earthly gain. Some of these migrants are believers. Pray that they might have a powerful spiritual impact on Libyans and on fellow migrants.

4 **The Christian community in Libya grows, but slowly.** Most believers are foreign, and are Catholic or Orthodox. The Protestant and Independent groups more actively practise their faith. Believers face many obstacles. The government, relatives, and Islamic groups all pressure them to return to Islam. In the past, persecution came mostly from government spies, but now it comes from Islamist groups. Pray for believers to stay strong in the faith, to grow spiritually, and to find fellowship with other believers for encouragement and strength.

Madagascar

Africa

Pop 20.1 million. **Capital** Antananarivo (1.9 mill).
Christians 10.8 mill. *Evangelical Christians* 2.3 mill.
Largest Religion Christian.
Fastest Growing Religion Muslim.

Largest Ethnic Groups Malagasy (97.5%, 38 peoples of mixed African, Indonesian, and Arab origin), French (0.5%), Réunionese (0.4%), Gujarati (0.3%), Chinese (0.3%).
Official Languages Malagasy, French. English also spoken.
All Languages 20.

Economy World's 11th poorest nation. Most people live by subsistence farming, fishing, and forestry. But cyclones, lack of clean water and sanitation, poor infrastructure, and careless farming techniques, all hinder progress. Mining and eco-tourism provide new sources of income.

Politics Highland Merina people gained control of island in the 19th century (still resented by lowlander peoples). Annexed by France (1896), and independent since 1960. Government has alternated between Marxist rule, coup/military takeover, and multiparty elections. Corruption continues as a major problem.

---

1 **This land of riches fights a battle with poverty.** Some call Madagascar the "8th continent". Its rich environment houses unique plant and animal species, and a unique mix of ethnicities. But most people live on an average of less than $1 US/day. The slash-and-burn farming technique destroyed about 80% of the rainforest cover and many species of plants and animals. Pray for leadership that will serve the people well, and development that lifts people out of poverty.

2 **The Church grows in the midst of political and environmental crises.** The Holy Spirit moved most among students, young people, and laypeople. Significant revival movements came to large churches in 1895, 1941, 1948, and in the 1980s. From revivals came a movement of lay "shepherds" in the mainline churches. Their emphasis on healing and exorcism led to conversions and new churches in some areas. Pray that this movement might continue to grow, and to be rooted in Scripture.

3 **Old beliefs still dominate, even within Christianity.** Many Christians compromise with reverence to ancestral spirits and with witchcraft. Pray for a new move of the Holy Spirit to awaken churches in decline. Hostile relationships divide the Church. Newer charismatic denominations face opposition from traditional denominations and the government. Churches split because of feuds between leaders. Pray for unity among leaders and churches. Pray that humility and a Kingdom mindset will replace pride and jealousy.

4 **Less-reached areas and peoples.** Pioneer workers must commit long-term to areas where living conditions are difficult, in order to demonstrate love for the people, language, and culture. Workers have opportunities in aid, development, vocational training, and education. The ministry of Mission Aviation Fellowship and Helimission provide vital service to this land with its many inaccessible areas. Pray for more radios and Christian broadcasts for isolated rural peoples.

- *The northern and southern ends of the island* host the least-evangelized Malagasy peoples. Animism with strong Muslim influence dominates the north and northwest, and 80% of the south remains non-Christian. Malagasy evangelists travel for days to reach these remote villages. Pray for health, and for bicycles, finances, and faith for them.

- *Malagasy ethnic religion* dominates among the Sakalava in the west, Tsimihety in the north, Tandroy and Tonosy in the south, and others. Shaman healers, witchcraft, and demonic oppression are common. Pray for these peoples to know the love and power of Christ.

- *Muslims* grow in numbers among Sakalava groups on the west coast, the Antemoro in the east, and the Antankarana in the north. Most practise folk Islam. A small specific outreach bears fruit among them. Pray for more. Pray also for the Muslim Comorians, Gujaratis, and Arabs, with few known believers among them.

Malawi
Africa

Pop 15.7 million. **Capital** Lilongwe (865,000).
Christians 11.9 mill. *Evangelical Christians* 3.1 mill.
Largest Religion Christian.
Fastest Growing Religion Muslim.
Largest Ethnic Groups Chewa-Sena (70.4%), Yawo (12.3%), Ngoni (7.8%), Central-Tanzania (4.8%), South Asian (0.7%), and many migrant peoples from Central/East Africa en route to South Africa.
Official Languages Chichewa and English. **All Languages** 24.
Economy Dense population with little development. Dependent on agriculture, which suffers from cycles of drought/heavy rainfall. Widespread AIDS a problem. Poverty and unemployment cause many to seek work in other countries.
Politics Independent from Britain (1964), followed by a ruthless 30-year dictatorship. Progress in economic stability, but political freedom suffered. Multiparty elections in 1994. Recent elections were peaceful and fair, and votes aligned with issues rather than ethnic or regional loyalties.

1. **Malawi remains a stable and peaceful land** in a region troubled by wars and violence. The people have a peaceful and rural nature, the democracy is healthy, and the president speaks out against corruption. Praise God for the peace that allows Christian ministry and national development to continue. The country still faces complex challenges of poverty combined with high population growth, AIDS, unemployment, and migration of many people into and through Malawi. Most leaders in Malawi are church members. Pray God would help them act with wisdom, humility, and long-term plans based on biblical principles. Pray that churches might be better equipped to face AIDS with helpful ministries.

2. **A wide variety of ministry** leads to steady evangelical growth! Christians enjoy freedom for outreach, youth ministry, house meetings, prayer movements, and more. The gospel impacts nearly every section of society. Pray for Bible translation and availability. The refugee community and rural Christians need and want Scripture, but poverty limits their access. Many Christians read well and seek quality Christian literature, but cannot afford books.

3. **The Church must address training for pastors and workers.** 17 Protestant and 4 Roman Catholic seminaries and Bible schools offer formal education. The traditional model of theological education cannot produce leaders fast enough for a growing Church. Pray for new models of training that work for poor pastors and those who cannot leave homes and families for study.

4 **Islam grows in Malawi.** The Africa Muslim Agency provides funds for primary education, scholarships for tertiary students to study in Muslim nations, aid, mosque building, and other means to promote Islam. Pray for a persistent witness of love to Muslims throughout Malawi. The Yawo people (80% Muslim) present the greatest mission challenge in Malawi. Mission agencies partner in outreach, but few people have come to Christ. Pray as the small Yawo Church comes to life!

Mali

Africa

Pop 13.3 million. **Capital** Bamako (1.7 mill).
Christians 352,000. *Evangelical Christians* 93,600.
Largest Religion Muslim.
Fastest Growing Religion Muslim.
Largest Ethnic Groups Sub-Saharan African peoples (89.4%, 55 groups including Malinke-Bambara, Gur, Soninke, Malinke, Fulbe, Songhai, others), Arab/Berber (10.5%, Tuareg and Arab, including Moor).
Official Language French. Bambara, Fulbe, Songhai are trade languages. **All Languages** 60.
Economy One of the world's poorest nations. 80% live by subsistence farming and fishing. One of Africa's major

cotton producers, but all farmers face difficulties due to drought, locust plagues, and growth of desert lands.
Politics The modern successor to the great Malian empire (AD 1230-1400). Independent from France in 1960. Multiparty democracy since 1991, when protests ended the military dictatorship. Tuareg unrest in the northeast over land and cultural rights regularly causes violence. Moors (north) and *Al-Qaeda*-linked groups add to the troubles. A transshipment point for drugs from South America to Europe.

---

1 **Mali experienced great upheaval in 2012-2013.** First, a military coup attempt in the south created instability. Then other rebels took control of the north. These rebels, a mix of Tuareg separatists and Muslim extremists, tried to impose strict Islamic law. Cruel acts were committed, and some Christians were targeted for death. Up to 500,000 people fled to the south or to other countries, including most Christians in the region. French military intervention, followed by a UN presence, stopped the rebels. Elections and a new government in 2013 brought stability and a new peace process. But long-term peace in Mali seems difficult because of the deep divides between north and south.

2 **Mali must overcome huge challenges** of high child mortality rates, malnutrition, and desertification. Around 20% of children will not survive to the age of five. Out of those who do survive, 1 in 3 will be malnourished. 67% of the land area is desert or semi-desert, and the desert continues to spread. Pray that Mali's leaders will have wisdom, and will know how to provide health, education, and employment to their people. The country needs long-term stability and foreign investment. Many Christian ministry opportunities exist.

3 **Mali is spiritually open, and the Church has begun to take root** in some of Mali's people groups. A second generation of Christians emerged. But Christianity grows at a slower rate than the overall national population grows. Many who make decisions for Christ eventually return to their former religion. Praise God that nearly 700 evangelical congregations now exist. A wave of evangelism moved through Mali in the 1980s. Most congregations today do not reach out or evangelize. Pray for a new wave to come!

4 **Mali remains mostly unreached.** Two-thirds of the population are unevangelized. Most of the 60 indigenous ethnic groups can be considered unreached, and only 5 of them have an evangelical population larger than 1%. Pray also for the many smaller, neglected groups with no or few known believers. Most Malians practice a tolerant brand of Islam unique to West Africa. Pray for a clear breakthrough among all peoples!

Mauritania

Africa

Pop 3.4 million. **Capital** Nouakchott (729,000).
Christians 8,400. *Evangelical Christians* 2,100.
Largest Religion Muslim.
Fastest Growing Religion Muslim.

Largest Ethnic Groups Hassaniya-speaking Arab (70%, 40% are Black Moor and 30% White Moor, who dominate in power), Sub-Saharan African (28.8%).
Official Language Arabic (Hassaniya dialect used by two-thirds of the population). French is language of government and commerce. **All Languages** 8.

Economy One of world's poorest countries. Based on subsistence farming and animal herding. Drought in the 1970s and 1980s devastated the country. Main exports are fish, iron ore, and some offshore oil production. Corruption affects the economy at all levels.

Politics An Islamic republic. Independent from France in 1960, then a series of military coups. Multiparty democracy in 1992, series of coups and elected governments. White Moors dominate the government, and ethnic/tribal tensions remain over past conflict and seizure of Black African lands and livestock.

---

1 **Mauritania must overcome huge economic and social challenges.** One-third of children lack enough food to eat, and widespread divorce leads to many social problems. Only about 1% of land can be farmed, and even that decreases as farmland becomes desert. New discoveries of oil could bring wealth, but could also increase corruption and further divide rich and poor. Slavery is illegal, but thousands most likely still live as slaves. Pray for freedom and justice for all those oppressed.

2 **All Mauritanian peoples remain basically unreached,** as Islam has dominated Mauritania for 1,000 years. Few people know a Christian or receive Christian media. Pray for greater spiritual openness and hunger for God. Pray that any who follow Jesus might be courageous in the faith. Believers in Mauritania face prison, beatings, or rejection by their family or tribe. Pray especially for unreached minorities:

- *The Haratine or Black Moors,* who used to be the slave class of Moorish society.
- *The African peoples of the Senegal River Valley.* Some suffered much persecution, but many who were exiled now return to their homeland. They have some openness to the gospel.
- *The nomads of the desert* descended from Berber and Arab Bedouin tribes. Their nomadic lifestyle isolates them from the gospel even more than others.
- *Mauritanians in other lands,* such as France, Spain, the USA, and other West African countries. Some Christians work among them in Senegal.

3 **Few expatriates live in Mauritania.** Most are migrants from West African countries who work jobs with lower pay, though some work as professionals. Others work in diplomatic services, development, and business. Foreigners suspected of converting Mauritanians to Christianity can face harassment, imprisonment, expulsion, and even attempted murder. Islamic terrorists increased extremist activities recently (including murder of a foreign Christian in 2009), which led many expatriate believers to leave the country. World Vision, Caritas, and others work in development, with human rights and justice issues, and in environmental protection. Pray that the lives of Christians might clearly demonstrate the love of Jesus. Pray also that the Lord might give them wisdom, protection, and make them powerful witnesses for His name!

Morocco (including Western Sahara) *Africa*

Pop 32.8 million (400,000 estimated in Western Sahara).
Capital Rabat (1.8 mill in Rabat/Salé).
Christians 29,000. *Evangelical Christians* 4,800.
Largest Religion Muslim.
Fastest Growing Religion Muslim.

Largest Ethnic Groups Arab (57.7%), Berber (41.4%).
Official Language Arabic. Berber used in many homes. French widely used. **All Languages** 10.

Economy Tourism, agriculture, textiles, and phosphate mining bring income. Morocco and Western Sahara have 70% of world's phosphate reserves. Large gap between the few rich and the large number of poor. Many seek work abroad.

Politics Independent since 1956 from French and Spanish rule. Limited democracy under a ruling monarch. Increased democratic freedoms introduced as a result of the Arab Spring uprisings elsewhere. Morocco has occupied Western Sahara since 1975, but the Polisario Front (representing Saharawis) fights for independence.

---

1 **Arab armies invaded in the 7th century,** introduced Islam, and erased a strong North African Berber Church. Moroccans feel proud of their country's heritage as a centre of Islamic civilization and learning, and they resist Christianity. Only a small percentage have heard the gospel. Moroccan Muslim groups disagree sharply between fundamentalist and moderate practices, but most citizens do not want religious violence to come. Pray for peace throughout the nation, and pray that those who seek violent solutions will not succeed.

2 **Moroccans became aware of the indigenous Church** when the media broadcasted negative and inaccurate reports about a large number of converts to Christianity. There may be about 2,000 Moroccan Christians, with 20 to 30 small house fellowships. New believers feel pressure from family, police, or religious authorities. Pray that believers might grow amid such persecution, as with the early Church, through faith, witness, mutual support, and encouragement!

3 **Discipleship of believers** is difficult in a context of persecution, isolation, and fear. Pray for believers to study the Word of God every day. Arabic and Berber Bibles are difficult to import, but both can be found on the Internet. Satellite TV, Christian radio, and the Internet reach many with the gospel, provide training opportunities for leaders, and connect scattered believers with one another. Believers often struggle to find jobs, education, and spouses. Pray for Christian families, who provide a base for strong house churches. Pray for God-given, Spirit-gifted leadership for every group of believers.

4 Specific unreached minority peoples:

- *The Berber peoples* were Christian until Islam came. Most Berbers practise a form of Islam mixed with folk magic (especially in rural areas), but are devout followers. Each of the 3 major Berber groups has a few believers. Rapid and loving Christian response to a 2004 earthquake created openness to the gospel.

- *The Maghreb Jews* once numbered more than 250,000. Most emigrated to Israel in 1948, and a few thousand remain in Morocco. No outreach to them exists at this time.

- *The nomadic desert tribes* of the south and east have little contact with the gospel.

- *Rural Moroccan Arabs* form part of the majority people group, but are particularly isolated from the gospel. Few ministries even try to reach them.

5 The government forbids missionary work, and recently expelled over 100 expatriate Christian workers on short notice. Still, some holistic ministries remain open to foreign Christian involvement such as work with the disabled. Sub-Saharan Africans and Asians come to Morocco for entry to Europe. They face abuse by traffickers, and harsh treatment by the government. Many are Christian and formed their own fellowships. Others come to faith through the ministry of Christians in Morocco. Pray for their positive witness to Muslims!

Western Sahara   *Africa*

1 Morocco invaded Western Sahara in 1975, and has occupied the territory ever since. A strong and persistent local movement (Polisario) fights for independence for the Saharawi people. Pray for justice, a fair solution, and for Saharawi refugees to be able to come home. The Moroccans and Saharawi have only a few Christians, but God has begun to break down the hostility between those who are on different sides politically. Pray for the Church to model the reconciliation of Christ. Opportunity exists for ministry to refugees through relief and development. Pray for more to serve among them.

Mozambique   *Africa*

Pop 23.4 million. **Capital** Maputo (1.7 mill).
Christians 10.9 mill. *Evangelical Christians* 2.6 mill.
Largest Religion Christian.
Fastest Growing Religions Christian and Muslim.
Largest Ethnic Groups Northern Bantu peoples (63%), Southern Bantu peoples (19.1%), Central Bantu peoples (15.5%), Portuguese Mestizo (1.6%).
Official Language Portuguese (less than 30% understand it).
All Languages 53.

Economy One of the world's poorest countries. Marxist economic theories, 30 years of guerrilla warfare, and colonial exploitation led to economic demise. Floods and droughts harm subsistence farming (80% of people farm). Dependent on foreign aid and crippled by foreign debt. Some improvement since 1995.

Politics Portuguese colony for 470 years. Independent in 1975 after long war for independence. Marxist-Leninist state until 1988, followed by years of intense warfare, which ended with a peace accord in the mid-1990s. Multiparty democracy and market economy since 1990.

1 **Praise God for peace** since 1992, after 30 years of war. The government now works to advance democracy, and economic and religious freedom. Years of suffering led to spiritual responsiveness. After harsh persecution under the Marxist-oriented regime, Christian faith spread rapidly. Mozambique was highly unevangelized, but now many people from all faiths and regions have begun to follow Christ!

2 **Mozambique's brokenness continues.** Pray for effective, practical programmes to assist those who live in the most severe poverty. AIDS is a major challenge, with 16% of the adult population HIV-positive. Malaria is even worse, with over 5 million cases a year. Diseases like diarrhoea and tuberculosis make the situation worse. Additionally, the trauma of violence and extreme poverty left many people emotionally or psychologically broken. Turn these challenges into prayers.

3 **Up to 80% of pastors/church leaders have little or no formal training.** Pray for more leaders who are godly and know the Bible. Most of the population learn orally. Pray for projects that build their biblical knowledge. Natural disasters in the 2000s stimulated Christian aid, and indigenous churches emerged inside refugee camps. Now pray for growth in maturity and truth, alongside cultural authenticity.

4 **Mozambique has a greater concentration of unreached peoples** than anywhere else in southern Africa. Pray for:

- *The Makhuwa.* Most mix Catholic faith with animism (in the interior), or follow Islam (along the coast), or even mix all three! These northern peoples represent nearly 40% of Mozambique's population. Preaching, aid, and miracles have brought many into the Kingdom! Pray for discipleship of new believers and churches.

- *The Yawo* of Niassa Province, along the shores of Lake Malawi, who are 96% Muslim. Only about 2% are Christian of any kind.

- *Northern/coastal Muslim peoples.* Swahili traders Islamized the area centuries ago. Few believers exist among the Mwani. The devout Koti saw a recent breakthrough, with perhaps up to 20 churches and 1,200 believers! The Ngoni expelled all priests after independence, and have no exposure to the gospel since then. (The few believers left due to social pressure.) The Makwe live in the extreme north, and are a forgotten people in a remote place.

5 **Mozambique needs expatriate missionaries,** especially for work among the unevangelized. Pray for missionaries who face disease, a hot and humid climate, difficult travel, and active spiritual powers. Workers must be willing to suffer as the national Church has done for decades. Foreigners must also learn to serve and truly partner with the national Church. Workers can serve well in leadership training, aid/relief, medical programmes, business development, children's work, and more. Bible translators work on at least 17 language projects.

Namibia

Pop 2.2 million. **Capital** Windhoek (354,000).
Christians 2 mill. *Evangelical Christians* 270,000.
Largest Religion Christian.
Fastest Growing Religion Ethnic religions.

Largest Ethnic Groups Ovambo (43%), Afrikaans-speaking Coloured (mixed race) (9%), Khoisan (8.9%), Kwangali (7.9%), Herero (7.6%), Afrikaner (7.3%).

Official Language English (few speak it, as most speak Afrikaans). **All Languages** 37.

Economy Mining for diamonds, uranium, and other minerals provide significant income. Cattle ranching, fishing, and tourism also important. Many still live in deep poverty.

Politics A former German colony (1883-1915). Then ruled by South Africa (1915-1990). Independent after a long war that severely disrupted the economy and society. Multiparty democracy brought some stability. Member of British Commonwealth.

---

1 **Stability and economic progress followed independence** in the 1990s, and Christians united in prayer at that time. But the country could fall into ethnic conflict and economic collapse if good government and community harmony do not prevail. Pray that the nation's leaders would address the gap between rich and poor, land ownership issues, and HIV/AIDS with wisdom and determination. People migrate to cities for work, but end up in shantytowns. Ovamboland (in the north) suffers the most poverty. Namibia suffers scars from its colonial past, from the legacy of apartheid, and from the terrorism before independence. Pray that in Christ both perpetrators and victims might find forgiveness and peace.

2 **Namibia has experienced several historical movements to Christ.** Lutheran and then Anglican missionaries gave birth to large denominations in the 19th century. Liberal theology and practices mixed with African spiritism confused many Christians, and weakened their faith. Charismatic fellowships brought new life, particularly to unreached areas and peoples. Pray for biblical faith to return to Namibia's many churches. Pray for all to hear the gospel again, and for many to turn back to Christ.

3 **The less-evangelized peoples.** Pray for:

• **The San** (Bushmen). Cattle ranching and mining threaten their traditional semi-nomadic way of life. The sinful habits that can come with a settled life bring many down. Some churches work among the San peoples, but with little spiritual response. Pray for outreach specific to their nomadic lifestyle and strong animistic faith.

• **The peoples of the Kavango and Caprivi Strip** in the northeast. Many are animists. Several churches and missions work among them.

• **The Himba (5,000) and Dhimba (15,000),** who live in the northeast and in southwest Angola. Most practise animism, though a few are Lutheran and Reformed Christians. Workers have nearly finished the Bible in Dhimba, and also Scripture songs in traditional Dhimba forms.

Niger

Pop 15.9 million. **Capital** Niamey (1 mill).
Christians 52,000. *Evangelical Christians* 22,000.
Largest Religion Muslim.
Fastest Growing Religion Muslim.

Largest Ethnic Groups Hausa (43.2%), Songhai (29.3%), Fulbe/Fulani (10.4%), Tuareg/Tamacheq (9%), Kanuri-Saharan (4.8%), Other Sub-Saharan African (1.7%), Arab (1.4%).
Official Language French. Hausa used widely. **All Languages** 21.

Economy One of world's poorest nations. Most barely survive on subsistence agriculture and livestock. Droughts and locust plagues cause further problems. Uranium deposits could bring future income. Dependent on aid and IMF loans.

Politics Centuries of Tuareg domination in the Sahel, followed by French colonial rule (1921-1960). Since then a series of military coups and periods of democratic rule. Intermittent Tuareg insurgency.

---

 1 **This Muslim land and its people are open for the gospel.** Many previously unreached people groups now have their first believers, and pastors (converts from Islam themselves) lead most congregations! Still, Islam dominates the land, and strict, aggressive Muslim groups increase. Pray that Niger may remain open for Christian mission, and that the Lord would remove every barrier to the knowledge of Him. The spiritual effects of folk Islam and demonic oppression hinder many from following Christ.

2 **Christianity grows,** but people come into the Kingdom by a trickle. Pray for the trickle to become a flood! Pressure to stay in Islam, or return to it, prevents many from following Christ. New believers feel isolated. Pray for groups to form, even if small, for those who need fellowship with other believers.

3 **All parts of the country still need missionaries.** Niger is one of the world's least-developed countries. Christian missionaries have ministered in love here (through aid, development, health, education), and won respect for the gospel. Pray for more labourers. Medical ministry and mission hospitals provide for critical needs. CAPRO reaches out to the many prostitutes in the capital, but they need more workers and funds. The government cannot afford to educate all children, so many (especially girls) receive no schooling. Various agencies run schools that offer education and opportunity to demonstrate the love of Christ. Pray for more Christians to embrace this opportunity to serve Niger!

4 **Least-reached peoples:**
- *The Tuareg/Tamacheq* once held riches, but now live in poverty due to drought, famine, and political changes. Selfless, holistic ministry led to several groups of believers among them!
- *The Zarma* follow Islam, but also maintain many of their traditional practices. Only a few hundred among them follow Christ.
- *The 5 Kanuri peoples* have a 1,000-year-long history of Islam. Some consider them resistant to the gospel, but they are receptive to sensitive witness. Pray for whole families and villages to follow Christ.
- *The Songhai* have very few Christians among them. Some missions serve them, but the work is difficult because this strongly Muslim people regard converts as traitors.

Nigeria
Africa

Pop 158.3 million. **Capital** Abuja (2 mill).
Christians 81.1 mill. *Evangelical Christians* 48.8 mill.
Largest Religion Christian.
Fastest Growing Religion Christian, Muslim.

Largest Ethnic Groups Over 520 ethnic groups. Yoruba (22.8%), Benue (17.8%), Hausa (16%), Igbo (14.9%), Fulani (10.4%), Chadic (4.5%), Kanuri (4%), Guinean (2.5%), Nupe (2%), Ijaw (1.8%), Adamawa-Ubangi (1.2%), Other Sub-Saharan African (1.7%).
Official Language English. Hausa, Yoruba, Igbo each used widely in their regions. **All Languages** 521.

Economy Very rich in natural resources, especially oil and gas. Massive levels of corruption made a small minority very rich. Most still live in poverty.
Politics Independent from Britain (as a Federation) in 1960. A multiparty democracy after years of military regimes. Rivalry among the Hausa/Fulani, Yoruba, and Igbo dominates Nigerian politics. Vast differences between the mostly Muslim north and the mostly Christian south. Tension and violence threaten to break apart the nation.

The 3 main regions of Nigeria came about as a result of colonial policy. The British kept the Hausa-Fulani Muslim rulers of the north, and allowed them to extend their rule over the peoples of the middle region. The south developed a more Western system of government. From 1967 to 1995 the states increased from 12 to 36, plus a Federal Capital Territory. 8 states appear to be primarily Muslim, 18 are primarily Christian, and 10 appear split around 50% each. Those who actually practise African traditional religions may be as high as 10% of the population, but these practices and beliefs also mix deeply with both Islam and Christianity.

CHALLENGES FOR NIGERIA

1 **Nigeria continues as one country,** which seems miraculous. This complex country has many layers. The nation always seems close to breaking apart politically. Deep divides exist between the north and south, but also among the 37 states/territory. Tension causes troubles between the 3 dominant peoples (Hausa, Yoruba, Igbo), but also among the hundreds of other ethnic groups. Since independence, Nigeria's rulers were mostly corrupt military leaders. Corruption in the election process creates a huge challenge for civilian governments. Pray for wise, just, and fair leaders who will help the country find a way through these very serious challenges. They will shape the future of the country.

2 **Nigeria has a global reputation as one of the world's most corrupt countries.** Bribery and fraud create problems at almost every level of society, and it is famous for email scams, international crime, and drug running. Not even a strong Christian or Muslim presence seems to stop it. It happens in politics, in banking, in the military, and even in religious groups! Multi-national corporations cooperate with corrupt Nigerians to divert much of Nigeria's rightful wealth into their own bank accounts. This cripples economic progress, damages society, and ruins lives. Many think that only violent or radical reactions will bring change. Pray that corruption will be removed at its root in Nigeria. Pray for God to raise up many who fear Him, and who have the courage to fight this evil.

3 **A deep religious divide separates Christians and Muslims,** and results in great harm. But the growth of Muslim extremist groups in the north of the country brings an even greater danger. *Boko Haram* and other like-minded groups commit acts of terrorism against Christians, against the federal government, and even against moderate Muslims. They use car bombs, suicide bombs, and assassinations. Their goal is to impose *shari'a* (Islamic law) on all citizens. Shari'a is already established in several northern states.

④ The fault line between Africa's Muslim world and Christian world runs across the centre of Nigeria. This line includes the capital region of Abuja and Plateau State. Jos is the main city of this state and is also an important city for Christian mission and ministry. Pray that wicked strategies to destroy the Church and to overthrow the democratic government would be defeated. Pray that the government would know how to defeat these plans. The evil one seeks to kill, steal from, and destroy both Christians and Muslims.

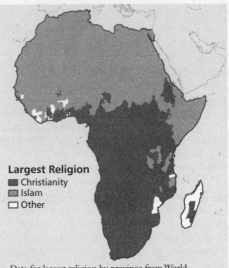

Largest Religion
- ■ Christianity
- ▦ Islam
- ☐ Other

Data for largest religion by province from World Religion Database. Published by Brill. Retrieved from www.worldreligiondatabase.org, 2014. USA.

THE CHURCH IN NIGERIA

① Church growth has been massive and remains so. A large majority of West Africa's evangelicals live in Nigeria. Catholics, Anglicans, traditional Protestant groups, and newer Pentecostal and charismatic groups all grow. Much growth comes from among Muslims and those who follow tribal religions. This growth often happened quietly, in less obvious ways. Praise God for the millions who have come to know Him in Nigeria!

② Africa and Nigeria's greatest spiritual challenge is discipleship, not Islam, not corruption, and not even the need for missions. The Church grew so fast that many new believers have little chance to be discipled. Much division and false teaching enters into churches. Prosperity teaching distorts the gospel. A form of Christianity mixed with African tribal religious practices is common. The Church needs a balanced and biblical approach to spiritual warfare, to healing and miracles, and to outreach towards other religions. Many Christians seem to live by other values than what the Bible clearly teaches. Pray that humility, simplicity, and holiness might become the motto of the Nigerian Church.

③ Persecution of Christians continues to increase, especially in the north. Some extremist Muslim groups have killed thousands of people, and have destroyed hundreds or even thousands of churches. Persecution unites Christians and drives them to the Lord in prayer, but it also threatens the very core of Nigerian society and statehood. Pray for restoration and recovery for those who suffer from loss, or from rape. Pray for forgiveness, and for deliverance from a spirit of revenge. Pray for believers to respond in the most Christ-like way possible. Finally, pray that the enemies of Christ who commit these terrible acts would become His followers!

④ A number of Christian movements impact the whole nation. Nigeria's prayer movement is one of the world's strongest. Some of the largest prayer meetings in Church history happened in Nigeria (meetings can gather over 1 million people at a time!). Many believe that positive political developments and church growth came about through focused prayer. Student movements like Scripture Union/Fellowship of Christian Students and Nigeria Fellowship of Evangelical Students win many to Christ. Student and prayer ministries both have great strategic importance to Nigeria's future.

5 The missions movement from Nigeria is Africa's largest and most dynamic. Nigeria sends over 5,000 missionaries through 115 denominational or independent agencies. About half serve in foreign countries, with many in West Africa. Vision 50:15 sets a goal to mobilize 50,000 Nigerians for missions in the next 15 years. Nigeria continues to increase its missionary training, and now has 50 such institutions in the country. Nigerians contribute much good missions research on the unreached. Pray for more churches to support Nigerian missionaries.

The Unfinished Task in Nigeria

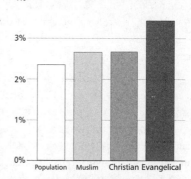

Annual Growth Rates

1 Pray for the many unreached groups in Nigeria. Churches have adopted 168 least-reached people groups for prayer and outreach, but a number of them remain unengaged by Christians. Pray for urgent but loving outreach to all those who need to hear the good news.

- *Muslims.* Islam has many expressions in Nigeria (Sunni, Shi'ite, Sufi, and militant), and all Muslims need effective outreach. Christians find some Muslims more open to the gospel because of the violence of Muslim extremists. Thousands have come to Jesus. Many of these converts face death threats, prejudice, and rejection from families and communities, and often need help with employment and shelter. Muslim suburbs in southern towns and cities need prayer and outreach.

- *The millions who still practise African traditional religions.* Numerous unreached groups practise animism (spirit worship). Christians usually find these groups open to the gospel, but Muslims often reach them before Christians do. The violence of radical Muslim groups hinders outreach to the peoples in the north of Nigeria. Pray for the Church to send out workers who can be well-prepared and effective in such a hostile, dangerous environment.

2 Media plays a greater role than ever in communication of Bible teaching, worship music and styles, and more. Nigeria has the third most Bible translation needs of any country, and one of the world's highest radio-listening populations. This oral, musical culture needs Christian radio and audio recordings. "Nollywood" is Nigeria's TV and film industry. Pray that Christians who work in this industry can help it become more God-honouring.

Rwanda

Africa

Pop 10.3 million. **Capital** Kigali (939,000).
Christians 9.2 mill. *Evangelical Christians* 2.8 mill.
Largest Religion Christian.
Fastest Growing Religion Muslim.

Largest Ethnic Groups Bantu (97.7%, 6 peoples including those formerly regarded as Hutu and Tutsi), Twa (2.3%, Pygmy).
Official Languages French, English, Kinyarwanda. **All Languages** 5.

Economy Coffee, tea, and aid are the main income sources. Most people survive as subsistence farmers on small parcels of fertile land. High unemployment, and crime in urban areas.

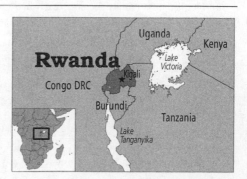

Politics A feudal Tutsi monarchy continued under German occupation (1899-1916) and Belgian Mandate (1916-1962). A long history of conflict between Tutsi and Hutu peoples culminated in the genocide of 1994. Since 2000, the government seeks to remove ethnicity from politics and society to make the country safe, and to rebuild. A member of the British Commonwealth.

1 **Rwanda made great progress** since the tragic events of 1994, when Hutu extremists seized power and began the genocide of the Tutsi minority and Hutu moderates. 800,000 perished in 100 days. Over 1 million fled, and more violence followed. Political stability since 2000 allows Rwandans a chance to rebuild. Rwanda's economy is now one of the fastest growing in Africa. Females make up over half the elected parliament, the world's highest rate. The government banned ethnic identification (Hutu, Tutsi, others). People are called Rwandans, and only Rwandans. Give praise for the people's commitment to reconcile and build peace. Praise God that churches help lead this movement.

2 **Recovery from the 1994 genocide** is difficult, but it displays people's willingness to forgive and move forward despite great pain and loss. Pray for healing. Deep wounds remain, and superficial words or actions cannot fix them. The normal judicial system could not cope with so many cases, so the government created *gacaca* (community-based courts) to try lesser offenders. Some succeeded. Others handled cases badly. Pray that the Lord might bring justice, and heal the wounds of those who did not receive fair treatment. Children and young people of the 1990s now form the young adults and future leaders of Rwanda. They carry a painful legacy and difficult burdens no young people should bear.

3 **The events of the 1990s reshaped the religious scene of Rwanda.** A country where 80% call themselves Christian, yet allowed and committed such evils, might be "Christianized" but clearly not converted. Many righteous Catholics, including priests and nuns, laid down their lives to protect others. But others stood by or even aided the perpetrators. Pray for renewal to transform the Catholic Church. Evangelicals grew rapidly in the aftermath due to evangelism, aid, ministry to the hurting, and their message of hope for all people. The East African Revival (1930s) began in Rwanda. Pray for another revival to come!

4 **Ministry challenges** need intercession. Thousands of spiritual leaders died or fled. Who will replace them? Pastors that remain struggle to cope with the desperate physical, social, psychological, and spiritual damage done. Pray for God to raise up godly men and women to serve in Rwanda's time of need!

- *Many women are at risk.* The genocide created many widows. Others live with husbands in prison. Rape victims number between 100,000 and 250,000, and many are psychologically traumatized and looked down on by society. Nearly half the rape victims contracted HIV. Females have fewer opportunities for education and work, and some fell into prostitution or were forced into it.

- *Orphans* from genocide, war, and AIDS may number up to 900,000. This is one-third of all Rwandan children. Their pain is deep, and the Church must learn how best to help them. 74% of orphans say they have no friends, and 40% feel life has no meaning. Pray for freedom in Christ and a new identity.

- *The Pygmy Twa* live in basic conditions in rural areas. Deforestation and unjust land eviction threatened the traditional jungle way of life for this small group. The Twa have fewer believers among them than other groups. Pray for Rwandan churches and expat missions to care for this vulnerable people in a humble and loving way.

Senegal  *Africa*

Pop 12.9 million. **Capital** Dakar (2.9 mill).
Christians 826,000. *Evangelical Christians* 26,000.
Largest Religion Muslim.
Fastest Growing Religion Christian.

Largest Ethnic Groups Over 56 ethnic groups. West-Atlantic (57.5%, including Wolof, Jola, Atlantic), Fulbe, also Fulani, Pulaar (24.9%), Malinke (9.8%), Other African (4.6%), Arab-Berber (1.8%).
Official Language French. Wolof spoken as first language by around 40% of population. **All Languages** 46.

Economy Based largely on subsistence agriculture. Main exports are peanuts and phosphates. Poverty and high unemployment lead many to attempt illegal migration to Europe. Remittances sent home and foreign aid bolster economy.
Politics Independent from France in 1960. A multiparty democracy with peaceful transfer of power to the opposition in 2000. Separatist conflict in the southwest Casamance province caused distress and disruption until parties signed peace accords in 2004.

---

1 **Senegal appears both open and closed spiritually.** The nation enjoys religious freedom and tolerates many faiths, and Senegalese feel proud about this. But few of the Muslim majority have ever come to Christ. The Muslim Sufi brotherhoods are organized, wealthy, and have political power. Over 85% of all Muslims belong to one of them. Even after long-standing Christian presence and outreach, a spiritual heaviness covers the land. Pray for the spiritual breakthrough that many wait for!

2 **The Casamance region** in the south endured years of troubles from groups who seek independence. Geography separates the Casamance from most of Senegal (The Gambia divides the country), but ethnic and religious differences also exist. Pray for long-term peace. Pray for sustained Christian ministry, as sporadic violence often disrupts the work.

3 **The largest Christian communities** exist among the Serer, Jola, Bassari, and Cape Verdean peoples. Most come from a non-Muslim background, belong to the Catholic Church, and do not practise their faith. Catholics have great influence through their good work in health and education. But Muslims often know Christians as "those who drink", not as "those who follow Christ". Few evangelical believers exist. Pray that the Church will hold on to its identity in Christ, and powerfully demonstrate Christ to the nation. Praise God that a variety of Christian training options serve both church leaders and members.

4 **Over 55% of Senegal's population are under age 20.** The younger generation has less commitment to formal religion, so they may be more open to the gospel. Pray that the God of the Bible will be the source of hope for young people with so much potential! Pray especially for more work among the usually poor *Talibés* ("tin-can boys"). Their families send them away to study the Qur'an with *marabouts* (teachers, who send the boys to beg for money and food on the streets). Pray also for God to raise up more ministry to the 30,000 street children in Dakar, and the 400,000 children considered at risk throughout the nation.

Unreached peoples:

- *Wolof,* who remain strongly Muslim. Only around 100 believers and a few new congregations exist, but change has begun. Christian resources (the New Testament, audio Scripture, Wolof worship music) give more opportunities than before to meet Jesus.
- *Fulbe.* Many live as nomads, and this requires creativity for church planters. The tiny number of believers slowly increases through the work of various groups.
- *Jola.* Out of 13 major dialects and languages, only 5 have any Scripture. Devotion to magical charms binds most people. 15 Jola-led congregations exist.
- *Maures,* who all follow Islam. The majority live in Mauritania, which is closed to the gospel, but many Maures could be reached in the Senegal River Valley.
- *Malinke peoples* (mostly in the south). Almost all practise Islam mixed with traditional folk religions.

6 **Thousands of emigrants** attempt dangerous, illegal sea voyages to the Canary Islands every year in search of work and a new life in Europe. Officials force some to return, and others die at sea. Those who make it face a hard and lonely life. Pray for compassionate ministry to Senegalese in Spain, and that they will be open to the gospel in their new situation.

Sierra Leone

Africa

Pop 5.8 million. **Capital** Freetown (901,000).
Christians 769,000. *Evangelical Christians* 229,000.
Largest Religion Muslim.
Fastest Growing Religion Muslim.

Largest Ethnic Groups Atlantic (38.4%), Mande (32.1%), Krio/Creole (11.4%), Malinke (8.3%), Fulbe (4.8%), Susu (3.2%).
Official Language English. 10% of population speak Krio (Creole) as a 1st language, and 90% as 2nd language. **All Languages** 26.

Economy Rich in natural resources (diamonds, gold, titanium, iron ore, cocoa, coffee, fish, other). Conflict and the failed political state resulted in economic collapse, and made it perhaps the most desperate country on earth! Order resumed from 2002, but much outside aid required to survive. Could prosper if it can overcome corruption and rebuild infrastructure. Widespread poverty and high unemployment (up to 80%).

Politics Founded as a home for freed slaves (1787). Violence from the nearby Liberian civil war (1990) spilled over and led to governmental collapse. Followed by years of military coups and guerrilla wars over control of diamond fields in the southeast, ending with a failed state. Intervention by the British military defeated the rebel forces. Democracy restored in 2002 with successful and peaceful elections.

---

1 **The nation now moves forward,** away from its tragic recent history. Thank God for the end of 11 years of chaos that claimed up to 100,000 lives, crippled many thousands, and harmed most of the population in some way. The Truth and Reconciliation Commission helps former fighters return to their communities and start again. Christian agencies work to rebuild the country and minister to spiritual, physical, and psychological needs.

2 **Sierra Leone has ranked as the world's poorest country** for most of the last 10 years. It has the highest infant and mother mortality rates, and widespread disease (malaria, HIV, others).

Life expectancy stays around age 47. Most people long for safety, stability, food, work, and for honesty from leaders. Corruption threatens to overturn the newfound peace. Pray for God to fulfil these longings, and for no further violence to come.

3 **Secret societies and their occult influence** shape the country deeply. Spiritual evils led to the greed and cruelty of the darkest times, and continue to influence society today. Many Christians compromised their spiritual purity, and the Church lost its power. Pray for God to bind these dark powers, and to break the influence of secret societies. Pray that Christians will live lives of faith, and will depend on Jesus alone for provision, protection, and power.

4 **Churches must be places of compassion, healing, and forgiveness** for the orphans, former child soldiers or slaves, the victims of rape and amputation, those who suffer mental trauma, and also for those who committed these deeds. Many congregations, buildings, organizations, and especially relationships must be rebuilt. The first Protestant Church in West Africa started in Freetown in 1785 among freed slaves. Yet after over 200 years of effort, only 13% of the country claim to be Christian. In addition to Bible training, pastors must prepare for counselling, spiritual warfare, and ministry to the poor and disabled. Sierra

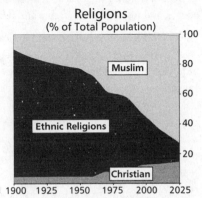

Religions
(% of Total Population)

Leone needs many more workers for holistic ministry, leadership training, and Bible translation.

5 **Pray for the least reached.** The more animistic people groups (Bom, Kuranko, Loko, others) come to Christ more quickly, but some also turn to Islam. Islam grew from 10% to 60% of the population in the 20th century, in part through the UN peacekeeping forces. Troops from South Asia built mosques wherever they were stationed. Pray that Christian witness to Muslim peoples (Fula Jalon, Krio Fulani, Mandingo, Susu, others) will be clear and bold, and also sensitive and humble. Most Christian outreach goes to animists, even though Muslims also respond to the good news.

Somalia

Africa

Pop 9.4 million. **Capital** Mogadishu (1.5 mill), Somaliland: Hargeisa (324,000), Puntland: Garoowe. [Figures are estimates, as no reliable source for population data exists.]
Christians 31,000. *Evangelical Christians* 4,300.
Largest Religion Muslim.
Fastest Growing Religion Muslim.

Largest Ethnic Groups Northern Somali (74.4%, with 4 major clan families), Southern Somali (20.4%, of 1 major clan).
Official Languages Somali, Arabic (though few speak it).
All Languages 15.

Economy Two-thirds of Somalis herd livestock, but face

problems of overgrazing and land becoming a desert. Some agriculture in south and northwest. The already weak economy was devastated by the ruin of civil wars. Most of the population depend on aid and remittances from relatives abroad.

Politics United as a single country in 1960 after independence from Britain (north) and Italy (south). War with Ethiopia and conflicts between warlords brought down the country. No viable government from 1991 until 2012. Somaliland (northwest) declared independence in 1991, but remains unrecognized. Puntland (northeast) set up its own government in 1998. Parliament and elected president installed in 2012.

1 **Africa's most failed state** may finally experience some stability. Somalia now has a parliament and recognized national leaders after 20 years without an effective central government. The militant Islamist group *Al-Shabab* (linked to *Al-Qaeda*) no longer controls the south, and the chaos appears less now. Pray that Somalia's rulers might learn from the past, govern for the good of the people, and respect human rights and religious freedom.

2 **The economic, social, and physical health** of the nation is in a terrible state after years of war and neglect. Around 500,000 people died from famines (1992, 2010-2012), and as many more from violence. Decades of chaos provided a cover for smugglers, bandits, pirates, and terrorists. The dangerous environment and strict enforcement of Islam prevent most aid work. Pray for protection and effective ministry for aid workers, many of whom are Christian. Most Somali women suffer female genital mutilation. Many endure rape, then divorce and abandonment by their husbands. Traffickers smuggle children out of Somalia and exploit or abandon them. Somalia has the lowest health budget of any nation and the highest infant mortality rate. Ask God to show His mercy to the peoples of Somalia.

3 **Somaliland and Puntland.** These 2 safer and more stable regions could help restore the south. Almost no Christians live in these northern regions. Pray that the peace in the north may move southward, and that peace will create open doors for the gospel!

4 **Praise God for the Somali Church** that grows amidst great tribulation. Missions work from 1897 to 1974 resulted in several hundred followers of Christ. The Somali Church went underground from 1991. Many believers fled the country. More and more Somali Christians die as martyrs, but the Somali Church refuses to disappear! Somali Christians feel a burden for their country, and proceed boldly. Possibly 4,000 Christians live in Somalia, and perhaps 8,000 outside the country. Some meet in secret, but others follow Jesus alone. Pray for perseverance, for protection, for discipleship, and for fellowship opportunities. Most Christians are men. Ask God to raise up Somali Christian families.

5 **Pray about these specific challenges:**

• *A negative view of Christianity.* When Somalis think of Christianity, they think of Western moral decline, European colonial powers, or the Ethiopian military. Pray for God to overcome these impressions so a greater breakthrough can come. Pray that refugees and others who receive aid from Christians will experience the love of Christ.

• *Nomadic lifestyle and Somali clans.* Most Somalis live as nomads, and 95% have ties with the Somali clan social structure. They struggle with Western forms of church, which can seem to emphasize individuals over families, and can appear tied to a building. Pray for understanding from Scripture of the many ways communities may follow and worship the One True God!

• *The Somali Bible.* It is sold in the USA and Kenya, but it cannot be distributed inside Somalia. Christian radio provides a vital way to reach Somalis from outside the country.

6 **The Somali diaspora** numbers about 6 million. Most are in Ethiopia, Yemen, Kenya, and Djibouti. 1.4 million people are displaced within Somalia. Several mission agencies seek to reach Somalis in various countries, where host communities often marginalize them. Pray that these ministries may impact Somalis, and may plant many Somali churches.

South Africa

Pop 50.5 million. **Capital** Cape Town (legislative, 3.4 mill), Pretoria (administrative, 1.4 mill), Bloemfontein (judicial, 443,000).

Christians 38 mill. *Evangelical Christians* 10.6 mill.

Largest Religion Christian.

Fastest Growing Religion Non-religious.

Largest Ethnic Groups Nguni (46.4%), Sotho-Tswana (24.3%), White/Caucasian (8.9%), Coloured/mixed race (8.9%), Asian (2.8%).

Official Language 11 languages (all major ethnic languages). English and Afrikaans main languages of higher education. **All Languages** 40.

Economy The richest and most industrialized country in Africa. Strong agriculture base and large deposits of gold, platinum, and chrome. High unemployment, with a vast gap between rich and poor. Corruption and impact of AIDS limit progress. Many white professionals and farmers are leaving the country.

Politics Union of South Africa formed in 1910. Parliamentary republic (white minority) created in 1961. The apartheid system limited political and economic rights of non-whites, and brought great pain and suffering to the majority. Government repealed the last laws that allowed apartheid in 1991, followed by free national democratic elections in 1994. Nelson Mandela's government worked hard for a free, non-racial government, and began the long healing process with some success. Governments and leaders since Mandela have disappointed many.

---

1 **Prayer initiatives** begun in South Africa went on to impact the whole world! The Global Day of Prayer started in Cape Town (2001), and now Christians from almost every country join to observe this on Pentecost Sunday each year. Other prayer movements like Transformation Africa and Jericho Walls also influence many nations. Biblical Christianity is strong in South Africa. Many Christian agencies minister to the needy sections of society. Beautiful stories tell of Christians who show love to victims of rape, crime, and AIDS, and also to prisoners, slum-dwellers, and the very poor.

2 **Pray for all in government and leadership,** that the priorities would be justice, righteousness, and economic improvement for all. Greater transparency, a more mature democracy, and free press, would all help combat corruption and deception. The nation faces high rates of rape and violent crime. Pray that the spirit of violence, both physical and sexual, might be bound under the authority of Christ.

3 **The effects of apartheid still strain the nation.** Pray for reconciliation among all races. Many call South Africa the "rainbow nation", and all races (black, white, coloured, South Asian) must now work to overcome mistrust, deep hurts, and fears. Evangelicals were slow to stand against apartheid, and this wounded many denominations. Pray for the whole Church to leave behind the conflicts of the past and to demonstrate the power of unity in Jesus.

4 **Christianity faces challenges.** How can a nation 75% Christian be crippled by such poverty, violence, crime, AIDS, and racial division? Pray for the Church to have a prophetic voice in a society that has abandoned moral absolutes. Some estimate South Africa needs 30,000 new churches to effectively reach and disciple the millions of unchurched, and leadership training challenges every church and denomination.

5 **South Africa sends out many missionaries.** All races and denominations send and support some missionaries. Around 2,000 South Africans serve abroad in missions, and nearly as many serve within South Africa. Pray for their provision, especially for missionaries from the Coloured, South Asian, and African communities. Pray also for more missionary outreach from the Black churches.

 Ministry challenges for the Church stem from the country's troubled history, its great diversity of peoples, and the wide gap between rich and poor.

- *Over 60% of South Africans are urban dwellers.* Apartheid policies enforced rural poverty among Africans. This continues in today's shantytowns, squatter camps, slums, and townships. Living conditions range from poor to terrible. Most are unemployed. Pray for churches, believers, and their witness as the light of Christ in these difficult places.

- *Immigrants,* legal and illegal, stream over South Africa's borders. Perhaps 5 million immigrants arrived from other African countries to escape war and poverty at home. Some estimate much more. Resentment towards immigrants exploded at times into riots and violence. Pray for the nation to recognize its responsibility to these needy people, as a powerful African country.

 Ethnic and religious groups for specific prayer:

- *Muslims* are less than 2% of South Africa's population, and very few Muslims have ever openly followed the Lord Jesus. Cape Malays (260,000 Muslims) live mainly around Cape Town as part of the Afrikaans-speaking Coloured community. A fellowship of agencies seeks to witness and disciple them. There is some fruit, but new believers face great pressure. 300,000 Muslim Asians live mostly in the Durban area of KwaZulu-Natal. Most are Gujarati, Urdu, or other Indian ethnic groups. A few churches reach out to them. Over 100,000 Black Africans became Muslim in recent years. Islam is one of the fastest-growing religious movements in South Africa.

- *Hindus* are 50% of the Asian population. A steady flow of Hindu people came to Christ, and now 19% of the Asian population is Christian! Demonization is a major problem, and many need freedom.

- *East Asians* have some Christian work among them. The Chinese include long-term residents, immigrants from Taiwan in the 1980s, and the recent immigrants from mainland China. A large Vietnamese community exists as well. Mainland Chinese are most responsive to outreach.

South Sudan *Africa*

Pop 12.2 million (UN, 2012). **Capital** Juba (254,000).
Christians 7.6 mill. *Evangelical Christians* 3.6 mill. [Figures are best estimates, as specific figures are not yet available following independence from Sudan.]
Largest Religion Christian.

Largest Ethnic Groups Nilotic (83.3%, 39 peoples, including Dinka: 42.3%, and Nuer: 15.7%), Sudanic (11.4%, 19 groups), Arab (3.9%), Adamawa-Ubangi (1.3%, 12 peoples).
Official Languages English, Arabic. Major languages: Juba Arabic, Dinka, others. **All Languages** 68.

Economy Potential wealth through oil, but hindered by conflict with Sudan, rivalries in government, and lack of economic development.

Politics Under joint British-Egyptian rule until Independence as part of Sudan (1956). Devastated by bloody civil wars until a 2005 Peace Agreement brought a ceasefire and opened the door for independence. The Republic of South Sudan gained independence on 9 July 2011. Both internal and external tensions continue.

1 **South Sudan is the world's newest country.** The nation was born in a great spirit of unity, happiness, and hope. Thank God for this freedom from the long, painful domination by the north. Sudan is now mainly Arab and Muslim, while South Sudan is mainly Black and Christian. Pray for the Church to have a good influence in society and leadership, to make life better for all people.

2 **The civil war between south and north lasted for 21 years.** Most of the 1.5 to 2 million killed were from the south. Half a million fled the country. Another 4 million fled their homes at some point. Every family in South Sudan suffers lasting effects from the horrors of war. The dispute over territory and oil continues with the north (Sudan), so the violence and bitterness continue.

3 **The legacy of war** remains, as civil strife broke out in 2013. Political rivalry between the president and deputy president intensified existing ethnic tension between the two main groups (Dinka and Nuer). The clashes between them, and between some army factions, took over 1,000 lives and displaced over 200,000 people. Peace talks started in 2014, but only true repentance, forgiveness, and reconciliation can overcome the spirit of bitterness and revenge. Pray for God to work miracles in the hearts of the leaders and of the people. Pray that the new constitution and government will be instruments of peace, justice, and fairness.

4 **South Sudan is one of the world's poorest nations.** Only 27% of the people (and only 8% of the women) can read and write. The country has more land than Spain and Portugal combined, but only has 100 km (62 miles) of paved roads. Less than 2% of the people have access to clean water, only 6% have access to improved sanitation, and 33% suffer from chronic hunger. Rates for the number of mothers who die in childbirth, for infant mortality, and for immunization against disease are the worst in the world.

5 **Christianity grew rapidly over the past 20 years** amid violence, warfare, persecution, and even genocide. Much of the country is Catholic, but other denominations include the Anglican Church, the Presbyterian Church, and the African Inland Church. Many became Christians as a rejection of Islam, which the North imposed on them. Most new believers previously followed traditional religions and spirit worship, and many need to learn much more about the gospel, the Bible, and Christian life and faith. Pray for good Bible teaching and leadership training. Pray that the churches will disciple young Christians to maturity in Christ.

Sudan   *Africa*

Pop 35.7 million (UN, 2012). **Capital** Khartoum (4.5 mill). **Christians** 2.6 mill. *Evangelical Christians* 1.9 mill. [Figures are best estimates, as specific figures are not yet available following independence of South Sudan.] **Largest Religion** Muslim.

Largest Ethnic Groups A complex mix of over 130 ethnic groups and sub-groups. Sudanese Arab (66.6%, 31 peoples), Other Arab (6.9%, 6 Shuwa peoples, 6 others), Horn of Africa-Cushitic (6.6%, 9 peoples), Ouaddai-Fur (5.7%, 13 peoples), Nubian (4.6%, 22 peoples), Nuba Mountain peoples (3.9%, 40 people groups, mostly small in number), Kanuri-Saharan (2.9%, 7 peoples), other Sub-Saharan peoples (2.9%, 16 Nilotic peoples, 5 Sudanic peoples, 7 others). **Official Languages** Arabic, English. **All Languages** 75.

Economy Good agricultural and mineral resources. Years of mismanagement, civil war, and famine have hindered progress. Many Sudanese live in poverty.

Politics Under joint Egyptian and British control from 1899 until independence in 1956. Continuous conflict between the Islamised, Arab north and the non-Arab, Black African south. A peace agreement ended fighting in 2005 followed by a referendum for southern independence in 2011 resulting in the formation of the Republic of South Sudan.

1 **Sudan lost 26% of its area and 25% of its population** when South Sudan became an independent country in July 2011. Thank the Lord a major new war did not break out when the country divided, but continue to pray for peace. The situation remains very tense, with many unresolved disputes between the 2 countries.

2 **War has been almost non-stop since Sudan's independence (1956).** The entire region is unstable, but most of Sudan's conflicts come from within. The government and military fought against minorities all around the country, and brought great suffering upon its own citizens for decades. They committed many terrible acts in the south (most of what is now South Sudan) and in the west (in Darfur). Pray for change that will bring peace to those still under threat, relief to those in need, and justice for those who have done this evil.

3 **The gospel spread through these many years of upheaval.** Although the conflicts created terrible suffering, they made the Church more mature. The wars scattered Christian refugees throughout the country, so even through suffering the good news spread. Churches formed in places and among peoples that previously had no Christians! Praise God that this growth occurs across many denominations. Pray for them to find unity through Christ. The Islamic government bombed churches and other Christian buildings in the South, and specifically targeted Christian areas for attack. But many believers kept their faith, and even took the gospel to other ethnic groups during these hard times!

4 **Pray for the Church in Sudan.** Believers must find ways to recover from the damage done by war and persecution. This includes both the physical damage from bombing, fire, and poverty, but also the spiritual and emotional trauma caused by such prolonged pain. Possibly the most strategic need is training. Spiritual leaders and pastors need training that suits the Sudanese context. In addition, the millions who came to Jesus from Islamic, animist, or weak Christian backgrounds need discipleship. Out of 114 languages, only 10 have the whole Bible. Christian radio/audio resources and TV/video material could help believers read and understand Scripture, gain a Christian worldview, and learn how to reach their neighbours (even their enemies!) for Jesus.

5 **Ministry opportunities exist,** but the control and influence of both the government and the majority religion make it difficult to get help to the people with greatest need. Khartoum has over 7 million people. Millions of displaced people come from other parts of Sudan and settle in poor shantytowns and squatter camps. Nearly half of Sudan's population is under 18 years old, so huge needs exist for education and youth ministry. With so much war, many children have no education at all. The years of conflict leave a situation where relief, aid, and development work remain vital.

6 **Most Sudanese are Muslims.** Many have found Jesus, but millions have never heard the good news. A large number of Africa's least-reached peoples live in Sudan, such as the Daju, Fur, Masalit, Midob, Tama/Kimr, and Zaghawa. Some peoples in the Nuba Mountains and in the south remain largely unreached. The Beja on the Red Sea Coast were once Christian, but now they practise folk Islam. Only a few of them follow Christ today.

Swaziland

Pop 1.2 million. **Capital** Mbabane (75,000).
Christians 1 mill. *Evangelical Christians* 302,000.
Largest Religion Christian.
Fastest Growing Religion Non-religious.
Largest Ethnic Groups Nguni (91.9%), Other Bantu (4%), Afrikaner (1.4%).
Official Languages siSwati, English. **All Languages** 8.
Economy An agricultural economy, but some mineral production and manufacturing. Majority of trade with South Africa. Droughts and floods affect the land. The high AIDS rate affects the economy.
Politics A British protectorate (1899-1968). Now a strong monarchy with a democratic government based on a disputed constitution, which was only signed in 2005. The monarchy's excessive wealth in a poor country presents a difficult issue.

1 **HIV/AIDS devastated the population** of this country, and the society lacks a young adult workforce. Reports say 26-40% of adults are HIV positive. Others claim that life expectancy is as low as age 32. Many times the eldest sibling leads a household of orphans. Talk about ministry and evangelism in Swaziland is not helpful if HIV/AIDS is not also addressed. Pray for treatment of the sick. Genuine Christian love, demonstrated in practical and gracious ways, could win many to the Lord. All churches must address the physical, emotional, and spiritual needs of AIDS sufferers.

2 **Christians sowed the gospel for 160 years,** and now a strong evangelical community makes up 25% of the population! Swaziland has a solid core of believers and regular church attenders. But too many other Christians live the same way as non-Christians. Some churches confuse the gospel with witchcraft and ancestor worship. Most believers are female – pray for men to be drawn into the Church. Pray for God's Spirit to bring revival. The young people of Swaziland have little opportunity to be young. Poverty, unemployment, and AIDS shorten their youth. Pray for godly models and mentors for them.

Tanzania

Pop 45 million. **Capitals** Dodoma (official, 210,000), Dar es Salaam (de facto, 3.3 mill).
Christians 24.4 mill. *Evangelical Christians* 8 mill.
Largest Religion Christian.
Fastest Growing Religion Christian.
Largest Ethnic Groups Bantu peoples (86.3%), Swahili (7.8%), Nilotic (2.2%), Cushitic (1.7%), Khoisan (0.3%), Other (1.7%, many South Asian, Arab, Chinese). Many African refugees.
Official Languages Swahili, English. **All Languages** 127.
Economy One of world's poorest nations, dominated by subsistence agriculture. Stability and dedicated leaders attract aid and investment. Economic potential exists through mineral deposits and a huge tourist industry.

Politics Union of Tanganyika and Zanzibar in 1964, after independence from Britain of each (1961 and 1963). The one-party socialist republic became a multiparty democracy since 1992. A stable country amidst many unstable ones, though Zanzibar remains a concern.

1 **Tanzania remains an "island of peace"** amidst troubled nations. It shelters over a million refugees who flee violence in their own lands, and serves as a base for Christian ministry in the region. Still, witchcraft mixes in with both Christianity and Islam in Tanzania. Spiritual superstition and occultism have great costs, and often lead to sexual abuse or even death for victims of these practices. Pray the government will be bold to confront evil, and wise to bring community harmony and religious freedom.

2 **The evangelical population grew** from 2.4 million in 1990 to 8 million in 2010, both in mainline Churches (Lutheran, Anglican) and Pentecostal denominations. New church-planting agencies came about since the 1980s, as did partnerships between nationals and expatriate missionaries. Praise God that the commitment to plant new churches and to reach the unevangelized peoples of Tanzania bore good fruit in recent years among both animists and Muslims!

3 **Leadership development and theological training** must become priorities in churches. Many pastors care for 10 or more congregations, often miles apart. Pray for opportunities for leaders to receive Bible training and personal development. Swahili is used in 96% of church services, though it is not the heart language of most. 51 languages have no Scripture and 32 more have only portions. Pray for more translation teams, and for projects to finish quickly and well. Pray for new songs and training resources in the heart languages of all Tanzania's peoples.

4 **The unfinished task in Tanzania.** National initiatives in the 1990s/2000s led to excellent research on Tanzania's ethnic groups. They discovered many peoples with few known believers. Remaining Task Mission set goals for national churches to plant 1 church for every 1,000 urbanites, and 1 for every 500 rural dwellers. Pray for:

- *Zanzibar* is famous for its spices, but also as an Arab base for its centuries-long African slave trade. 3 original Swahili peoples live on the two main islands, and almost all are Muslim. Radical Islam divides the people, and spreads fear and violence. Christian numbers increased to 60 congregations, mostly Pentecostal. Pray for their perseverance, and for a witness of love.

- *The Muslim peoples of coastal regions* live under the curse of the historic slave trade. They are among the least evangelized of Tanzania's peoples. Pray that Christians from other ethnic groups among them may be used of God to bless them with the gospel.

- *The South Asian community* speaks a range of Indian languages (mostly Gujarati, but also Hindi, Punjabi). Most are Hindu or Muslim, with few Christians.

5 **Widespread poverty** is a challenge and an opportunity. The country needs help for schools, universities, hospitals, roads, drinking water, and agriculture. Holistic ministry can bring transformation to all levels of Tanzanian life. Tanzania has Mission Aviation Fellowship's biggest operation (8 aircraft, 3 bases, 77 staff). They transport Christian workers where there are no good roads, maintain medical programmes, and reach out to the scattered Maasai, Iraqw, and Barabaig groups.

Togo

Pop 6.8 million. **Capital** Lomé (1.7 mill).
Christians 3.1 mill. *Evangelical Christians* 723,000.
Largest Religion Christian.
Fastest Growing Religion Muslim.

Largest Ethnic Groups Over 57 ethnic groups. Guinean (47.4%, 22 peoples mostly in the south), Gur (45.5%, 21 peoples mostly in the north), Yoruba (4.4%), Fulani (1.2%).
Official Language French. **All Languages** 43.

Economy Dominated by agriculture (coffee, cocoa main crops). Self-sufficient in basic foodstuffs. Phosphate and cement exports also bring income. Unwise use of money in past years caused living standards to decline since the early 1990s.

Politics German colony (1884-1914). Independent from France in 1960. One-party rule from 1967 until a democratic constitution was introduced in 1992. After the president's death (2005) ended his 38-year rule, a military coup installed his son as president. Bloody protests followed. His party retains the majority rule after elections (2007, 2010, 2013), despite opposition protests.

---

1   **The political and economic situation** remains unstable. The military coup and unfair elections created resentment between the southern (Guinean) and central-northern (Gur, who dominate politics) peoples. Pray that God breaks down the bitterness between them. Poverty leaves orphans and unwanted children (over 300,000) vulnerable to human traffickers, and makes prostitution common. Pray for an end to these evils, and for effective ways to fight poverty.

2   **The Church in Togo** did not grow much between 1960 and 1990. When new denominations from outside Togo began to plant churches in the 1990s, both new and traditional denominations began to grow! Pentecostal groups from Nigeria, Ghana, Benin, and Burkina Faso arrived and expanded the Church even more. National goals to reach every home and plant a church in every village brought some unity and growth, but division remains a problem. Pray that newer and older churches might work together for God's glory.

3   **Too few evangelical mission agencies send workers.** This open, responsive, needy country has many opportunities (in church planting, discipleship, education, aid/development, Bible translation, ministry to children and youth), and also many unreached. Where are the workers? Pray for:

- *Strong powers of darkness work within Togo,* and must be challenged through intercessory prayer and the power of the gospel. Secret societies among the Ewe, Fon, and other tribes oppose the gospel. Most of the population still participate in animistic and voodoo rituals, and many Christians join in. Togo and Benin have the highest percentage in Africa of unevangelized who follow traditional religions. Ghanaian and Benin believers of the same language groups are potentially the best fit as missionaries and evangelists.

- *Muslims* dominate the marketplace and education. Oil-rich Muslim countries send money to build mosques, schools, and charity projects. Prosperous Muslim businesses recruit young Christians to work there who eventually convert to Islam. But few Christian workers focus on Muslim evangelism among the 13 Muslim-majority people groups, or within the high concentrations of Muslims in urban areas.

Tunisia

Africa

Pop 10.4 million. **Capital** Tunis (767,000).
Christians 23,000. *Evangelical Christians* 1,200.
Largest Religion Muslim.
Fastest Growing Religion Muslim.
Largest Ethnic Groups Arab (97.8%), Berber (1.9%).
Official Language Arabic. French widely used. **All Languages** 10.
Economy Stable and developed despite few natural resources. Tourism, textiles, olive oil, and phosphates earn the most. Tunisia has the best chance for stability of the Arab Spring countries.
Politics Independent from France (1956), followed by a republic with a strong presidential government and single-party state. Human rights abuses in the repression of a fundamentalist Muslim movement. Free, democratic elections (2011) won by an Islamist movement in coalition with other groups, but unrest remains.

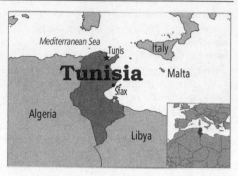

1 The Arab Spring began in Tunisia (December 2010). The country had one of the most progressive and open societies in the Arab world, but Tunisians felt frustrated by high unemployment, corruption, political oppression, and poor living conditions. Protests led to government changes, and inspired similar protests across the whole Arab world. Tunisia's new constitution is truly progressive, and positive fruit came from the suffering of the Arab Spring. However, unemployment and economic decline remain big challenges to the new government. Pray for frustrations to somehow draw people towards Christ.

2 Many Tunisians have grown more devoted in their Islamic faith. Salafist Islamist groups became more bold and violent in their attempts to enforce their views. The government resists political enforcement of Islam, but fundamentalist groups gain followers, especially among the restless, dissatisfied younger generations. Pray for the Church to reach Tunisia's youth while their hearts and minds wrestle with such deep issues.

3 The Church in Tunisia was widespread in the early centuries after Christ. But without deep roots in the local culture and no Scripture translated into local languages, Christianity slowly faded until Islam finally overcame it. Most Christians in Tunisia today are expatriates, but about 500 committed indigenous believers again exist. A large international development organization relocated to Tunis, and increased the number of expatriate Christians (mostly African) in the country. Pray they may find opportunities to relate to their Tunisian neighbours. Pray that the Church might grow again in this land!

4 A century of missionary work produced very little fruit, but continued intercession can break through the long-standing barriers to the gospel! Pray for commitments to Jesus that will last. Few Tunisian believers remain faithful for more than 10 years due to spiritual, cultural, and family pressures. Pray that Tunisian believers might overcome their fear of sharing their faith. Opportunity exists for more Christian workers to serve Tunisia, particularly in teaching, development, and healthcare. Pray for more Christian workers, especially from Arabic-speaking countries.

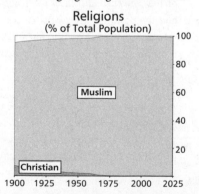

Religions
(% of Total Population)

5 **Specific unreached areas and peoples.** The Church must use media to reach Tunisians, especially radio programmes, satellite TV, and the Internet.

- *Women* have more freedom here than in most other Muslim countries, but cultural and traditional restrictions still make it difficult to reach them with the gospel.

- *The southern part of Tunisia* is a spiritual desert. The cities of Sfax, Gabes, and Gafsa need witnesses.

- *The Berber communities* have Christian ancestors, but have very few Christians now.

- *Some regard Kairouan as the 4th most holy city in Islam.* Many go there for blessings, healing, and help. Pray that their search might lead them to find Jesus!

Uganda   *Africa*

Pop 33.8 million. **Capital** Kampala (1.6 mill).
Christians 28.6 mill. *Evangelical Christians* 12.5 mill.
Largest Religion Christian.
Fastest Growing Religion Muslim.

Largest Ethnic Groups Bantu (65.6%), Nilotic (24.1%), Sudanic (6.8%), Other African/South Asians/Westerners (3.5%).
Official Languages English, Swahili. **All Languages** 45.

Economy A mainly agricultural economy (80% of workforce), with fertile land and regular rainfall. Progress in the 1960s destroyed in the 1970s. Progress since the 1990s slowed by conflicts, AIDS, and disease. Poverty remains widespread.
Politics Independent from Britain in 1962. A brutal dictatorship (1971-1978), with ethnic conflicts that continued until 1986. Gradual peace and stability since then. Multiparty democracy introduced in 2005.

1 **Revival and church growth** continues from 1986 to the present. Uganda has widespread prayer movements, a strong evangelical presence in the Church of Uganda (Anglican), and renewal movements in the Catholic Church. Some consider it one of the most truly Christian nations in the world. Public prayer is common even in government and judicial buildings, and many people attend church. Pentecostal and charismatic churches grow the fastest, both the megachurches with thousands of members and the small house and storefront churches.

2 **Uganda works hard to recover** from many years of war, violence, and heavy-handed government. Pray for peace within the troubled region and the nation. The Lord's Resistance Army (LRA) became an occult-powered militia group that spread terror and committed countless evils in the region. Many Christian NGOs and ministries provide aid, shelter, counselling, spiritual ministry, and education. Pray for God's people to be at the heart of the nation's restoration.

3 **The Church** experiences wonderful breakthroughs and significant obstacles. Most Ugandans identify themselves as Christian, but many struggle with greedy attitudes and non-biblical lifestyles. Government and churches worked bravely to reduce the infection rate of AIDS from 25% of the population (1992) to below 10% (2001). But millions still suffer with the illness, and infection rates could easily rise again. The prosperity gospel and other false teachings lead many astray. Pastors and leaders need affordable and practical biblical training.

4 **Ministry to young people and children** must be a priority. The LRA abducted thousands of children for use as child soldiers or sex slaves. Pray for these former child soldiers as they re-enter normal family and community life. Pray for the street children of Kampala, and the 2 million AIDS orphans. Pray for effective youth programmes in churches, for the ministry of Scripture Union in schools, and for workers who reach out to university students.

5 **Missions vision.** The Ugandan Church endured great suffering in the past, and emerged large and strong. Nearby nations still suffer greatly, and Uganda's missionary potential is enormous! But few Ugandans serve abroad or cross-culturally in mission. Ask God to call many, and pray for the Church to train them and send them out.

6 **Other religious groups.**

- *Muslim* numbers and influence grow quickly. Arab states pour large sums of money into education and Islamic organizations. The Kakwa, Aringa, and Madi peoples in the northwest and the Soga in the southeast have significant numbers of Muslims. Pray for sensitive, specific outreach to them.

- *Animistic tribal religious practices* seem to increase, and believers mix them with Christian faith and practice. In some dioceses, the number of pagan shrines is double the number of church buildings.

Zambia

Africa

Pop 13.3 million. **Capital** Lusaka (1.5 mill).
Christians 11.5 mill. *Evangelical Christians* 3.4 mill.
Largest Religion Christian.
Fastest Growing Religion Muslim.

Largest Ethnic Groups Bemba (30%), Tonga (11.8%), Nyanja (10.7%), Lozi (5.7%), Nsenga (3.4%), Nyiha (3.6%), Tumbuka (2.5%), Kaonde (2.3%), Lunda (2.1%), Lala (2%), Foreign origin (1.7%), Khoisan (Bushmen) (0.5%).
Official Language English. **Trade languages** Bemba and Nyanja spoken by large segments of population. **All Languages** 72, including dialects.

Economy Copper mining and refining remain the major

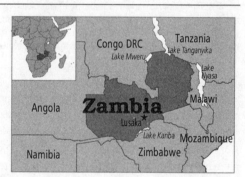

sources of foreign exchange. Agriculture employs many workers. Corruption, AIDS, lack of sea access, and debt drive economy downward. Some opportunities come with investment from China and India, and from natural resources. **Politics** Independent from Britain in 1964. Single-party state until 1991. Since then multiparty elections. Corruption continues despite efforts to change.

1 **Zambians widely accept Christianity,** even in public institutions and the media. Evangelicals grew from 3.8% in 1960 to 25.7% in 2010. Former president Chiluba declared Zambia a Christian nation in 1991, and Zambians practise freedom of all religions. Zambia enjoys a legacy as a stable and peaceful nation surrounded by countries troubled by war and unrest. But national transformation along biblical lines still has not come. Too few know the Word of God, or how to live a Christian life. Superstitions and occult practices open the door for the enemy to work evil in people's lives. Pray for Christians to live pure and holy lives that depend on God alone for spiritual power and blessing. Pray that Zambia will truly be a nation that honours God.

2 **The nation must tackle poverty and its causes.** Up to 86% of the population live below the poverty line, and as many as half of all children are malnourished. Over 100,000 die from AIDS-related health issues every year. All major denominations adopted policies to combat the spread of AIDS and to assist those infected. Praise God that compassion and action now replace much superstition and bad information about AIDS. Zambia has 710,000 orphans, mostly due to AIDS. Over 90,000 live on the streets. 75% of Zambian homes care for a relative orphaned by AIDS. Many agencies help through development, healthcare, education, job training, microfinance, and more.

3 **Evangelical congregations thrive and grow.** Many evangelical believers live in the northwest, and among the Tonga peoples of the south. The large Church among the Nyanja peoples in the east also continues to grow. Pray for more churches among the Lozi and southwestern peoples, and among the Bemba and northern peoples. Many call themselves Christian, but do not practise their faith. Others participate in sects or indigenous churches that mix biblical faith with traditional beliefs and practices that dishonour God. Zambian believers need truly African, truly biblical ways to worship God and practise their faith.

Zimbabwe

Africa

Pop 12.6 million. **Capital** Harare (1.6 mill).
Christians 9.9 mill. *Evangelical Christians* 3.9 mill.
Largest Religion Christian.
Fastest Growing Religion Non-religious.

Largest Ethnic Groups Shona (68.2%), Nguni (14%), Chewa-Sena (8.2%), Sotho-Tswana (3.3%), Other (European, East Asian, South Asian, Coloured) (1.6%), Other African (0.6%).
Official Language English. **Trade languages** Shona spoken widely, Ndebele in the west. **All Languages** 22.

Economy An economic disaster, even with rich agricultural land and mineral deposits. Corruption, mismanagement, devastation from disease, and costly military action in the Congo, all resulted in massive unemployment and hyperinflation. The land redistribution programme (2002) sent the nation into a downward spiral.
Politics Formerly known as Rhodesia. The white minority claimed independence for Rhodesia (from Britain) in 1965. This led to fierce guerrilla warfare and eventually to independence (1980) as Zimbabwe. Until 2008, a one-party state and dictatorship led by Mugabe's ZANU-PF party. Now multi-party elections, but ZANU-PF remain in power.

---

1 **Zimbabwe faces a constant state of emergency.** This country once exported food, but now cannot feed its own people, even with international aid. A government land-reform programme (2002) claimed 5,500 farms from white owners, and allowed over 100,000 war veterans to settle on the land. The country turned to chaos. Millions left Zimbabwe, including many leaders in education, business, healthcare, and agriculture, as well as spiritual leaders. Squatter camps now occupy good farmland. Millions who remain live in poverty. Unemployment at one point reached 90%. Many schools and universities closed, and some hospitals cannot operate. State-endorsed violence and human rights violations often target political opposition, the media, and social activists. Pray for Zimbabwe's national leaders, that God might bring humility and a servant attitude, or else put leaders in place who will govern for the sake of the people, and for restoration of the nation.

2 **Zimbabwe faces one of the world's worst AIDS crises.** Around 1 million AIDS orphans need care, and over 2,000 people die from AIDS-related illness each week. Thank God the rate of infection began to slow in recent years. Life expectancy in Zimbabwe got as low as 40 years. So much death robs the nation of trained professionals and leaders, and devastates the workforce. Pray for wisdom to help the nation cope with this great loss of life. Pray for churches to engage with the moral, spiritual, and economic effects of AIDS.

3 **Praise God, the Church grew through the trials!** The Church must be a prophetic voice for the political and economic life of the nation. Responsibility falls to churches to feed the hungry, care for orphans, protect the vulnerable, and heal the sick. Zimbabwe's churches work in these areas, with support from South African ministries and others. Target 2000 led to 10,000 new churches planted in Zimbabwe! This was followed by Target 2010, a plan to strengthen churches in community work, prayer, mission, leadership development, and healthy church growth. Pray for church unity. Divisions and splits make cooperation hard at a time when unity is vital!

4 **Young people** watched a country decline into misrule. They represent a large portion of the population, but many lack hope for a better future. The Fellowship of Christian Unions (FOCUS/IFES), Scripture Union, and African Enterprise (Foxfire ministries) all work with students and young people in evangelism, leadership training, life skills, and compassionate ministries. Many of the country's Christian leaders were impacted by such ministries when they were younger. Pray for this legacy to continue and to grow. Pray for effective teaching and discipleship of those called to serve the Lord as church leaders.

The African Islands

British Indian Ocean Territory, Cabo Verde (Cape Verde Islands), Mauritius, Mayotte, Réunion, São Tomé and Príncipe, Seychelles, Saint Helena. (Comoros and Madagascar are written separately.)

The African island nations represent a diverse set of histories, ethnic groups, and societies:

- 2 poorer former Portuguese colonies off the west coast of Africa
- 3 richer former French or British colonies in the Indian Ocean to the east of Africa
- 2 British Overseas Territories, one isolated island off the west coast and one in the Indian Ocean
- 2 French Overseas Departments, both in the Indian Ocean to the east of Africa

At the same time, they share in common many spiritual challenges in need of our prayers.

1 **Almost all of these countries have a Catholic majority** (except Mauritius, Mayotte, Saint Helena, and the British Indian Overseas Territory). However, many do not practise their faith. Many others blend Christianity with Hinduism, superstition, African witchcraft, or the occult. But God continues to renew the Catholic Church, and the charismatic movement and house church movements also produce genuine faith. Pray for the many islanders who call themselves Christian, but who do not yet know the power of Christ in their lives to deliver and save.

2 **Newer religious groups grow rapidly.** Praise God that this includes evangelical groups! But it also includes cults, which often mix Christian teaching with falsehood. Pentecostals from Brazil, the USA, France, and Nigeria have all had a big impact on the spiritual life of these islands, as has the Church of the Nazarene. Pray that more indigenous leaders and pastors may be trained to lead the congregations as they grow in size. Pray that believers might mature, and that churches might grow, even when they are in isolated locations. Pray for unity between church groups, which has been lacking in the past.

3 **The isolation of these islands makes discipleship and leadership training difficult.** The high cost required to deliver Christian resources to these remote places limits their availability. The Bible Society in Mauritius distributes over 200,000 Scripture portions each year to all the island territories of the Indian Ocean. Bible translation work continues in a modern Creole (Mauritius) and for the Seselwa OT (Seychelles). Gospel radio is an important tool. The Internet, where it is accessible, is a precious lifeline to Christian materials. Mauritius hosts several Bible schools and TEE programmes, but the other nations struggle to find resources to train new leaders.

4 **Outer islands and minorities** often get neglected for outreach and need prayer:
- *The Rodrigues Islanders of Mauritius* (38,000) are largely Creole. They live in poverty and isolation on a remote island. Many blend biblical teachings with unbiblical traditional beliefs.
- *In São Tomé and Príncipe,* less-reached groups include the more remote Príncipe islanders, the Angolares (rural fisherfolk), and *serviçais* (contract labourers). Each has its own distinct Creole dialect.
- *Muslims, Hindus, and Chinese minorities* across the many islands need loving outreach from believers who demonstrate the true gospel.
- *The Chagos Islanders* were evacuated to Mauritius from the British Indian Ocean Territories in 1966-1970. For the last 10 years, they have unsuccessfully fought to return. (The Chagos Islands

are occupied by the British, who lease it to the American military.) The Chagos live in very difficult conditions with high rates of poverty and unemployment. Almost all are Catholic. Pray for their return and resettlement, and for continued opportunities to respond to the gospel. A Bible-based ministry called *Mo Pense Toi* (which means "I Think and Care About You") seeks to serve the 8,000 Chagossians.

5 **Young people face extra challenges** as crime rates and sexual immorality rise in their societies. There is often little hope of an improved life for youth in these remote communities. Intravenous drug use in Mauritius is 2nd-highest in the world. But as traditional values wear down, some become more spiritually open. Pray for fruitful ministry by the Christian agencies seeking to reach young people.

6 **Migrant communities.**

- *Caboverdians.* Nearly half a million live in migrant communities in the USA (266,000), Portugal (80,000), Angola (46,000), Senegal, and France. The money they send home is vital to Cape Verde, one of the poorest countries in Africa. Pray that many in the diaspora will become true disciples of Jesus.

- *Saint Helena.* Mainly British-origin people (8,000) live in the remote Atlantic Islands of Saint Helena and its 2 dependencies (Ascension and Tristan da Cunha). The heritage of Christianity slowly fades from this land. Pray for Saint Helena's Baptists and the Salvation Army, where most evangelicals worship.

- *British Indian Ocean Territory.* Pray for Christ to be known and worshipped among the several thousand American (USA) and British (UK) service personnel, and the contract workers from Mauritius and the Philippines.

7 **Mauritius** has many religious groups and ethnic groups, which creates a challenge for evangelism (48% Hindu, 32% Christian, 17% Muslim). Pray for wisdom and discernment among Christians. Indians face difficulty to become followers of Christ because Hindus here have strong ethnic and family ties, and much influence over government and culture. Even so, large numbers of Hindus have come to Jesus through the bold witness of evangelical/Pentecostal churches. Some other churches and independent house groups also experience modest growth. Evangelical groups face some opposition and hostility from the Hindu-biased government.

8 **The indigenous people of Mayotte** (99.9% Muslim). Mayotte has religious freedom. The government even allows open-air evangelism (practised by the Assemblies of God). But response has been slow, and most Christian converts eventually return to Islam. Magic and spirit-possession dominate the version of Islam practised in Mayotte. Because of generous economic aid from France and the EU, the people possess little initiative and entrepreneurship. Pray for a spiritual breakthrough. Mayotte's Shimaore language has no Old Testament, and the Shibushi language has no Scriptures at all. Pray for God to call more workers to Mayotte for long-term ministry, especially French-speaking Africans. The name Mayotte means "place of death". Pray that it will become a place of spiritual life in Christ.

QUOTES ON PRAYER

The man who mobilizes the Christian church to pray will make the greatest contribution to world evangelization in history.
Andrew Murray

You do not test the resources of God until you attempt the impossible.
F. B. Meyer

A man is what he is on his knees—nothing more and nothing less.
Robert Murray McCheyne

It is well said that "asking is the rule of the kingdom". It is a rule that will never be altered in anybody's case. If the royal and divine Son of God cannot be exempted from the rule of asking that He may have, you and I cannot expect the rule to be relaxed in our favour.
C. H. Spurgeon

In no other way can the believer become as fully involved with God's work, especially the work of world evangelism, as in intercessory prayer.
Dick Eastman

Prayer succeeds when all else fails. Prayer has won great victories and has rescued, with notable triumph, God's saints when every other hope is gone.
E. M. Bounds

Prayer is not overcoming God's reluctance, but laying hold of His willingness.
Variously attributed

Prayer does not fit us for the greater work; prayer is the greater work.
Oswald Chambers

Every great movement of God can be traced to a kneeling figure.
D. L. Moody

Prayer is weakness leaning on omnipotence.
W. S. Bowd

Beware in your prayers, above everything else, of limiting God, not only by unbelief, but by fancying that you know what He can do. Expect unexpected things "above all that we ask or think".
Andrew Murray

Intercession is truly universal work for the Christian. No place is closed to intercessory prayer. No continent—no nation—no organization—no city—no office. There is no power on earth that can keep intercession out.
Richard Halverson

There has never been a spiritual awakening in any country or locality that did not begin in united prayer.
A. T. Pierson

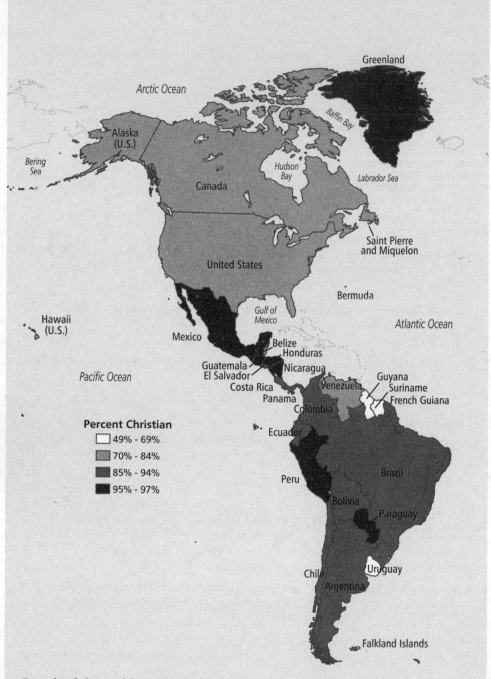

Percent Christian

- 49% - 69%
- 70% - 84%
- 85% - 94%
- 95% - 97%

For a detailed map of the Caribbean, see p. 114.

THE AMERICAS

Pop 940.3 million.
Christians 809.6 mill.
Evangelical Christians 191.9 mill.
Largest Religion Christian.
Fastest Growing Religion Non-religious.

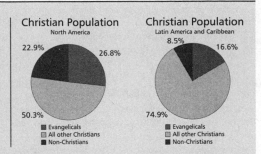

Christian Population
North America

22.9%
26.8%
50.3%

- Evangelicals
- All other Christians
- Non-Christians

Christian Population
Latin America and Caribbean

8.5%
16.6%
74.9%

- Evangelicals
- All other Christians
- Non-Christians

NORTH AMERICA
Nearly 16% of world's land surface. Contains 3 of the world's 13 largest countries (Canada, USA, Greenland). 49 cities over 1 million, 2 of those over 10 million.

All Languages 443. **Languages with Scriptures** (of indigenous North American languages) 9 Bibles, 31 New Testaments, 48 Old or New Testament portions, 27 works in progress.

THE CARIBBEAN
26 sovereign states, overseas departments, and dependencies. 4 cities over 1 million people.

All Languages 47. **Languages with Scriptures** (of indigenous Caribbean languages) 2 Bibles, 2 New Testaments, 7 works in progress.

LATIN AMERICA
22 countries spread across Central America, Spanish-speaking South America, and Brazil. 15% of world's land area. 61 cities of over 1 million people. Mexico City and São Paulo are two of world's largest cities.

All Languages 503. **Languages with Scriptures** (of indigenous South and Central American languages) 32 Bibles, 291 New Testaments, 130 Old or New Testament portions, 276 works in progress.

The Americas includes two continents and 58 countries and territories. The different regions have much in common, but also possess great diversity.

Indigenous peoples range from the Inuit of the Arctic polar region to the Fuegians on the tip of South America. Hundreds of distinct ethnicities and languages make their homes between these two extremes.

European countries colonized the Americas during an era of exploration and settlement, but it was also an era of oppression and even extermination of the native peoples. This history still affects many issues throughout the Americas. Slaves brought over from Africa, and their descendants, play a major role in the story of these lands.

Almost all people speak at least one of the four main colonial languages: English, Spanish, Portuguese, and French. Other factors that link this continent include the free trade zones, the extensive drug trade, and widespread immigration.

Argentina

Pop 40.7 million. **Capital** Buenos Aires City (13.1 mill).

Christians 36.3 mill. *Evangelical Christians* 3.7 mill.
Largest Religion Christian.
Fastest Growing Religion Non-religious.

Largest Ethnic Groups White Argentinian (72.1%), Amerindian (7.1%), Other Hispanic (7.0%), Italian (4.7%), Middle Eastern (3.3%).

Official Language Spanish. **All Languages** 40.

Economy Abundant resources and educated workforce. Strong recovery since 2001 after deep losses. Wide gap between rich and poor.

Politics Independent from Spain in 1816. Stable democracy restored in 1983 after decades of incapable government.

 Argentina suffered one crisis after another with a military takeover (1976), the disappearances of many political opponents, a failed war over the Falkland Islands (1982), and an economic disaster (1999-2002). But these events led the nation into spiritual hunger and drew many back to God. They also strengthened the people's commitment to justice and democracy. Pray that the Spirit will continue to draw many to Himself.

 Evangelical Christians grew from less than 1 million in 1980 to 3.7 million by 2010. Renewal, evangelism, and prayer touched the nation. Argentinean evangelists, teachers, and missionaries touched the world! Godly, unified leadership is necessary for the future. Pray for students in the hundreds of seminaries, Bible schools, and programmes. Local Councils of Pastors and the National Evangelical Alliance (ACIERA) now meet to pray and co-ordinate ministry. Pray that leaders may hear what the Spirit speaks to the Church, and act together in faith.

3 **Argentina appears sophisticated, but faces spiritual struggles.** The occult, Mormonism, Islam, and Spiritism compete for the souls of people. Weak faith and attractive, pleasure-seeking lifestyles influence Christianity. God brought victories to past battles through intercession, so pray for protection and spiritual health for each one caught in the battle.

4 **Amerindians from the Chaco** suffered many years as a poorly treated minority. Most of these 26 groups follow a mix of Catholicism and animism (worship of spirits in nature). The Church Mission Society, the Mennonites, and other agencies brought the gospel to this region, and now there are believers and churches among these peoples. Pray for the indigenous Church to mature, and for ongoing Bible translation in several languages.

5 **Buenos Aires** is one of the world's largest urban areas, and the gospel does not reach many who live there. The cultured upper class are harder to reach. The Jewish community (one of the world's largest) has few believers. Some churches started work among the 500,000 slum dwellers, homeless, and street kids, but more work is needed. Chinese, Korean, Japanese, and Vietnamese communities continue to grow with only one agency reaching out to them.

6 **Argentina could become a major mission sending country.** Praise God for the missionary vision of the national Church! Ask Him to fulfil the goals Christian leaders have set to prepare, send out, and support many workers. Pray that pastors and churches may gain a vision for the unreached peoples of the world.

Belize

Pop 313,000. **Capital** Belmopan (20,000).

Christians 263,000. *Evangelical Christians* 59,000.
Largest Religion Christian.
Fastest Growing Religions Non-religious.

Largest Ethnic Groups Mestizo/Ladino (46.7%, mostly Guatemalan and Honduran background), Belize Creole (25%), Amerindian (10.6%), Garifuna (6%, Black Carib), European (4.9%), East Indian (3%), Chinese (2.7%).
Official Language English; Spanish spoken by majority.
All languages 12.

Economy Solid economic growth, but highest cost of living in Central America. Widespread poverty.
Politics A stable parliamentary democracy. Formerly British Honduras, but independent since 1981.

1 **Most Belizeans profess Christianity,** but only 10% of the population attend church regularly. People need to encounter the true gospel in ways that are meaningful and sensitive to their culture. The Spanish-speaking immigrants sometimes mix Truth with superstitions, the Mayans with paganism, and the Garifuna with black magic. Pray for revival and spiritual conviction for any confusion in beliefs.

2 **Evangelicals** grew from 4.6% of the population (1960) to 19% of the population (2010). They now work to overcome present challenges. The cultural and denominational diversity in Belize creates barriers among churches. Pray for efforts to draw together Hispanic, English, German, and Mayan-speaking believers. 70% of pastors must work another job. They see the need for training, but distance and cost make it difficult to participate in programmes.

3 **Many missions trips focus on this small nation.** Much medical and literacy work is positive, but their constant presence creates reliance on foreign believers and not the national Church. Pray for fruitful partnerships where everyone can contribute for Kingdom purposes.

4 **The less-reached peoples** include the Garifuna, Mayans, Chinese, and Indians (who are almost all Hindu or Muslim). Each group needs clearer and more culturally thoughtful ministry.

Bolivia

Pop 10 million. **Capital** La Paz (administrative, 1.7 mill); Sucre (legal, 288,000).
Christians 9.1 mill. *Evangelical Christians* 1.6 mill.

Largest Religion Christian.
Fastest Growing Religion Ethnic religions.

Largest Ethnic Groups Mestizo (43.7%, includes Mestizo, whites and Afro-Bolivians), Highland Amerindian peoples (49.8%), Lowland Amerindian peoples (3.8%), German (2%).
Official Languages Spanish, Aymara, Quechua. **All languages** 41.

Economy Once the richest area of South America, but now its poorest nation. Discoveries of natural gas deposits raise hope for future growth.

Politics Independence from Spain in 1825 after a long war for freedom. Over 200 successful coups or revolutions in 160 years after that. Stable democracy since 1985. Increased respect of rights for indigenous groups and the poor.

---

1 **A harvest of new believers came, but early missionaries struggled** against persecution and harsh conditions first. The Andes Evangelical Mission (now SIM International) pioneered most ministries. Aymara and Quechua peoples both experienced major church growth. Lowland tribes are largely evangelized. Praise God for 50 years of growth in many sections of the Bolivian population! Pray for maturity of leaders who must now pass on the faith to the next generation with Christian practices that honour God and their heritage. Foreign workers can now help train leaders, reach out to young people, and serve in holistic ministries.

2 **Both the churches and the government want to help the poor.** 70% of Bolivia's population live in poverty, and half of those live in extreme poverty. Bolivian farmers earn more money for the coca leaf than for other products, but some uses for coca are illegal. Rich gas deposits in the east lead to tension among the white elite, the highland peoples of the west, and the mixed and Indian peoples of the east. Pray that individuals in power and those in poverty will find courage to reject temptations and make wise decisions.

3 **The spiritual grip of the enemy remains strong** after centuries of paganism, and continues its hold on the Church. Christians now recognize that spiritual warfare is necessary to gain ground. Pray that the Church will wake up to the enemy's deep influence, bind the strong man, and pray until God transforms Bolivia.

4 **Evangelical Christians** grew greatly in number and influence, but face challenges. Some follow false teachings or fail morally without good discipleship and Bible knowledge. Ask God to set apart thousands of new leaders for His use. Evangelicals must help lead Bolivia's battle against poverty, injustice, and evil by allowing Kingdom values to guide their words and deeds.

5 **The less reached in Bolivia** include the powerful and wealthy upper classes, the indigenous peoples living in remote areas, and the urban migrants who live at the edges of cities and seek work. Unemployment, urban violence, and easily available drugs tempt many youth. Over 67% of the population are under 30. The majority of children live in poverty and suffer malnutrition. Perhaps 100,000 live on the street. Almost all the boys try drugs, and many of the girls experience sexual abuse. Pray for churches to see the importance of youth and children's ministries. Also ask God to work through radio ministry in less-reached places where low literacy, poverty, and isolation limit access to the gospel by other means.

Brazil

Pop 195.4 million. **Capital** Brasilia (3.9 mill).

Christians 178.6 mill. *Evangelical Christians* 51.3 mill.
Largest Religion Christian.
Fastest Growing Religion Non-religious.

Largest Ethnic Groups European groups (50.2%), Mixed race (38%), African (6.4%), Arab (4%), Amerindian (0.4%) – 275 tribal groups speaking 185 different languages.
Official Language Portuguese. **All languages** 193.

Economy Sustained growth stabilized the economy. Now emerging as an economic superpower.
Politics A federal republic. Multiparty democracy since 1985 after decades of military rule.

1 Brazil's *evangélicos* grew from 2 million in 1960 to over 50 million in 2010. They are one of the largest evangelical populations in the world, and very strong in prayer meetings and movements. Large gatherings, women's networks, events like the Global Day of Prayer and March for Jesus, all bring masses together to pray and celebrate Jesus. Praise God for Brazilian prayer warriors!

2 Brazilian society improved in recent decades, but faces huge challenges. Accountability and transparency in the government has started to change the widespread corruption. Justice and economic opportunity increased. But poverty affects tens of millions, and many still live in crime-filled *favelas*. Criminals especially exploit street children and indigenous peoples, and up to 250,000 people may be affected by debt slavery. Brazil is the world's 2nd-highest consumer of illegal drugs and has the highest rate of firearm homicides. Spiritual, social, and economic breakthroughs must come. Pray that future governments will pursue an end to corruption. Pray for a wise response from the Church to combine church planting and development through effective Brazilian and expatriate work.

3 Brazil is spiritually open, but this can be both good and bad. Millions practise Spiritism and Catholicism at the same time! Many follow cults influenced by African animism and witchcraft. Pray for the Holy Spirit to expose the lies of these cults and of the Spiritist priests and guides. Pray for those people in spiritual bondage to be delivered through the power and truth of Jesus.

4 The Catholic Church desperately needs renewal. Many leave for evangelical churches, other faiths, or become non-religious. Only a minority of Catholics faithfully practice their religion. The Church needs 100,000 more priests to meet their needs. Praise God for almost 1 million "Bible circles" (study groups). Pray that this focus on Scripture study may shape the lives of Catholics. New life comes from the charismatic movement (now over 15 million), and growth of evangelical Catholics.

5 Evangelicals face difficult challenges. Too many groups give more attention to numerical growth than to discipleship. This leads to immature churches, spiritual error, and believers who move from one church to another. "Prosperity teaching" adds to the problem. Celebrity lifestyles, scandal, and lack of accountability among pastors damage churches. Pray for leaders devoted to humility and faithfulness. A greater commitment to pastoral training is encouraging, but with over 200,000 congregations much work remains. Pray also for greater unity and cooperation. The diversity in churches is a blessing, but it sometimes leads to rivalry and jealousy.

6 **Brazil became a leading mission-sending nation** in one generation. Almost 2,000 Protestant, Independent, and Anglican missionaries went out. Brazilian faith, energy, adaptability, and talent (sport, music, dance) opens doors! Unfortunately, poor preparation and lack of support sometimes hinder their efforts. Pray for more churches to have a vision for missions. Ask the Lord of the harvest to send out and provide for Brazilian missionaries. Pray that they persevere and bear fruit.

7 **Many regions of Brazil still lack an evangelical presence.** The poor and less-developed northeast region has the lowest percentage of evangelicals, especially Piauí and Ceará. Pray for greater response to Pentecostal outreach there. Cities have many churches, but many needs. Up to one-third of the populations of Rio de Janeiro and São Paulo live in crime-filled slums. The rich and powerful, and the ethnic minorities often have few evangelicals. The battles between ganglords and police often make victims of the innocent. Brazil has 8 million children at risk, 7 million child labourers, and 600,000 girls in prostitution. Some churches and agencies help children through orphanages and job training ministries, but it is not enough. Pray for Christian ministry to every area of need.

8 **Indigenous peoples.** The Amazon Basin has 36,000 communities without a church. Most can only be reached by boat. Church planting is difficult because of the isolation and poverty, but several organizations send missionary boats. Pray also for sensitivity as numerous agencies minister to the Amerindian groups spread across Brazil. These indigenous peoples suffered centuries of oppression, exploitation, and worse. Problems continue to this day. Brazilians need to see these peoples as national treasures instead of a nuisance. Ask God also to bless the 45 current Bible translation efforts, and to send workers to help with the 10 languages that still need the Scriptures.

9 **A greater vision is needed to reach immigrants** to Brazil. The largest Japanese community outside Japan lives in Brazil (around 1.5 million). Many claim to be Catholic, but their spiritual practice is combined with Shintoism and Buddhism. Over 200,000 ethnic Chinese now live in Brazil, and multiple agencies plan to reach out to them. The Jews have few followers of Christ among them, and the same is true of the Muslim Arabs and Turks. Pray that the Church may find effective means to reach these groups.

Canada   *The Americas*

Pop 33.9 million. **Capital** Ottawa (1.2 mill).

Christians 24.4 mill. *Evangelical Christians* 2.6 mill.
Largest Religion Christian.
Fastest Growing Religion Muslim.

Largest Ethnic Groups European origin–British (36%), European origin–French (15.8%, majority in Quebec), European–Mixed origin (14.5%), Other European (13.7%, includes many Germans, Italians, Ukrainians), Chinese (3.2%), South Asian (3.1%), Indigenous (2.9%).
Official Languages English, French. **All languages** 169.

Economy One of world's leading industrial nations with lowest public debt of G8 nations. Abundant natural resources point to a strong future. Service industry provides most employment.

Politics Constitutional monarchy (member of British Commonwealth) with multiparty parliamentary democracy. Differences between French-speaking Quebec and the other English-speaking provinces present occasional threat to national unity. Large areas of land restored to First Nations peoples.

1 Christian influence on Canadian society declined across the last century. The non-religious population grew the most as Christians left the Church, but other religions grew quickly through immigration and high birthrates. The mainline churches, especially the United Church and Anglican Church, became more liberal in their beliefs about God and the Bible. They also declined in numbers.

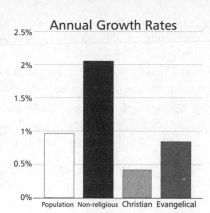

Annual Growth Rates

Population · Non-religious · Christian · Evangelical

2 Catholicism is the largest religious influence in the country. Immigrants bring new life to the Catholic Church. Urban churches are multicultural and lively. Charismatic renewal ministries like Catholic Christian Outreach and National Evangelization Teams contribute to the church growth around the country. Pray for much-needed revival, in the Church first and beyond to society again.

3 Evangelical Christians were 25% of the population in 1900, but only 8% today. Some evangelical and charismatic groups do grow, but overall the Christian population loses influence for the gospel. Words like "evangelical" and "born-again" sound suspicious to people, and the media shows hostility to biblical Christianity. Pray that Christians overcome these suspicions with humility, patience, wisdom, and love. Evangelicals in Canada come from different ethnicities, cultures, denominations, and age groups. Pray for this diversity to be a testimony to the truth and power of the gospel!

4 Quebec has the strongest Catholic heritage. Over 80% call themselves Catholic, but church attendance in Quebec is the lowest in all Canada. Secular and modern ideas dominate the French majority culture. Some view evangelical churches as cults. The small number of evangelicals in Quebec come from French, English, and immigrant Protestant churches, and the Catholic Church also. Quebec often wants to separate from Canada. Pray for unity, fellowship, and collaboration among evangelicals, and for this province to make a good contribution to the history of redemption in Canada.

5 Canadian indigenous peoples suffered shameful treatment in the past. Both the government and the Church (mostly European-background) abused these peoples in painful ways. To move forward, people must repent and forgive. Pray for the Truth and Reconciliation Commission begun in 2010. First Nations peoples have 600 reserves in Canada, all with small populations. Many Canadian indigenous peoples are called Christian, but many do not practise their faith. Pray for leaders and churches that represent First Nations culture to plant others like them! Six languages received the New Testament in the last 10 years. Translators now work on 6 more, but 27 native languages have no Scripture. Missions evangelize and plant churches in the difficult northern parts of the country. Revivals came among the Inuit in the Arctic. Pray that the power of the gospel will transform Inuit communities! Large numbers of First Nations people live in cities like Toronto, Winnipeg, Edmonton, and Regina. Many live in poverty and struggle with substance abuse. Some ministries reach out to them, but evangelicals usually overlook this challenge on their doorstep.

6 The nation of immigrants now welcomes immigrants. Canada has one of the world's highest rates of immigration and receives many refugees. Most live in Toronto, Montreal, and Vancouver. Pray especially for:

- *The Chinese population* (1.4 million). Almost 400 congregations exist among them. They face challenges of 2nd-generation immigrants who sometimes leave the Church, and separation from wider Christian fellowship.
- *South Asians* (over 1 million), Canada's largest bloc of unreached peoples. Most are Hindus, Sikhs, and Muslims. Vancouver is the world's 2nd-largest Sikh community.
- *Muslim peoples.* Most are of Arabic background, but now more Afghans, Kurds, Somalis, Sudanese, East Africans, and Southeast Asian Muslims also come to Canada. Very few ministries or churches reach out to them. The few believers among them came mostly from Lebanon or Palestine.

Pray for urban churches to reach out to these unreached peoples God placed near their churches and homes! Canada once felt proud of the way it sent aid and peacekeeping forces, and many missionaries, around the world. But the number of missionaries decreased. Pray for more churches and individuals to join in the evangelization of the unreached around the world.

Chile
The Americas

Pop 17.1 million. **Capital** Santiago (6 mill).
Christians 14.9 mill. *Evangelical Christians* 3.2 mill.
Largest Religion Christian.
Fastest Growing Religion Non-religious.
Largest Ethnic Groups Hispanic (95.9%), Amerindian (3.2%).
Official Language Spanish; but Mapudungun increasingly recognized.
Economy Well-developed economy based on mining. Poverty still widespread.
Politics A republic since 1810. Democracy since 1989 after decades of a repressive regime.

1 **Chile now sustains a democratic government,** a stable and growing economy, and recent education and poverty reforms. The past years under Pinochet (1973-1988) were a painful era of injustice and repression. The regime murdered more than 3,000 people and abused thousands more. Forgiveness and grace are necessary for national wounds to heal.

2 **New freedoms for the people** brought positive and negative changes. Crime and drug abuse continue to increase. Almost 15% of births are to mothers under age 19. Many people now separate themselves from religious groups like Catholicism and Pentecostalism. Pray that Chileans will honour the positive aspects of their traditional family and society. Pray that the government, churches, and missions will address the massive gap between the rich and poor.

3 **The Roman Catholic Church** lost members and influence. Only 12-13% of Catholics now regularly attend mass. Many Catholics became evangelicals or Pentecostals, but many became non-religious. Among other problems, the Church did not do enough to help the poor or oppose injustice during the Pinochet regime. Pray for Bible study to happen on a deeper level, so that many might find their faith renewed and discover the living Jesus!

A Pentecostal revival came to the Methodist Church in 1909 and began a dynamic, indigenous movement. Growth continues across almost all denominations with evangelicals in them! Evangelicals now face good opportunities to influence society. Sadly, Chile has the most divided Pentecostal movement in the world. Churches and denominations split and split again to form hundreds of independent Pentecostal groups. Pray for commitment to unity across all Christian groups.

The Chilean Church lacks missions vision. Chile could do more to send and support missionaries. COMIBAM (*Cooperación Misionara Iberoamericana*) and other agencies set up missions training programmes that raised some interest. Almost 90% of evangelicals belong to indigenous groups that reach many but do not work together locally or globally. Pray for links with the global Church for mission and ministry. Pray for the work of foreign missionaries in Chile to encourage a missions vision.

Ethnic minorities in Chile find life is difficult, and often face prejudice.
- *The Mapuche* (Mapudungan speakers) are about 70% Catholic, but the old religion and shamans still have the most influence. Translators completed the Mapudungan New Testament in 1997.
- *Rapa Nui* (Easter Islanders from Polynesia) now live mostly on the mainland. Their culture and language disappear as tourists, the film industry, and the pains of alcoholism and AIDS overrun their society. Four evangelical congregations and some missionaries now serve them.
- *Palestinian immigrants.* Santiago now has over 70,000 Christian Palestinians, the largest concentration in the world outside of Palestine.

Colombia
The Americas

Pop 46.3 million. **Capital** Santa Fé de Bogotá (8.5 mill).
Christians 43.7 million. *Evangelical Christians* 3.5 mill.
Largest Religion Christian.
Fastest Growing Religion Ethnic religions.
Largest Ethnic Groups Mestizo: Eurindian (57.6%), Spanish-speaking white (20%), Mulatto: European/black (14%), African-Colombian (4%), Zombo: Afro-Indian (1.9%), Indigenous Amerindian (1.6%).
Official Language Spanish. **All languages** 83.
Economy Rich in resources. Oil, coal, and cocaine are main exports. Colombia supplies 90% of US cocaine, so poor farmers face temptation to grow it. Drug trade

often controlled by guerrilla groups or the private armies of drug lords. Wide gap between rich and poor.
Politics Independent of Spain in 1819, and a separate state in 1831. 170 years of divided politics, dictatorships, and civil wars. Some supported violent Marxist guerrilla groups, others sided with drug cartels. The peace process begun in 2004 brought stability and a decrease in violence.

Colombia has more stability. Murder, kidnapping, and crime rates recently decreased. Thousands of guerrillas and paramilitaries put down their weapons in the peace process. Problems continue, but the progress encourages many. Pray for the government to be strong in the stand against violence, and to be just as it moves the nation forward. CEDECOL (the Evangelical Confederation of Colombia) made a formal statement against violence and outlined a peace process.

It will raise the role of the Church and encourage cooperation, but it will also make evangelicals more of a target. Pray for peaceful solutions.

2 **Pray for God to break Satan's hold on Colombia.** Former fighting groups turned into gangs that profit from cocaine and kidnapping. Cocaine production increases, and now even threatens the land in national parks and nature reserves. Thousands die from drug-related violence, and leave many as orphans and widows. Bogota has one of the highest numbers of street children in Latin America. Colombia has the world's 2nd highest number of internally displaced people (3 million). Another 3 million left the country. Believers face intimidation, property destruction, murder, and assassination. Dozens of pastors and priests die every year. Pray for all who suffer from loss, that the Lord will meet their needs. Proclaim the Lordship of Christ over the spirits of violence, revenge, lawlessness and corruption, and the occult practices. These all brought the nation to a low point.

3 **The Roman Catholic Church** lost members and influence. Changes in the constitution (1991) ensured religious freedom, and many Catholics left to join evangelical groups. Catholics generally hold traditional values, but only about 25% practise their faith. A strong charismatic movement grows among the active Catholics. Pray for renewal inside Catholicism that wakes up the Church.

4 **The Church continues to grow,** even during times of crime, terror, and murder. Evangelicals are 7.5% of the population, and charismatics are near 18%. Local indigenous churches grew the most. Local, citywide, and national outreaches produced many congregations and new believers. Bellavista Prison in Medellin was once called "hell on earth". Believers prayed for the prison and witnessed there, and former criminals turned to Christ. They pray, fast, and evangelize, and the prison now has a Christian radio station and Bible Institute! The country-wide vision *Amanacer Colombia* seeks to plant 18,000 more churches in Colombia. Pray for leaders.

5 **Physical and spiritual enemies of the gospel target missionaries.** Foreign missionaries live with the threat of kidnapping, murder, and financial abuse. Colombian missionary vision grows. While some Colombians work abroad, most work cross-culturally in their own country. Several Amerindian groups remain closed to foreigners, but Colombian missionaries try to reach every tribe. Pray for courage and faith for both native and foreign missionaries. Pray especially for Christians to reach out to the Muslim community (35,000), who come mostly from Syrian, Lebanese, or Palestinian backgrounds.

6 **Amerindians** suffer oppression and discrimination. Colombians often disregard their contribution to culture and society. Most are poor, less educated, and vulnerable to violent conflict and land abuses. Some of the 94 groups have strong, well-led churches that work together and send out missionaries to others. 37 Amerindian languages do not have a New Testament, and 25 have no Scripture at all. Violent groups kidnapped or killed some Bible translators. Some groups persecute Amerindian Christians and force them to return to their former religious practices. 15 of the 94 Amerindian groups remain isolated and unevangelized. Pray for each of these precious groups to find the gospel before they disappear forever.

Costa Rica

Pop 4.6 million. **Capital** San José (1.5 mill).

Christians 4.4 mill. *Evangelical Christians* 689,000.
Largest Religion Christian.
Fastest Growing Religion Non-religious.

Largest Ethnic Groups Costa Rican (76.9%), Mestizo (9.4%), Other Latin American (7.6%), Jamaican/Creole (1.3%), Amerindian (1.1%). 500,000-700,000 Nicaraguan refugees and migrant workers.
Official Language Spanish. **All languages** 13.

Economy Recent growth in tourism and tech sector helped the depressed economy. 20% live in deep poverty. Leading country for ecological conservation.

Politics Independence from Spain in 1821. A stable, multiparty democratic government.

 Evangelicals in Costa Rica grew to 15% of the population, and established one of Latin America's most effective mission movements. But the Church needs prayer. Most Costa Rican churches are good at winning "converts", but they fail to disciple them well. Pastors survive on minimal incomes and have little help, so they struggle to provide consistent pastoral care. Christians often fall away in difficult times or move to different churches.

Charismatic renewal touched the Roman Catholic Church. Many found personal faith in Christ and this strengthened the Catholic Church. 73% of Costa Ricans are Catholic, but most do not practise their faith. Pray that charismatics who stay in the Catholic Church may bring further renewal to mainstream Catholicism.

Ministries and missions. The Costa Rican Evangelical Alliance brings together many evangelical denominations for outreach and mission. Pray for a new programme, *Costa Rica Century XXI*, that promotes development of churches. Costa Rica offers some of the best Christian training options in Latin America with 26 Bible schools and seminaries and a very extensive TEE programme. The country's stability provides an ideal base for many regional and global ministries, and national ministries and missions increase as the Costa Rican Church matures.

Pray that these peoples might see indigenous and biblical churches among them:
  • *Amerindian tribes* are small in number, but each of the 5 groups is culturally unique and special to God. An active indigenous Church grows among the Cabécar. The Bribri now have a New Testament after nearly 100 years of translation work!
  • *The Mekitelyu African Caribbean community* (on the Caribbean coast). Few have a life-changing faith in Christ. Pray for revival in these Protestant churches.
  • *The Chinese population* increased rapidly, and there are now some growing evangelical fellowships. Pray that workers from Costa Rica and the Chinese diaspora will come and reach these people.
  • *Arab, Iranian, and South Asian immigrants* have come to Costa Rica. Most are Muslim or Hindu.

Two-thirds of Costa Ricans are under age 30. Alcoholism, drug addiction, violence, and immorality harm this generation. Many social problems exist on the "Street of Bitterness" near the national university. Pray for sustained outreach from Christian student and youth ministries (IFES, Cru, and others).

Cuba

Pop 11.2 million. **Capital** Havana (2.1 mill).

Christians 6.3 mill. *Evangelical Christians* 981,000.
Largest Religion Christian.
Fastest Growing Religion Christian.

Largest Ethnic Groups White Hispanic (62%), Mulatto & Mestizo Hispanic (25%), Black Hispanic (11%), Asian (1%, primarily Chinese).
Official Language Spanish. **All languages** 4.

Economy Lack of essentials affects many, but high standards of health and literacy. Tourism now important.
Politics Independent from Spain in 1898. Fidel Castro brought Communism to power in 1959.

1 **Cuba faces a difficult future.** Communist Party leaders hold power, but this economic approach cannot last forever. The economy is one of the weakest in the Caribbean, and too few young people remain to support the older generation. Deep poverty led to a successful black market with widespread crime, drugs, and prostitution. The regime imprisoned more than 500,000 for political reasons, and over a million became refugees in the USA. Pray that the Cuban diaspora might find Christ and influence their original homeland. Pray for reasonable reforms, freedom, forgiveness, and for every industry built on sin to be overcome by good.

2 **The majority of Cubans confess Catholicism,** but the faith is often deeply mixed with Spiritism. African Caribbean religions such as *Santería,* and other cults similar to Haitian voodoo, may have more than 3 million followers. Pray that Christians may show love, understanding, and spiritual power to see many delivered from this satanic bondage. Less than 10% of Catholics go to mass, but the few true believers now see growth after difficult decades. Pray that the Catholic Church will become a place where millions find Jesus.

3 **Praise God for growth in evangelical churches!** Protestants doubled in number from 1995 to 2010, and many new believers are young people. Persecution refined the Church and it grew stronger in unity and a life of prayer. Christians with few outside resources still minister in bold, creative ways. God brought maturity and confidence through suffering. Pray that this faith community would be a light to the nation.

4 **The choice to follow Jesus is still a sacrifice** even while persecution is less than in the past. The government makes it difficult to build new churches, and sometimes imprisons leaders. The dozen evangelical and 2 Catholic Bible schools or seminaries face government obstacles, and lack funds and teachers. Churches urgently need Bibles and Spanish-language materials. Pray for courage and endurance for suffering believers. Praise God for leaders who remained in Cuba and carry on the long, hard work of serving the people.

Dominican Republic
The Americas

Pop 10.2 million. **Capital** Santo Domingo (2.2 mill).
Christians 9.6 mill. *Evangelical Christians* 931,000.
Largest Religion Christian.
Fastest Growing Religion Non-religious.
Largest Ethnic Groups Dominican (87.5%), Haitian (10.2%, most are undocumented, illegal migrant labourers), Spanish (0.8%), US citizen (0.7%).
Official Language Spanish. **All Languages** 8.
Economy Steady growth since 2004 after 20 years' decline. Wide gap between rich and poor.
Politics Democratic governments since 1961 after long, repressive dictatorship.

1. **The Dominican Republic has suffered 500 years of turmoil.** First, one million indigenous Arawak Taino people died from foreign diseases and Spanish rule. Sugar cane plantation owners later imported African slaves. Both European colonial powers and later Dominican governments exploited the land and people. Pray for economic and political justice to visit this nation that has suffered for so long.

2. **The Catholic Church** has influence, but nearly half of Catholics do not practise their faith. Up to 25% claimed by the Church say they have no religion. Many others follow a dangerous combination of Christianity and Afro-Spiritism similar to Cuban *Santería* and Haitian voodoo. Pray for renewal through the power of Scripture and the Holy Spirit. Thank God for the Catholics who faithfully follow Jesus.

3. **The number of evangelicals doubled in the past 20 years!** Many people are open to the gospel when it is presented simply and in love. But only a small number who respond will participate in local churches. Believers struggle to live well in their society where corruption, violent crime, and promiscuity are common. Evangelical churches often work from poverty, which can create dependent relationships on foreign organizations. Some spiritual leaders migrate to the USA or Puerto Rico for a better life. Pray for provision and faithfulness for those called to minister in poor areas. Pray for a missions vision, and more Dominican missionaries to be sent out.

4. **The less-evangelized:**
   - *Haitian immigrants or descendants.* Hispanics, even Christians, usually discriminate against them. They bring many of Haiti's problems with them, but respond well to the gospel. Pray for the Dominican Church to engage the Haitians with faith, love, and grace.
- *The unchurched majority* often profess Christianity, but the occult is strong. Up to 4,000 villages have no evangelical witness. The middle and upper classes have fewer evangelicals, but the Christian & Missionary Alliance and Foursquare Missions minister to them. Pray for Christian workers at the 37 universities and colleges. More than 200,000 students need to be reached. IFES and Cru have fewer than 1,000 students in their groups.
- *The Chinese* have only 2 congregations. The International Mission Board works among them.

Ecuador

Pop 13.8 million. **Capital** Quito (1.8 mill).

Christians 13 mill. *Evangelical Christians* 1.2 mill.
Largest Religion Christian.
Fastest Growing Religion Non-religious.

Largest Ethnic Groups Spanish-speaking (56.4%), Amerindian: Quichua (40.5%), English-speaking (1.5%), German-speaking (0.7%), Other Amerindian groups (0.5%).
Official Language Spanish. **All languages** 25.

Economy Major exports are bananas, oil, flowers, shrimp. Oil benefits foreign companies and a minority of Ecuadorians, but at cost to Amerindian peoples and the environment. Some economic growth since 1999, but poverty remains.

Politics Independent from Spain in 1830. Ecuador lacks stable government. Presidents do not last in the job and changes come often. The Quichua now have a small political voice. Ecuador needs constitutional reform.

---

1 Praise God for these answers to prayer:
- *The gospel impact on the Quichua* is a modern miracle. In 1967, only 120 people out of 3 million followed Christ. Today some Quichua areas are over 50% evangelical! Avant Ministries worked among them for over 100 years. Over 240,000 people go to churches planted through Avant.
- *The small jungle tribes.* Ecuador received worldwide attention in 1956 when the Waorani (Auca) killed 5 young foreign missionaries. Now almost all these tribes have churches and the Scriptures through the work of various missionary groups.
- *HCJB Radio* began in Ecuador in 1931, the first of the great Christian mission radio broadcasters. Today the ministry blesses Ecuador and the whole world.

2 **Ecuador once had Latin America's smallest percentage of evangelicals,** but it grew steadily across the last 50 years. Most growth is in cities and among the Quichua. Divisions over denomination, culture, and personality hinder the gospel. Many churches exist independently without accountability to others. Pray especially for Amerindians and Spanish-speaking churches to work together with cultural sensitivity. The majority of evangelicals are Amerindian, but Spanish-speaking evangelicals have more power. Pray for unity, and for evangelistic passion for the still unreached parts of the country.

3 **The Catholic Church** loses members to marginal sects and evangelical groups. Pray for increased spiritual life among Catholics, and for growth of the charismatic movement inside the Catholic Church. False teachings attract both Catholics and evangelicals. Pray for the error of these groups to be made known, and for believers to address them with truth and love.

4 **Pray for good church-mission relationships.** Ecuador sent 10 cross-cultural missionaries in 1996, and over 100 in 2005! Congregations now understand better the commitment and cost. Both foreign groups and AMEE (Evangelical Missionary Association of Ecuador) support churches in their mission vision. Foreign missionaries also serve in supportive ministries, church planting, and pioneer work. HCJB, *Radio Biblica Cristiana,* and others produce over 1,200 hours per week of Christian programming in 12 languages. Christian TV programmes on 3 channels teach and encourage believers.

5 The less-evangelized:

- *Slum-dwellers of Quito and Guayaquil.* Over 60% of Guayaquil are extremely poor, and live in slums built on a polluted marsh. Few Christian workers serve these deprived people.

- *The Afro-Ecuadorian peoples* are only 0.03% evangelical. Many are Catholics, but in truth practise Spiritism. Pray for a spiritual breakthrough in this group!

- *28,000 people live on the Galapagos Islands.* Praise God for a ministry among them through Missionary Ventures International. Many tourists who visit there oppose biblical Christianity.

- *Loja Province* remains isolated from most of Ecuadorian life, and is only 0.1% evangelical. *Operation Esperanza*, a partnership among several mission agencies, reaches out to isolated villages through prayer, radio, evangelism, and holistic ministry.

El Salvador

The Americas

Pop 6.2 million. **Capital** San Salvador (1.6 mill.).
Christians 5.9 mill. *Evangelical Christians* 2 mill.
Largest Religion Christian.
Fastest Growing Religion Non-religious.
Largest Ethnic Groups Hispanic (90.1%), Part-Indian (4.5%), Pipil/Aztec (4.0%), Lenca (0.8%).
Official Language Spanish. **All Languages** 7.
Economy Exploitation and war held back development for decades. Improvement from 1991 to 2005 reduced the poverty number by half. Over 30% of Salvadoreans live outside the country due to economic migration.
Politics Independence from Spain in 1821 and from the

Federation of Central American States in 1838. Corrupt dictatorships led to organized revolt from 1980 until the peace accord in 1992. Democratic government now more established.

1 **Peace, stability, and democracy** came since 1992, after the suffering of civil war. Elections now replace assassinations. God answered prayer! The country must prioritize recovery from the wounds made by centuries of oppression and 12 years of civil war. Over 75,000 died in fighting or by death squads. 20% of the population fled. Pray for repentance, reconciliation, and a fair society based on respect for human rights.

2 **Evangelical churches** grew through the civil war. God worked a modern miracle! Believers planted up to 9,000 churches in the 1990s. The country still needs more evangelical congregations, but the work has slowed down. El Salvador has some of Latin America's largest megachurches. Elim and *Tabernáculo Bíblico Bautista* each have over 100,000 in their networks. Megachurches can influence society through their good resources and platform in the community. Pray for unity and vision for outreach among all churches so the nation might belong to Jesus. *El Salvador* means "the Saviour" in Spanish.

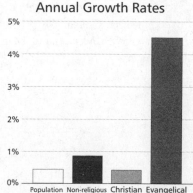

Annual Growth Rates

Churches need leaders. The war, poverty, and few staff limited training opportunities. Pray for the Bible schools, seminaries, and TEE programmes. Pray for God to provide all material needs and staff needs in this time of economic stress. This ministry needs more missionary input.

Social changes inside and outside the country need prayer and action.

- *3.3 million Salvadoreans live abroad,* many in the USA. Many work illegally, and sometimes others exploit them. Their absence also affects families left back home.

- *A large number of youth* (up to 70% of young men) join *maras* or street gangs. Many of them have fathers who live abroad. The Church must create new methods to serve teenagers, young adults, and the 115,000 university students. El Salvador was mostly rural just one generation ago, and now 60% live in cities.

- *The Amerindian population* suffered many abuses in the last century. Pray for the Church to begin a sensitive church-planting ministry among them.

Falkland Islands   *The Americas*

Pop 3,000. **Capital** Stanley (2,000).
Christians 2,000. *Evangelical Christians* 329.
Largest Religion Christian.
Fastest Growing Religion Non-religious.
Largest Ethnic Groups British (95%), Other (5%).
Official Language English.
Economy Mostly based on fishing and sheep farming. No unemployment.
Politics Self-governing British Overseas Territory. Claimed by Argentina.

Dispute harms this remote group of islands. The UK and Argentina both claim rights. This led to conflict in 1982, and tension continues. The 2009 constitution reflects the strong desire of the Islanders for self-government. Pray for wise and fair agreements, and for understanding among all three groups. Pray for the Christians who work and pray for the reconciliation of all involved.

The country has three main denominations: Anglican, Roman Catholic, and Tabernacle United Free Church. Most people are shallow in their religious faith. Pray for believers in their witness to fellow Islanders, and to the fishermen, oil workers, military, and tourists who visit from different nations.

French Guiana

Pop 231,000. **Capital** Cayenne (64,000).

Christians 211,000. *Evangelical Christians* 10,000.
Largest Religion Christian.
Fastest Growing Religion Islam.

Largest Ethnic Groups African Caribbean (62%), European (15.1%, mostly French background), Chinese (5%), Brazilian (5%), Indian (4%), Afro-American Maroon (3.2%), Amerindian (2%), Laotian Hmong (1.5%), Javanese (1%).
Official Language French. Guianese French Creole widely spoken. **All languages** 15.

Economy Developed coastal strip and undeveloped jungle inland. The Guyanese Space Centre (launch centre for the European Space Agency) is major source of income and development. Tourism is potential growth industry.

Politics French Overseas Department. Formerly French penal colony. High subsidies from France/EU give little incentive for independence for most of population.

1 **Praise God for church growth** among the Creole and Amerindians, especially Caribs/Galibi. Haitians, Antilleans, Hmong, Brazilians, and interior tribes (Maroons) also responded to the gospel. Evangelicals grew steadily in the past 20 years. Workers from many denominations now see people come to faith in previously unreached people groups. Pray for a co-operative spirit among evangelicals, and for unity through the Suriname Bible Society.

2 **French Guiana has a new image** as a developed multicultural society, rather than as a place for imprisoned criminals. This change also brought French secularism and moral challenges. Many young people cannot find employment and are restless. Graphic pornography from French satellite TV disturbs the moral framework. Families suffer with high rates of illegitimate births and many single-parent homes. Harm to the environment, illegal immigration, and human trafficking for the gold mine industry all cause problems.

3 **The least-reached peoples:**
 • *French Guianese Creole youth* see the riches of French society, but cannot afford them. IFES/*Union des Groupes Bibliques Universitaires* (UBGU) work on public university campuses. Pray for Biblica to complete development of the Gospels in Guianese French Creole.
 • *Amerindian and Maroon tribes.* The Wayana (1,100), Wayampi (700), and Emerillon (500) need the gospel. They practise spirit worship (animism). Maroon tribes live in the country's interior. Tribal Christians from Suriname work among them.
 • *Immigrant communities.* The Chinese have only 1 known congregation. French and European communities work with the space programme, and few follow the Christian faith.

Greenland

Pop 57,000. **Capital** Nuuk (15,000).

Christians 55,000. *Evangelical Christians* 3,000.
Largest religion Christian.
Fastest Growing Religion Non-religious.

Largest Ethnic Groups Greenland Inuit (88%), Danes (8%).
Official Languages Greenlandic Inuktitut (3 dialects), Danish. **All languages** 2.

Economy Based on fishing and support from the Danish government.
Politics Overseas administrative division of Denmark with self-government. More liberty since 2009.

1 **Almost every settlement in Greenland has a Lutheran church** – but many lack real spiritual life. Pray for renewal. Modern culture clashes with Greenland's old ways, and many now battle with immorality, sexual abuse, alcoholism, mental illness, and suicide. Some indigenous believers and foreign missionaries serve in counselling, healing, and deliverance, and see wonderful fruit by the work of the Holy Spirit. Pray for this to continue. Thank God for new airstrips that opened remote settlements for ministry.

2 **Evangelical witness is recent.** Greenland had about 20 born-again believers in 1984, but now has an evangelical movement in several denominations. The Greenlandic Church learned to express itself in biblical ways suited to its culture. Pray that the unique culture of the indigenous Inuit people might now be made complete in Christ. Pray that God will change many lives through the Greenlandic Bible (finished in 2001).

Guatemala

Pop 14.4 million. **Capital** Guatemala City (1.1 mill).

Christians 13.8 mill. *Evangelical Christians* 3.5 mill.
Largest Religion Christian.
Fastest Growing Religion Non-religious.

Largest Ethnic Groups Spanish-speaking Ladinos (53%), Amerindian-Maya (36.3%), Amerindian–other indigenous (8.4%).
Official Language Spanish. 23 recognized Amerindian languages. **All languages and dialects** 42-52.

Economy Agriculture provides half of nation's jobs. Majority still in poverty, and indigenous peoples particularly oppressed. Trans-shipment point for drug trade, as 70% of cocaine to USA passes through Guatemala.

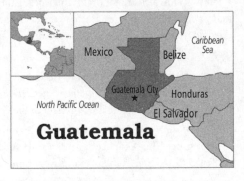

Politics Independent from Spain in 1821 and from the Federation of Central American States in 1838. Destructive guerrilla warfare from 1960 until a 1996 peace agreement. The 2007 elected government seeks national unity and opportunities for Mayan people.

1 **Authorities now appreciate and cooperate with evangelicals and committed Catholics** to address social problems such as street children, substance abuse, and illiteracy. The Mayans faced oppression and exploitation for centuries. Now both the government and churches seek justice, and respond to the wrongs done. God answered prayer!

2 **Guerrilla war** erupted in 1960 after years of mistreatment towards the poor and indigenous peoples (especially Mayans). Over 200,000 people died, mostly at the hands of the military (armed by the USA). Over 40,000 people disappeared (likely killed). The war displaced 1 million people inside Guatemala. 250,000 became international refugees. All involved must recognize and repent from sins of the past, and repair the damage. Pray especially for evangelical leaders from both Mayan and Spanish-speaking communities as they work to heal the nation.

3 **Violence continues today.** Guatemala has the highest murder rate in all of Latin America. Youth gangs (*maras*), drug traffickers, and "death squads" cause enormous problems. Murder is common, and life is cheap. Matters are worse for children at risk like the 15,000 street children, the many orphans, and the majority of 6- to 18-year-olds who live in poverty. Ask God to bind the spirit of murder and cause the peace of Christ to prevail!

4 **The Catholic Church** declined in number and influence. A large charismatic movement grew, but the Church put limits on it, and many of them left to join evangelical churches. Others rediscovered early Mayan religions, or mixed the Mayan gods with Catholic saints. Pray for new life to fill the Catholic Church.

5 **Praise God for the growth among evangelicals** who now are almost 25% of the population, in 25,000 congregations! The 1976 earthquake, the pain of war, and the witness of believers and missionaries all drew many to Jesus. Growth came quickly among Pentecostals, but faith is not always deep. Many mix pagan practices and beliefs with biblical faith, or follow attractive teachings on prosperity. Churches that fail to disciple new believers may lose them in the next two decades. Pray that pastors and leaders will demonstrate Christ-like humility, and rise above foolish divisions and greed.

6 **Pioneer missionaries** helped sow the recent harvest of believers. Presbyterian missionaries birthed Theological Education by Extension (TEE) here in the 1960s, and now Christians worldwide use TEE. 6 seminaries and many Bible schools serve the Church. SIL International oversaw translation of the New Testament for many Amerindian groups. National believers now carry on much of the training and translation work. Outreach touched every Mayan tribe, and indigenous Christianity grows among some with the help of Bible translations. Some tribes have few believers. Pray for these churches to mature, and to contribute to the wider Church outreach in Guatemala. Pray also for good ways to train leaders of poorer rural churches.

7 **The Guatemalan missionary movement** began in 1982 with a vision for the world. The first mission formed in 1984 (*Agencia Misionera Evangélica*). CONEM (the National Commission of Mission to the World) co-ordinates the national missions effort. Guatemala has 3 missionary training centres. Pray for growth of the missionary movement, and for a new conference that helps pastors catch a vision for mission.

Guyana

Pop 761,000. **Capital** Georgetown (132,000).

Christians 401,000. *Evangelical Christians* 151,000.
Largest Religion Christian.
Fastest Growing Religion Non-religious.

Largest Ethnic Groups South Asian (42.5%, mostly rural farmers from India), African (29.7%, most in civil service, government, and urban areas), Mixed (16.5%), Amerindian (8.9%, most live in the interior).
Official Language English. Creole used by 90% of the population. **All languages** 19.

Economy Supported mainly by mining and agriculture. Good potential hindered by a 20-year Marxist economic experiment. Slow improvement since 1992. Severe floods (2005) brought $415 million damage.

Politics Dutch rule (1750-1814), then British rule until independence (1966). Colonial import of labour for the sugar industry created current racial diversity and political tension.

---

1   **Guyana faces various threats.** Venezuela and Suriname both claim large parts of Guyana's land. The two main political parties divide along racial lines (Indo-Guyanese versus Afro-Guyanese). The climate sometimes ruins the economy, like the disastrous floods in 2005. Many people emigrated, including many of the most talented. Pray for hope to come to Guyana, and for the gospel to transform society.

2   **Praise God for His good work in Guyana!** Pentecostal, charismatic ("clap-hand"), and evangelical denominations grow, even while the population size decreases. Most churches divide along racial lines, but the multiracial congregations that do exist provide some of the few ethnic bridges in the country. The Guyanese Evangelical Fellowship works to bring unity across denominations. Pray for all believers to show the power of the gospel in their unity, in their words, and in holy living.

3   **Pray for the peoples:**

• *Many Afro-Guyanese and mixed-race Guyanese are Christian,* but have a weak faith. They often mix Christian beliefs with other religions. Obeah Spiritism and witchcraft, Rastafarianism (from Jamaica), foreign sects, and the racist group Nation of Islam all attract people away from Jesus. Pray for the true gospel to impact these communities.

• *The Indo-Guyanese population is mostly Hindu.* Pray for their evangelization. Some are Christians or Muslims. Guyanese Muslims remain the least-reached group in the nation.

• *The Amerindian peoples are mostly Catholic,* but some became Pentecostals through the work of Assemblies of God, Church of God, and others. Churches in the south are missionary-minded! Pray for indigenous Christian leadership and mature churches that can keep their cultural identity and still survive the impact of modern society.

4   **Christian missions and ministry affect society positively.** Missions have freedom to work in every area. The testimony of love from Christian medical workers opens doors for the gospel. Guyana has the 2nd-highest AIDS rate in the Caribbean. Malaria affects many. Most denominations work among youth. Family life, education, employment, and future hope are big challenges for young people. IFES reaches 12,000 students every week in 200 groups at primary, secondary, and tertiary levels.

Haiti

Pop 10.2 million. **Capital** Port-au-Prince (2.1 mill).
Christians 9.7 mill. *Evangelical Christians* 1.6 mill.
Largest Religion Christian.
Fastest Growing Religion Ethnic religions.
Largest Ethnic Groups African Caribbean (94.3%),
Mulatto (Eurafrican) (5.4%).
Official Language French. Many speak Haitian Creole,
English, or Spanish.
Economy Poorest state in the Western Hemisphere.
Remittances from Haitians abroad and aid funds are
major sources of income.
Politics The first black republic in the world, created in
1804. Since then a history of bloodshed, dictatorships, and military coups.

1 **The 2010 earthquake** was a horrific disaster. Over 230,000 lost their lives, and over 1 million lost their homes. The people of Haiti responded with prayer and repentance. The president called for three days of prayer and fasting and over 1 million people attended. Pray this turn to God will change the spiritual life of Haiti! Healing from such hurts needs time, care, and the love of God. Efforts to rebuild will take years. Pray for generous help from wealthier nations and aid agencies. Pray for hope out of tragedy. Haiti must rebuild a better country with wisdom and justice.

2 **Tyranny, cruelty, and spiritual bondage fill Haiti's history.** The Spanish genocide against the indigenous Arawaks, Spanish and then French slavery, and Haiti's own brutal leaders promoted a spirit of violence for centuries. Voodoo (a religion of spirits) creates fear throughout society. Many Catholics practise some voodoo. Pray that the power of the Holy Spirit might overcome the forces of evil. Pray for the Holy Spirit to cleanse the Church. Ask God to bind the powerful spirits underlying voodooism in Jesus' name, so the nation can be wholly dedicated to the Lord.

3 **Evangelicals and Protestant churches** grew in number through evangelism, acts of love, and an open stand against voodooism. Foreign and local believers work together better than before, and see more fruit! The Church reaches out well to the rural poor and illiterate. Churches have many needs, though. Denominations break apart and divide Christians. Poverty, language (Creole), and literacy limit training for church leaders. Pray for the 20 Bible schools or seminaries and the many TEE programmes that seek to meet the need. The Protestant Federation and the Council of Evangelical Churches now give Protestants a platform to speak with one voice to the government about social and religious initiatives. *Vision Haiti* brings Christians of many denominations together to pray for deliverance. Pray for spiritual purity and for the love and power of Christ to shine through believers.

4 **The country's economic situation** leads many to despair. Corruption is widespread and crime is high. Millions escaped to the USA and other Caribbean countries, and some now suffer as illegal refugees. Others stayed but turned to drugs to escape problems. These difficulties attract Christian aid agencies such as World Vision, Tearfund, and many others. They need sensitivity and wisdom to respect the creativity and independence of Haitians they work with. Aid needs to include ecology, agriculture, healthcare, AIDS, education, and children at risk. Pray that Christian work will have long-term impact on the nation, and draw people to the Saviour. Pray also for more workers called to reach the Haitian diaspora.

5. **Haiti's youth and children** need special prayer. Teens face poverty, unemployment, illiteracy, and turmoil. Many turn to guns and gangs. 10% of Haiti's children (300,000-400,000) are *restaveks* (from the Creole word "stay-withs"). People can buy and sell these children who labour without education or healthcare. Ask God to bring compassion and love to these little ones.

Honduras

The Americas

Pop 7.6 million. **Capital** Tegucigalpa (1 mill).
Christians 7.4 mill. *Evangelical Christians* 1.8 mill.
Largest Religion Christian.
Fastest Growing Religion Non-religious.
Largest Ethnic Groups Spanish-culture (89%), Amerindian (7.9%), Arab-Palestinian (0.8%), Jamaican (0.5%).
Official Language Spanish. **All languages** 13.
Economy One of the Western Hemisphere's poorest countries with most of population below poverty line. Economic activity from agriculture, services, tourism, and remittances.
Politics Independent from Spain in 1821. 134 revolutions and revolts by 1932. Military rule for most of 20th century. Democratic civilian government since 1984, but faces challenges from a powerful military and from US interference. High levels of corruption, unemployment, and crime.

1. **Evangelical growth** began with the Evangelism in Depth programme of 1963. In 1960, evangelicals numbered 32,000. Now they approach 1.8 million! Pray for the *Confraternidad Evangelica*. It represents 90% of Honduran evangelicals, and promotes fellowship and cooperation. Honduran churches lack unity. Countless denominations create problems of jealousy and isolation. Hurricane Mitch (1998) destroyed many towns, villages, and churches. Many still need to rebuild even after more than 10 years. World Relief, Tearfund, and others help with the work.

2. **The most basic problem for Honduras is deep poverty.** Children form more than half the population, and most live in poverty. Many try to reach the USA to find family members there, but often end up suffering in prison in Mexico or Guatemala. Honduras has more *pepenadores* (garbage dump children) than any nation in the Americas. Violent gangs exploit vulnerable children as members and sex workers. Honduras has 60% of Central America's AIDS cases. Organized crime and *maras* (gangs) link with drug cartels and hold power in society. Pray for moral courage for Hondurans to stop the spread of AIDS. Pray for righteousness, and for wise government that works equally for rich and poor.

3. **The Catholic Church** continues to lose its influence. Only about 20% of Catholics are actively involved in the Church. Many migrated to evangelical churches. Pagan practices attract others, and the lack of indigenous church workers is a problem. Catholics and evangelicals agree on most social and community matters. Pray for the Holy Spirit to bring revival to the Catholic Church! A revival would transform Honduran society.

4. **Several mission agencies train and send cross-cultural workers.** Pray that the whole Honduran Church would gain a greater vision for outreach and mission. Church leaders need

training. Many seminaries and Bible schools struggle to find staff, and foreign missionaries could help meet this need. Divisions between denominations cause problems for training, but TEE programmes and networks can help the situation.

5 **Many Amerindian peoples came to Christ,** and churches grow among them. Pray for the work of Baptists, Christian Fellowship Mission, Miskito Missions, and others among the very poor. MOPAWI (*Mosquitia Pawisa*) began on Christian principles, and works to develop and protect local cultures. Praise God that the indigenous peoples of the eastern rainforest won rights to preserve their endangered land and cultures. Pray for healthy development of churches among them, and for an end to all forms of abuse.

Jamaica *The Americas*

Pop 2.7 million. **Capital** Kingston (582,000).
Christians 2.3 mill. *Evangelical Christians* 765,000.
Largest Religion Christian.
Fastest Growing Religion Non-religious.
Largest Ethnic Groups Jamaican (93.7%), Haitian (2.0%), East Indian (1.7%), Chinese (1.2%), Euro-American (1.0%).
Official Language English. 97% speak Jamaican Creole. **All languages** 7.
Economy Revenue comes from tourism, remittances, mining, and agriculture. Rising crime rates, under-employment, and the large public debt are challenges.
Politics Parliamentary democracy since independence in 1962. Politically stable with problems of gang warfare, illegal drug dealing, and corruption.

1 **Jamaica has a wonderful Christian heritage,** with a rich history of sending missionaries. It has the most evangelicals and the best-resourced churches in the Caribbean. The Bible Society (Kingston) provides Bibles to most mini-states of the region with a special vision for young people. Praise God that many foreign workers entrusted leadership to national leaders, and the Jamaican Church became its own. Pray that the 15 Bible schools and seminaries, and the Keswick teaching conferences may be strongholds of biblical theology, godly lifestyle, and mission sending for the Caribbean!

2 **Christianity in Jamaica needs renewal.** Only a minority of Christians attend church or live a Christian life. The country faces moral and social collapse. Powerful drug cartels use Jamaica to ship drugs to the USA, which leads to violence and other crime. Rape and domestic violence are widespread. Pray that government and church leaders will reject compromise. Christians must work for unity and integrity in the Church, and also to address and combat political and social problems. The very poor have little exposure to the gospel except by radio. Pray for courage, moral purity, and determination to turn the country back to God.

Mexico

Pop 110.6 million. **Capital** Mexico City (19.5 mill).

Christians 105.1 mill. *Evangelical Christians* 9.2 mill.
Largest Religion Christian.
Fastest Growing Religion Non-religious.

Largest Ethnic Groups Mexican(American)/Spanish *mestizo* (65.1%), Euro-American (13.6%), Detribalized Amerindian (9.9%), Amerindian-speaking indigenous peoples (9.4%).

Official Language Spanish (world's largest Spanish-speaking nation). **All languages** 297.

Economy Free market and free trade improved economy based on oil, industry, manufactured goods, tourism and agriculture. Income and wealth distribution unequal. Organized and armed drug cartels control much of US border region.

Politics The Spanish and smallpox destroyed the developed Aztec Empire in the 16th century. Independent from Spain in 1821. Northern territories lost to USA in 19th century. One-party federal democracy until 2000, when Mexicans elected opposition leader. Now a federal republic with elected leadership. Small guerrilla movements in the south promote Amerindian land and culture rights.

 Mexico faces social and economic challenges. The government sees the difficulty of traditional solutions and now invites Christians and churches to help meet human needs. 60% of Mexicans struggle with poverty, both rural poor and slum-dwellers. Native Amerindians face greater poverty, less education, and more political unrest. Evangelical ministry among them has a good response, but also opposition. Pray that Mexicans, both indigenous and *mestizo*, might find their identity and purpose in the love of Christ and the purposes of God.

2 **The massive illegal drug trade** brings huge amounts of money into Mexico's economy. Over 500,000 people are now addicted to cheap drugs. The wealthy, powerful cartels that control the drug trade are ruthless. They kill each other as well as police, armed forces, journalists, and helpless citizens. Corruption in government leads to millions embezzled, and corruption in police forces allows growth in organized crime. Pray for integrity, courage, and wisdom to address these great challenges.

3 **Mexico and the USA** often resent each other, but they need each other. Only cooperation and trust will overcome the wickedness of the drug cartels and human trafficking rings on both sides of the border. The USA spends large sums of money on border protection. More than 1 million try to cross the US border each year, and hundreds die in the attempt. Around 13 million Mexican migrants work in the USA. Some towns in Mexico have few able-bodied men left at home. Millions in Mexico depend on money sent from relatives in the USA. Some US states' economies depend on the informal economy driven by migrants. Mexican migrants sometimes find Jesus while away from home, and bring evangelical Christianity back with them. Pray for justice in all relations between these countries.

4 **The Catholic Church** dominated the country for 300 years, and now is very diverse. Most Mexicans are culturally Catholic but only 10% regularly attend church. Christ-centred renewal grew within the Catholic Church, and the Alpha course draws Catholics to Christ. Many Mexicans blend the gods and goddesses of Amerindian spiritism into a folk version of Catholicism. Pray for the Holy Spirit to break the influence of these ancient gods and the spirit world. Pray for renewal to spread through the Mexican Catholic Church.

5 **Evangelicals** numbered 800,000 in 1960. They now number over 9 million, and the movement still grows! The Catholic Church oppressed ministry work in the past, but the government now gives freedom at local, state, and national levels. Both international denominations and indigenous movements grow well. The Evangelical Fraternity of Mexico (CONEMEX) works for unity and for good relations with the government. A Pentecostal fellowship also brings together the millions of Pentecostals. Large events such as the March for Jesus/March of Glory and prayer movements draw believers together. Geographical distance and broken relationships divide many families, and many are first-generation believers who need help to grow in their commitment and faith. Pray for godly church leaders, and for more pastors willing to work among the poor in rural or slum areas. City jobs and bigger churches attract many new pastors.

6 **Believers endure prejudice, disturbance, loss or damage of property and churches** in the southern states, particularly Chiapas, Oaxaca, and Guerrero. Persecution often comes when they refuse to join community religious events that involve a mix of Christian and pagan practices. Pray that believers will demonstrate the meekness and love of their Saviour when mistreated. Pray for full religious freedom at local and national levels.

7 **More and more Mexican churches send and support missionaries.** COMIMEX (*Cooperación Misionera de México*) links together most mission agencies and many denominations for prayer, training, and to get more churches involved. *Pueblos Musulmanes Internacional* is one of several significant international agencies born in Mexico. Few churches support pastors and missionaries well, especially poorer churches in rural areas and urban slums. Pray for a release of finances from Christians into Kingdom work. Pray also for a biblical perspective on matters of money.

8 **Some sections of the population have few committed Christians.** Many Mexicans seek something better than the empty religious traditions of the past. Pray for evangelical growth to continue in both numbers and spiritual maturity.

- *The "Rosary Belt" region* in central Mexico covers Zacatecas, Jalisco, Aguascalientes, Guanajuato, Colima, Michoacán, and Querétaro. Spanish colonial and religious influence remains strong there. None of these states are more than 2% evangelical, and Querétaro is only 0.25% evangelical.

- *Indian peoples* are considered Catholic, but they sometimes practise a folk religion where the old gods and spirits have Catholic names. COMIMEX finds that 15 out of 298 people groups do not have a Christian witness among them. 98 others have a church that still needs outside help to reach its own people.

- *Around one-third of Mexicans are aged 15 or younger.* Many young people in Mexico respond to evangelical faith, but not enough churches reach out to them in creative and relevant ways. Mexico may have 800,000 street children, mostly in Mexico City. They each need love and help. Up to 11 million child labourers help support their families, but drop out of school to do so.

9 **A remarkable history of Bible translation work** began in 1936. Workers have completed 120 New Testaments and provided 190 language programmes across the years! 11 languages still need a Bible, and 20 need Bible portions. Pray for translation agencies to enjoy good relations with government agencies. Pray that the Scriptures will transform individuals, congregations, and the nation.

Nicaragua

Pop 5.8 million. **Capital** Managua (944,000).

Christians 5.7 mill. *Evangelical Christians* 1.7 mill.
Largest Religion Christian.
Fastest Growing Religion Christian.

Largest Ethnic Groups Latino-Mestizo (67.5%), Latino–white Latino (16.5%), Amerindian (5.9%), Middle Eastern (0.8%).
Official Language Spanish. English-speaking communities on East Coast. **All languages** 7.

Economy One of poorest states in Americas due to 2 centuries of dictatorships, civil wars, and natural disasters. Progress since 1991 after economic collapse in the 1980s. Dependent on remittances from workers abroad.

Politics Independent republic since 1838. Corrupt dictatorship ended in 1979 after bitter civil war. Suffered from Cold War politics and US interference. Government alternated between left-wing and right-wing regimes. Current cooperation between the political left and right may be progress, or may be an alliance for deceitful purposes.

1 **God brought many people to Himself,** even through suffering. Believers increased through mass crusades, Evangelism in Depth programmes, and local church outreaches. Volcanic eruptions, earthquakes, and hurricanes led many to question life and eternity. War, conflict, and political struggles turned many towards the compassion of Christians, and hope in Christ. Evangelicals grew from 2% in 1960 to 30% today, and growth continues.

2 **The horrible events of 1978-1998** divided politics, communities, churches, and families. Many people have lost loved ones or property, and they suffer deeply. Distrust keeps groups divided. Both the Catholic Church and evangelical megachurches influence politics, and some believers now work in government. Pray that Christians might commit to be a righteous influence in Nicaragua. Organizations such as CEPAD (The Evangelical Committee for Relief and Development) and the Assemblies of God sponsor programmes to help. Churches minister to the most needy, and try to help their members who live in extreme poverty.

3 **Ministry challenges for the Church:**
- *Those devastated by civil war.* Former Sandinistas (Marxist group) and Contras (US-sponsored opposition group) continue to suffer loss. They need believers to minister love and spiritual healing to them after the bitter war where all sides suffered deep pain.
- *English/Creole and Miskito churches* in the Caribbean eastern provinces. These Moravian, Anglican, and Catholic churches often confuse the gospel with local ethnic religions. The Sandinista government persecuted the Miskito peoples especially.
- *Garifuna* churches are few. Most of the Garifuna ethnic group are still animistic, or trapped by the spirit world. Translation of the New Testament is in progress.
- *Chinese immigrants* (over 11,000) have no churches among them.
- *Young people* (under age 30) are 75% of the population. Few families or churches give stability to youth. Pray for Nicaraguan youth to bring future transformation and redemption to society.

4 **Missions and outreach.** The *Movimiento Misionero Transcultural Nicaraguense* (MMTN) links mission agencies and churches to send missionaries and work in unity. Foreign missionaries work in Bible teaching, leadership training, and partner with Nicaraguans for development projects. These projects empower Nicaraguans towards economic and spiritual progress.

Panama
The Americas

Pop 3.5 million. **Capital** Panama City (1.4 mill).

Christians 3.2 mill. *Evangelical Christians* 677,000.
Largest Religion Christian.
Fastest Growing Religion Non-religious.

Largest Ethnic Groups Latino-Mestizo (56.8%), Panamanian Caucasian (8.8%), Amerindian (10.9%), Caribbean (9.4%), European/American (6.6%), East Indian (4%), Chinese (1.5%).
Official Language Spanish. **All languages** 18.

Economy Service-based economy, mainly banking, commerce, and tourism. Developed infrastructure and strong prospects from Panama Canal (global trade). 40% live in poverty. Drug cartels have influence.

Politics Republic with constitutional democracy. Formerly part of Colombia. Politically stable.

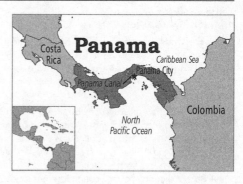

1 **Pray that Panama may bless the world.** The country motto is "Panama, Bridge to the World, Heart of the Universe". Panama possesses great diversity, and great potential. Its location, the Canal, and stability attract many races. Some come for honest purposes, but others come for criminal reasons such as the drug trade and sex trafficking. Pray for the government to rid the country of corruption and to oppose wickedness.

2 **The large Christian population in Panama** does not impact the society well enough. Spiritual interest and responsiveness allowed evangelicals to grow from less than 5% of the population in 1970 to nearly 20% in 2010. Yet evangelical congregations often focus more on their own "success" than on working together for their communities and society. The Catholic Church lost its strong influence. Many members compromise with false teachings of New Age, astrology, and psychics. Divorce, domestic violence, and children outside of marriage are common in society. Christians often fail to demonstrate biblical and godly living. Pray for the Holy Spirit to intervene.

3 **Panama has missionary vision.** Over 94 Panamanians serve cross-culturally at home and abroad. The network PAAM (Panamanians Reaching the World) brings together dozens of ministries and denominations for this task. Pray for the following groups inside Panama:

- *The Amerindians.* They respond well to the gospel, and churches still grow. New Tribes Mission and Avant plan to phase out their work as indigenous churches mature. Pray for indigenous leadership and indigenous expressions of Christian faith. Pray for the Bible in each language.

- *The Chinese.* Most still speak Hakka (60%) and Cantonese. There are only 11 congregations among them, and only a handful of workers.

- *The South Asians.* Most speak Gujarati. The majority are Muslim, some Hindu, and others Sikh. No known groups reach out to them.

- *The 9,000 Jews.* Most of these Orthodox Jews are hard to reach. Pray for a Panamanian outreach called Messianic Association "Remnant of Israel".

Paraguay

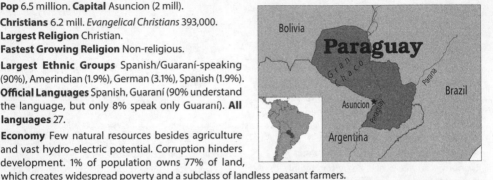

Pop 6.5 million. **Capital** Asuncion (2 mill).

Christians 6.2 mill. *Evangelical Christians* 393,000.
Largest Religion Christian.
Fastest Growing Religion Non-religious.

Largest Ethnic Groups Spanish/Guaraní-speaking (90%), Amerindian (1.9%), German (3.1%), Spanish (1.9%).
Official Languages Spanish, Guaraní (90% understand the language, but only 8% speak only Guaraní). **All languages** 27.

Economy Few natural resources besides agriculture and vast hydro-electric potential. Corruption hinders development. 1% of population owns 77% of land, which creates widespread poverty and a subclass of landless peasant farmers.

Politics Independent from Spain in 1811. Devastating wars (1864-1870, 1932-1935) and a corrupt dictatorship (1954-1989). Recent democratic and economic reforms move Paraguay slowly forward in political and trade networks.

1. **Paraguay suffered under two centuries of war and bad government.** National leaders were corrupt, foolish, or both. Thank God for recent changes. Pray for Paraguay's current leaders, that they will be upright and wise, and will serve the suffering people of the country.

2. **The Roman Catholic Church** dominates the spiritual and political life of the country. It has long opposed corruption and immorality in the nation. Sadly it has also opposed evangelical work. Catholicism in Paraguay mixes Christian faith with strong devotion to Mary and occult-related bondage to old deities and customs. Few of the Spanish-Guaraní majority have a living relationship with Christ. Pray for a spiritual awakening.

3. **Many of Paraguay's believers are immigrants:** Germans (Mennonites and Lutherans), Brazilians (Pentecostals), Ukrainians (Baptists and Pentecostals), Koreans (Presbyterians), and Chileans. Mennonites work with indigenous peoples in the Chaco region. Koreans reach out also. Pray for mission vision in the immigrant churches, to reach out across cultures with the gospel.

4. **Thank the Lord for evangelical church growth.** Pentecostal/charismatic churches from Brazil, Chile, and Argentina especially grew well. Pray for Christian unity and collaboration among many different evangelical denominations. An association of pastors works to promote national strategies to evangelize the whole country, and to assist isolated rural churches. Pray that local churches will embrace the challenge of the unreached and needy within Paraguay and beyond. Workers planted churches among many of the 21 indigenous Amerindian groups. Pray for the gospel to root and grow in these and the remaining minority groups.

5. **The country still needs missionaries** to serve the Paraguayan Church and strengthen national leadership. Opportunities exist for church planting, leadership training, holistic mission, and especially education. Many poor school-aged children work instead of studying. Schools, teacher training, and improved education and literacy will help transform Paraguay. The Christian Mission Society, Latin American Mission, and others work in these vital areas.

Peru

Pop 29.5 million. **Capital** Lima (8.9 mill).

Christians 28.2 mill. *Evangelical Christians* 3.4 mill.
Largest Religion Christian.
Fastest Growing Religion Ethnic religions.

Largest Ethnic Groups Highland Amerindian peoples (49.4%), Mestizo (32%), white Peruvian (13.5%), Chinese (2.9%), Lowland Amerindian peoples (1%), Afro-Peruvian (0.7%), Japanese (0.3%).
Official Languages Spanish, Quechua. **All languages** 93.

Economy Revenue from fishing, mining, agriculture (coffee), and tourism. Strong growth since 2000. Cocaine production and oil exploitation in the Amazon basin remain serious issues.

Politics Fully independent from Spain in 1824. Long history of dictatorship and repressive military rule. Democratic government failed to bring improvement, and 2 Marxist groups brought 15 years of violent guerrilla warfare. Future governments must deal wisely with poverty, corruption, ecology, and instability of neighbouring countries.

---

1 **Peru made notable progress** when President Fujimori dealt strongly with Maoist terrorist groups. The government then brought abusive, corrupt politicians (including Fujimori) to justice. Many people still suffer from the effects of the terror groups and "death squads". The country urgently needs a stable government to carry out just policies after so many years of corruption, dictatorship, and threats to security. Over 50% still live in poverty, and 20% in extreme poverty. Amerindian groups face racial injustice, and urbanization brings many poor migrants to urban areas. Pray for justice and righteousness for the crushed and oppressed.

2 **Foreign exploitation.** International companies willingly endanger environments for oil and mining. This threatens the existence of vulnerable peoples who live in these areas. Foreign demand for cocaine encourages poor farmers to grow coca for profit. Drug wars and trafficking create a complex situation with no easy solution. Ask God to tear down structures of sin, to expose evil, and to provide good solutions to complicated problems.

3 **The Catholic Church** faces a crisis. Many members left to join evangelical churches. Others follow foreign sects, atheism, or old Andean pagan practices. Only 5% of Catholics attend church. Most clergy are foreign. Praise God for the positive impact of a charismatic movement (the Christian Life Movement). Pray for many to find the light and liberty of the gospel found in the Bible.

4 **Evangelicals** grew strong during times of violence, even though the army and the guerrilla fighters between them martyred 750 evangelical leaders and put others in prison on false charges. The first evangelical church began over 100 years ago. There were 78,000 evangelicals in 1960, and 3.4 million in 2010! Peruvian believers engage in social and political issues, and the state sees their contribution as a force for positive change. After peace came, growth slowed. Pride came along with the success, and sharp division exists within and between some denominations. Pray for a national body that will bring together diverse groups of believers. Churches must focus on discipleship, accountability, and quality teaching. Pray for a new work of the Holy Spirit to reignite the Church.

5 **Praise God for church growth** in the highland and lowland Amerindian groups.
  • **Quechua and Aymara (highland) peoples** descend from the Incas. Superstitions and pagan

practices still bind millions. But the Quechua Church thrives today. Whole villages turn to Christ! The Quechua Church flourishes as Christianity becomes indigenous to the people through music, Scripture, styles of worship, and even forms of church. Pray for continued ministry to both urban and rural Amerindian groups. Pray for reconciliation through Christ between Quechua speakers and Spanish speakers after centuries of oppression. Pray for unity of all Christian ethnic groups in Peru.

- *Lowland Amerindians* responded to the ministry of South American Mission, Swiss Mission, and others. Now local missionaries also reach their own and related tribes. Leaders developed a network of Amerindian churches from 17 groups (FAIENAP). Pray for the work to and among these peoples. They carry the huge burdens of the exploited Amazon region.

Puerto Rico *The Americas*

Pop 4 million. **Capital** San Juan (2.7 mill).

Christians 3.8 mill. *Evangelical Christians* 1 mill.
Largest Religion Christian.
Fastest Growing Religion Non-religious.

Largest Ethnic Groups 98.7% of population are Latino in orientation, language, culture. Hispanic Puerto Rican (70.4%), African–Puerto Rican (15.5%), Mixed Puerto Rican (10.3%).

Official Languages Spanish, English. **All languages** 13.

Economy Free market economy with manufacturing, trade, and tourism. Among highest per capita incomes and costs of living in Caribbean.

Politics Former Spanish colony. Related to USA since 1898. Administered by an elected governor although US president is chief of state.

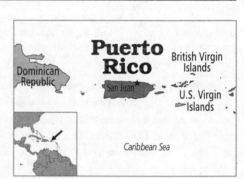

1 **The churches make little impact on the nation's social needs.** The very high rates of substance abuse, corruption, crime, and poverty confront the gospel in a country 97% Christian and 25% evangelical! Over 45% live below the poverty line. 62% fail to complete secondary school. Drug addiction, alcoholism, and HIV/AIDS rates rank among the highest of any US state or territory. Puerto Ricans moved to cities and to mainland USA to find work. As many now live abroad as in their homeland. High levels of corruption disrupt local government.

2 **Evangelical churches grew from 0.1% in 1900 to 25.2% in 2010!** Puerto Ricans traditionally follow Catholicism. A large charismatic movement grew inside the Catholic Church, but most new growth is among independent groups. Puerto Rican mission vision also grew. Pray for effective training and support of new mission ventures. Media ministries use TV, local radio, and Internet sites to offer practical answers to life and faith questions. IFES and indigenous student movements reach most campus students. Pray for ministries to continue shaping future leaders, and for discipleship movements to transform the lives of believers.

Suriname

Pop 524,000. **Capital** Paramaribo (263,000).

Christians 260,000. *Evangelical Christians* 72,000.
Largest Religion Christian.
Fastest Growing Religion Non-religious.

Largest Ethnic Groups East Indian (29%, mostly from Bihar), Surinamese Creole (19%), Maroon (16%), Indonesian (15%, mostly Javanese), Mixed-race (11.3%), Amerindian (4%), Chinese (2.7%).
Official Language Dutch. Sranan Tongo (a Dutch Creole) is the trade language. **All languages** 20.

Economy Recent economic growth. Bauxite, oil, timber, marine and agricultural products, and eco-tourism provide revenue. Unsecure borders allow for illegal gold extraction and drug trafficking.

Politics Independence from the Netherlands in 1975. Socialist military dictatorship (1980-1987), then unstable period of coups and unsuccessful elections until 1994 agreement for democratic government and peace. Former dictator elected as president in 2010.

1 **Praise God for His work among the Maroon peoples and the tribal Amerindians.** Almost 60% of the Maroon peoples now follow Jesus. They live in the interior of Suriname. World Team, local churches, and others sowed the gospel for many years, and now there is good fruit! The southern Amerindian churches embraced the Great Commission, and now send missionaries to tribes and villages in French Guiana, Brazil, and other parts of Suriname.

2 **Suriname faced confusion in the years after independence.** Many people lost their way with morals and ethics. Race and religion still divide people, and this blocks political and social progress for the nation. Powerful crime rings traffic drugs and smuggle gold, and they appear unstoppable. Pray for godly leadership for this young nation.

3 **The Surinamese Church** needs good leaders from all cultural backgrounds. Leaders need strong biblical faith, and an open heart to the many peoples of Suriname. Almost half of the population is called Christian, but many do not understand their faith. The Catholic and Moravian denominations grow, but slowly. Newer Pentecostal and charismatic churches grow rapidly. Some Christians mix their Christian beliefs with spirit worship. Pray that Christian leaders seek unity in the body of Christ. Pray for hunger for the Word of God among leaders and their congregations. National movements (for women, for men, for young people) unite believers to pray and take action in their nation.

4 **Pray for Christian cooperation in outreach** to every ethnic group in Suriname.
- *Amerindian groups.* Most have Christians among them. Movements to Christ grew strong among the Wayana, Akurio, and Trio groups. Others churches struggle with strong temptations to old sinful customs or material pleasures. The Carib and Arawak groups on the coast still need the most outreach.
- *Javanese.* Most are Muslim, but not strong in their faith. New generations of Javanese Christians reach out to their own people. The Suriname Javanese New Testament came in 2000, and the Old Testament will come next.

<font />Suriname

- *The Indian community* now has a few believers. World Team and a Hindustani organization want to plant enough churches that every Hindustani could walk to a church. Pray for this vision. Local churches often do not reach out to the Indian community. No groups witness to the Muslims of the Indian community. Pray that God will remove barriers of prejudice and misunderstanding.

- *Chinese churches* now join with other local churches and missions to reach the Chinese in Suriname. Most Chinese in Suriname come from the southern coastal provinces of China.

United States of America *The Americas*

Pop 317.6 million. **Capital** Washington, DC (4.5 mill).

Christians 246.6 mill. *Evangelical Christians* 91.8 mill.
Largest Religion Christian.
Fastest Growing Religion Non-religious.

Largest Ethnic Groups US Caucasian (58.1%, a melting pot of many peoples), Latin-Caribbean American (14.7%), African-American (12.2%), Eurasian (6.6%), Jews (1.8%), East Asian (1.6%), Arab (1.4%), Malay (1.1%), South Asian (0.7%), Southeast Asian (0.7%), North American Indigenous (0.6%).
Official Language English. The Spanish-speaking Hispanic population is 11.2% (34 mill). **All languages** 176. 13% of population use a language other than English in the home.

Economy World's largest and most diverse economy driven by technology, industry, natural resources, agriculture, and services. Gap now large between rich and poor. The USA accounts for 25% of the world's GDP, and nearly 50% of world's military spending. The 2008-2009 US recession affected many economies around the world.

Politics Independent from Britain in 1776 as a federal republic. A world leader with strong democratic tradition, emphasis on private initiative, and civil liberties. Checks and balances in political system limit abuse of power, but also limit some political progress. Threat of terrorism at home and abroad sees US forces engaged overseas, a foreign policy that creates backlash from some parts of the world.

1 **Biblical Christianity has influenced the USA** more than any other nation. Evangelicals (28.9% of population) exist in all major ethnic groups and levels of society. The Pilgrim Fathers of America wanted a land with freedom to practise their Christian faith. This foundation supported the growth of one of the largest Christian movements in history. The USA has 17.6% of the world's Protestants and 16.8% of the world's evangelicals, and a large proportion of the world's missionaries. More than 2,000 recognized institutions offer theological degrees in the USA and Canada. 30,000-50,000 students graduate each year with a desire to impact the world for Christ. America's Christian values shaped modern democracy, human rights, and economic development. Generosity, evangelistic work, and big visions help the gospel progress. Pray that these may continue!

2 **The spiritual heritage of the USA is under attack** from atheist, New Age, and other groups who use their media power to discredit Christians and erase Christianity from American public life. Pray that Christians in America will speak the truth in love, and preserve the Christian legacy and free speech of their country. Pray for Christ-like attitudes and conduct in all conversations and actions with these groups.

3 **America has a massive cultural and social influence**. No other country is a greater force for good in the world, and no other country does more to spread sin. America has made the world a better place through aid and development, innovation in technology and media, universal education, information, defence of human rights, and opposition to tyranny. America has also hurt the world through insensitive cultural domination, selfish individualism, corporate greed, and spreading of pornography, casual violence, and obsession with possessions, wealth, and poverty. America's desire for illicit drugs and fossil fuels causes wars abroad, keeps corrupt regimes in power, and inflicts suffering on indigenous peoples of other lands. Pray that God might shape this nation to be a greater force for good, and destroy these sinful practices that pollute much of the world.

4 **American churches and Christians** now connect with each other more through renewal and revival movements and networks centred around shared values and theology. They connect less through denominations. Most denominations struggle to keep members. These newer movements thrive. Millions of believers participate in megachurches with their networks and satellite churches, or in house church movements. Charismatic and Pentecostal movements continue to rise across the various Christian traditions and denominations. Pentecostals/charismatics were 10% of the population in 1970, but 20% by 2010.

5 **New expressions of Christian and evangelical faith** emerged in recent years. These groups show commitment to spirituality and holistic ministry, and practise their faith with worship and engagement in their communities. They show less loyalty to the political or denominational barriers dividing previous generations. The lively and active ethnic minority churches grow and mature. African-American, Hispanic, and Asian churches reach their own people, reach their communities, and help shape American Christianity. Asian-Americans send many missionaries, and Latino and African-American churches now send more missionaries than before.

6 **The American Church needs revival.** Worship and sermons can appear more like a performance than true fellowship, and pastors often function more like CEOs than shepherds. Americans mix biblical Christianity with strong individualism, a love of money, flexible morals, and national pride. This mix produces a Christian faith that justifies selfishness, immorality, and arrogance. Christians often live like non-Christians regarding marriage and divorce, sexual morality, and attitudes toward possessions. Pray that Christians may be set apart, then repent of selfish living, and change their thoughts and lives. People often turn away from Jesus because of what they see in the American Church. Disappointed Christians leave and go to house churches or practise faith alone. Pray for a return to biblical holiness.

7 **Divisions and denomination splits** harm Christian unity. Denominations debate topics like homosexuality, gender roles, spiritual gifts, views on the end times, prosperity theology, and creation-evolution. But they overlook topics like world evangelization and service to the most vulnerable. The American Church has a rich history of biblical activism, but a recent history of ugly battle in "culture wars" over important issues. Pray for God to raise up ministries and churches that balance biblical truth on moral issues with God's passion to show love to the needy and the lost.

8 **Racial and ethnic minorities.** Most live in cities, but 10% of US counties now have racial and ethnic minorities as the majority. Pray for the needs of these groups, and the churches among them.

- **The African-American community** (38 million) suffered greatly from its origins in slavery, then later racial discrimination. The civil rights movement and the election of the first black president brought great change in attitudes, but many still face the cycle of unemployment, poverty, family instability, and crime. African-Americans more often are Christian than any other racial group. They form many of the largest and most lively evangelical churches in the USA. Pray for churches to serve the neediest communities. Young people have the greatest risk of poverty, drugs, and violence. Many young, inner-city, black males are in prison or in gangs.

- **Hispanics** represent the largest minority group in the USA. Most emigrated from Mexico, but not all came legally. Some struggle with poverty. 40% of Hispanic evangelicals in the USA converted from Catholicism when evangelical church services focused on their language, culture, and personal needs. Almost half of Hispanic Catholics identify with the charismatic movement. Millions of US Hispanics have a living, active faith! Pray for effective discipleship among the 50 million Hispanics in the USA. Many of them may return to their homelands, effectively as missionaries.

- **Native Americans,** also called American Indians, have suffered for centuries in their encounters with white people. Before Europeans came, they numbered at least 20 million. By 1890 only 250,000 remained. Most died from diseases brought by Europeans. White people broke many treaties and promises across the years, and the natives lost almost all their lands, their identity, heritage, culture, and self-respect. Resettlement onto isolated and infertile land created dependence on the government. Today the indigenous peoples face unemployment, poverty, disease, alcoholism, and hopelessness. Some choose suicide. Only 5% of Native Americans follow Christ, though more now find indigenous ways to worship, and can feel both Christian and Native American. Pray for the full reconciliation of native and immigrant peoples, and for ministries of healing and deliverance. Pray for an indigenous movement of the gospel to complete the evangelization of all 550 recognized tribes. God has raised some Native American ministries and a prayer network to reach their own people. No clear people movement to Christ has come yet amongst the aboriginal peoples of Alaska.

- **Asian minority churches** spring up across US cities. Korean churches now number 4,000, Chinese churches 1,000, and they grow quickly! Filipino is America's 2nd-largest immigrant nationality after Mexican, and churches grow rapidly in these communities. Churches exist in some places for Arabs, South Asians, Vietnamese, and Iranians. Korean-Americans send the highest proportion of missionaries of any ethnicity in the USA. But US Asians still have the fewest Christians among them of any of the larger ethnic minorities.

Pray for a unity of believers that rises above race or ethnicity. Pray for a new move of the Spirit of God in these churches.

9 **The less reached.** Many of the least-evangelized peoples in the world settle in the USA. Other groups need specific attention and witness, even in a country where Christian media reaches most of the population.

- **Modern immigrants groups.** America is a nation of immigrants, with the greatest ethnic-origin diversity of any nation in history. 31 ethnicities have a population over 1 million in the USA. It is the only industrialized nation with large population growth, mostly through immigration. Mexico, China, Philippines, India, Colombia, Haiti, Cuba, and Vietnam top the list of US immigrants. Millions come from unreached countries that limit missionary access. Pray that churches will wake up to this opportunity to share the love and power of Christ with these less-reached peoples among them.

- *International students.* Around 700,000 come to America from almost every country in the world. Over half come from Asia, with 103,000 from India, and 99,000 from China. Many encounter the gospel for the first time. The Association of Christians Ministering Among Internationals links ministries such as International Students, Inc., InterVarsity (IFES), Cru, Navigators, and others. Pray for conversions, and for discipleship ministries that equip these students to witness well when they return home.
- *Jews* (5.2 million). The largest concentration of Jews outside Israel live in the USA. In Miami and New York, 9-10% of the population is Jewish. More Jews are won to Christ in the USA than anywhere else since New Testament times! 250,000 worship in Christian churches, or in Messianic synagogues that preserve Jewish customs and culture.
- *Arabs* (4.4 million). Many are Muslim, but two-thirds are Christian.
- *Muslims.* Numbers increase through immigration and conversion of African-Americans from Christianity to Islam. Two-thirds of US Muslims are foreign-born. Population estimates range from 1.3-7 million, and there are 1,200 mosques. Many more Muslims integrate into mainstream life in the USA than Muslims in Europe, but extremist sects fund and control some mosques to spread their teachings. 5-10% of Iranians in the USA are Christian, many by conversion from Islam. The USA has 40 Iranian Christian fellowships. 20% of the prison population now follows Islam, which spreads especially among African-American prisoners. Somalis, Afghans, Bosnians, and other majority Muslim peoples have large refugee communities.
- *South Asians* (5.5 million). Well-educated and wealthy immigrants come to the USA for work in business, technology, medicine, or education. Almost all are Muslim, Hindu, or Sikh, and most have never heard the gospel.
- *The cults.* Some identify themselves as Christian but contain false and extra-biblical teachings. Mormons and Jehovah's Witnesses make many converts. Scientology does not claim to be Christian, but has great influence with American celebrities. The occult and the supernatural attract US youth culture. Christians must be well informed and specifically engage these groups to lift up Jesus who is the way, the truth, and the life.

US Christians have pioneered and supported missions efforts on a grand scale for more than a century. The number, variety, and commitment of US missionaries and agencies affects every nation on earth. Prayer networks and movements emerged in different places and across different Christian traditions. Pray for wisdom and long-term involvement of Christians as salt and light in every corner of US society.

Uruguay

The Americas

Pop 3.4 million. **Capital** Montevideo (1.6 mill).

Christians 2.2 mill. *Evangelical Christians* 210,000.
Largest Religion Christian.
Fastest Growing Religion Ethnic religion (Afro-Brazilian Spiritism).

Largest Ethnic Groups White Uruguayan (86.9%), Italian (2.6%), Afro-Uruguayan (1.8%), Galician (1.2%), Argentinian white (0.9%), Spaniard (0.9%), German (0.9%). The Charrua Amerindians (indigenous people) were destroyed after the arrival of Spanish settlers.
Official Language Spanish. **All languages** 12.

Economy High standard of living for Latin America. A costly, extensive welfare system. Little industry, but good water supplies and potential mineral resources. Greatly affected by larger neighbouring economies.
Politics Independent from Spain in 1828. Democratic government with civil liberties for most years since then.

1 **Uruguay has the most secular society in South America.** While some positive progress came in areas like political transparency and economic development, modern developments like the legalization of abortion, same-sex marriage, and cannabis use came as well. Uruguay's rates of depression, suicide, abortion, and divorce are some of the highest on the continent. Most Uruguayans follow a "do-it-yourself" spirituality influenced by New Age ideas. The nation is 55% Catholic (the lowest in Spanish-speaking Latin America), and only 2% attend mass. Afro-Brazilian Spiritism attracts many people. Pray for the Holy Spirit to expose religious deceptions and defeat the demonic powers behind them.

2 **Uruguay resisted the gospel for a long time,** but changes came in the last 20 years. Many non-religious discovered again a spiritual dimension to life, and churches grew. The Evangelical Alliance planned to double the number of congregations between 1998 and 2005. They met their goal and also saw the number of believers double! Pray the harvest will continue, and that godly pastors and leaders step forward to disciple new believers and churches. The 20 or so seminaries and Bible schools must help meet this demand.

3 **Missionaries to and from Uruguay.** Thank the Lord for the church planters who come from other Latin American countries. SIM International, the Assemblies of God, and others also send workers. Pray that foreign workers will serve the new Uruguayan churches with respect for the unique culture and people in Uruguay. Two Uruguayan mission agencies now send workers (*Avance* and *Desafío Mundial*), and others work with international agencies at home and abroad. Pray for a vibrant missionary-sending movement from Uruguay!

4 **Pray for the less reached.** Jewish, Chinese, Japanese, and Palestinian communities have few believers, and little outreach among them. The number of poor people still grows, and slums emerge in urban areas. Pray that the many new churches will reach the poor. The largest unevangelized group is probably the upper middle-class along Montevideo's coast. Their wealth isolates them from the gospel. Pray for the Lord to use His Church to transform Uruguayan society for His glory.

Venezuela
The Americas

Pop 29 million. **Capital** Caracas (3.1 mill).

Christians 24.6 mill. *Evangelical Christians* 3.1 mill.
Largest Religion Christian.
Fastest Growing Religion Non-religious.

Largest Ethnic Groups Hispanic (96.5%), Others-from European, Middle Eastern, Asian ethnicities (2.7%), Amerindian (1.8%).
Official Language Spanish. **All languages** 47.

Economy The world's 4th-largest oil producer. Still, the country suffers energy shortages. High inflation and unemployment. Large investment in social structures should benefit the poor in time.

Politics Independence from Spain in 1821 (as part of Gran Colombia). Separate state in 1830. Revolutions and harsh dictatorships until 1958. Stable democracy from 1958 until the 1998 coup led by Hugo Chavez. Socialist authoritarian rule since, with support for anti-Western leaders.

1 **Venezuela's evangelical breakthrough** came later than other Latin nations (1980s), but growth continues. Some indigenous churches grow by 10% every year! Believers set a goal in 2002 to plant 25,000 churches by 2015. Many feel they will reach it. Research by *Amanecer* (Dawn Ministries) made the Church aware of needs for every region. Churches also started new social and mission ministries. Evangelicals now influence both society and politics.

2 **Venezuela is unstable and deeply divided.** Recent presidents (first Chavez, now Maduro) and their policies have strong supporters and strong critics in almost equal number. Oil exports boost the economy, but poverty is widespread. 60% of city dwellers live in slums. Venezuela ranks as the 2nd most corrupt nation in Latin America (after Haiti). Significant drug and human trafficking passes through Venezuela. The government invests in programmes for the poor, but significant change has not yet come. Pray for sensible policies that strengthen the nation and also strive for peace at home and abroad. Pray that the most needy people will receive care.

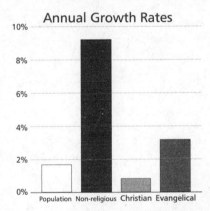

Annual Growth Rates

3 **Spiritual forces battle in Venezuela.** Both rich and poor visit witch doctors in the thousands of spiritist and occult shops. One animist cult (*Maria Lionza*) has 500,000 followers. Only 10% of Catholics attend mass. Fewer people go to church in Venezuela than in any other Latin American nation. Millions of former Catholics chose evangelical faith or no religion at all. New Age spirituality attracts the educated and rich. Satanists actively try to destroy the Church. Caracas has Latin America's largest mosque. Pray for the Holy Spirit to bind all the powers that blind Venezuelans to Truth, and to reveal Christ to all.

4 **Believers must commit to discipleship and wise choices** to face poverty, political struggle, and spiritual warfare. Praise God that cooperation between churches is higher than before. The Church needs unity to face opposition. Spiritual error and misguided leaders confuse many churches with prosperity teaching and other unbiblical practices. Two main seminaries serve the Protestant and Pentecostal churches, and other groups run Bible institutes and schools. Correspondence courses and training programmes help many pastors who cannot study full time. Pray for the Lord to bless the Church's missions vision, especially among interested young people.

5 **Evangelical ministry to 30 Amerindian tribal peoples** met opposition from anthropologists, politicians, the government, and some Catholic priests. The government brought an end to the work of New Tribes Mission and Mission Aviation Fellowship in 2005. Pray for every Amerindian people to hear the gospel, and for churches to reach the last unevangelized tribes. Venezuelans carry forward the work left by expats.

6 Pray also for outreach to other parts of society.

- *Cities.* Caracas, the capital, is one of the least-reached areas. Over 1 million live in slums. Caracas has fewer than 300 churches for 3.1 million people. Gangs or drug lords control entire areas in the city.

- *Prisoners* live in crowded, brutal conditions. They endure torture and violence. VOCEP and other groups share Christ in these dangerous places, and many come to faith! Pray for the safety of new believers in prison and for their spiritual growth.

- *The Arab community* (more than 130,000) is prominent in business. Most originally come from Lebanon and Syria. Many are Orthodox and Maronite Catholics, but most are Shi'a and Sunni Muslims. Some ministries (WEC International) have a vision to reach them, but work has not begun.

- *Western immigrant groups* like Italians, Portuguese, and Spanish have almost no evangelical believers or outreach among them. There is one Messianic Jewish assembly.

Anguilla, Antigua & Barbuda, Aruba, the Bahamas, Barbados, Bermuda, British Virgin Islands, Cayman Islands, Curaçao, Dominica, Grenada, Guadeloupe, Martinique, Montserrat, St Barthélemy, St Kitts & Nevis, St Lucia, St Maarten, St Martin, St Vincent, Trinidad & Tobago, Turks & Caicos Islands, Virgin Islands of the USA. (Cuba, Dominican Republic, Haiti, Jamaica, and Puerto Rico are written separately.)

The Caribbean islands offer a wide diversity of cultures and experiences, but they share important features. They clearly share geography. These small islands all fall within a tropical zone. This affects island life deeply. Even more deeply, the islands share a colonial history. England, France, the Netherlands, and Spain competed and fought imperial wars on and for these islands. These wars shaped Caribbean population, economy, culture, religion, and more. The following needs deserve prayer. They apply to the smaller islands listed, and also to the larger islands that have their own section.

1 **Many islands live with vulnerability.** Tropical storms and other natural disasters hit hard. This brings human suffering and property loss. It also brings financial disaster for poorer economies that depend on tourism and agriculture. Any changes in population, in culture and values, in climate and weather, in government and the economy, can have a great effect on small islands.

2 **Social issues challenge Caribbean societies.** Most of the population descends from slaves brought from Africa by European powers. Former treatment of slaves shaped modern values and patterns of life. Children often do not know or see their fathers, and mothers raise them alone. Immorality causes broken families, and broken homes can lead to more immorality. Too many get involved with violent crime, gangs, guns, and drug and alcohol abuse. The social and justice systems of many nations lack strength to face these challenges effectively.

3 **Economic inequality causes problems in the Caribbean.** A large gap divides the few people who are rich (often white people) and the many poor, and causes resentment and envy. This situation looks too much like the colonial era. Some islands promote themselves as tax havens for offshore banking, which attracts much-needed money. But sometimes criminals and others involved in evil work also use these banks. The islands often survive through tourism, but tourists bring other challenges. The rich use these tropical paradises like playgrounds. This creates good jobs, but it also models that the main values in life are material wealth and pleasure seeking.

4 **Most people call themselves Christians in these islands,** but how much real faith is found? Christianity is in the majority, but real followers of Jesus are in the minority. Caribbean communities lack spiritual hunger and need revival. Public life and family life need more impact from Christian values. Evangelical and charismatic Christian groups grow steadily in many places, but mainline denominations do not grow. Praise God for the strong Christian presence and history of these islands! Pray now for a new work of the Holy Spirit.

5 **The Caribbean needs ministry work.** Churches need unity more than anything else. Denominations and different churches do not cooperate well, though it has begun to happen in a few places. Christians do not grow as quickly or deeply spiritually as they should. Two great bottlenecks limit Christian growth in the Caribbean. Believers need opportunities for serious discipleship, and church leaders need opportunities for training. Many work as a pastor and hold another full-time job. God blessed the Caribbean islands with many Christian radio stations. Radio programmes can be used to share the gospel, to teach about the Bible and Christian life, and to encourage believers and those who struggle.

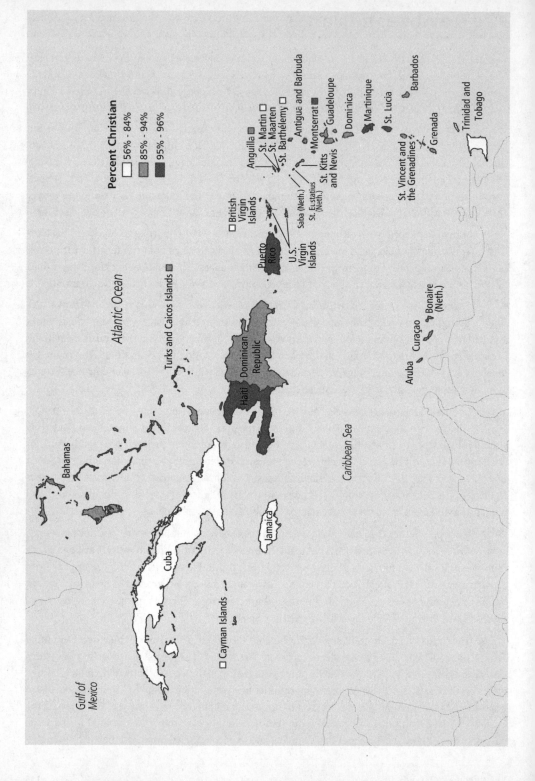

Percent Christian

- ☐ 56% - 84%
- ▦ 85% - 94%
- ■ 95% - 96%

Gulf of Mexico

Atlantic Ocean

Caribbean Sea

Bahamas

Cuba

Cayman Islands ☐

Jamaica

Turks and Caicos Islands ▦

Haiti

Dominican Republic

Puerto Rico

U.S. Virgin Islands

British Virgin Islands ☐

Anguilla

St. Martin ☐
St. Maarten
St. Barthélemy

Saba (Neth.)
St. Eustatius (Neth.)

St. Kitts and Nevis

Antigua and Barbuda ☐

Montserrat ■

Guadeloupe

Dominica

Martinique

St. Lucia

Barbados

St. Vincent and the Grenadines

Grenada

Aruba
Curaçao
Bonaire (Neth.)

Trinidad and Tobago

6   **The balance of society affects Caribbean life.** Younger generations do not understand their Christian background. Many call themselves Christian, but do not know what that means. Some of the most talented Caribbean leaders and workers move to North America or Europe for better jobs and lifestyle. Their home islands feel the great loss. For some Caribbean islands, more people now live abroad than live at home on the islands. Tensions often exist in countries with different racial groups. Minorities who arrived most recently are most vulnerable. Haitian immigrants face prejudice, and they need to be reached with the love of Jesus. So do the Asian and Middle Eastern immigrants who live in the Caribbean and sometimes face discrimination.

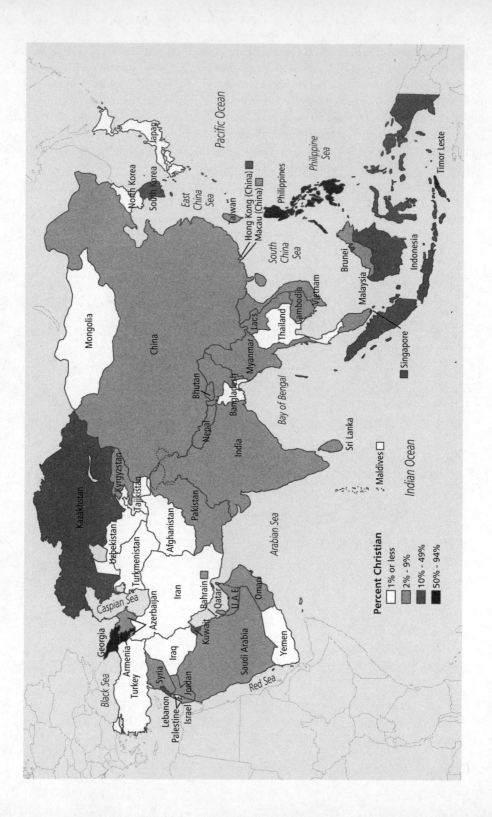

Percent Christian

- 1% or less
- 2% - 9%
- 10% - 49%
- 50% - 94%

Pacific Ocean

Philippine Sea

Timor Leste

Indonesia

Brunei

Malaysia

Singapore

Philippines

Hong Kong (China)
Macau (China)

South China Sea

Vietnam

Cambodia

Laos

Thailand

Myanmar

Taiwan

East China Sea

South Korea

North Korea

Japan

China

Mongolia

Bhutan

Bangladesh

Nepal

India

Sri Lanka

Maldives

Indian Ocean

Bay of Bengal

Arabian Sea

Pakistan

Afghanistan

Tajikistan

Kyrgyzstan

Kazakhstan

Uzbekistan

Turkmenistan

Iran

Caspian Sea

Azerbaijan

Armenia

Georgia

Turkey

Black Sea

Lebanon

Palestine

Israel

Syria

Jordan

Iraq

Kuwait

Bahrain

Qatar

U.A.E.

Oman

Saudi Arabia

Yemen

Red Sea

ASIA

Pop 4.2 billion.
Christians 368.1 million. *Evangelical Christians* 146.9 mill.
Largest Religion Muslim.
Fastest growing religion Christian.
[For this book, Asia does not include any of Russia's territory, but does include the Middle East/West Asia and the Caucasus nations of Armenia, Azerbaijan, and Georgia.]
Asia has approximately 24% of the world's surface area, but over 60% of the world's population. It contains more than 250 cities of over 1 million people, 11 of which are over 10 million. Asia has the world's largest city, Tokyo/Yokohama (around 37 million people).

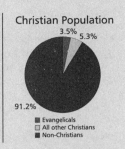

Christian Population

3.5% 5.3%

91.2%

■ Evangelicals
☐ All other Christians
■ Non-Christians

All Languages About 2,322 distinct languages (33.6% of the world's languages). **Languages with Scriptures** 161 Bibles, 270 New Testaments, 220 Old or New Testament portions. Work is underway on 418 language projects. At least 879 languages still need further translation work.

Asia is a continent of extremes. It has the world's highest peak and the ocean's deepest point. It has many of the world's richest billionaires and many millions of the world's poorest people. It has some of the most advanced societies, as well as some of the most undeveloped areas. It has the world's largest cities, but the largest rural populations as well. It has the world's biggest populations (China and India), as well as very small countries like Singapore and Brunei.

This region holds examples of almost every possible political regime, from various forms of democracy to total state control, and from monarchy to theocracy (rule by religious leaders). Asia is set to become the dynamic hub of global politics and economics, but it has seen the most military conflicts on its soil of any continent in recent history. The increasing economic power of China especially, but also India, will greatly influence the rest of the continent. The growing global demand for oil and gas means that areas like the Arab Peninsula, Iraq, Iran, and Central Asia will also continue to play a major economic role.

Asia is the birthplace or heartland of all major world religions. This means diversity in the number of religions practised here, but also in ways societies and governments handle religious faith and freedoms. Persecution and religious oppression are most intense in Asia. It is also the continent where Christian growth has been the fastest and most miraculous, from Iran to China and from Mongolia to Indonesia.

Afghanistan

Pop 29.1 million. **Capital** Kabul (3.7 mill).
Christians <15,000. (Most are foreigners. Military not included.)
Largest Religion Muslim.
Fastest Growing Religion Muslim.
Largest Ethnic Groups Pashtun/Pathan (42.7%), Tajik (26.2%), Hazara (12.9%), Uzbek (6.4%), Aimaq (5%), Turkmen (2.1%), South Asian (2.1%, 28 peoples), Baloch (1.2%). These numbers do not include the significant number of military personnel and expatriate NGO workers in the country.
Official Languages Pashtu (used by 50% of population), Dari (Afghan Persian, used by 70%). **All Languages** 41.

Economy Shattered by decades of war. Redevelopment focuses on rebuilding infrastructure and public buildings. Potential future exports from gas and mineral deposits, but the country currently relies heavily on foreign aid. Conflict with armed opposition (particularly the Taliban) hinders recovery and economic growth.

Politics Rival foreign empires have fought over this strategic land for nearly 3,000 years. The monarchy was overthrown in 1973. A republican government ended in a Marxist coup in 1978, and the Soviets (1979-1989), the Mujahedeen (1992-1996), and the Taliban (1996-2001) all brought violence and destruction to the nation. Invasion by US-led forces led to a new democratic government and constitution (2002-2004). Despite presence of NATO troops, the Taliban continue to operate. Afghanistan struggles with corruption.

 The upheaval of the last 35 years reduced the country to ruin and destitution. War led to over 1 million deaths, and left up to 4 million orphans. Most people live in poverty, with little employment opportunity. 60% of Afghans are under age 20, and have only known life with war. The more stable areas see some economic progress, even though the country still suffers from a degree of conflict. Pray that the Afghan people might experience genuine freedom and a better quality of life.

Health risks and human development. Praise God that health services have begun to improve, and more children now attend school than ever before.

- *Children* die from preventable diseases (diarrhoea, cholera, dysentery, pneumonia), but lack of healthcare and clean water also cause many deaths.

- *A high proportion of people suffer with disabilities.* Little provision is made for their care or rehabilitation. Pray for compassionate help for those who lost limbs as a result of war. Over 1 million dangerous landmines and explosive devices still litter the countryside.

- *Afghanistan grows 90% of the world's opium-producing poppies,* and has up to 1 million heroin and opium addicts. Poor farmers continue to grow this crop, even though Islam prohibits it. Pray for the success of alternative agricultural projects.

The status of women deserves special prayer. The Taliban largely banned them from public life. Life expectancy for women is only 44 years. Numerous women die in childbirth in Afghanistan because women cannot receive healthcare from male doctors. Female literacy is under 20%, and one-third of women suffer from violence. Widows face very difficult circumstances, and suicide is common. Special radio programmes share with women from the Bible, about the love and value God holds for them. Pray for justice and freedom from oppression, and especially that women might find Christ.

4 **Perhaps several thousand Afghans now follow Christ!** Numbers are difficult to document, but 20 years ago it was likely less than 50. Some hear Christian radio or receive dreams and visions of Jesus. Others hear the gospel from returned refugees. The Church in Afghanistan remains almost entirely underground. Expat believers must be careful in their faith and witness. Pray that, despite persecution, the body of Christ might mature and grow. Praise God for the completed Dari Bible after decades of work! The New Testament exists in Pashto, but no full Bible translation exists in any minority language.

5 **A number of Christian relief and development agencies** minister to the blind, crippled, sick, illiterate, and needy. Practical demonstrations of Christian love break down prejudices, and prepare hearts for the gospel. In recent years some workers died as martyrs, and entire organizations had to leave the country. Pray for courage in the face of violent opposition and adversity, and wisdom to demonstrate the love of Christ well.

6 **Afghanistan is one of the least-reached countries in the world.** Development of Christian media in many formats (digital audio, mobile phone memory, radio, video, literature, the Internet) will help with evangelism and discipleship. Pray for the 70 unreached peoples of this land, including:

- *Pashtuns,* who dominate politics. Pashtuns on both sides of the Afghanistan-Pakistan border form what some call the largest Muslim tribal society in the world (up to 46 million people).

- *Tajiks* (in the northeast). This group remain over 99% Muslim.

- *Hazaras* (Shi'a Muslims of Mongol descent). They were severely persecuted by Sunni Muslims across the centuries, massacred by the Taliban, and show greater openness to the gospel.

- *Uzbeks and Turkmen* (of the north). Only a tiny proportion follow Christ.

- *The 6 Aimaq tribes of the west, and the Baloch and Brahui of the south.* Very few if any believers exist in these isolated groups.

Armenia
Asia

Pop 3.1 million. **Capital** Yerevan (1.1 mill).
Christians 2.9 mill. *Evangelical Christians* 268,000.
Largest Religion Christian.
Fastest Growing Religion Non-religious.
Largest Ethnic Groups Armenian (97.8%, a Caucasian people), Other (2.2%, Azerbaijani, Kurd, Russian, Ukrainian).
Official Language Armenian. **All Languages** 12.

Economy Progress set back by destructive earthquake in 1988, by Soviet-era infrastructure, and by blockades by Azerbaijan and Turkey. Based on agriculture, refining and processing metals, and tourism. Helped by remittances from Armenians abroad. Widespread under-employment and low incomes.

Politics Armenia has rarely been independent in its 2,500-year history. Recent political life dominated by conflict with Azerbaijan and tensions with Turkey. Largely stable, democratic government, with diplomatic ties to Russia.

1 **Pray for good relationships with nearby countries.** Centuries of bitter conflict, oppression, and massacres left Armenians with hatred and mistrust of these nations. From 1915-1917, the

Turks killed up to 1.5 million Armenians in what many see as an unrecognized genocide. Conflict with Azerbaijan (especially over control of Nagorno-Karabakh) remains unresolved, with up to 800,000 Armenians and Azeris still displaced. Diplomatic solutions have failed, and both nations refuse to back down. Pray for an answer to this situation. Pray that Armenians would forgive. Pray for God to establish trust, cooperation, and trade between Armenia, Turkey, and Azerbaijan.

2 **Armenia was the world's first Christian nation,** with a Christian legacy of more than 1,700 years. Praise God for the survival of the Armenian Church through the centuries, despite frequent and harsh oppression. Pray that Armenian Christians might become a source of light and blessing to the region. Evangelical Christianity thrives among the Armenian diaspora (up to 8 million), with many congregations in the Middle East, North America, and elsewhere. Armenian Christians have only now begun to recognize the blessing of their Christian heritage and the mission responsibility that goes with it.

3 **The Armenian Apostolic Church was a cultural refuge** in times of persecution. But the very traditional nature of the Church sometimes keeps people from an encounter with the living Christ. This Church will almost certainly remain the dominant religious force in Armenian life. Pray for deep spiritual renewal and for godly leaders. Pray also for unity between the two main groups (Eastern and Western, which use different dialects), and for the Church to engage in fellowship with smaller, non-Orthodox denominations in Armenia.

4 **Evangelical numbers grew rapidly** since independence. Much of this growth was through the Armenian Church-Loving Brotherhood, a movement within the Apostolic Church. They emphasize Bible study groups, publish evangelical literature, witness to others, distribute Bibles, and work among the poor. The movement has a couple of hundred workers, and thousands more associated with it, particularly younger people. Other growth came through new Pentecostal/charismatic groups. Baptists and the Armenian Evangelical Church also grew, but not as quickly. Pray for growth and maturity for all these groups, and for unity among them.

Azerbaijan

Asia

Pop 8.9 million. **Capital** Baku (2 mill).
Christians 245,000. *Evangelical Christians* 19,000.
Largest Religion Muslim.
Fastest Growing Religion Muslim.

Largest Ethnic Groups Turkic (86.8%, Azeri are 86%), Iranian-Median (5%), Eurasian (4.4%, Russian, Armenian, Ukrainian; almost all Armenians live in Nagorno-Karabakh), Caucasus peoples (3.7%). More than 15 million Azeris live abroad, mostly in Iran.
Official Language Azerbaijani (with 20 dialects). **All Languages** 34.

Economy Dominated by oil production. Baku was world's original "oil-boom" city (over a century ago). Only a few benefit from oil wealth. About 40% of the population live in poverty, though this number has reduced in recent years.
Politics Long history of foreign rule by Arabs, Mongols, Persians, Turks, and Russians. Independent from USSR in 1991, followed by internal coups and conflict with Armenia. Leaders have shifted politically away from Russia, and towards Turkey and the West.

1   **Azerbaijan remains a politically and economically unsettled nation.** Conflict with Armenia led to war in 1990 over the region Nagorno-Karabakh, which declared independence. No one has committed to find a political solution. The economic boom from oil may dry up before 2025. The country needs to invest its wealth in long-term infrastructure, and in development of other sources of income. Pray for stability, and for a genuine will to make peace in and around Azerbaijan.

2   **God raised up an Azeri Church,** even amidst trials! Only 40 known Azeri believers lived in the country in 1991. Now estimates range between 3,000 and 6,000, with the majority in Baku. Even more ethnic Azeris follow Christ inside of Iran. Some Azeri believers create their own music, literature, poetry, and other indigenous forms of worship. Even so, most Christians in Azerbaijan are primarily of foreign ethnicities (Armenian, Russian, Georgian, others). Pray for good fellowship among all the believers.

3   **The Church faces opposition.** Many churches live with intimidation, surveillance, and unfair treatment by government officials. Strict registration laws (2010) make life difficult for Christian groups, but even for Muslims and other religious groups as well. Still, believers have some freedom to share the gospel sensitively. Most Azeris connect Christianity with Russian imperialism, with Armenian enemies, and with Western political powers. Pray for a humble, wise, and loving Christian witness to the majority Muslim population.

4   **Unregistered house church networks** continue to spread, and they have a vision to reach every town and village in the nation! The Azeri Church is open for foreign believers to partner with them in ministry. Pray especially for:

- *Azerbaijan's towns and villages.* Most have never been evangelized.
- *The poor.* Many lack clean water, and struggle to find employment. Good opportunities exist to show Christian compassion to the many thousands displaced by the conflict of the 1990s.
- *The Caucasus peoples.* Most are Muslim and unevangelized. Pray for the Lezgi, Avar, Tsakhur, Kryz, and Buduq peoples.
- *Nagorno-Karabakh.* Pray for believers to proclaim the gospel here, where some freedom exists to do so. The Orthodox Church has deep ties to Armenian identity. Pray for renewal.

Bahrain   *Asia*

Pop 807,000. **Capital** Manama (167,000).
Christians 79,000. *Evangelical Christians* 24,000.
Largest Religion Muslim.
Fastest Growing Religion Hindu.
Largest Ethnic Groups Arab (50%, Bahraini Arab are 40%), Iranian (15%, Farsi, Kurds, other), South Asian (15%, Indian, Pakistani), Bahraini Farsi (10%), East Asian (7%, Filipino, Korean, Chinese), European (1.5%).
Official Language Arabic. **All Languages** 12.
Economy First to produce oil in the Gulf, and will be first to run out. Made effort to diversify with finance/business, IT, healthcare, and education. Freest economy in the Middle East. Unemployment and poverty increase as oil and water supplies decrease. About half the workforce is foreign.

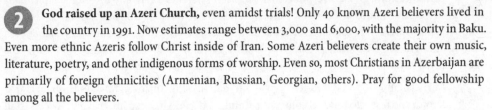

Politics British Protectorate until 1971. Absolute rule by an Emir from 1975 to 2001. Now a constitutional monarchy with 2 levels of parliament (the lower one elected). A Sunni family rules the country, but two-thirds of the indigenous population are Shi'a. Tensions continue to rise, with occasional violent clashes between protestors and government forces.

1 **Bahrain enjoys greater freedoms** than almost all Gulf countries, and therefore is spiritually strategic. Praise God for the local believers! Some worship with the various established churches, and others gather in more informal networks. Pray especially for unity and cooperation among these groups, as a testimony to their fellow Arabs. Many Saudis and Kuwaitis visit to enjoy the more relaxed environment. Pray for them to meet Christians, and to encounter the gospel.

2 **Christian ministry in Bahrain** has good foundations. The American Mission Hospital is well-known and respected after a century of faithful service. High-speed Internet gives access to all kinds of Christian resources. Chat rooms are especially popular since users can privately ask questions about Jesus. Pray that this may continue, and that the thoughtful witness of believers will bear fruit!

3 **Among the large expatriate community** (mostly from South and East Asia, the Middle East, Africa, and the West) a good number of Christians meet both formally and informally. Pray that expat believers might have courage and wisdom to share their faith outside their own culture group. Great potential exists in the area of education, as locals prize good education and much schooling is in English.

4 **The labour force** is 59% foreign, drawn from more than 50 nations. Most are on temporary contracts, and often must endure poor treatment, poor pay, and unrealistic expectations from people back home. Pray that believers within these national groups may win people for Christ. The least evangelized of these communities are the Iranians, Sri Lankans, and Hindus and Muslims from India and Pakistan.

Bangladesh

Asia

Pop 164.4 million. **Capital** Dhaka (14.6 mill).
Christians 1.1 mill. *Evangelical Christians* 633,000.
Largest Religion Muslim.
Fastest Growing Religion Muslim.

Largest Ethnic Groups All ethnic groups/cultures/castes: 399. Muslims and Hindus have distinct cultures and dialects. Bengali (94.3%, 136 peoples; Shaikh are 85.6%), Other South Asian (2.6%, 180 peoples), Urdu Muslims (2%, 35 peoples), Other (1.1%, including 46 Tibetan/Himalayan peoples, other Asians, and Westerners).
Official Language Bangla. English also used. **All Languages** 46.

Economy One of the world's poorest nations. Suffers

from over-population and natural disasters (floods, cyclones). Income from agriculture, textiles, clothing, jute, and remittances from those who work abroad.
Politics Part of Pakistan for 24 years. Gained independence in 1971 after a bitter civil war, followed by political instability with 18 military coups. Military dictatorship ended in 1991. Now one of the Islamic world's only democracies, but it suffers from political unrest and personal tensions between leaders in the two main political parties. Often rated among the world's most corrupt nations.

1 **The cycle of poverty** will continue unless fundamental changes occur. Bangladesh has few natural resources, and nearly half the population live on less than $1/day. The country sits on level ground beside the gigantic Ganges and Brahmaputra Rivers, and floods and monsoon rains regularly devastate the nation. The political situation offers little hope, as it seems more focused on arguments between wealthy clans than on improvements for the people. Pray for long-term transformation in this land of desperate need.

2 **Over 20,000 registered NGOs** try to meet the many social needs. Christian NGOs have provided aid and development since independence, and businesses started and run by Christians provide another way to serve people in need. The micro-credit strategy (loans to help people start small businesses) has improved the situation for many people, especially women. Extreme poverty and high levels of corruption put millions of child labourers or sex workers at risk of being forced into slavery, with little chance for escape.

3 **Praise God for growth in the number of believers,** both inside and outside the formal churches! The majority of Bangladeshi Christians traditionally come from a Hindu background, and usually from the lower caste peoples. But significant church growth occurred among 8 tribal groups, with notable growth among another 18 groups. At the same time, tens of thousands from a Muslim background now call on Jesus as Lord! Some found Christ through highly contextual "Jesus mosques", others through friends or relatives, even visions and dreams. Pray for these movements to grow and mature.

4 **Pray for leadership for the churches.** Earlier movements brought thousands of people into the Church. But the lack of trained, godly leadership eventually left many believers with a weak and shallow faith. Poverty limits the number of full-time ministers and theological students, but churches also lack spiritually mature lay leaders.

5 **The Bengali people** (240 million globally) remain the largest unreached people group in the world. Even 200 years after William Carey came as a missionary to the Bengali they still honour his memory, but a breakthrough for the gospel has not come.

- *Pray for Bengali Muslims.* Many follow "folk" Islam (a blend of Sufi Islam, indigenous cultures, and Hinduism). Most have never heard the true gospel. Pray for the few Bengali believers to depend on God in their poverty, to be strong when faced with persecution, and to find community with followers of Christ from different backgrounds.

- *Pray for Bengali Hindus* (228 Hindu groups, of which 204 are unreached), who face violence and persecution as a religious minority.

6 **Christians and other minority groups** (even other, smaller Muslim groups) face persecution, even though the constitution grants religious freedom. But praise God that more churches have begun to reach out with the gospel after years of little interest! Pray especially for:

- *The tribal peoples.* The Bengali population grows quickly, and pushes into traditional tribal lands. This threatens the existence of the tribal peoples. Some have large Christian populations, while others remain unreached. Pray for a just settlement over the land.

- *Bihari Muslims* (Urdu-speaking). Most live in former refugee camps, as Pakistanis do not want them, and Bangladeshis consider them traitors. Pray for their reconciliation with the Bengali people, and for openness to the gospel among them.

- *Rohingya Muslims.* As many as 250,000 have fled the Buddhist government in Myanmar. They live in refugee camps, where many face starvation. They have never been evangelized.

Bhutan

Asia

Pop 708,000. **Capital** ThImpu (93,000).
Christians 15,000. *Evangelical Christians* 13,000.
Largest Religion Buddhist.
Fastest Growing Religion Christian.

Largest Ethnic Groups Bhutanese (50%), South Asian (27.5%), South Himalayan (15.7%), Tibetan (6.5%).
Official Language Dzongkha. Nepali also widely used. **All Languages** 35.

Economy Based mostly on simple agriculture, but tourism and hydroelectricity also contribute. Tourist numbers are strictly controlled. Around 23% live in poverty, but rated one of world's happiest countries.

Politics A Buddhist monarchy with a parliament. India plays a major role in external affairs. Large-scale Nepali immigration over the past century and their desire for greater democracy resulted in severe government measures against non-Bhutanese peoples since 1985. Up to 150,000 ethnic Nepalis have been expelled, and their culture/language suppressed inside Bhutan.

---

 1 **Pray for true spiritual freedom in this "Land of the Dragon".** The Buddhist monarchy, the government policies to keep Bhutan isolated, and the strong hold of Vajrayana Buddhism resulted in Bhutan being one of the world's least-evangelized nations. Bon (an indigenous religion) was replaced by Buddhism, but maintains a strong occultic/demonic influence. Pray for King Wangchuk and his salvation. Among the 5 largest Tibetan/Himalayan peoples (Dzongkha, Tshangla, Lepcha, Kheng, Gurung), only the Lepcha have a significant Christian population. Pray for a fellowship of believers to witness among every ethnic group of the Bhutanese! A New Testament exists in Dzongkha (official language), but most languages have no Scriptures.

2 **Bhutan was closed to almost all Christian witness** until 1965. 25 years followed where some Indian and other expatriate NGOs had limited freedom to witness. Since 1990, restrictions increased again. The government had allowed mission agencies to provide health, agriculture, and education programmes, but only a few small aid projects continue. Pray that God will once again open doors for Christian ministries to sensitively bring the love of Christ into Bhutan! Indian believers, Nepalis, and others give gospel literature to the Bhutanese. Many Christians in Bhutan came to the Lord this way. Pray that Bhutanese students and workers in India and around the world might hear the gospel and respond positively.

3 **Bhutan denies religious freedom to Christians,** and persecutes them in various ways. Only a few churches can have buildings, and most fellowships meet in homes. Evangelism is illegal. Bhutanese who become Christian may lose the benefits of citizenship (free education, health care, employment, and even access to electricity and water). Some face mistreatment and even beatings. Praise God that despite this, groups of believers form and spread across the country! Pray for the growth of the Church in this land.

Brunei

Pop 407,000. **Capital** Bandar Seri Begawan (23,000).
Christians 46,000. *Evangelical Christians* 25,000.
Largest Religion Muslim.
Fastest Growing Religion Non-religious.

Largest Ethnic Groups Malay (69.6%, dominant in government and civil service), Chinese (15.6%), Filipino (7.9%), Indonesian (2.3%), British (1.7%), Indo-Pakistani (1.2%).
Official Languages Malay, English. **All Languages** 17.

Economy One of Asia's richest states. Free education and healthcare, no income tax for most, and subsidized housing, fuel, and basic food. Oil and gas are 90% of exports, but deposits may soon be exhausted. Efforts to diversify economy focus on eco-tourism and self-sufficiency in rice growing.

Politics Refused to join Malaysian Federation in 1963. A Protectorate of Britain until full independence (1983). The Sultan rules as an absolute monarch, and maintains traditions of a Muslim monarchy that dates back to the 15th century.

1 **Islam dominates life in Brunei.** The Islam practised here is conservative, but not radical. Pressure results in a slow stream of converts to Islam from among the tribal and Chinese minorities. The constitution guarantees religious freedom, but it is illegal to evangelize and illegal for a Muslim to convert to another religion. Government agents often go undercover in other religious groups to monitor them. The Sultan is considered the world's 2nd wealthiest royal. He established a world-class university, and now works to hand over rule smoothly to the crown prince. Pray for conversions to Christ in the large royal family. Pray for spiritual openness and for religious freedom.

2 **The Christian Church exists under very difficult conditions.** Evangelism is illegal, and the government does not permit foreign Christian workers. Pray for continued growth, even with the restrictions. Most Christians come from local tribal peoples and Chinese. Pray for new believers from among all ethnic groups and segments of society!

- *The Malay majority are Muslim.* The few Malay Christians keep their faith private. Pray for the Spirit to move in the hearts of Malays. Expatriate Filipino believers and Brunei-born and foreign Chinese Christian businessmen could reach them.

- *The Chinese* still mostly follow the traditional religions of China or no religion at all. Less than 20% follow Christ.

- *Tribal peoples* have either converted to Islam, or they remain isolated in jungle villages. The Church has a witness to many villages. Pray for it to bear fruit.

- *The expatriate workforce* will likely grow. The largest groups are Muslim Bangladeshis and Indonesians, Hindu Indians and Nepalis, Buddhist Thai, and Catholic Filipinos.

Cambodia

Pop 15.1 million. **Capital** Phnom Penh (2 mill).
Christians 471,000. *Evangelical Christians* 240,000.
Largest Religion Buddhist.
Fastest Growing Religion Christian.
Largest Ethnic Groups Khmer (86.9%), Vietnamese (4.2%), Chinese (4.1%).
Official Language Khmer. **All languages** 25.

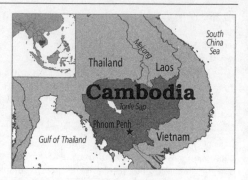

Economy One of the world's poorer countries, dependent on foreign aid. Significant progress in economic development, but not yet helping the rural poor. Agriculture, clothing factories, and tourism earn the most. Illegal logging and the sex trade make a small number very wealthy, and cause many to suffer.

Politics A ceremonial monarchy. Powerful kingdoms ruled from 1st to 14th centuries, then 500 years caught in regional and global conflicts. The extreme Marxist Khmer Rouge (from 1975) oversaw one of the most horrible massacres of the 20th century. Democracy since 1993.

 Spiritual darkness persists in Cambodia, from the many spirit shrines, the powerful grip of Buddhism that opposes Truth, and the widespread loss of morals. Only prayer will lift it. The enemy of souls makes people suffer under terrible abuses and oppressive poverty. The drug and sex trades hold power over many people. Criminals exploit the high number of unprotected children and young people. Pray for the light of the gospel to shine on individual lives and all social structures in Cambodia. Christians can make a difference in the areas of justice, rehabilitation, orphanages, healthcare, and development. Cambodia also needs outside help with projects in agriculture, fisheries, water management, and education.

2 **Cambodian people need freedom and deliverance from past sin, hatred, suffering, and abuse.** This comes through the blood of Jesus. The violent Khmer Rouge regime (1975-1979) destroyed millions of its own people. Ask God to heal deep psychological wounds through the Holy Spirit and counselling ministry. Many of the former Khmer Rouge who took part in genocide now follow Jesus. Pray for them to live in the fullness of God's forgiveness for past crimes. Christians can bring peace and reconciliation. Churches can teach children and young people how to live in a healthy family.

3 **The Cambodian Church survived great trial and grew!** Missionaries worked for 47 years before breakthrough began, then genocide came and destroyed most of the Church. 90% of Christians died or fled to Thai refugee camps. God reaped a great harvest among those in the camps, but only a few thousand believers survived inside Cambodia. But churches spread to all 19 provinces during the 1990s, and now 470,000 Christians worship God there! Churches need mature and well-trained leadership. Most educated people died in the Khmer Rouge slaughter. Pray for pastors to have wisdom, holiness, and power in the Spirit.

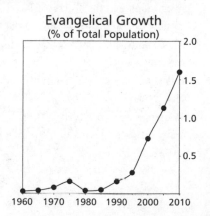

Evangelical Growth
(% of Total Population)

4 Mission Kampuchea 2021. The national Churches share this vision to see a church in every village and people group in Cambodia by 2021. Currently 11,000 villages need a church. Pray for the less-reached Buddhists, the 18 unevangelized tribal groups, the Muslim Cham people, and 6 Chinese language groups. Cambodian churches and Christians from abroad can partner to share Jesus with these people groups. Pray also for Chinese believers from abroad to come as apostles to the Chinese peoples in Cambodia.

China, Hong Kong *Asia*

Pop 7.1 million. **Capital** None.
Christians 877,000. *Evangelical Christians* 434,000.
Largest Religion Chinese religions.
Fastest Growing Religion Non-religious.

Largest Ethnic Groups Chinese: Cantonese (88.7%), Other Chinese groups (6.5%, including Hakka, Chaochow, Fujianese, others), Filipino (2.1%), Indonesian (1.4%).
Official Languages Chinese, English. Cantonese is the official local dialect, but Putonghua (Mandarin) has become more common and influential.

Economy One of the world's richest cities and largest economies. Ranks as world's most free economy. Hong Kong finance supports China's rapid economic growth. Wealth generated through international trade, finance, and industry. A gap grows between the very rich and the very poor.
Politics Britain gained control of Hong Kong from China in 1842. China resumed control in 1997, but existing legal, political, and economic structures must remain until 2047. China has responsibility for defence and foreign policy. One of Asia's most open and free societies, with religious freedom.

---

1 The rightful return of Hong Kong (HK) to China came with most freedoms left in place, and with continued religious liberty. Praise God for this, and for the opportunity Christians have to demonstrate their faith to all of China. Some people feel unsure about the future of these freedoms. The Chief Executive and all others in leadership must balance responsibility to leaders in Beijing and responsibility to their own people in HK. Pray for wisdom and courage to take the right path.

2 Money has shaped Hong Kong's past. HK became very wealthy as a British colony, and its busy port brought in the wealth of the nations. Sadly this also created a culture built around wealth. The desire for more and more material possessions drains the spiritual life, and churches suffer. At the same time, the Christian community has resources to use for good works among the needy people of HK, and for those who suffer in the region, and around the whole world. Pray that Hong Kong's wealth will find its place – at the feet of Jesus.

3 The majority follow Buddhism, Daoism, Confucianism, or Chinese folk religions, with over 700 temples and monasteries, and countless shrines, dedicated to various powers. Many residents follow no religion. Other faiths are present, but mostly among immigrant groups. Christians are 10% of the population, but the Church runs the majority of schools and social organizations, and 25% of the hospitals. Pray for Christians to boldly share Jesus, even when they face these spiritual powers that oppose Christ's lordship.

4 **Church growth** slowed down since the 1960s, but unity among churches increased. Large churches and megachurches with cell groups grow the fastest. The cost of real estate in crowded HK creates challenges for church growth. Many congregations meet in smaller numbers, in whatever spaces they can find. Bitter divisions between churches caused many problems in the past, but God brought reconciliation to some conservatives and charismatics through forgiveness and prayer.

5 **Small Hong Kong has a big impact for the Kingdom!** Hong Kong churches send many missionaries, and provide finance for outreach, discipleship, media, and literature ministries, especially to serve the Chinese-speaking world. Around 60% of congregations engage in or support mission activity! The CCCOWE (Chinese Coordinating Committee on World Evangelization) has headquarters in HK, and links together Christians in the 40-million Chinese diaspora, for fellowship and outreach to less-evangelized Chinese communities. Pray for wisdom to serve the growing Church throughout China.

6 **Pray for the parts of HK society with great spiritual needs:**
- *The working class and the poor.* Many still live in crowded situations, and lack hope for change. A number of ministries work among the most desperate people.

- *Immigrants from mainland China,* with 150 more people that arrive each day. They face prejudice from others, and live in bad conditions. Yet they probably respond more positively to the gospel than any other group! Around 10,000 mainland Chinese also arrive daily as workers or tourists. Pray they might encounter the gospel while in HK.

- *The Southeast Asian population* (mostly Filipino and Indonesian domestic workers). Many follow Christ, but struggle with loneliness and mistreatment by employers.

- *The Muslims.* Most are Hui Chinese, Pakistani, Malay, Indonesian, or Middle Easterners.

China, Macau

Asia

Pop 548,000. **Capital** Macau (548,000).
Christians 29,000. *Evangelical Christians* 8,500.
Largest Religion Chinese traditional religions.
Fastest Growing Religion Buddhist.

Largest Ethnic Groups Chinese (93.6%, over half born outside Macau), Macanese (Eurasian) (2.4%).
Official Languages Chinese, Portuguese. Majority speak Cantonese, but Mandarin also widely spoken.

Economy One of world's richest countries in 16th–17th centuries. Now dominated by gambling and tourism, driven by visitors from mainland China. A gateway city for China's economic zones such as nearby Zhuhai.

Politics Europe's first and last colonial possession in Asia. Rented by the Portuguese in 1557, and a Portuguese colony in 1887. Considered a Chinese Territory under Portuguese administration since 1974, but reverted to Chinese rule in 1999 as a Special Administrative Region. High degree of economic and political autonomy.

1 **Macau is the first Christian territory in Asia to become non-Christian.** 95% of the population were Catholic in 1600, but only 5% called themselves Christian by 2010. Protestant missions to China started in Macau. Here missionaries baptized the first Chinese convert, translated the first Chinese Bible, and buried the first Protestant missionary to the Chinese. Many now follow Buddhism,

Daoism, or traditional Chinese religions. The gambling industry, fear of the local god "A-Ma", and high turnover of leaders in churches, all hinder the spread of the gospel. Pray for believers to win back this territory for the Saviour.

 Many people call Macau the "City of Sin". The gambling industry earns far more profit here than in Las Vegas (USA). Addiction and desperation ruin lives, but only a few churches minister to gambling addicts. Rahab Ministries reaches out to mainland Chinese trafficked in as prostitutes. Pray for this ministry, and for more groups to reach the vulnerable people brought from China or Southeast Asia. High salaries in casinos encourage young people and even Christians to work there, but the jobs often lead them to neglect education or church involvement. Pray for alternative work opportunities.

 The Church grows in number and unity. Macau does not have a strong Church like Hong Kong, or fast growth like mainland China, but both the Chinese-speaking congregations and the churches operating in other languages do grow. Pray for the Church to survive and grow, and to bless China and the whole world.

The less reached:
- *Tourists from mainland China.* Religious freedom allows ministries to distribute the gospel in various formats.
- *Indonesians and Vietnamese,* who work in domestic labour and often face mistreatment or abuse. They need specific outreach.
- *The Macanese* (mixed Portuguese-Cantonese). They are often Catholic, but few practise their faith. They have 1 evangelical church, but little outreach among them.

Republic of China, Taiwan *Asia*

Pop 23.6 million. **Capital** Taipei (2.6 mill).
Christians 1.4 mill. *Evangelical Christians* 649,000.
Largest Religion Chinese religions.
Fastest Growing Religion Buddhist.
Largest Ethnic Groups Chinese: Taiwanese (66.2%, settled in Taiwan over 300 years ago), Chinese: Hakka (15%, settled in Taiwan 200 years ago), Mainland Chinese (15%, refugees from mainland China from 1945 to 1950), Austronesian mountain peoples (1.7%, 14 recognized tribes and 11 unrecognized).
Official Language Mandarin. Hoklo and Hakka widely spoken. **All Languages** 28.

Economy One of world's most active export economies. Close economic ties to mainland China (primary export market).
Politics Under Japanese rule (1895-1945), then granted to the Nationalist Government of China. Taiwan became the refuge of the Nationalist Chinese government (Kuomingtang/KMT) after mainland China fell to the Communists (1949). This led to international diplomatic isolation and internal divisions. Now a multiparty democracy. Despite the tensions, China and Taiwan have close economic and cultural ties.

 Taiwan's controversial political status causes problems both within China and internationally. Taiwan functions as an independent state, but by law is a province of China. If Taiwan declared independence, it could result in a hostile military response from China. Pray for wisdom for the leaders involved, and for good relations for the long term.

2 **Taiwan remains a stronghold of Buddhism and Taiwanese folk religion.** Over 90% of Taiwanese follow some combination of Buddhism, Confucianism, Daoism, and traditional religions. Buddhism now grows strongly among educated professionals. Most traditional folk religions have many gods, and people pay offerings to ghosts or seek advice from the spirit world. Taiwan remains the only major Han Chinese population in the world without a significant spiritual breakthrough. Visitors from mainland China often comment on the spiritual darkness here.

3 **Praise God for a new era of Christian growth** after decades of little activity! This growth includes megachurches and house churches, charismatics and conservatives, and it crosses ethnic, language, and economic barriers. Many churches now put more emphasis on prayer, evangelism, and community outreach. Taiwanese churches and agencies have a vision to carry the gospel to mainland China and other parts of Asia.

4 **Pray for the Church to overcome its current challenges.** Many Taiwanese focus strongly on career and wealth, and on their children's education. They have little time left for spiritual matters or for ministry. Gambling and the sex industry are common in Taiwanese society, and tempt new believers away. Ask God to pour out His Spirit to create a true hunger for Him. Believers need discipleship, but too few pastors or full-time workers exist to meet the need. Rural congregations suffer the most.

5 **Less-evangelized people groups.** Most Christians live in bigger cities and speak Mandarin. Far fewer churches exist in rural areas, or among peoples who speak Taiwanese or Hakka. Pray for:
- *The Taiwanese working class,* who speak Hoklo/Hokkien. This group is 60% of the population, but only 0.5% are Christian.
- *The Hakka communities.* They are only 0.35% evangelical, and want to preserve their language, culture, and religion.
- *The Muslim community.* Some outreach exists to the Indonesian Muslims, but none to the Hui (the largest Muslim group).
- *The Penghu Islanders,* who are fisher folk, and highly superstitious. Most churches among them closed down.
- *Foreign brides* (up to 320,000, mostly from mainland China and Vietnam). Few know about Jesus. Taiwan Expatriates Caring Committee partners with national churches to minister to them.

6 **The indigenous Austronesian peoples of Taiwan (25 tribes)** live in the mountains of the east and in some cities. 80% are Christian after long work by Presbyterians among them, but many lack Scriptures and Bible teaching. They struggle to preserve their traditional ways of life when faced with social changes such as family breakdown, alcoholism, and migration to the cities.

China, PRC

Hong Kong and Macau are integral parts of China, though their statistics are not included here. Taiwan's status is debated. These 3 are each handled separately (see p. 127 for Hong Kong, p. 128 for Macau, and p. 129 for Taiwan).

Pop 1.3 billion. **Capital** Beijing/Peking (12.4 mill).
Christians 105 mill. *Evangelical Christians* 75 mill.
Largest Religion Non-religious.
Fastest Growing Religion Christian.

Largest Ethnic Groups China has close to 500 indigenous, distinct ethnic groups, but 55 "nationalities" officially recognized. East Asian (93.1%, 41 peoples, includes Chinese, Chinese-Hui, Manchu, Mongolian, Korean, Japanese, Taiwanese), Southeast Asian (3.3%, 167 peoples in southern provinces from Zhuang, Miao/Hmong, Tai, Yao-Mien, Bouyei, others), Tibetan/Himalayan (2.5%, 238 peoples in western and southwestern provinces from Nosu, Tibetan, West China/Yi, others), Turkic (1%, 26 peoples in northwest, mostly Uyghur), Other (0.1%, includes Western, Iranian-Median, Malay peoples, African, Arab, Jews).

Official Language Putonghua (Mandarin Chinese). Local languages in the 5 Autonomous Regions. Some estimate 600 different spoken Han dialects, with 1 written language common to all. **All Languages** 296.

Economy Maoist/Marxist economics from 1948 were unsuccessful. Since 1978, a more practical "Chinese Socialism" developed with more relaxed policies on agriculture, industry, and business. The last 3 decades of change and growth greatly raised China's living standards, especially in the coastal region and a few larger inland cities. China is now the world's 2nd-largest economy. China faces crises ahead (with the environment, healthcare, property ownership, urbanization, an unsustainable need for resources, others). Corruption, illegal activity (drug and human trafficking), unjust business practices, human rights violations, and serious social problems all create challenges for the future. But China's ability to manage nearly 1.4 billion people, and to lift hundreds of millions out of poverty, is a noteworthy accomplishment.

Politics Once China came under Communist control (1949), the Party rebuilt the nation along Marxist lines. The Cultural Revolution (1966-1976) under Mao Zedong caused great suffering (up to 20 million Chinese died). After Mao, reforms brought economic, political, and cultural progress, but with strong response (even violent) to political, ethnic, and religious dissent. Extensive reforms since the 1990s eased some restrictions, but the state controls most sectors of life and society. China's challenges include ethnic tensions within the country, strained relations with neighbouring nations, and many social ills.

China is the world's 3rd-largest country by area. The climate and geography are extremely diverse, from tropical in the south to sub-arctic in the north, from a highly industrialized and modern eastern seaboard to sparsely populated western deserts and mountain ranges.

This ancient civilization has regained its place of importance in the world after nearly 2 centuries of decline. China has emerged as a world superpower. Its economic and foreign policies will shape the world in the 21st century.

1 **Some call this the "Chinese Century"** because of China's rising role on the world stage. It has more people than any other country, and massive influence on world economics and politics. China invests billions of dollars in Africa, Asia, and Latin America to develop trade, but also to gain influence. But it also remains politically oppressive and corrupt. The Communist government represses minority ethnic groups and squashes dissent. The army crushed the 1989 student protest in Tiananmen Square (Beijing). It has a poor human rights record, and imposes harsh laws and punishments. Pray for God to work in and through the Chinese government.

 Praise God for positive changes in government and society in the last 15 years. Growing numbers oppose the widespread corruption in business and government, and the deception and cheating in academia and other areas. China's civil society now grows, which leads to greater social awareness, and care for families and communities that comes from people instead of the state. Christians now are active in most every area of Chinese society. The state recognizes the usefulness of faith-based organizations to address social problems. This is a great opportunity for the Church!

 Tensions in Chinese society need urgent attention and wisdom. Pray for peaceful resolutions that benefit China practically and spiritually. Pray about:

- *Political and economic reform.* The state promotes capitalism, but resists the political change needed to support economic freedoms.
- *Freedom of information.* The government encourages Internet use, but actively controls and censors it.
- *China's atheist Communist Party.* The number of Christians in China is larger than Communist Party members (70 million). Schools teach atheism, but Christian growth continues (even within the Communist Party!).
- *Ethnic unrest.* Minority peoples fight to retain their homelands and cultures, while massive numbers of Han Chinese (the majority people) immigrate into their areas to weaken their ethnic identity. Conflict within Tibet and Xinjiang continues.

 The biggest human migration in history is happening in China today. In just a couple of generations, hundreds of millions of rural dwellers have relocated to China's urban centres. Many millions cannot support their families through farming. Migrants to cities end up without basic social services or educational opportunities, which creates overcrowding and unemployment. Migrants without proper housing become vulnerable and problematic.

5 **China has a "one-child policy" to control population size.** Each married couple can have only 1 child, or 2 in some cases. Many families desire a healthy son, and so they abort, abandon, or traffic female or disabled babies. The Chinese perform over 13 million abortions every year, and many accept it as a form of birth control. The future situation will be a great burden on Chinese society. Pray for wise long-term policies:

- *Gender imbalance.* Some studies predict that 20-30 million men will be left single by 2020. Cases of rape, abduction, female slavery, incest, prostitution, dangerous homosexual behaviour, and the rapid spread of AIDS may all increase.
- *The workforce.* The number of young people available for some jobs in industry and the military will decrease significantly.
- *Care for the elderly.* Fewer young people will be available to help. Some desperate families abandon elders the way they do young children.

 China's massive social and health needs overwhelm the government and society. Some faith groups form NGOs, or serve communities informally. The gospel offers strength in Jesus to face life's challenges, and to demonstrate love for others in Christlike service.

- *Disease and poor health.* Millions suffer with tuberculosis, and hundreds of thousands are HIV positive. Drug use has increased (over 1 million users).

- *The disabled.* One-fifth of the world's disabled people live in China. Over 1.2 million of the babies born each year have disabilities. 40 million suffer with mental illness, and medical care for them is inadequate. Chinese society historically rejects the disabled. Most of these individuals suffer needlessly, without love, care, or dignity.

- *The vulnerable.* Women, orphans, refugees (especially from North Korea), and the very poor are most at risk. Pray for those who try to stand for justice on their behalf. Pray for rescue for those in danger.

- *The depressed.* China has the highest number of suicides in the world, and the majority are rural women. Family and community pressures rise as society changes. Pray for many Christians to get involved in drug rehabilitation, marital counselling, and suicide prevention.

- *The overlooked,* including the elderly without care, victims of natural disasters, migrants in over-crowded slums of massive cities, minority communities, and those in the harsh prison system. Jesus sees and remembers them all. Pray that the Church might do the same!

7 **China faces environmental disasters.** The enormous agricultural and industrial progress also created serious land, air, and water pollution. As a result, many people die, get ill, or suffer birth defects. The growth of deserts (northern areas) already affects millions. Pray that the government will make brave decisions for the long-term well-being of the population and environment.

THE CHURCH IN CHINA

1 **The survival and growth of the Church in China** are awesome events in our generation! The atheist government strictly controls religious groups, and banned all religious activity during the Cultural Revolution. Christians then started underground house-church networks designed to survive the persecution. Through radio ministries, Christian workers, and believers devoted to outreach, the Church did more than survive; it grew! The government re-allowed registered churches in 1978 as a way to regain control over Christianity. But the unregistered churches just continued to grow. In fact, there is no growth story like it in all of church history. 2.7 million evangelicals in 1975 grew to over 75 million in just 35 years!

2 **Praise God for the faith and commitment of Chinese believers.** They endured perhaps the most widespread persecution of Christians ever. But God strengthened and increased the believers, and the Holy Spirit inspired passionate prayer and bold evangelism. Persecution and pressure are less now than before, and some say that this is a step towards true religious freedom. Yet even today, the state considers unregistered churches illegal, Christians face arrests and fines, and churches face forced closure and destruction of their buildings.

3 **Pray for the Chinese Church:**
- *The Three-Self Patriotic Movement and China Christian Council (TSPM/CCC)* together form the only state-recognized Protestant Church. It can legally print and distribute Bibles, and can register and build church buildings. But the government limits its teaching, outreach, and discipleship activity. Since its restoration in 1978, it continues to grow. In the past, the atheist regime imposed some doctrines and practices on the TSPM/CCC that hindered its impact on society. Pray for revival and renewal, and future growth.
- *The traditional house-church networks* formed the core of the Chinese Church for many decades. Preachers travelled far and wide across China. The intense persecution isolated them

from the global Church, and forced them to adopt indigenous ways. They focus strongly on prayer, revival, simple living, and on Christ! Most house-church Christians love their country, but their first loyalty is to God. They do not want to register with the government. Their illegal status leads to persecution. The mass migration to the cities will force these networks and churches to adapt. Some rural congregations get left without a leader, and some migrants struggle without a church group in the city. Pray that the strong commitment to God's Word, the power of the Holy Spirit, and the boldness to spread the gospel will all continue to shape this growing, changing movement.

- *Other smaller, less-organized house-church networks* still make up a significant part of the Chinese Church. Many formed through radio broadcasts and related ministries, often among minority groups. More recently, new networks form within the workplace, such as within factories or offices owned or managed by Christians.

- *The urban professional Church* is an important recent development. Many professionals and academics turned to God for the first time, often while students or professors living abroad. They returned to China eager to engage urban society with their new faith! These well-educated believers can influence government, business, media, the legal system, academia, and civil society. They can relate differently to the government than the TSPM/CCC or house-church networks can. Many have strong commitment to social welfare.

- *The Catholic Church* was divided when the Chinese government set up the Catholic Patriotic Association (CPA) that was independent of the Vatican (1957). The majority of Catholics went "underground", and stayed loyal to the Pope. They suffered severe persecution. These groups fought with each other, and the Pope now encourages them toward reconciliation. Many Catholics are passionate, charismatic believers.

4 **Relationships among the different parts of the Chinese Church** were tense and strained for many decades. But they more recently began to strengthen. TSPM/CCC churches and house-church networks worked together after the earthquakes of 2008 (Wenchua in South China) and 2010 (Yushu in the northwest) to help serve communities in need. Thousands came to Christ. Was this a turning point? Pray for genuine reconciliation at the foot of the cross.

5 **Many Christians do not have enough Bible knowledge to answer difficult life questions.** Pray especially for transformed relationships between spouses, and between children and parents. Society accepts extra-marital sexual relationships as normal. Divorce rates are high, and families break apart. Increased wealth creates new pressures. Corruption is normal. The Chinese Church has many mature, wise Christian leaders and elders, but not enough of them. Pray for access to God's Word, and for guidance from the Holy Spirit.

6 **The Church faces a crisis in leadership training.** Many believers are first-generation Christians. Some TSPM groups report 1 trained leader for every 7,000 believers, and even up to 40,000 in some areas! The 18 official seminaries in China graduate fewer than 1,000 students per year. Bible training and discipleship are vital for the entire Chinese Church. Pray for good distribution of Bibles, and for programmes to equip the hundreds of thousands of lay leaders. Young people face pressure from family and society to choose a career path with a good salary instead of a life in ministry. Women provide much leadership, because almost 75% of Christians are women. Pray for strength and wisdom for them to manage their responsibilities. Pray for men and women to serve together in the Church.

7 **Aggressive cults such as Eastern Lightning and Lingling spread false teachings.** Some cults have similar teachings to biblical Christianity, and others are full of deception. They confuse people, and lead to wrong perceptions about Christianity. These cults grow quickly in many provinces, especially Henan and Jilin. Often, churches are their targets for new members (sometimes even through kidnapping and brainwashing). In some areas of Inner Mongolia, the Eastern Lightning has gained control of most house churches. Cults have the most success where Christians lack Bible knowledge and trained leaders. Pray for Christians to know the Truth, and to see the lies. Pray for radio and literature ministries to strengthen believers in God's truth.

8 **Chinese Christians have increased contact with evangelicals around the world.** After decades of isolation, this is a great blessing! Chinese Christian leaders can enjoy greater fellowship and prayer with Christians from other nations. But increased contact also brings obstacles and the danger of exploitation. External finance and resources bring blessings and complications. Pray for wisdom and love in all relationships with foreign Christians.

9 **Missions vision is strong,** and the Chinese Church sends out workers to both unreached minorities within China and unevangelized nations beyond. Some house-church networks have supported missions outreach to other provinces and to ethnic minorities for a long time. The Back to Jerusalem vision aims to send up to 100,000 missionaries from China throughout the unevangelized world. Some think China may become the greatest sending nation of the 21st century! Pray for good preparation to equip Christians and churches for this cross-cultural task. Pray for sensitivity and humility, especially for the dominant Han Chinese.

THE LESS EVANGELIZED

China now has the world's 3rd-largest Christian population! But only about 8% of China's people are Christian, and believers are not evenly spread throughout this enormous country. Many Chinese are atheist, but more than 500 million follow religions other than Christianity. These include ancient practices such as Daoism, Buddhism, and Confucianism. The newer Falun Gong movement also attracts many. At least 20 million are Muslim. This section highlights some of the less-evangelized sections of the population. Pray that all turn toward the Truth.

1 The "lost generation". The Cultural Revolution was Mao Zedong's final policy, and it caused great suffering. Millions died in those years, and education was crippled. Pray that the "lost generation" of that era might find hope and peace in Christ.

2 **Children and young people (under age 15) number nearly 300 million.** They face different pressures from the hardship of previous generations. Youth crime and sexual immorality have increased drastically in both rural and urban areas. One of China's greatest needs is for adults to disciple children and youth. Pray that busy Christian parents give time to their families. Atheism remains a strong part of Chinese education, so pray for good Bible teaching for youth and children. In cities, more parents now want private schools. Pray for Christians to start excellent schools that attract Chinese families.

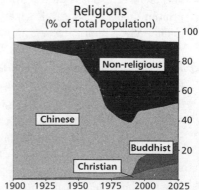

Religions
(% of Total Population)

3 **Islam is an official religion in China,** but conflict with some ethnic minority groups makes it a sensitive matter. Almost all Muslims come from the indigenous Uyghur, Kazak, Uzbek, Kyrgyz, Tajik, Tatar, Salar, Dongxiang, and Hui groups. Few Christians in China live and work among Muslim peoples. Ask God to call more workers to serve these often isolated and sometimes oppressed minorities.

4 **Around 10% of the indigenous population in China are not from the Han Chinese ethnicity.** They represent 135 million individuals, in 474 distinct peoples. Most remain unreached. 217 of these peoples have no known believers. Ask God to raise up intercession and outreach to them. Pray especially for Scripture translation into their heart languages.

5 **The Chinese diaspora (40 million) lives in every nation.** The Arab Gulf states employ countless Chinese labourers. New Chinese economic activities in Africa and Latin America bring them to these lands. Many Chinese are moving into Russian Siberia. Many countries have strong Chinese Christian communities. But in others, the Chinese remain unevangelized.

6 **China needs well-equipped Christian workers from around the world.** The government does not welcome foreign Christians as missionaries. But they can serve China in many ways.

- *Foreign experts.* China recently appealed for 150,000 foreign experts in fields such as biotechnology, energy, agriculture, IT, and especially finance. Schools want foreigners to teach English, Japanese, and other languages, as well as a range of university courses. China also needs development work, especially among minorities and migrants. Pray for many Christians to respond to this appeal, and to serve well in their field.

- *Students.* Over 75,000 students from over 175 countries study in China. Ask God to use foreign Christian students as a powerful witness.

- *Chinese family members who visit ancestral homes.* Millions return to China as tourists. Believers sometimes see amazing spiritual response among relatives in China.

Pray for foreign Christians in China to serve with humility, to learn the language and culture, and to persevere in times of challenge.

7 **Pray that all who seek God's Word will find a Bible.** The development of the Church in every people depends on it. Pray for:

- *Bible distribution.* Most urban Christians now have a Bible, yet millions of believers still need one. Some rural house-church members share 1 copy among 10 or even 100 believers! Amity Printing Company has permission to print more than 10 million Bibles each year, and around 8 million stay in China. The days of "Bible smuggling" as the main supply are mostly over, but a need for Scripture in China remains.

- *Bible translation.* Over 200 minority languages of China have no Scripture! Many have no written language. Bible translation for most people groups in south and southwest China has not even started.

- *Audio and visual materials.* Christian radio supports evangelism and teaching throughout China. Praise God for those who broadcasted into China for many years, without knowledge of the results. Today we can see the fruit! Christian stations today broadcast many hundreds of hours in Han Chinese dialects. Some Christian radio and video resources exist in a few languages without Scripture, but too few. Television, digital media, and the Internet can reach hundreds of millions who have little contact with Christians.

The Regions of China

China has 34 administrative divisions: 22 provinces, 4 municipalities, 5 autonomous regions, 2 Special Administrative Regions (Hong Kong and Macau), and the claimed Taiwan Province. 11 of these are large enough on their own to rank among the 25 most populous countries in the world!

It is difficult to count Christians in China. The TSPM and the government prefer to publish lower numbers. Some Christian agencies prefer larger numbers. In 2010, state officials published statements on the number of Christians that were very close to what Christian researchers also claimed. We believe the figures included below reflect as accurate a picture as could be obtained.

NORTHEAST CHINA

Heilongjiang, Jilin, Liaoning

Over 120 million people. Around 8% of them are Christian.

 This region (near North Korea and Russia) was the homeland of the Manchu people (Manchuria), who conquered and ruled all of China from 1644 to 1911. Heilongjiang Province has good farm land. Jilin Province borders North Korea. Liaoning Province attracts economic migrants for industry, agriculture, and the busy port (Dalian). The Church here grew rapidly, with both locals and foreigners (Korean) active in ministry and church planting.

Praise God that almost a third of the 2.4 million Koreans in Northeast China are Christian! Around 30,000 North Koreans escape to China each year, and Christians help them. It is very dangerous for all, with severe punishment for those caught. Many of the refugees are women, and end up as domestic or sexual slaves. Pray for all who escape from North Korea to find freedom, safety, and the light of the gospel in China.

Pray especially for:
- *The Manchu, the 2nd-largest minority group in China.* Most live in the Northeast. Praise God for a significant response to the gospel recently, with new believers in both Manchu congregations and Han-majority churches.
- *The small indigenous Mongolian and Altaic peoples.* Most practise folk religions and follow shamans. Many resent the Han Chinese "takeover" of their homelands.
- *Changchun and Jilin City* (large cities), which have a much lower percentage of Christians.

NORTH CENTRAL CHINA

Hebei, Shaanxi, Shanxi, 2 Municipalities (Beijing, Tianjin)

Over 173 million people live in North Central China, with about 8% of them Christian.

China is ruled from Beijing. Pray for the nation's leaders to seek the good of the people. The wealth and influence of Beijing attracts millions of rural migrants, as well as people from business and academic communities throughout China and the world.

This region is the birthplace of Christianity in China! Nestorian Christians built their first church in Xi'an (Shaanxi) in AD 635, but terrible persecution wiped out this witness. Hebei is

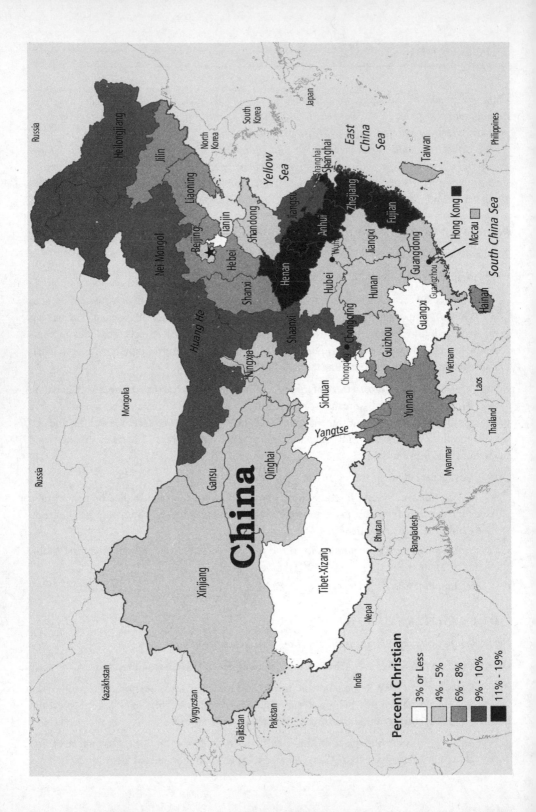

the heart of Catholicism in China, with a large proportion of Catholics. In the last 20 years, the Church here has become one of the fastest growing in China!

3 **The Church of this region endures strict government control and harsh persecution.** In Shanxi Province, thousands of Chinese Christians died as martyrs in the Boxer Rebellion (1900), and waves of persecution continue to come. It is one of the most strictly policed provinces in China, yet the Church grew to nearly 6 million here!

4 **Pray about the challenges of this region:**

- *Spiritual strongholds.* In Shanxi Province, Mount Wutai is a holy mountain for Buddhism, Mount Hengshan is holy to Daoism, and Dazhai became a holy place for followers of Mao during the Cultural Revolution. Shaanxi Province was a key location in the triumph of Communism. Pray for God Almighty to show His sovereignty over these places.

- *Poverty and hardship.* Shanxi's heavy industrial activity led to pollution, disease, and harsh working conditions for factory workers and miners. Poverty in Shaanxi is widespread. Many feel hopeless and desperate, but ministry among them bears good fruit.

Northwest China

Gansu, Qinghai, 1 Autonomous Region (Ningxia Hui)

Over 40 million people live in this region. Around 5% are Christian.

1 **Christian compassionate ministry brought many in this region to Christ.** Church growth in the poorer province of Gansu is small, but more and more come to Christ as Christians care for the sick and needy. Along the Yellow River (in the north of Ningxia), Christian ministry to the poor led a significant number of the farmers and working-class people to faith.

2 **Qinghai Province** is a unique region where the Tibetan, Han, Mongol, Hui, and Turkic worlds meet. Qinghai has the highest ethnic-minority population of any full province in China. In the 1940s, only a few hundred Christians lived here. Growth has been significant mostly among the Han Chinese. Many thousands of prisoners endure great hardship in the labour and prison camps in this province. Pray for the believers who suffer in prison, that their faith in God might grow and bless those around them.

3 **The less reached:**

- *The Dongxiang and Bonan* (mostly in Gansu) come from a mixed Mongolian background, and are strongly Muslim. No one has ever tried to evangelize these isolated peoples.

- *The Muslim Hui* (13.2 million) live in every province of China, even though Ningxia is their official homeland. They descend from a mix of Persian and Arab Muslim traders, Mongolians, and Chinese. Believers number less than 1,000, but a few fellowships and congregations exist today. A few years ago there were none at all. Most Hui who become Christian join Chinese churches, and lose their Hui identity.

- *Tibetan peoples* mostly follow Lamaistic Buddhism. They are strongly bound by powers of the spiritual high places of the Tibetan religion. Gansu has one Tibetan Church, and some Tibetan groups have very small numbers of believers.

East China

Anhui, Fujian, Jiangsu, Jiangxi, Shandong, Zhejiang, 1 Municipality (Shanghai)

Over 400 million people live here. Over 10% are Christian.

1 **Christian growth in East China has been amazing for several decades now!** Every province but Jiangxi had enormous church growth, and even there the Church grows in some areas. TSPM, Catholics, and especially house churches all flourish. Fujian was one of the first provinces to receive the gospel from Protestant missionaries (19th century). Two of China's largest house-church networks started in Anhui, where the Church keeps growing despite strong persecution. 20% of Zhejiang is Christian, the highest of any province (likely more born-again believers live here than in any European country!). Nanjing (in Jiangsu) is a key city for Christianity in China. The national seminary for the TSPM and the Amity Press (the biggest printer of Bibles) are both here. Christians from these areas, especially Zhejiang, work to evangelize other parts of China.

2 **Pray for the wealthy coastal provinces that face Taiwan, South Korea, and Japan:**
 - *Shandong and Jiangsu.* Shandong was the birthplace and home of Confucius, whose philosophy and writings deeply shaped Chinese culture. Ask God to break the spiritual stronghold of Mount Tai, China's most holy mountain in the Daoist and Confucian traditions.
- *Zhejiang Province.* 90% of businesses are privately owned, and its wealth is more evenly spread than in most provinces. It is among China's most stable provinces.
- *Fujian Province* is closely connected to Taiwan (80% of Taiwanese trace their roots to Fujian). Many of the Chinese diaspora in Southeast Asia and even globally come originally from Fujian (Hokkien, Teochew, Hakka, others). Many Taiwanese have come back to restore or build Buddhist and Daoist temples and shrines in their ancestral lands.
- *Shanghai Municipality* is China's largest city. It has the nation's largest port, and is a global centre for finance and trade. China's largest expatriate population lives here. It also has an enormous rural migrant population (5-6 million), as well as more than 3 million residents over age 60.

3 **The inland provinces of Jiangxi and Anhui** are poorer than those on the coast. Floods, food shortage, and poor administration all leave people desperate. Jiangxi has a strong Communist heritage. Weak and sometimes corrupt leaders make policies which often lead to massive protests by farmers and peasants.

Central China

Henan, Hubei, Hunan, 1 Municipality (Chongqing)

Pray for the 250 million people of Central China. Around 10% are Christians.

1 **Henan is the powerhouse of church growth in China!** Some refer to Fangcheng county as the "Jesus Nest". The state declared Henan an "Atheistic Zone" in the 1960s. Revival began during the Cultural Revolution with mass conversions, miracles, and vision for evangelizing China. Henan now has the largest TSPM and house-church populations. Outreach from Henan is one of the great stories of the expansion of Christianity! Church-planting teams (often young women) went out from Henan, followed by Bible teachers. Praise God for this massive, nation-changing growth.

2 Hunan Province was Mao's birthplace, and it remains isolated and hostile to foreigners. Pray for spiritual breakthrough in this province. The Church was traditionally very small here, but has started to grow rapidly in the last generation. But cults and Confucianism also grow rapidly among young people. Peoples in the remote western mountains remain hardly touched by the gospel.

3 Pray for the needs of this region:

• *Henan Province endures much suffering.* Frequent floods along the Yellow River cause great damage.

• *The 3 million Tujia* (Hunan and Hubei) are one of the largest peoples in the world without a written language. They have no Bible. A few are Christian, but most worship the spirits, with particular reverence for white tigers.

• *The registered Church grew in Hubei before 1949,* but not as much since then. Authorities keep tight control, especially over cities. Ask God to break the political and spiritual chains that bind the people. Some house churches grow where Christians ministered to flood victims.

• *Changsha* (the capital of Hunan) was the place where Mao converted to Communism. Hudson Taylor, an early British missionary to China, is buried here. It is closed to foreign influence, and has perhaps only 50,000 Christians out of a population of over 6 million.

• *Chongqing Municipality* (on the Yangtze River) is the industry and trade centre for west and southwest China. It was the world's fastest-growing urban area from 2000 to 2010. The state forced 1.4 million people to find new homes because of the Three Gorges Dam project, and most ended up in Chongqing. Pray for hearts open to the gospel as a result of this traumatic change.

SOUTH AND SOUTHWEST CHINA

Guangdong, Guizhou, Hainan, Sichuan, Yunnan, 1 Autonomous Region (Guangxi Zhuang)

Over 350 million people live here. Only around 4.5% are Christian.

1 The region struggles with many social evils. Corruption, crime, sexual immorality, drug trafficking, and human trafficking are common. Christians are fewer here compared to the rest of China. Sichuan has the lowest Christian percentage of all the Han-majority provinces. Catholics arrived in Sichuan in 1696, and Protestants evangelized Guangdong and Sichuan in the 1800s. But the British seized Hong Kong, and made war on China to force it into the opium trade. This history hinders the spread of the gospel. Rapid development brought great wealth, many migrants, but also moral decline to Guangdong, Hainan (an island that attracts rich mainland tourists), and Chengdu (now the key city for all of western China).

2 Praise God for growth of the Church:

• *In Guizhou,* among 2 Miao peoples and several Yi peoples, mostly in the northwest. A number of peoples previously with no believers now have small but growing churches.

• *In Hainan,* despite the difficult divisions between TSPM and house churches, as well as Christian leaders. Pray for Christian unity.

• *In Chengdu* (Sichuan), where the TSPM churches and house-church networks both grow.

Pray for Christians in South China peoples to become missionaries to the unreached.

3 The unreached peoples of South and Southwest China number tens of millions of individuals, in hundreds of different groups, each with different cultures and languages. Difficult geography and poor transportation keep many villages isolated from the gospel. The Holy Spirit worked powerfully among some tribal groups of Yunnan in the last century (Lisu, Hmong, Wa, Jingpo, Nu). Other peoples have a large number of Christians, but it remains only a small beginning.

- *Guangxi* is one of China's least-developed and most remote provinces, and perhaps up to 90% unevangelized. The Zhuang people are China's largest ethnic-minority population. Pray for Christians to reach even the most remote corners of this region.

- *Yunnan's minorities* number 16 million, in at least 208 peoples. Steep mountains, different languages, old hatreds, and spiritual bondage all hinder the gospel. 95 peoples in Yunnan have no known Christians.

- *The Nosu peoples* (Sichuan) once dominated their area and made slaves of Han Chinese until the Communist government gained control here in 1953.

- *The Li people groups* (Hainan) have a history of rebellion against Chinese rule. No Scripture exists in the 7 main languages of the Li.

- *Tibetan people groups* (Sichuan) are unreached. Many of these people groups are related, but they cannot understand each other's languages. The Bible is available for the Khampa and Amdo Tibetans, but no other group has access to it.

- *Hundreds of other minorities,* such as the Miao and Hmong (mostly in Guizhou), and the Yao-Mien (mainly in Guangxi), need to hear the gospel. Pray for the small Christian churches in them to become strong, effective witnesses.

THE 3 OUTER AUTONOMOUS REGIONS

Inner Mongolia (Nei Mongol), Tibet-Xizang, Xinjiang Uyghur

Over 48 million people live here. Only around 6.6% are Christian.

1 Government policies and massive Han immigration threaten the cultures of these indigenous peoples (Mongols, Uyghurs, Tibetans). These groups often react with hostility, violence, or through a stronger expression of their traditional religion.

2 More ethnic Mongolians live in Inner Mongolia (4 million) than in Mongolia. Their religion mixes Buddhism with ancestor worship, magic, and the influence of shamans. Pray for God to bind the spiritual powers that blind Mongolians to the truth. Mongolians are under-evangelized, but open to the gospel. Christianity grows rapidly in Inner Mongolia, but mostly among the Han Chinese.

3 The Muslim Uyghurs once had a strong Church. Christianity was present in the 6th century, strongest in the 13th century, and persisted even into the 1930s. Violent persecution killed or scattered the believers. Now perhaps 200 to 300 Uyghur believers live in Xinjiang. Pray that the small Uyghur house churches here will grow strong.

4 Most indigenous peoples of Xinjiang are Muslim, and are unreached by the gospel. Some Kazakhs, Hui, Kyrgyz and others have begun to find life in Jesus, but the religious and political situation here requires perseverance, sensitivity, and great faith. Christian ministry by expatriates and even the Han Chinese Christians remains very difficult here. Pray for the global Church to wake up to the great spiritual needs of Xinjiang.

5 **Tibet was briefly an independent Buddhist state until 1950,** when China invaded. Many Tibetans resist the occupation. The government has destroyed over 6,000 monasteries. More than 1 million people may have died, and another 100,000 Tibetans now live in exile in Nepal, India, and the West. Tibetan Buddhism has a powerful hold on the people. The high places of the Tibetan plateau are known to be a spiritual stronghold, highly resistant to the gospel. The ancient religion (Bon) still has demonic and occult influence. 1,800 monasteries and 46,000 Buddhist monks remain in spite of Communist persecution. After centuries of failed attempts and very little fruit, perhaps just over 3,000 Christians exist among the 5 million ethnic Tibetans in the world.

Georgia

Asia

Pop 4.2 million. **Capital** T'bilisi (1.1 mill).
Christians 3.3 mill. *Evangelical Christians* 65,000.
Largest Religion Christian.
Fastest Growing Religion Non-religious (0% growth). All other significant religious groups have negative growth rates.
Largest Ethnic Groups Caucasus (81.7%, Georgian, Mingrelian, Abkhazian), Turkic (6.4%), Armenian (5.4%), Pontic Greek (2.5%), Slavic (1.9%, majority Russian), Iranian-Median (1.2%, majority Ossetian).
Official Language Georgian. **All Languages** 25.

Economy Productive soil and good climate for fruit, tea, cotton, wine, and tourism. Industry and service sectors also strong. Tax reform, anti-corruption efforts, and some privatizations gained higher international standing for the country. Strategic location along an old Silk Route road good for European-Asian transit of goods, oil, and gas.
Politics Independent since 1991 after centuries of domination by surrounding empires. Significant democratic progress since 2004 elections after "rose revolution" (2003). 2 breakaway regions (Abkhazia and South Ossetia) have support and recognition from Russia, and this political dynamic will greatly shape Georgia's future.

---

1 **Positive social, economic, and political changes continue** since 1991. Less corruption and more democratic reform point towards a more peaceful future. Openness to spirituality and Christianity in particular increased greatly! But inter-ethnic conflicts of the past generation displaced nearly 250,000 people. The August War of 2008, when Russian troops briefly occupied much of the country, reversed some of the good economic progress. Pray for peace, and for progress to come again.

2 **The history of the Georgian Orthodox Church** stretches back to AD 150! The Church faced opposition under Communism. Some became martyrs, while others compromised with the Communists. After independence, many Georgians returned to the Church of their ancestors, and some minority groups also converted. For most Georgians this was an expression of nationalism, and not of active spiritual faith. Pray for access to the Word of God, that many may find the truth of the gospel through it.

3 **The small Protestant Church also struggled** under Communism. Since independence, it faces opposition from parts of the Orthodox Church. Evangelical ministries find it difficult to secure buildings, or to receive the permits necessary to hold meetings. Some legal changes in 2005 offer hope of greater freedom. Pray for mutual respect between the Orthodox and other churches. Pray for all churches to put aside their own plans, and to work together for the benefit of the Kingdom.

4 **Pray for the spiritual needs of ethnic minorities:**
 - *Abkhazians* (northwest) are mostly Orthodox, with a Muslim minority, though under the surface most follow more pagan practices. Outreach to them would require cultural insight and spiritual breakthrough.
- *Jews* have long known peace here, but now face increased prejudice. No known witness to them exists.
- *The Kish* are mostly Sunni Muslim, and are closely related to the Chechens. Many live in poverty, in and near the Pankisi Gorge.
- *The Mingrelians* (400,000) are largely non-religious in practice. The JESUS film was the first ever film in their language!
- *The Svaneti people* live in the west in remote mountain villages. Only 1 missionary couple is known to work among this unreached people.

India
Asia

Pop 1.2 billion. **Capital** Delhi (22.2 million).
Christians 71 mill. *Evangelical Christians* 26.3 mill.
Largest Religion Hindu.
Fastest Growing Religion Christian.

Largest Ethnic Groups The most ethnically diverse nation on earth, with over 2,500 distinct people groups! Hindi (37%, 297 groups), Bengali (14.3%, 162 groups), Telugu (5.4%, 135 groups), Marathi-Konkani (5.3%, 110 groups), Rajasthan (5.3%, 110 groups), Tamil (4.6%, 89 groups), Gujarati (4.1%, 127 groups), Kannada (3.1%, 162 groups), Malayali (3.1%, 97 groups), Urdu Muslim (3.1%, 142 groups), Jat (2.8%, 104 groups), Munda-Santal (1.4%, 11 groups), Punjabi (1.4%, 120 groups), Oriya (1.4%, 284 groups), Gond (1.4%, 6 groups), Bhil (1.3%, 4 groups), Tibetan/Himalayan Peoples (1.1%, 252 groups), Iranian-Median (0.9%).

Official Languages 22 official languages by constitution. Hindi is the official language (spoken by 40% of population). English a secondary official language. **All Languages** 456 (18 languages have over 10 million speakers). The SIL Ethnologue lists 438 living languages. 70 have Bibles, 120 have New Testaments, 89 have Old or New Testament portions, and 136 have Scripture work in progress.

Caste Around 4,700 castes and about 25,000 subcastes function as groups that define the social order. People are born into a group, sometimes related to the family occupation. There are 4 main categories: Forward Castes, Other Backward Castes, Dalit/Bahujan/Scheduled Castes, and Scheduled Tribes. Discrimination of people based on caste is illegal by the constitution, and the government has policies in place to help the groups that suffer the most from the system. But caste-based discrimination continues throughout much of India.

Economy Traditional agricultural economy. Rapid transition from early 1990s to become more financially diverse, particularly in industry and services. India is a nuclear power, has a space industry, and is a world leader in the IT sector. Rapid growth brought new wealth to many, and increased the middle class. The rural poor and urban slum-dwellers still number in the hundreds of millions, and 40% of the population live below the poverty line. Inadequate infrastructure (such as travel, power, sanitation), together with corruption and social prejudice, remain enormous obstacles to progress.

Politics Independent from Britain in 1947 as a democracy. Hindu extreme nationalist movements grew in strength and influence, and the Hindu nationalist BJP (Bharatiya Janata Party) gained political power in the 1990s. A coalition government led by the Indian National Congress party (INC) then won 2 elections. That government emphasized economic growth and social progress on issues such as caste and freedom of religion. 2014 elections brought a BJP-led alliance back into power, on a platform of stronger economic growth and social development. Long-standing tensions with Pakistan continue, especially over the issue of Kashmir.

Over 1 billion people make their home in India's 28 Union States and 7 Union Territories. 45 of India's cities have a population of over 1 million. At the same time India remains just over 30% urban, and the majority of people still live in a rural context. India has an ancient, complex, and easily misunderstood past. Add to that its present diversity of languages, ethnicities, and religions, all mixed together with the caste system. A detailed analysis of its population is a hugely difficult task.

INDIAN SOCIETY, ECONOMY, AND GOVERNMENT

1 **India is the world's largest democracy.** Political, economic, and social challenges all place a heavy burden on the government. India experienced recent progress in many areas, but we must continue to pray for its leaders to deal strongly with corruption, inefficiency, and prejudice. (100 of the 543 Members of Parliament had criminal cases against them in 2010.) Many Indians today experience greater religious freedom and positive economic growth. More Indian NGOs and the government attempt to address injustices practised within the caste system. Pray that the government will choose to build on the progress of recent decades, especially to preserve and protect human dignity, rights, and freedoms.

2 **India's last decade is an economic success story** that will significantly impact the global economy in the future. Most people traditionally work in agriculture, but the industrial and services sectors (especially IT) continue to expand. India now has the 4th-highest number of millionaires of any country, and an enormous middle class. The younger generation is more educated and more open-minded, but also more materialistic. India also has the world's highest number of poor, and the world's widest gap between rich and poor. For millions, India's economic growth changed nothing. Infrastructure continues to be a problem (travel, power, sanitation), and corruption affects every level of society. 40% of the population live below the poverty line, and 40% of children do not have enough food to eat.

3 **The caste system** remains a major issue. The Dalits/Bahujans/Scheduled Castes and Scheduled Tribes together are 25% of the population. Others oppressed these groups for thousands of years, and used the caste system (and Hinduism) to justify their harmful actions. The UN, the Indian government, and international NGOs have all taken action to address the situation. Churches also work to establish human rights, education, health, and employment, and also for salvation of the Dalits. The Church has an opportunity to show that the love of Christ extends to all people, regardless of caste, race, language, gender, and economic status. Pray for Christians to remove all caste discrimination from the Church, where it sadly does exist. The Dalit Freedom Network educates Christians about issues related to Dalit rights and freedoms.

4 **India has more human need than any other nation.** We must respond to India's suffering with intelligent action and sustained prayer!

- *Poverty affects hundreds of millions.* In India, many people are not just poor but have nothing. The largest cities have enormous slums, but most poor people still live in rural villages. They usually come from the Dalit/Bahujan/Scheduled Castes and Scheduled Tribes, and often end up as "debt slaves" to corrupt land owners. Both their debt and the slavery pass to the next generation, so this will not end without change. Pray that those who suffer might see God's justice and love demonstrated to them.

- *Health concerns affect masses of people.* The lack of adequate sanitation and clean water increases diseases, which mostly impact children and the poor. Around 900,000 people per year die from drinking unclean water, or from breathing polluted air. India has the world's 3rd-largest HIV-positive population and one-third of the world's tuberculosis cases. Leprosy originated in India, which has over 1,000 leper colonies. Most of the 15 million cases of blindness could be prevented with enough doctors or optometrists.

5 **Women and children suffer the most.** No country can match India's tragic need. Pray for state programmes and loving Christian ministries to address these desperate needs. Pray that God will change attitudes and practices in society to reflect His care for women and children.

- *Children in crisis.* Of the 400 million children, possibly up to 35 million are orphans. 11 million are abandoned (90% are girls). 3 million live on the streets. Some families sell children into slavery to pay off family debts. Two-thirds of all children suffer physical abuse, and half suffer some kind of sexual harassment or abuse. Over 1 million end up in prostitution (mostly Nepalis and Bangladeshis).

- *Women and girls.* Society prefers male children, so some families abort, abandon, or even kill girl babies. The female population today lacks 35 million girls when compared with the male population. Women have lower rates of literacy and education, and domestic abuse is a widespread problem. Some young girls get dedicated to the ancient service of temple prostitution.

6 **Instability and unrest threaten peace** inside and outside the country. India dominates South Asia and the whole Indian Ocean region. Relations with Pakistan are continually tense and at times violent. China also disputes some of India's northern borders. The armed Communist militant groups within Central and Eastern India continue to grow in number and threaten national security. A number of minority separatist groups in the northeast use violence to promote their various causes. Throughout India, Hindu militant groups follow the ideal that "India is Hindu only", and use intimidation or violence against Muslims, Christians, and other minority groups.

HINDUISM AND RELIGION IN INDIA

1 **Hinduism is the world's 3rd-largest religious system,** though it is more like a network of many religious beliefs and practices. Some focus on philosophies, others on rituals and traditions, others worship idols, and others mix these together with tribal or village spirit worship (or the occult). Hinduism can allow for any beliefs or teachings, so many consider it a religion of tolerance and peace. A few of its concepts have become part of modern global culture (yoga, gurus, the ideas of karma and reincarnation, transcendental meditation). But its paths do not provide for true fellowship with the Creator God.

2 **India's constitution gives full religious freedom.** Praise God that Indian Christians are free to proclaim the gospel. But some state governments discriminate against Christians, Muslims, and other minorities. They pass anti-conversion laws, or sometimes refuse state benefits to Dalits who become Christian. Pray that India's leaders protect religious freedom and religious minority groups. Persecution largely comes from militant Hindu groups who want to rid India of all "foreign" faiths. The government must deal firmly with violence against Dalit and tribal communities, and provide equal opportunity for all Dalits, regardless of their religion.

3 **India has the world's 3rd-largest Muslim population** (over 160 million, or over 14% of the population). Muslims ruled much of India for over 600 years, but now they live as a frequently oppressed minority. Most live in Uttar Pradesh, West Bengal, and Bihar. They remain some of the least-evangelized peoples in the world. This is a tragedy, because they are more accessible in India than elsewhere! More Indian and global agencies have committed to work among them in recent years. Pray especially for:

- *The 77 million Shaikh* in Andhra Pradesh, Tamil Nadu, Jharkhand, and Bihar.
- *The 10 million Ansari.* God brought a breakthrough among them in Delhi!
- *The 9 million Mappila of Kerala.*
- *The 7 million Kashmiri Muslims.* They have become more militant in their Islam.
- *The 7 million Sayyid* in Tamil Nadu and West Bengal.

4 **Christianity** in India is best known for William Carey's legacy of service in the early 19th century. Indians view his many contributions to society as positive. More recently, Christianity is associated positively with the work of Catholic missionaries, and even evangelical holistic ministry in education and health. But most Hindus consider Christianity a foreign, Western faith. Pray that Indian and foreign Christians would demonstrate true spirituality and the transformation that Christ brings.

5 **India has the world's largest populations of Sikhs, Zoroastrians, Jains, and Baha'is.** Pray for:
- *The Sikh community* (over 22 million). Most Christians do not understand Sikhism. But today, the number of Sikhs who follow Jesus (both secretly and openly) continues to increase.
- *Buddhist Tibetans* (about 100,000, largely refugees from Tibet). Only a few dozen among them follow Christ. Dharamsala in Himachal Pradesh is the present headquarters of the Dalai Lama.
- *The 6 million Jains and 70,000 Parsees.* They have great influence in society, industry, and business. The Jain religion is ancient, with a strong emphasis on moral purity and non-violence. Parsees practise the ancient Persian Zoroastrian faith.

THE CHURCH IN INDIA

1 **The Indian Church is highly diverse,** with a long legacy. Much of Indian Christianity results from people movements of the last 300 years, often started by local revivals. Some Christian groups today have remarkable growth, while other groups decline in numbers.
- *The Orthodox Churches* trace their origin to the tradition of the Apostle Thomas, who was said to minister here in the 1st century. Orthodox Christians (over 2.2 million) have the strongest presence in Kerala and southwest India.

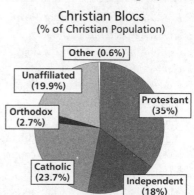

Christian Blocs
(% of Christian Population)

Other (0.6%)

Unaffiliated (19.9%)

Protestant (35%)

Orthodox (2.7%)

Catholic (23.7%)

Independent (18%)

- *Catholics* represent the largest Christian group in India (nearly 20 million). People respect their charity work, especially Mother Teresa's care for the poorest of the poor. Catholics run more than 5,000 healthcare facilities. The charismatic movement in the Catholic Church began in 1972. It spread to almost every congregation, and brought both new life and increased outreach.
- *Evangelical denominations and congregations multiplied.* God uses several networks and alliances to mature and mobilize believers through prayer, pastors' retreats, and conventions. They also coordinate training, literature production, missions, and outreach (the Evangelical Fellowship of India links over 224 denominations, the Pentecostal Fellowship of India links the major Pentecostal groups, and so on).
- *Newer Pentecostal and charismatic fellowships* sprang up quickly, and spread throughout India, especially in the last 15 years.

- *The Yesu Darbar* gathers tens of thousands of Jesus' followers in North India. They model biblical worship and fellowship patterns in an Indian style.
- *Millions of followers of Jesus (Yesu Bhaktas)* are secret believers, or unbaptized Christians outside the established denominations. Pray for discipleship for these people as their numbers increase.

(2) **Bible-believing churches and groups continue to grow,** even in regions that previously resisted the gospel (Uttar Pradesh, and other North or Central Indian states)! Growth among lower-caste Hindus and tribal peoples is especially strong. Millions of Indians became more open to the message of Christ through strategic use of Christian literature, radio, and TV programmes, and through Christian videos, films, and cassettes. Much of this growth came after hundreds of new and often massive prayer movements (frequently driven by women and children) began to pray for the evangelization of the country. Praise God for answered prayer!

(3) **The established Church faces a need for change.** In many denominations, Christians follow Western forms of worship, lifestyle, and church organization. Outreach to non-Christians has decreased greatly for some groups, and many congregations have few to no new believers. Past disputes over power and property led to bitter divisions in the Church. Pray that the Holy Spirit might bring new life to traditional forms of Christianity.

(4) **Persecution of Christians** (especially in Orissa, Karnataka, and Gujarat) draws believers together in greater unity. It also caused the Church to reflect on its current methods for evangelism and ministry. Pray that Christians might unite and take courage when faced with violent persecution (over 1,000 attacks a year occur, mostly in the BJP-ruled states). Some militant Hindus attempt to "reconvert" Christians by force. Pray that believers will stand firm in Christ, whatever the cost, with love and forgiveness. Pray that their persecutors might repent and find Christ.

(5) **Training for Christian workers is an urgent need.**
- *The life and health of the Church depend on pastors, teachers, evangelists, and missionaries.* Many new believers come to faith through large rallies, healings, or miracles, but have few opportunities for Christian discipleship. Most leaders and pastors received very little preparation for their work.
- *Pray for the formal training institutions.* India now has over 100 degree-level seminaries! Many are evangelical. Bible schools number over 1,000. Many teach practical skills (such as church planting) in addition to theology. Training centres for indigenous workers (to train church planters) now also play a significant role. But much more is needed. Pray for creative, effective models to reach the country's pastors and leaders with Bible teaching.
- *All Christians need training to be effective ambassadors for Christ in their society.* The Indian Church must learn to have greater impact in the workplace and in national life. Currently most Indians associate Christianity with the deprived and lower classes of society (80% of Indian Christians come from Dalit or tribal communities). The gospel has not yet made a significant impact on business, politics, arts, or culture.

(6) **Christian missions, church planting, and research initiatives** in India have all grown and matured since the 1960s, when foreign groups largely controlled much of this work.
- *Over 1,000 Indian mission agencies send out 100,000 church planters, evangelists, and social workers.* Tens of thousands of new congregations now exist as a result! A truly Indian Church follows Christ, and lives out the gospel. Over 500 Indians serve as missionaries in foreign countries.

- *Networks like the Indian Missions Association (IMA) encourage cooperation and fellowship.* Several agencies collect data on each state, city, language, and people group of India. The Church has never before had such clarity about the unfinished task of evangelism! Pray for mature leaders, good member care, and cooperation for the gospel's sake.
- *Only 1,000 expatriate missionaries serve in India.* Many find it difficult to obtain visas. Business and medical visas provide good opportunities for workers who authentically serve in those areas.
- *The All India Christian Council* serves all denominations, with over 5,000 agencies, NGOs, denominations, and institutions that work for human rights, social justice, religious freedom, and protection of minorities. Unity now grows where there was a spirit of division.

India's Least Evangelized

1 **India has more unreached individuals than any other nation.** The south and northeast have a higher proportion of Christians than the more populated north and west. Pray that the Church worldwide might rise to this task! Pray for:

- *The North India Ganges plains,* or the states through which the Ganges flows (Himachal Pradesh, Uttarakhand, Uttar Pradesh, Bihar, and West Bengal). Together they account for 283 million people. None of these states is more than 1% Christian. However, the Church now grows here more than ever, with some megachurches and several networks of house churches. Some Christians have a vision for 1 million churches planted in the north by 2020.
- *The great cities,* where the very rich live close to the very poor. Millions come from rural areas to cities every year, and most end up in slums. Mumbai and Hyderabad have significant Christian populations, while Kolkata, Delhi, Varanasi, and Lucknow have little Christian witness.
- *The middle classes* (up to 350 million people). Half the cross-cultural missionaries worked among tribal groups, and many of the rest among the neediest sections of the population. Few today work among the urban middle class and the higher castes. This needs to change, but most workers feel unprepared for such challenges.

2 **India has the largest concentration of the world's least-evangelized peoples.** 159 people groups in India have over 1 million people, and 133 of them remain unreached. Every state has unreached people. The lists below may seem like a collection of strange names, but each group has millions of people, and most of them have no access to the gospel (no Scripture, no church, no Christian radio or TV, no missionaries). Each family and individual is precious to God. Pray especially for:

- *The Brahmin* (50 million). They are the priestly caste, and the highest caste in the Hindu world. Only about 18,000 follow Jesus.
- *The Forward Castes.* They have negative views of Christianity, and believe that Christians reject Hindu culture for Western colonial ideas. Ask God to break through barriers to faith in Christ! Pray for the Rajput (43 mill), Mahratta (29 mill), and the Hindu Jat (16 mill). Pray for the Mahishya (10 mill), Kayastha (8 mill), Nair (8 mill), Agarwal/Bania (5 mill), Arora (4 mill), Bhumihar (3 mill), Vellalan (2.5 mill), and Hindu Khatri (2.1 mill).
- *Backward Caste peoples.* Praise God for the 55,000 believers among the Banjara (20 mill, a Gypsy people), and a breakthrough among the Lingayat (10 mill, with hundreds of fellowships).

Pray for the Yadava (59 mill), Kurmi (18 mill), Teli (18 mill), Kunbi (16 mill), Kapu (16 mill), Nai (12 mill), Pashtun (12 mill), and Mappila (10 mill), Kairi (8 mill), Sonar (7 mill), Gujar (7 mill), and Vakkaliga (6 mill).

- *Scheduled Castes/Dalits.* They respond more openly to the gospel, sometimes in large numbers! Pray for these groups, all less than 0.1% Christian: Dhobi (12 mill), Mahar (9 mill), Pasi (8 mill), Namasudra (5 mill), Rajbansi (5 mill), Bagdi (3.5 mill), and Pod (3 mill).
- *Scheduled Tribes.* Many remain unevangelized or underevangelized. After years of ministry, the Bhil (14 mill) and Gond (14 mill) have many churches, but both remain only 1% Christian. The 12 million Koli are only 0.3% Christian.

3 **The Bible Society has worked in India since 1811.** It helps distribute over 30 million Scripture portions or Bibles every year, together with other organizations. But Bible translation remains a major challenge. India has 456 languages. 70 languages have a Bible, and 120 languages have the New Testament. At the current rate of work, translation would not be completed until the end of this century. Pray for more workers. Over half the population cannot read well, so audio resources (like Talking Bibles) are vital. India is a world leader in IT, and has over 100 million Internet users. Pray for more Christian websites for evangelism and for discipleship, in many of India's languages.

The Regions of India

Most Indian states are larger than the majority of countries of the world! More people live in Central and North India, but more Christians live in South or Northeast India. Each state is distinct, but many share similar challenges or answers to prayer. The many issues facing society and the Church described above remain true for each state.

Please note that religious figures from census data available in 2009 were lower than information we received from people within each state. For that reason, the percentage of Christians shown below comes from the World Christian Database (2010).

SOUTH INDIA

Andhra Pradesh, Goa, Karnataka, Kerala, Tamil Nadu, 3 Union Territories (Andaman and Nicobar Islands, Lakshadweep, Puducherry)

Over 200 million people. Praise God that around 12% of them are Christian.

1 **Many Indian mission agencies work in Andhra Pradesh,** and many people come to Christ! Every district now has churches. But 16 people groups remain unreached and unengaged. Millions of Hindus come to Andhra Pradesh every year to worship at Tirupathi. 200 Christian organizations have bases in Hyderabad (the state capital), a key centre for Christian ministry. 40% of Hyderabad are Muslim, and it is also a key centre for Islam in South India. Very little is done to reach out to Muslims.

2 **Tourists come to beautiful Goa,** both from India and around the world. This helps the economy, but also brought an increase of evil activities such as drug trafficking and child prostitution. Pray that all those involved might be delivered to new life. Goa was a Portuguese colony (1510-1961), and has many Catholics. Many people here mix Hindu beliefs with Christian teachings. Praise God for the new Konkani Bible (the language of most Christians and many others). Translators worked for 18 years to complete it. Pray for its effective use.

3 **Karnataka has the most spiritual need of any state in South India.** Bangalore (capital) is the fastest-growing city in India, and the centre of the IT and software industries. Over 800 Christian ministries have headquarters here! Bangalore's Christian community came first from the middle and upper classes, but now many from the lower castes and many slum dwellers have become believers, especially through the ministry of charismatic churches. Traditional Christian communities tend to be isolated from the rest of society. 79 people groups remain unreached and unengaged in Karnataka.

4 **Kerala has a long Christian history,** and more Christians than any other state in India. The majority are from Syriac Orthodox churches. Pray for God to bring new life and passion to these ancient churches. Christians of earlier generations invested in the educational system, and Kerala is now the most well-educated state in India, and the most favourable to women. Some tension exists between the traditional Christian Churches (Orthodox, Catholic, Protestant) and the newer, fast-growing Independent groups (usually charismatic). Pray for unity.

5 **Politics affects the Church and mission in Tamil Nadu state.** Hindu extremists threaten the Church with anti-conversion laws. Pray that the current religious freedom continues. The Church grows despite the social pressures, especially among Dalit and tribal peoples. Muslims and higher

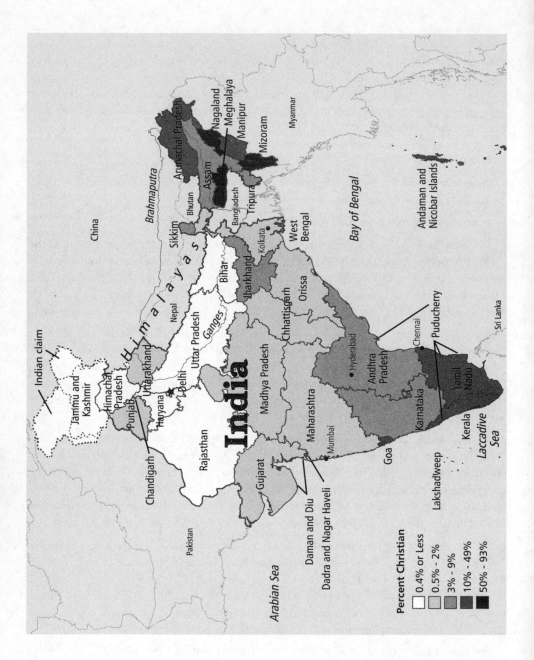

Percent Christian

0.4% or Less
0.5% - 2%
3% - 9%
10% - 49%
50% - 93%

caste Hindus receive very little outreach. Tamils founded many of the Christian organizations throughout India. Pray that the Church of Tamil Nadu presses forward with its mission vision and outreach.

6 **Pray for these Union Territories:**

- *Andaman and Nicobar Islands* (38 islands in the Bay of Bengal). Over 20% of the population are Christian. 4 isolated people groups remain unreached. They have small populations, but the government forbids all mission work among them. The Hindu and Muslim populations (around 300 people groups) also need outreach.
- *Lakshadweep* (12 coral islands and 36 islands in the Arabian Sea). Over 98% of the population are devoted Muslims. No long-term ministry to them has ever been permitted or attempted.

NORTHEAST INDIA

Arunachal Pradesh, Assam, Manipur, Meghalaya, Mizoram, Nagaland, Tripura

Over 40 million people. Praise God that around 20% of them are Christian.

1 **Many ethnic rebel movements disrupt life in Northeast India.** They each have different aims, and often fight each other. Sometimes they attack Christians, or any non-indigenous peoples. Local people resent immigrants (Bengali-speakers from Bangladesh, Hindi-speakers from other parts of India). Sadly, conflict among "Christian" tribes hinders outreach to Muslims and Hindus. Pray that those who take up arms for many causes would instead find peace and unity in Christ!

2 **Many tribes of Northeast India became Christian in the 20th century!** Revivals brought new life, even while many early converts suffered persecution. 87% of Mizoram are Christian, one of the highest proportions anywhere in the world! Thousands of Mizo, Naga, and Manipuri go out as missionaries to other parts of India and the world. But young people have begun to leave the Church. Immorality, the pursuit of material possessions, and drug or alcohol abuse are widespread problems, as are false teachings, cults, and even devil worship.

3 **Pray for these less-reached groups:**

- *The Buddhist peoples of Arunachal Pradesh* (near Bhutan) have little opportunity to hear the gospel. Those who leave Tibetan Buddhism usually face rejection and persecution.
- *Assam remains the major spiritual challenge in Northeast India.* After 2 centuries of missions, Christians are only a small minority. Most tribal peoples remain unreached. Few Christians witness to the 9.7 million Muslims (who speak mostly Bengali) or the Hindu majority (who speak Assamese). The tea-estate workers are migrant peoples or tribal minorities from other states. Most are open to the gospel, but few Christians are there to share it.
- *The Meitei* (Manipur) have followed Hinduism for 3 centuries, but recently had a revival of their traditional religion (Sanamahi). Most Meitei reject Christianity as a religion only for tribal peoples, and only a few Christians exist among them.

CENTRAL INDIA

Chhattisgarh, Gujarat, Jharkhand, Madhya Pradesh, Maharastra, Orissa, Sikkim, West Bengal, 2 Union Territories (Dadra and Nagar Haveli, Daman and Diu)

This area, from Mumbai to Kolkata, has over 400 million people. Only 2% of them are Christians.

1 **Kolkata is West Bengal's capital city,** and was once the capital of India. It is named after and dedicated to Kali, the Hindu goddess of destruction. Many people live in slums in this crowded, polluted city, and up to 1 million people live on the streets. 67 people groups throughout West Bengal are unreached and unengaged. Workers sometimes neglect tribal peoples, but they usually respond well to the gospel.

2 **Bengalis are the world's largest unreached ethnic group** (250 million). 67 million live in West Bengal, where Christians are less than 1% of the population. Ask God to remove every barrier to the gospel (the proud culture, demonic powers, a spirit of independence, and need for effective demonstration of the gospel). Praise God for a new, easy-to-read Bengali Bible translation.

3 **Orissa has more intense persecution of Christians** than anywhere else in India. In many districts, Christians must either reconvert to Hinduism, leave their village, or face death. Pray that churches might grow in unity, and in their ability to withstand persecution. Despite the troubles, the Church multiplies rapidly, mostly among tribal and Dalit peoples. 709 of the 799 people groups in Orissa have no Christians, according to a census. Pray for the effective use of audio Scripture, and Christian radio and TV programmes, as illiteracy is common.

4 **Chhattisgarh and Jharkhand** both have minerals, forests, and good farm land. But the people are largely poor and under-educated. Rebel groups are very active in the forest and jungle regions, and violent conflict (which can include persecution of Christians) causes problems. The Christian Church remains small here, but house churches have begun to spread. Chhattisgarh is known as "Home of the Tribals". Pray that the light of the gospel shines into every tribal group, in both states.

5 **Madhya Pradesh was one of the last states to open up for missions.** It is strongly Hindu, with strict laws that limit conversions to Christianity. Madhya Pradesh has many large tribal peoples, and more tribal groups than anywhere else in the world. Most practise a version of animism that was influenced by Hinduism. Many practise witchcraft, Shaktism (worship of female energy), and Saivism (worship of the god Shiva). Christians planted thousands of new churches in 20 years. Praise God for house church movements among some of the tribes. The whole state needs pioneer mission work. Pray for open doors for the gospel!

6 **Maharashtra's name means "state of large territory",** and it is huge in land area, in population, and in influence.

- *Mumbai* (capital) has the Indian stock exchange and the Indian film industry (Bollywood). But it also has Dharavi, India's largest slum (over 1 million people). In fact, over half the population of Mumbai live in slums! Mumbai has 200,000 people caught in the sex trade, 100,000 street children, and 300,000 AIDS cases. At the same time, Mumbai has the 2nd-highest Christian population of all India's megacities. Pray that Christians may be salt and light in their city!

- *Smaller cities and rural areas* have not yet experienced the same scale of mass people movements to Christ. At least 73 peoples remain unreached and unengaged, and 40,000 villages are unreached. Pray for the 175 or more Indian agencies and churches who reach out to them.

7 **Gujarat remains a place of religious tension and persecution.** The state government and the police support Hindu militant groups that intimidate Muslims and Christians in Dalit and tribal groups. Gujarat was the birthplace of the leader Gandhi. Pray for the peace and tolerance he promoted to become a reality here! Religious oppression at times prevents Christian outreach, and creates division among believers. But persecution sometimes brings new life and revival. Pray for labourers to the unreached, especially:

- *The Jains.* The Saurashtra (peninsula that reaches into the Arabian Sea) has over 1 million Jains. Ahmadabad is a major Jain centre, with over 100 temples and little Christian work.
- *The Muslims.* Pray also for God to send workers to the 76 distinct people groups. Muslims are the largest and least-reached population in Gujarat.

NORTH INDIA

Bihar, Haryana, Himachal Pradesh, Jammu and Kashmir, Punjab, Rajasthan, Uttar Pradesh, Uttarkhand, 2 Union Territories (Delhi, Chandigarh)

Over 400 million people. Only around 0.5% of them are Christian.

1 **Jammu and Kashmir endure tragic suffering and conflict.**

- *Pakistan and India both claim possession of Kashmir* since the partition of India (1947). Islamic militants fight to either join Pakistan or have an independent state. So far 40,000 have died, and 800,000 lost their homes in this war.
- *Christians have always been few,* but in some places whole villages have now come to faith! Many feel tired of the hatred and violence, and find hope and peace in Christ. Christian growth usually meets persecution from families and communities. Pray for the protection of new believers and Christian workers.
- *Almost all groups in Jammu and Kashmir remain unreached.* The Kashmir Valley region is 97% Muslim, the Jammu region is 66% Hindu, and the Ladakh region is 46% Buddhist. Pray especially for a breakthrough among the more isolated Buddhist peoples.

2 **Punjab is the home state of the Sikhs,** and the only state where they are a majority. Their famous Golden Temple is in Amritsar (capital). In the past, Christians paid little attention to Sikhs. Some agencies and churches reached out to them, and now several Christian leaders from the Sikh community profess and proclaim the good news both in Punjab and abroad! Most other Christians in Punjab came from mass movements to Christ in the 19th century. Today many churches and missions have a vision to plant churches in all villages and urban areas of Punjab. 14 people groups remain unreached and unengaged.

3 **Rajasthan is India's most popular tourist destination,** for Indians and foreigners. Christians here remain a small minority, but the Church grew rapidly in the last decade. Praise God! Hindu militant groups persecute Christians so harshly that even secular groups and some moderate Hindus protest against the treatment. Pray that all attempts to destroy God's people would result in greater church growth. Ministry in Rajasthan continues to increase, despite the persecution. Jaipur (capital) has 3.2 million people and around 22,000 Christians. Higher castes show almost no response to the gospel. Most are Hindu, but some are Jain or Muslim. No Bible portions exist for the major languages of Rajasthan.

4 **Delhi** is the capital of India, and the centre of power and finance for the nation. Major Christian revival and growth in Delhi would in turn affect the rest of India. Delhi's massive population growth created a serious crisis. Most people who arrive in the city must live in illegal housing areas which grow into slums (now over 3,000). Most lack water, electricity, sewage, and legal status. Crime rates are very high. Many national Christian organizations have headquarters here, and Delhi has over 3,000 churches. Pray that Christians will be moved to share and demonstrate the gospel in the slums.

 Haryana is one of India's least-evangelized states. Only 32,000 identify themselves as Christian among its 22 million people. 6,000 villages have no Christian witness. But 15 Christian training centres have work here. Pray for them to equip many new workers for outreach. A significant number of Sikhs in Haryana have come into the Kingdom. Pray that this number increases, and has an impact on Sikhs elsewhere. Few known Christians exist among the 1.7 million Brahmins or the 750,000 Shaikhs.

 Himachal Pradesh is called the "land of the gods", and Hindu pilgrims come to visit the holy sites. Pray that the people may be released from bondages, and find freedom in Jesus.

- *This was India's least-evangelized state for a long time,* but this may no longer be true. Indian mission agencies sent many workers to preach the gospel, and now over 600 churches and house groups meet to worship Jesus!

- *Of the 115 people groups, only 15 have believers.* The Dalai Lama (leader of Tibetan Buddhists) lives in Himachal Pradesh. Pray for the gospel to reach the 100,000 Tibetan refugees in India.

 The people of Uttarakhand claim to be guardians of the Hindu gods' land, and so they resist the gospel.

- *Uttarakhand's Hindu holy sites and a holy Sikh shrine all attract millions of pilgrims* each year. The world's largest Hindu gathering (the Kumbh Mela) takes place in Haridwar every 12 years. Pilgrims who come seek release from the cycle of suffering. Pray that they will find it in Jesus!

- *Uttarakhand's population is largely upper caste.* Christian workers must be fluent in Hindi, and share the gospel in more intellectual ways.

- *Despite the small Christian population, Dehradun (capital) is a strong centre for Christian activity,* with several theological or Bible training institutions. Pray for their vision to train Christian workers to reach North India.

 Uttar Pradesh (UP) is the home of Hinduism, and has a long historical connection to Buddhism and Jainism also. Sadly, it has given no home to the gospel.

- *Millions of Hindu pilgrims visit Varanasi,* the holy city of Hinduism on the Ganges River. But very few find the living water only Jesus can give. This key state needs vast amounts of prayer, and thousands more Christian workers.

- *The scale of human need and suffering* here is immense. Water-borne diseases are widespread. Most of the world's polio cases occur in Uttar Pradesh. The majority of children are undernourished. Christian witness must go together with acts of mercy.

- *The size of the unfinished task in UP should drive us to prayer.* If UP were its own country, it would have the 3rd-largest unevangelized population in the world. 191 groups remain unreached and unengaged. This single state likely represents the world's greatest missionary challenge. Praise God that more churches, mission agencies, and prayer networks (both national and expatriate) now focus some work on UP.

Pray for Bihar, India's poorest state. Bihar was once the seat of the great Mauryan and Gupta empires, and it played a large role in India's struggle for modern independence. Buddhism and Jainism both began here. Its modern political history, however, is known for incompetence, corruption, division, and community conflict. Many call Bihar "the graveyard of missions" because of the obstacles that prevent evangelization (deep poverty, lack of Scriptures, strong spiritual opposition, persecution by the Hindu majority, others). Malaria and other diseases endanger the lives of Christian workers as well as all Bihari people. Pray that the Lord might show His powerful love for Biharis through ministry to them.

10 **Over 4,000 Indian missionaries now serve in Bihar.** Excellent research and analysis highlighted the needs. Christians give greater focus to prayer, church planting, and holistic outreach. The high-caste Hindus (16.5 mill) hear the gospel more often now, but few respond. The Muslims (16.5 mill) are among the poorest and the least-reached people in the world.

11 **Sikkim is a small state in the Himalayas.** The Church grows rapidly here. Some former Buddhist monks and religious leaders have found Christ. Most Christians here come from the Lepcha people, who are the original inhabitants of the region and traditionally follow Buddhism. Pray that these believers will share the gospel with other Himalayan Buddhist peoples. Spiritual breakthrough here is very difficult, but not impossible. Pray for God to work powerfully!

Indonesia   *Asia*

Pop 232.5 million. **Capital** Jakarta (9.2 mill).
Christians 36.9 mill. *Evangelical Christians* 13 mill.
Largest Religion Muslim.
Fastest Growing Religion Christian.

Largest Ethnic Groups Diverse population, with over 750 distinct peoples. Indo-Malay (94.3%, includes Javanese, Sunda, Indonesian, Madura, Batak, Minangkabau peoples), Chinese (3.9%), Pacific Island peoples (0.6%, 258 peoples), Other (1.2%, includes Arab, Indian, European, US citizen, mixed race).
Official Language Indonesian (Bahasa Indonesia). Its increased use brings unity to the nation. **All Languages** 722.
18 are spoken by more than 1 million people. 247 spoken in Papua region alone.

Economy Based on natural gas, forest products, agriculture, and textiles, with large mineral reserves. The service industry is the largest employer. Steady economic progress since 1980s, and enormous potential. Political and religious instability, corruption, and a need for economic reform. Wealthy urban areas, but half the population lives on less than US$2/day. Serious environmental damage (from cutting down forests) in Kalimantan, Sumatra, and elsewhere.
Politics Colonial rule by Portuguese, Dutch, British, and Japanese across 16th–20th centuries. Independent since 1945. Ruled by General Sukarno and then General Suharto until 1997. Since then transitioned to an elected government (the world's 3rd-largest democracy). The politically active military and Islamist groups throughout the country could threaten peaceful progress. Religious tensions and mass relocation programmes (due to overpopulation) could also lead to violence.

Indonesia is large and diverse. It has 17,500 islands scattered across 10 million square kilometres of ocean. The population speaks 722 languages, and lives on 6,000 different islands. Indonesia has the world's 2nd-largest rainforest and vast coral reefs. The government faces an enormous challenge to hold this diverse nation together. It must balance national unity with each region's unique identity. Indonesia's history includes discrimination, injustice, human rights abuses, and violent conflict. Pray for the government to act with righteousness, and to honour each of the peoples and communities it represents.

Praise God for many positive changes. These include continued church growth over 50 years, especially some large people movements to Christ! Give thanks for a democracy which allows a Christian voice in society. Thank God that intense persecution did not stop Christian growth, and led to more unity among believers. Praise Him that many moderate Muslims in Indonesia also hate the extremism and violence of radical Islamists in their country. Give thanks for the spread of the Indonesian language, which also allows the gospel to spread more easily.

Millions of Indonesians need a new place to live. Pray that Christians might show the love of Jesus to these displaced peoples.

- *The "Transmigration Scheme".* Since Java and Bali are highly crowded, the government organized the relocation of over 8 million people to Sumatra, Kalimantan, Sulawesi, and West Papua where more space is available.

- *Natural disasters.* As a result of earthquakes, tsunamis, and floods, millions since 2001 have become homeless or displaced and 200,000 have died.

- *Community violence and religious persecution.* More than 500,000 Christians from Maluku and central Sulawesi suffer personal loss, bitter trauma, and loss of their ancestral homelands to Muslim groups.

- *Migrant workers.* 400,000 legal migrants (and more illegal ones) seek work abroad. 80% are female, and they often work in people's homes. Their loneliness can open their hearts to loving witness by Christians in other nations.

A spiritual battle rages for Indonesia. Ancient occult powers oppose the gospel, while the extremist Muslim groups seek to remove Christianity from society. Ask God to bind these powers. Islam in Indonesia has many forms. Some Muslims are devout in their faith. Some identify themselves as Muslim, but mix Islamic ways with traditional folk religions or even Hinduism. Others have a more secular view and lifestyle. The government requires that all citizens follow 1 of 6 religions (Islam, Hinduism, Buddhism, Confucianism, Catholicism, or Protestantism). This actually led many traditional animists to consider the gospel!

Islamists slowly gain influence, which causes religious freedom to decline. They persecute Christians and other religious minorities, even other moderate Muslim groups. The secular government and Muslim leaders need courage to stand against the Islamists. Pray that they would stop Islamist violence where they can. Whole towns and regions no longer have a Christian presence, and many have lost lives and property. Some Christians have responded with attitudes and actions of hatred or revenge. Pray for heartfelt repentance among Christians who have hurt their

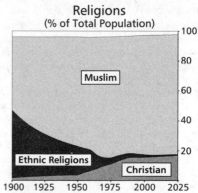

Religions
(% of Total Population)

witness in this way. Pray for Christians to respond with love, and in all ways to represent the gospel.

Pray that the Church continues to grow amidst the intense opposition and persecution. Pray for:
- *Revival.* Some areas have been Christian for centuries (in North Sulawesi, North Sumatra, West Timor, Maluku). Many denominations there lack spiritual life. They struggle with immorality, divisions, and even indigenous occult practices.

- *More mature, spiritual leaders.* The rapid growth of newer Pentecostal and charismatic churches created a need for discipleship and training for both lay leaders and pastors.
- *New believers from a Muslim background,* who often face rejection and persecution from their communities. They can also find it difficult to fit into Christian culture and churches. Pray for whole households to come to Christ, and to follow Christ within their own culture.

 A vision to evangelize Indonesia brings churches together. From 1996 onward, national and regional consultations began to focus on unreached Indonesian peoples. The Indonesian Peoples' Network does excellent research, and many Indonesian ministries now send workers to unreached peoples. Pray that the Indonesian Church might lead the effort as expatriate workers partner with them. Pray for:

- *A living and witnessing church in every people group.* Nearly 100 million people in Indonesia can be considered unevangelized.
- *A church in every village.* Over 45,000 villages (out of 76,000) still have no church.
- *A united Indonesian prayer movement,* with a prayer group in every neighbourhood. The national prayer network (formed in 1990) has already spread to over 450 cities.
- *A missionary vision.* About 3,000 long-term missionaries work mostly in Indonesia. Pray for churches to reach the hundreds of unreached peoples in their own country and in other lands.
- *Bible translation.* Translators work on 150 projects, but 414 other languages have definite or possible need for translation work.

God continues to bless the work of foreign missions in Indonesia, despite the obstacles. Pray for open doors for those whom God calls to this nation. Sumatra, Sulawesi, and the West Lesser Sunda Islands need more missionaries, especially those with an Asian background. The relationships between churches and mission agencies need prayer, especially in West Kalimantan, Papua, and Maluku. Pray specifically for:

- *Missionary flying.* Some mission work in Kalimantan, Sulawesi, and Papua would be almost impossible without it.
- *Practical ministries* (community development, health, education, relief). They provide opportunities to share the gospel. Pray especially for the ministries who serve the millions of Indonesian children at risk.
- *Christian radio.* The dense rainforests isolate rural communities, and too few pastors serve these areas. Radio is essential to reach and disciple some people.

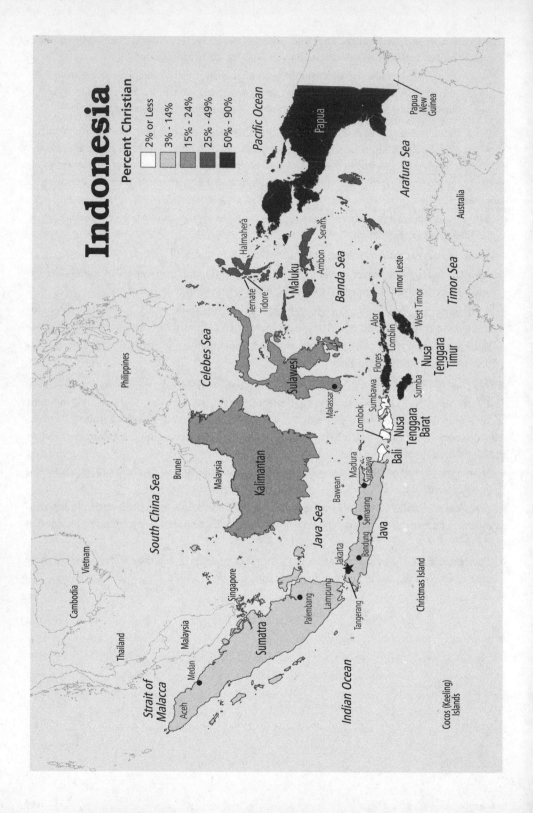

The Islands of Indonesia

Each major island or island group is unique and complex with different needs for prayer.

SUMATRA

 Sumatra is the largest unevangelized island on earth. Most of its largest people groups are strongly Muslim. Others practise folk Islam. Many spiritual strongholds must be broken. Christianity is strong here among previously animist peoples (the Batak, Nias, Mentawai), and among the Chinese. The Batak people are successful and migrate all over Indonesia. But their ethnic pride, strong devotion to old customs, and frequent conflict with Sumatran Muslims all hinder their Christian witness. The Chinese live in most cities, and operate 60% of businesses. Pray for Christians to reach beyond their own ethnic groups and witness to the non-Christian peoples around them.

Of the 49 unreached peoples of Sumatra, 29 have no indigenous church, and 8 have no known gospel workers.

- *The 3.5 million Aceh people* are strongly Muslim, and spread Islam to other Indonesian peoples.
- *The 8 million Minangkabau of West Sumatra* are well-educated, well-travelled, and successful. They are devoted Muslims, with less than 1,000 Christians.
- *The Muslim Mandailing of northern Sumatra* are proud to have almost no Christians among them.

JAVA

Java is not the largest island, but it has the largest population. Praise God that the Church on Java continues to grow. Nearly 50% of Chinese-descent Indonesians and 5% of Javanese are Christian. The many religions of Java historically tolerated each other. But this has changed. Persecution now comes in the form of laws that prevent Christians from building, which sometimes results in the destruction of churches and Christian property. Christians of many traditions now draw together for prayer, worship, and mutual support. And the love among them attracts many Muslims to Christ, despite the persecution. Christian love for the needy and most vulnerable people in society has a powerful effect. This is a time of harvest!

Jakarta and other urban centres (Surabaya, Bandung, Semarang) are key cities for the evangelization of Indonesia. Individuals from almost every Indonesian people group live in Jakarta, which is now over 13% Christian. Jakarta's massive wealth and influence impacts the economic realm, and a spiritual movement here now impacts the whole country.

The major unreached people groups of Java traditionally resist the gospel. Pray that churches reach out to the less evangelized in small towns and rural villages.

- *5 Javanese ethnic sub-groups* remain strongly Muslim (with very small numbers of believers), which stands in contrast to the millions of Javanese Christians who come from the other 3 Javanese sub-groups.
- *The Sunda* (West Java) are one of the largest unevangelized groups in the world.
- *The Madura* come from East Java, but are transmigrated elsewhere. They are strongly Muslim, but influenced by magic. They have a reputation for anger and violence. Pray that Christians might overcome fear and show Christ's love to them.

The Lesser Sunda Islands

1. **The unique culture and beauty of Bali attracts millions of tourists.** Most bring a godless, self-seeking way of life. A few bring the gospel. Bali has 49,000 Hindu temples, as most Balinese practise a version of Hinduism. Occult, magic, and spiritism all influence the people. Balinese Christians are few. Converts to Christ often face persecution when they change their way of life. Bali needs the power of the gospel to set its people free. 1 million Balinese live on Sumatra, Sulawesi, and Lombok, and have more openness to the gospel in those places.

2. **The largest West Lesser Sunda Islands are Lombok and Sumbawa.** The 3 largest people groups remain largely unevangelized, even after 20 years of outreach. Fewer than 300 follow Christ among these Muslim peoples. Many young people convert to Islam in order to get married.

3. **The largest East Lesser Sunda Islands are Flores, Sumba, and West Timor.** Only a handful of the 65 languages have a New Testament. This hinders the gospel.

- *Flores* is 80% Catholic, but many mix Catholic teachings with pagan practices that sometimes involve snake worship. No language of Flores has Scripture.
- *The Spirit moved on Sumba* in the late 1980s, and Protestants doubled in number!
- *A Spirit-led revival on West Timor* (1960s) brought renewal in the Church and thousands of conversions.

Kalimantan

1. **The indigenous peoples of Kalimantan Island speak around 80 different languages** and many dialects. Christians are a majority in many groups, and a sizeable minority in others. Christian leaders need training, but the isolation, spiritual opposition, and lack of indigenous Scriptures slow down development.

2. **Dozens of ethnic groups remain largely unreached:**
   - *The Banjar* are one of Indonesia's least-evangelized peoples. The few who follow Jesus live as secret believers among this strongly Muslim people.
- *Transmigrants* number over 1 million. Very few of them are Christian. They live in settlements and oil-rich towns. Pray that local believers might overcome resentment and reach out in love.
- *Animist peoples* are geographically isolated. Their living conditions are difficult for outsiders. Pray for more pioneer workers to go to them, especially with medical and education programmes, and ministry to orphans.

Sulawesi

1. **Sulawesi has over 110 people groups.** Most coastal peoples are Muslim, and Christians are a majority in the northeast and the central highlands. Violent conflict between Muslims and Christians (1990s and 2000s) left over 1,000 people dead. Christians feel unfairly treated and harshly punished. Pray for a Christlike response. Bible translation is an enormous unfinished task. Pray for the less-reached Muslim Bugis, Makassar, and Gorontalo peoples. The Makassar are one of a few strongly Muslim groups to show some response to the gospel.

MALUKU

1 The terrible violence and ethnic cleansing of 1999-2000 changed the Maluku Islands forever. Rioters destroyed many churches and mosques. Over 20,000 Christians died. Christians and Muslims now mostly live in separate villages. This helps peace, but hinders outreach. Pray for healing for the many who suffered. Pray for Christians to love their Muslim neighbours. The Maluku Protestant Church was founded in 1605. It is Asia's oldest Protestant denomination.

WEST PAPUA (IRIAN JAYA)

1 Praise God for many people movements in West Papua in the last 100 years. Over 90% of indigenous peoples are Christian! They face tribal conflict, political tensions, a mix of Christianity and animist practices, and oppression by others. Workers have located and contacted 100 less-reached smaller ethnic groups. Many need evangelism and church planting. Christian aviation is necessary in this land with few roads. Bible translation for the many small language groups remains an immense task.

2 Environment and population issues threaten stability in West Papua. Pray about:

- *Transmigrant communities* (Javanese Muslims) sent by the government because of overpopulation in Java. The Javanese often have low regard for the Melanesian Christians, and oppress them. Pray that the sad story of the West Papuan peoples might be made known to the world, so that other governments and international groups might end this injustice. Pray that God may call some Christians to bring the gospel to those transmigrants who took land and privileges at the expense of the indigenous Papuans.

- *Corrupt forces that work together to exploit the land* (logging and mining). They take profits for themselves, and leave the province and native peoples with little benefit. Pray for sustainable logging practices that will bring profits to the people who have occupied the land for centuries.

Iran
Asia

Pop 75.1 million. **Capital** Tehran (7.2 mill).
Christians 385,000. *Evangelical Christians* 118,000.
Largest Religion Muslim.
Fastest Growing Religion Muslim.

Largest Ethnic Groups Approximately 100 ethnic groups. Persian (52.4%), Azerbaijani (22.2%), Luri-Bakhtiari (6.6%), Kurd (5.9%), Qashqal (2.3%), Arab (2.3%), Domari/Gypsy (2%), Baloch (1.5%).
Official Language Persian (Farsi, Dari, Tajik are major dialects). **All Languages** 79.

Economy Great wealth from oil and natural gas. Only 20% of the economy is in the private sector. Corruption and political-religious ties put off potential foreign investors. Rapid urbanization and population growth created millions of jobless young people in cities. Iran's strategic location (between East and West) could help create future economic growth.

Politics The Shah lost power in the Islamic Revolution, and Iran declared itself a theocratic Islamic Republic in 1979 under the Supreme Leadership of the Ayatollah. Invasion by Iraq in 1980 led to war. Since that time, power shifts between "moderate" reformists (who seek more social freedoms) and hard-line conservatives.

Religious leadership (under the Supreme Leader) controls the police, army, and judicial system. Human rights abuses are frequent. The Green Revolution of 2009 showed dissatisfaction with religious and political conservatives. In 2013 a more moderate president was elected. Ongoing tensions with the West over the development of nuclear power.

 Massive numbers of Iranians came to Jesus in recent years! From only 500 Muslim-background believers in 1979, estimates suggest the number is now at least 100,000, and some say as many as 1 million. The Church in Persia has not grown this fast since the 7th century. In Iran, a person can receive a death sentence for apostasy (abandoning religious faith). This growth is a remarkable move of the Holy Spirit, with many signs and wonders, dreams and visions.

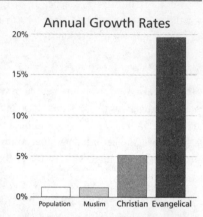
Annual Growth Rates

The 1979 Islamic Revolution promised peace and prosperity, but 30 years later it still has not come. Instead, a legacy of bloodshed, cruelty, injustice, corruption, and economic hardship left many disappointed with the conservative religious leaders and their narrow version of Islam. An estimated 13 million Iranians live below the poverty line. Around 200,000 of Iran's best-educated young people emigrate every year. Iran has one of the highest rates of opium addiction in the world, 200,000 street children, and widespread (but hidden) prostitution. Iran is an ancient, noble, and proud civilization. But in the modern era, these struggles have made many people, especially young people, very open to the gospel. Pray that Iranians' desires for greatness, prosperity, freedom, and even for righteousness might ultimately be met through worship of Jesus.

Religious persecution grew more intense since 2005, especially toward the Baha'i, Sufi Muslims, and Christians (particularly believers from a Muslim background). The government rules that only Armenians and Assyrians can be Christian. Ethnic Persians must be Muslim. This makes almost all Christian activity illegal, especially in Persian languages. Yet the regime's harsh treatment of Christians only seems to increase church growth! Pray that the body of Christ might continue to multiply and mature despite persecution.

The majority of the wider Christian community are Christian Armenians, with a smaller number of Assyrians and Chaldeans. They have different cultures and languages from the Muslims around them. They live with a measure of peace in their communities, but often emigrate to give their families a more stable life. Pray that Jesus might shine through their lives, and that they might have a burden for their Muslim neighbours.

Evangelical churches before the revolution were mostly small and struggling. The traumatic changes and suffering that followed gave these churches a brief period of renewal, outreach, and many conversions! Many then adopted house church models because of intimidation from the government and the martyrdom of several church leaders. Pray for creative access to programmes that will develop capable, well-trained leaders for the underground Church.

Iran contains some of the largest unreached, unengaged peoples in the world. Missions are not free to minister in Iran, but some tentmaking opportunities exist. Pray for the door to Iran to open in God's perfect timing.

- *The Zoroastrians (Parsees)* follow an ancient Persian religion founded 1,000 years before Christ.
- *The Baha'i religion* started in Iran, but the government seeks to drive its followers out. Very little Christian love and witness to them exists among either the 300,000 in Iran, or the 5–7 million worldwide.
- *The nomadic and semi-nomadic Luri, Bakhtiari, and Qashqai* live in the Zagros Mountains. Only a few dozen known believers exist from these groups. Persian Christians have begun to reach out to them.
- *The Turkic Azeri and Turkmen* in the north have had almost no positive contact with Christianity. Azeris form the largest minority group within Iran.
- *The Gypsy communities* have no Christian workers committed to outreach among them.
- *The Persian-speaking Jews* descend from those exiled to Babylon 2,700 years ago. Their numbers decline as more and more move away to escape harassment, but a number have become active, witnessing Christians!

7 **Ministry to Iranians increased greatly,** both inside Iran and abroad. Christian satellite-TV broadcasts and Christian websites in Persian languages have an incredible impact, and even reach to remote villages with the gospel. Millions listen to Christian radio despite government restrictions, and send in thousands of response emails and letters. Scripture has become more available, mostly smuggled into the country. Several ministries reach out to the Iranian diaspora (around 4 million) through evangelism, outreach training, church planting, discipleship, and leadership training. Many diaspora Christians visit Iran and powerfully minister to Iranians there.

Iraq   *Asia*

Pop 31.5 million. **Capital** Baghdad (5.9 mill).
Christians 500,000. *Evangelical Christians* 53,000.
Largest Religion Muslim.
Fastest Growing Religion Muslim.

Largest Ethnic Groups Arab (74.3%), Iranian-Median (22%, includes Northern, Southern, and Central Kurds), Turkic (2.5%, Turkmen in centre and north).

Official Languages Arabic. Kurdish in the Kurdish Autonomous Region (KAR). **All Languages** 26.

Economy Based on oil (since Genesis 11!). Economy devastated by military spending, decades of war, and international sanctions. Ordinary people live in poverty. Corruption, high unemployment, and history of conflict between armed factions are all challenges for future growth.

Politics The site of the ancient Syrian, Assyrian, and Babylonian empires. Modern Iraq was created by the Allies after WWI, and gained independence as a monarchy in 1932. Overthrown by Baathist military regime (1958), which became a dictatorship under Saddam Hussein. He used massive military force to protect his rule, to repress Kurds and Shi'a Muslims, to launch a war against Iran (1980-1988), and to invade Kuwait (1990). UN forces defeated Iraq and imposed sanctions until 2003, followed by a US invasion. A representative and constitutional democracy since 2005 elections, but the longstanding divisions and rivalries, combined with Islamist terrorism, make the country difficult to govern peacefully.

1 The emergence of Iraqi Arab evangelicals in recent years (now over 50,000) is an answer to prayer! Many of them come from Muslim and even extremist backgrounds, but they encountered Christ through evangelical witness, gospel radio, and especially through dreams and visions of Jesus. Pray for leaders for the churches. Many fled the country and others died, often targeted by Islamists. Many times the Christian widows of these leaders continue with the pastoral and discipleship work.

2 Significant political changes began in 1991, and the country's future remains uncertain.

• *War with the West* brought greater autonomy for the Kurdish area, a representative government, and some reforms in the economy, education, and healthcare. But the US invasion led to a time of violence by Islamist militants, while Sunni and Shi'a groups turned on each other.

• *Many deep divisions run through Iraqi society* (Kurds against Arabs, Shi'as against Sunnis, secular politicians against Islamist groups). Christians and other religious minorities lack true religious freedom. They face demands for bribes, kidnapping, destruction of their property, rape, and murder. Most Muslim political leaders want to see progress, but extremist groups continue to make the country unstable.

• *Sunni Muslim fighters* seized partial control of Iraqi territory in summer 2014, and announced an Islamic State (covering parts of Iraq and Syria). Their brutal treatment of other ethnic and religious groups (including Christians) forced thousands to flee for their lives, and brought further chaos to the region.

3 Nearly every person bears scars from traumatic experiences. Women suffer forced marriage, abduction, honour killing, violence, and rape. Many children do not attend school, and less than half have access to safe drinking water. More than half the population live in poverty. Only the power of the gospel can truly transform Iraq.

4 The Christian community in Iraq survives from the 1st century! The majority are descendants of the Nestorian Church, one of the greatest missionary denominations of history. (They won 6% of Asia's population to Christ 1,000 years ago!) But with severe persecution, most Christians fled to Syria, Jordan, or the West, and this historic Church is now largely scattered. The Iraqi Church represents diverse denominations, ethnic groups, and political loyalties who struggle to get along. Pray for a united Church that can respond to hatred and persecution with boldness, forgiveness, and love. Ask God to preserve Iraq's biblical heritage, and to restore life to the suffering Iraqi Church.

5 All peoples are unevangelized except Assyrian and Armenian minority groups. Pray for:

• *The Shi'a Arabs of Basra and the south* suffered death and destruction within their communities under Saddam Hussein, even though they are the majority people.

• *Sunni Arabs* gained the most from the former dictatorship, but have now lost much of their influence.

• *The Madan or Marsh Arabs* probably descend from the ancient Sumerians. A repressive government policy toward them reduced their population from 450,000 (1950s) to less than 90,000 (2010). No known Christians exist among this people.

• *The 1.4 million Bedouin* have no churches, no outreach to them, and only a handful of believers.

• *The Yazidi* practise a religion that originated in India centuries ago. Muslims persecute them harshly, especially after 2003. Only a small number follow Christ.

• *The smaller Domari (Gypsy) and Mandean populations,* who are marginalized in Iraqi society.

6 The freedom of the Kurdish Autonomous Region (KAR) is a sensitive issue for the nation and region. The line where Arab and Kurdish areas of control meet is the most violent place in Iraq. With more freedom in the region, a significant and exciting movement of people to Christ now grows among Kurds!

Israel

Asia

The Palestinian Authority, although under Israel's administration, is treated separately.

Pop 7.3 million. **Capital** Jerusalem (783,000), but not recognized internationally.
Christians 149,000. *Evangelical Christians* 31,000.
Largest Religion Jewish.
Fastest Growing Religion Non-religious.
Largest Ethnic Groups Jews (75.5%, 28 groups), Arabs (20.4%), Others (4.1%, includes European, African, Chinese, Thai, Filipino, North and South American).
Official Languages Hebrew, Arabic. Many immigrant languages are spoken. **All Languages** 48.

Economy Modern, sophisticated industrial state. Well-developed high-tech, bio-tech, chemical, and agricultural sectors. However, high defence spending, the cost of new immigrants, and a crisis over lack of water all hinder further growth. Israel lacks natural resources. Large gas and oil deposits (under Mediterranean Sea) could change Israel's energy status.
Politics Founded in 1948 as a Jewish state, which ended 1,900 years of statelessness and exile for the Jews. 6 wars with neighbouring countries between 1948 and 2006, plus the Gaza War (2009), keep the country in constant wartime readiness. Israeli society remains deeply divided on the peace process, solutions to the Palestinian problem, the future of Jewish settlements in the Disputed Territories, and the future of Jerusalem and the Golan Heights.

1 Interest in the gospel increased within Israel, especially among Jews, and especially the last few years. At least 12,000 Jews recognize Jesus as their Messiah. Messianic Jews are now an undeniable part of Israeli society, but growth also brings persecution. Pray for boldness in witness, and perseverance in faith despite the opposition. The return of Jews to Israel was a significant period in Jewish history. Many see it as a fulfilment of prophecy. Pray for the nation's spiritual restoration (Romans 11:25-31).

2 The Christian Church in Israel is fragmented. About 80% are Arab, 8% Jewish, and 12% expatriates. They worship in over 120 Hebrew-speaking fellowships, as well as congregations in Russian, Amharic (Ethiopian), and various European languages. 5 Catholic groups, 9 Orthodox groups, over 20 denominations of Protestants/Independents (and over 100 mission agencies) all exist together inside of Israel. Pray for spiritual unity that will overcome divisions of history, ethnic conflict, national origin, and different interpretations of the Bible.

3 Both sides in the Israeli-Arab conflict claim the land, and all human efforts to resolve this conflict have failed. Palestinian population growth, Hezbollah's strength, Al Qaeda's threats, and Iran's aggressive comments all point to potential future trouble. At the same time, a quiet change in relationships between Messianic Jews and Arab Christians also grows inside the Holy Land.

Through several initiatives, these 2 groups seek a path for reconciliation and friendship. They set an example for the rest of the region. But some others question, or even oppose, these developments. Pray that Jesus, who destroyed the dividing wall of hostility between God and man, and between Jew and Gentile, might also bring reconciliation between Israelis and Palestinians.

 Major outreach challenges.

- *The ultra-Orthodox Haredi* are only 10% of the population, but they have strong political influence. They are like modern Pharisees, who strictly observe and preserve their religious laws and identity. Pray for many more to become like Nicodemus (John, chapters 3, 7, and 19).

- *The Ethiopian Jews (Beta Israel)* arrived as immigrants over a decade ago. Now they are largely a poor, urban underclass. Fewer than 2,000 (out of 120,000) are Messianic believers.

- *The Arabs* are over 90% Muslim. But Arabs also make up the majority of Christians in the Holy Land. They face pressure from all sides, as Israelis discriminate against them, Islamists persecute them, and the international community largely overlooks their situation.

- *The Druze community* are closed to outsiders, but a small movement to Jesus has begun among them.

- *The 8 million Jews outside Israel* live mostly in the USA, the former USSR, and other Western nations. Perhaps 100,000 now have links with Messianic congregations, and a much larger number attend other Christian churches. Pray for Gentile churches to have greater sensitivity to the Jewish remnant within the global Church.

Japan
Asia

Pop 127 million. **Capital** Tokyo-Yokohama (36.7 mill).
Christians 2 mill. *Evangelical Christians* 596,000.
Largest Religion Buddhist.
Fastest Growing Religion Non-religious.
Largest Ethnic Groups Japanese (98.5%), Foreign (1.5%, includes Korean, Chinese, Filipino, other Asian, Western), Ainu (0.02%, aboriginal inhabitants). Possibly 1 million illegal immigrants (Pakistani, Iranian, Bangladeshi, Southeast Asian).
Official Language Japanese. **All Languages** 16.

Economy One of world's most powerful export economies, despite lack of natural resources or oil. The 1990s became "The Lost Decade" with zero growth and high unemployment, but many individuals had private savings that protected them from losses. A low birth rate and an ageing population are major social and economic concerns for the future.

Politics Constitutional monarchy with a parliamentary democracy. Years of stability and economic growth after WWII turned Japan into an economic superpower. Increased nationalism and political tensions create domestic and foreign challenges.

---

1 **Japan faces many crises.** Even its leaders called it "a superpower without a moral compass". Many lack hope or confidence in the future. Young people struggle the most, in particular with problems such as a suicide epidemic (over 30,000/year), mistreatment by peers, and teenage prostitution. High suicide and divorce rates in other age groups confirm the crisis. The constant threats of earthquakes, economic decline, and social isolation leave many people open to spiritual matters. The government alone cannot solve Japan's social problems. This gives the Church a chance to engage with society.

2 **Spiritual powers and principalities in Japan** hinder the gospel. The powers associated with idolatry in temples and ancestor worship in homes remain strong. Many Japanese claim no religion, but actually follow some rituals of Buddhism and Shintoism. Even the idea of a Creator God is foreign to the Japanese worldview. Many new religions get started in Japan each year, often based on Buddhism, but also on the occult, the worship of extra-terrestrial aliens, and other strange ideas. Ask God to remove the spirit of delusion!

3 **Japan has the world's lowest birth rates and highest life expectancies,** so the population rapidly ages. The social and economic challenge this creates is enormous. By 2055, half of Japanese will be retired and collect a pension. No other country has faced this before. Pray for more Christian nursing homes and hospices. Japan will need many care workers, and this will create a mission opportunity for believers from other nations. Japan's low birth rate results in a small younger generation with their own challenges and issues. Those aged 18-23 are the most open to the gospel, but few actually become active believers. The bonds that once held Japanese society together have lost much of their strength.

4 **The Church in Japan grew between 1945 and 1960,** but both Catholics and Protestants experienced little overall growth since then. Today, up to half of those baptized leave their churches within 2-3 years. During WWII, a union of Protestant churches compromised their faith with Shinto and emperor worship. After the war, many denominations made statements of repentance of their participation in war and of idol worship during the war. Repentance is an important concept for Japanese Christians, and many believe that national repentance for this sad time of history is a key for spiritual breakthrough.

5 **Japan has had a Christian presence for 500 years,** but people still think of it as foreign. Society values conforming and consensus. Very few families come to faith, so individual Christians feel exposed. At least 70% of all churches have an average attendance of less than 30 people. Most churches will not have even 1 baptism in a typical year. Of those who do attend, women outnumber men by 7 to 1. Churches tend to reflect the Western culture that was introduced years ago, and relate less to 21st-century Japanese culture. But praise God for the 300 Japanese who serve as missionaries in 34 countries around the world!

6 **Japan is the largest unevangelized nation completely open to missionaries.** Yet the spiritual, cultural, language, and financial difficulties require great commitment and perseverance. The Japan Evangelical Missionary Association (JEMA) coordinates 46 mission organizations, which represent over 1,100 missionaries. Most work in church planting and evangelism. Hundreds of jobs are available for those who can teach English. Long-term missionaries are a great need, since it takes many years to learn the language and understand the culture. Over 1 million Japanese live abroad (in the USA, Brazil, China, others), and each year around 1,600 return home with a new faith in Christ!

7 **The less-evangelized areas and peoples of Japan.** 3% of Japanese identified themselves as Christian in a recent poll, and 10% see Christianity as a possible religious option for themselves. Many believe that Japanese society will soon see an amazing awakening to the gospel!

- *24 cities in Japan have no church at all,* and 595 towns and villages also have no church.
- *The ruling class* have little exposure to the gospel. Pray for the emperor and royal family, politicians, and business leaders. Pray for a revived Church to transform the nation.

- **Koreans in Japan** descend from those brought here by force (1903-1945). Even into the 3rd and 4th generations, Japanese often treat them poorly. South Korean missionaries planted 500 churches among them.

- **Chinese** worship in about 30 churches, with around 2,000 believers. But Japan probably has the least-evangelized Chinese population of almost any nation.

- **The Ainu** were Japan's first people, who settled in north Japan. Their heritage is now at risk of extinction, and they number only 25,000. The number of Ainu (if any) believers is unknown.

- **Sexually exploited women, and those who use them.** The *yakuza* criminal network has imported 200,000 foreign women to become sex slaves. Prostitution of women and children across East and Southeast Asia thrives partly because of Japanese men's immorality.

- **Muslims** increase mostly through immigration, and the Church does little to reach them.

- **Christian sects** (such as Jehovah's Witnesses, Mormons) have grown faster than evangelicals or Catholics, and have the largest "Christian" presence in some areas. Little ministry to them exists.

8 **Traditional and modern arts** are important to Japanese culture. One-third of books and magazines in Japan are manga (graphic novels), so pray for *The Manga Bible* and "The Gospel Edition" manga comic. Praise God for a new emphasis on evangelism in many churches, and creative ministry that connects well with Japanese mindset and culture. Christian music (especially Black Gospel choirs) has a strong support base in Japan, and Christmas music is also a popular point of contact for the gospel in mainstream Japanese society.

Jordan
Asia

Pop 6.5 million. **Capital** Amman (1.1 mill).
Christians 145,000. *Evangelical Christians* 19,000.
Largest Religion Muslim.
Fastest Growing Religion Muslim.
Largest Ethnic Groups The mass relocation of Palestinians, Kuwaitis, Iraqis, and Syrians means no precise figures exist for the present situation. Arab (95.4%, including Palestinians, East Bank Jordanian, Iraqi, Bedouin), Jordanian minorities (2.2%, including Adygei, Armenian, Kurd, Turkmen, Chechen), Non-Jordanian (2.4%, including Assyrian, Greek, Western, Pakistani, others).
Official Language Arabic. **All Languages** 16.

Economy Based on tourism, phosphates, and agricultural products. Jordan has no oil and little water. Poverty and unemployment are significant issues.
Politics Part of Turkish Empire until 1918. Independent from Britain in 1946. Now a constitutional monarchy. King Abdullah has executive powers. Turmoil in the Middle East profoundly affects life, with massive influx of refugees and economic disruption. A moderate Arab nation and Western ally, and a stable country surrounded by unstable countries.

1 **King Abdullah's rule began with promise and hope,** but the wars in Iraq and Syria placed great pressure on the nation. Over a million immigrants flowed in, and half still remain. Suicide bombings by Muslim extremists (2005) showed Jordan's vulnerability to violent troubles. Jordan serves as a regional centre for many Christian activities and ministries, and much Christian work in the Middle East would suffer if religious freedom in Jordan changed. Pray for the peace of this land, and for the King and government.

 Jordan's Christian population dropped between 1980 and 2010. Lower birth rates, Christians who left Jordan, and a large influx of Muslim refugees all contributed to this change. Still, Christians serve in all parts of society, even in parliament or other positions of influence. The evangelical Church even doubled in size between 1995 and 2010! Most newer believers come from communities with a culturally Christian background, but recently more Muslims came to faith. Pray that all Christians in Jordan, whether in traditional churches, evangelical churches, or believers from a Muslim background, might cooperate to make Christ known throughout society.

The vast majority of Jordan's population remain unreached. Pray for:

- *The Muslim majority.* Perhaps only 10% of churches have meaningful interaction with Muslims. Pray for the protection of new believers amid persecution from family, work, and society.

- *The millions of Palestinians* (the majority population in Jordan). Even after generations outside their homeland, many struggle with bitterness and frustration. Jordan's Queen is Palestinian.

- *Iraqi refugees.* Local churches and international missions work among them. Pray that the government might grant permission to churches to provide education to refugees, a ministry on Christians' hearts.

- *The Bedouin* (300,000). Churches more easily reach those who settle (*fellahin*), but many still live as nomads.

- *Dom Gypsies* remain a hidden, poor, excluded people. Pray for the Scripture (especially in audio format) in their language, and for holistic ministry that meets their spiritual and physical needs.

Kazakhstan
Asia

Pop 15.8 million. **Capital** Astana (658,000).
Christians 1.9 mill. *Evangelical Christians* 105,000.
Largest Religion Muslim.
Fastest Growing Religion Muslim.

Largest Ethnic Groups Kazakh (56.2%), Russian (27.2%), Ukrainian (3.5%), German (2.4%), Uzbek (2.2%), Tatar (1.7%), Uyghur (1.4%).
Official Language Kazakh. **All Languages** 43.

Economy Enormous oil and mineral reserves. One of the world's fastest-growing economies. A minority profit from the growth while the majority suffer from poverty and the nation's ecological disasters (toxic waste, radiation, pollution, desert expansion).

Politics Independent from the USSR in 1991. A multiparty democracy, but the only president since 1991 has continued with authoritarian rule.

An economic boom from the abundant natural resources brought transformation to Kazakhstan. The government invests in some public works, but much of the wealth makes a few people incredibly rich while most remain poor. Pray that the government will act on behalf of all its citizens. Pray for protection against the corruption and material greed that comes with such wealth.

Some people say that "to be a Kazakh is to be a Muslim". Most Kazakh follow a version of Islam strongly influenced by *shamans* and indigenous practices. Other Muslim countries invest huge amounts of money to send Muslim missionaries to Kazakhstan. They successfully convert even some ethnic Russians to Islam. After the Soviet Union broke up, the number of registered mosques grew – from 46 (1989) to 1,282 (2002)! Pray for freedom from historic spiritual bondages.

The Christian population in Kazakhstan historically had an ethnic European majority, but recently it began to shift towards an Asian one. Korean churches grew, as did most charismatic, Pentecostal, and some Baptist groups, mainly among Central Asian ethnic groups. People often consider Orthodox Christianity the religion of the Russians, and consider evangelicals a dangerous sect. Believers face persecution from authorities, from some strict Muslims, and from unbelieving family members. Pray that believers may stay united, even through opposition and increased diversity. Mixed churches in urban areas bring together ethnicities that once did not get along, but now have oneness in Christ!

The population is diverse, with 76 different peoples. Kazakhs (and ethnic minorities) are strategic for outreach to Central Asia and the Muslim world. Pray especially for:

- *Kazakhs.* Pray for the Church among them to grow and mature. From almost no believers in 1990, by 2010 about 15,000 met for worship in over 100 Kazakh-speaking congregations!

- *Russians and Ukrainians.* Large numbers returned to their ancestral homelands since the early 1990s. Most that remain are non-religious or Orthodox. Pray for renewal among the Orthodox. The fast-growing evangelical/charismatic/Pentecostal churches also impact many Russians.

- *Unreached minorities.* A number of Uzbeks and Uyghurs turned to Christ, and some began to take the gospel back to their own people! Pray that the gospel might be shared in heart languages, in the many towns and villages of Kazakhstan.

Pray for Christians to demonstrate Christ's love and mercy. Families suffer brokenness, as many people battle alcoholism and drug addiction. Heroin is as easy to obtain as alcohol. The expatriate Christian community is diverse. Russians, Americans, Koreans, Germans, and other nationalities each contribute to ministry in their own way. Pray for humility as they serve the indigenous Church. Opportunities exist for outreach, training, discipleship, for work as professionals, and in compassionate ministries.

Korea, North
Asia

Pop 24 million. **Capital** Pyongyang (2.7 mill).
Christians 356,000. *Evangelical Christians* 246,000. [All figures are estimates. The true number of Christians is unknown.]
Largest Religion Non-religious.
Fastest Growing Religion Christian.
Largest Ethnic Groups Korean (99.8%), Chinese (0.2%).
Official Language Korean.
Economy Probably the most centralized and isolated economy in the world. Heavily dependent on aid. Economy in decline due to high military expenditure and low agricultural and industrial productivity. The world's number one seller of missiles. Profits from illegal drugs, cigarettes, counterfeit money, and gambling

establishments also decline as other countries tighten regulations. Food shortages and widespread malnutrition force some limited economic reform.

Politics Occupied by Japan (1910-1945). On Soviet insistence, Korea was partitioned after WWII. A Communist regime since 1948. North Korea invaded the South in 1950, and civil war lasted until 1953. The dictator oversees one of the most repressive regimes in the world. It has dedicated itself to the idea of *Juche* (self-reliance). With many problems, sudden change could come at short notice.

---

1 **North Korea today is like a nightmare.** The state creates a cult around the young "Supreme Leader" (Kim Jong-un) and his dead grandfather (Kim Il-Sung), and does not allow the people to interact with the outside world. More than 3 million people have starved to death since 1994. Aid agencies can sometimes bring in food, but the government and military take much of it. Pray that food will reach the desperate, hungry people. Pray that in God's timing a change would come to completely free and transform this land.

2 **The Korean revival (1907) began in the Church in North Korea!** People in those days called Pyongyang the "Jerusalem of the East". But most Christians fled to the South during the Korean War, or died as martyrs. Now if you even say the name "Jesus" aloud you may die for it. We do not know much about the underground Church, but we know it survived and even grows. The government holds up to 100,000 Christians in labour camps. Pray for North Korean believers to persevere in probably the most difficult country for Christians.

3 **Christians minister to North Koreans despite the restrictions.** Some foreign Christians serve through aid and development projects. Christian radio reaches far into North Korea. Christians smuggle Bibles into the country, or send them in attached to balloons. Chinese businessmen have open and easy access to the country, which could be a strategic opportunity. Many thousands of believers worldwide created a prayer network to form an unbroken chain of prayer for this nation.

4 **Pray for the 300,000 North Korean refugees in China.** Those who escape still face danger from both Chinese and North Korean agents who try to trick and capture them. Up to 90% of women refugees end up sold as slave-wives or into the sex trade. But some find Jesus through the kindness of Christians who help them. A brave few return home to North Korea to share the gospel.

Korea, South

Asia

Pop 48.5 million. **Capital** Seoul (9.8 mill).
Christians 15 mill. *Evangelical Christians* 8.2 mill.
Largest Religion Non-religious. [Many Koreans have no formal religious ties, but do have a connection to Confucian values and teachings.]
Fastest Growing Religion Non-religious.

Largest Ethnic Groups One of the world's most ethnically homogenous (same culture) nations. Korean (97.8%), Other (2.2%, a mix of Western, Chinese, Japanese, and South or Southeast Asian).
Official Language Korean. **All Languages** 4.

Economy Transformed from a poor, devastated nation

in 1953, into the 11th-largest economy in the world. Rapid industrial growth and modernization. Few natural resources. The country depends heavily on exports, its highly educated workforce, and innovation in technology.

Politics A thousand-year-old history of invasions and interference from nearby nations. The Japanese occupation (1910-1945), the division of Korea (1945-1948), and the Korean War (1950-1953) all shape Korean attitudes and politics. Strong military-civilian governments from 1950 to 1987, then a more open multiparty democracy.

1 **Society and culture in South Korea changed rapidly** in the last generation. Economic growth was remarkable, but global success also exposed corruption in politics and industry. A wide gap now separates the rich and poor. Korean society was traditionally conservative, but positive modern developments also brought new problems such as more suicides, Internet addiction, the fast-growing sex industry, high use of cosmetic surgery for vanity, and less sensitivity to violence in the media. Pray for wisdom for leaders, and justice for the most vulnerable. South Korea leads the digital revolution. Evangelism by mobile phone already happens, and churches and ministries provide media-rich Internet sites and live TV.

2 **Many South Korean Christians pray and prepare for a reunited Korea.** In the 1940s, foreigners imposed the division of Korea into North and South, which led to a destructive war between them. The zone between the 2 countries is now the world's most heavily guarded border region. The future is unpredictable. Conflict could start again, but the North Korean state could instead collapse and open the opportunity to again unite the Koreas. Pray that political and Christian leaders might be ready, and make wise decisions for the healing of all Korea.

3 **Praise God for the unique Korean Church!** From the 1st Protestant congregation in 1884, South Korea now has as many as 50,000. God blessed the Church with a series of revivals, and refined it through times of persecution. Now its leadership is well-trained, and its strong missions vision is an example to the world. Korea has 6 of the 10 largest churches in the world, and Christians impact all levels of society. The South Korean Church commits itself to sacrificial and passionate prayer, with early morning and evening prayer meetings, every day and all night!

4 **The Korean Church faces major spiritual challenges.** The spiritual excitement of previous generations has cooled off for the current one. The Church has nearly stopped growing now, and churches often split from conflict. Some prideful Christian leaders seek financial success and prosperity as signs of God's favour. Some church leaders possess too much authority, with too little accountability, and their church members rely on the pastor more than on the body of Christ working together. Pray for humility, reconciliation, and a spirit of cooperation. The Korean Church is large, influential, and wealthy, but Christians do not yet work together well enough to effectively address South Korea's social problems.

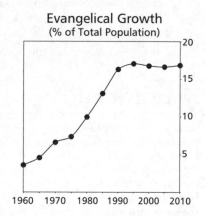

Evangelical Growth
(% of Total Population)

5 **Praise God that South Korea has sent out over 20,000 mission workers!** Over 170 agencies send missionaries cross-culturally. Most have a theology degree or pastoral training before they even start mission training. But what works in Korea does not always work in other lands. Pray for good preparation for cross-cultural mission. Pray also for the 6 million Koreans who live and work abroad. Many of them are Christian, and the churches among them also support and send out missionaries. Mission Korea brings agencies and campus ministries together to mobilize young

Koreans for world mission. Pray for a new generation that will go to the field, pray for the nations, and support missions work.

Some less-evangelized groups need special ministry.
- *Many Koreans still consult shamans.* Some estimate as many as 300,000 shamans, and 300 shamanistic temples, within 1 hour of Seoul.
- *More than 250,000 illegal migrants from other Asian countries* often work in very bad conditions. Some local churches show them love and offer practical assistance.
- *Korean Muslims* (about 40,000) grow in number as a result of Islamic missionary efforts among Koreans in the Middle East. Few people reach out to them.
- *Over 2 million South Koreans* follow new religions which mix traditional beliefs, Christianity, and Buddhism.

Kuwait

Asia

Pop 3.1 million. **Capital** Kuwait City (2.3 mill).
Christians 421,000. *Evangelical Christians* 46,000. (Most Christians are expatriates.)
Largest Religion Muslim.
Fastest Growing Religion Christian.
Largest Ethnic Groups Kuwaiti (35%), Foreign Arab (22%, includes Egyptian, Syrian, Lebanese, Palestinian), Bidoon (4%, stateless Arab refugees). Others (South Asian, Filipino, Iranian, Western Chinese, others) make up 39% of the population.
Official Language Arabic. **All Languages** 7.
Economy Made wealthy by oil (Kuwait has 10% of the world's reserves). Total dependence on oil and foreign labour.
Politics Independent from Britain in 1961. Constitutional monarchy and parliamentary democracy, with the Sheik and his family exercising great control. A Western ally.

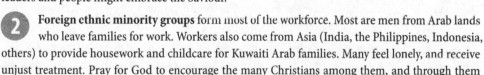

 Kuwait gained great material wealth in the last century, but wealth did not answer its problems. Government members disagree over modern and traditional ways of life. The political activity of Islamist groups increases. Young people feel frustrated and bored. Pray that Kuwaiti leaders and people might embrace the Saviour.

 Foreign ethnic minority groups form most of the workforce. Most are men from Arab lands who leave families for work. Workers also come from Asia (India, the Philippines, Indonesia, others) to provide housework and childcare for Kuwaiti Arab families. Many feel lonely, and receive unjust treatment. Pray for God to encourage the many Christians among them, and through them bring the love of Christ into the homes and lives of Kuwaitis.

The Bidoon people do not have a state. Their name means "without". Over 100,000 of them live in Kuwait, but with no believers known among them and almost no ministry to them.

Praise God that the Kuwaiti Church continues to grow! A few Kuwaiti believers now make themselves known publicly, but most stay underground. Kuwaiti Arabs often meet Christians while abroad for travel, business, or study. Pray for Kuwaitis who hear and want to respond. Pressure from culture and family prevents many from following Christ.

 A hundred years of medical mission history gave modern foreign Christians a good reputation! Authorities allow churches to grow, but evangelism of Muslims is illegal. Pray for greater freedom for witness and the release of land for buildings. Catholics, Orthodox, Anglicans, and Protestants together formed the Fellowship of Christian Churches in Kuwait. They work in cooperation for the good of society, especially to help the poor. Most churches are South Indian or Filipino, but pray that indigenous Kuwaiti believers can help lead the ministry of the gospel to the peoples of Kuwait.

Kyrgyzstan   *Asia*

Pop 5.6 million. **Capital** Bishkek (864,000).
Christians 292,000. *Evangelical Christians* 40,000.
Largest Religion Muslim.
Fastest Growing Religion Muslim.
Largest Ethnic Groups Great ethnic diversity given its population size. Kyrgyz (64.8%), Uzbek (13.6%), Slavic (13.5%, down from 24.3% in 1989 as Russians and Ukrainians returned to their homelands), Dungan/ Chinese Muslim (1.1%), Uyghur (1%).
Official Languages Kyrgyz, Russian. **All Languages** 32.
Economy A mainly agricultural country, but future potential from mining, hydro-electricity, and tourism.

Mountainous geography, isolation, and corruption prohibit development. Widespread poverty and unemployment (up to 500,000 seek work abroad).
Politics Independent from the USSR in 1991. The 1st Central Asian republic to replace its post-Soviet regime (2005). Troubled by economic hardship, criminal influence over the economy, and rise in power of Islamic militants (in the Fergana Valley). Created Central Asia's first parliamentary democracy in 2010, after protests and a coup. Ethnic and community tensions have led to some violence.

---

1 **The government needs courage, resources, and even miracles** to make right the economy and society. The regimes that followed Communism have so far only brought more corruption, crime, and poverty. Many people migrate from rural to urban areas, which results in large slum populations in Bishkek. Others leave the country to find work. Pray for Christians to find good, legal jobs. High rates of alcoholism, drug trafficking, gambling, and prostitution create huge challenges. The poor, elderly, and disabled suffer the most. Pray that believers can address these challenges, and positively affect their society and economy.

2 **The vast majority of Kyrgyz are Muslim** by culture, but underneath the surface most people fear the "evil eye", use charms, and practise ancestor worship. The occult, demonic forces, and shamans hold great influence. Muslim missionaries from several nations come to strengthen and purify Islam. Pray for believers to stand firm, and to demonstrate the power and love of Christ. Kyrgyzstan has more religious freedom than many nearby countries, even with its government restrictions. Ask God to increase the harvest of believers among the peoples of Kyrgyzstan!

3 **Christianity** was limited to the non-indigenous communities before 1990 (mostly Russians, Ukrainians, Germans), but Kyrgyz believers now form a significant proportion of the nation's

Christians! Only 45 Protestant congregations existed in 1990, but now they number almost 300, and many more with the illegal house churches included. More churches now worship in Kyrgyz, with many effective Kyrgyz Christian leaders. Pray for unity and cooperation among the different denominations, cultures, and ethnicities.

4 **Missionary concern** grows among believers of Kyrgyzstan, for their own people, for other Central Asian peoples, and beyond. Several hundred expatriate Christians (from Asia, the Americas, and Europe) have jobs in this country, and seek to minister sensitively. The greatest potential for service may be in community development, medical services, and business. Pray for the less evangelized, who mostly live in rural areas:

- *The partly nomadic Kyrgyz* usually live in more remote villages. Few have heard of Christ.
- *The Fergana Valley* (south) spans also across Tajikistan and Uzbekistan. The Tajik and Uzbek minorities (770,000 combined) are mostly unreached. Islam is most strict here, and the few successful church plants meet significant opposition.
- *The Dungan* descended from Chinese Muslim refugees. A significant multi-agency effort to reach them began in 2000.
- *Many smaller ethnicities* around the country have little to no specific outreach: Tatars, Chinese, Uyghur, Jews, and others.

Laos
Asia

Pop 6.4 million. **Capital** Vientiane (831,000).
Christians 218,000. *Evangelical Christians* 170,000.
Largest Religion Buddhist.
Fastest Growing Religion Christian.

Largest Ethnic Groups Lao-Tai (59.2%), Mon-Khmer (28.1%), Hmong-Mien (4%), Tibetan-Himalayan (2.7%), Vietnamese (1.6%), Chinese (1.5%).
Official Language Lao. **All Languages** 89.

Economy Subsistence agriculture accounts for 80% of employment. The Communist regime has begun to open the country for investment and private enterprise, with some economic growth. Poor infrastructure and corruption hinder progress. Problems with illegal trafficking (persons and narcotics), and with drug use. One of Asia's poorest countries.

Politics Independent from France in 1954. Lao and Vietnamese Communist forces in complete control by 1975. The Communist Party still has full political control, and limits freedoms.

1 **Praise God for rapid church growth,** even under government restrictions and persecution! Indigenous Laotians lead almost all churches and evangelism efforts. The government recognizes 2 Protestant groups. The largest is the Lao Evangelical Church, where most of the Christian growth occurs. Growth also happens through "underground" house groups. Over 90% of all trained leaders left Laos in 1975, and most congregations lack a trained pastor. Pray urgently for leaders both in the recognized churches and in the house church networks. Pray that new believers will grow strong in faith, and not fall away. The Church suffers through persecution, but recognizes that it drives them to prayer and total dependence on God.

2   **Much of Laos remains unevangelized,** even with good church growth. This Communist land has 5,000 Buddhist temples and just 250 church buildings. Most people practise a mixture of Buddhism and tribal religions. With 143 peoples who speak 89 different languages, evangelism of the whole country is a challenge for the Church. At least 31 languages still need Bible translation teams. Pray for:

- *The Lao.* Others describe the nation's dominant people (Lao) as gentle and peace-loving, but these same Lao actively persecute Christians. Pray that God uses Lao believers (now more than 40,000) to bring the gospel to the rest of Laos.

- *The Tai tribes,* who are similar to the Lao in language and ethnic background. They speak 15 languages, and most remain unevangelized. Almost no Christian resources exist in their dialects.

- *The northern peoples.* Many responded to the gospel in China and Thailand, but the political situation prevents missionary work among them in Laos. Pray for change.

- *The many small southern tribes.* These groups first received the gospel between 1957 and 1963, but war stopped the church planting among most tribes. Most live with deep fear of the spirits. Pray that they find freedom through Jesus.

3   **Christian workers** could help address the many needs, but the government forbids missionaries. Some believers serve the nation through aid and development work, bomb removal (bombs dropped by the USA during the Vietnam War), business training, and English teaching. Asian believers (from nearby China and Thailand, also the Philippines and South Korea) can play a major role. Pray that foreign workers and churches would serve the Laotian people in the best possible way.

Lebanon

Asia

Pop 4.3 million. **Capital** Beirut (1.9 mill).
Christians 1.4 mill. *Evangelical Christians* 21,000.
Largest Religion Muslim.
Fastest Growing Religion Non-religious.
Largest Ethnic Groups Lebanese Arab (66.4%), Palestinian Arab (12.2%), Druze (7.7%), Armenian (4.5%).
Official Language Arabic; French and English are widely used. **All languages** 9.
Economy A strong commercial centre of the Middle East. Wars brought upheaval and instability.
Politics Republic with power balanced among religious communities. Constant political trouble, with interference and influence by Syria, Iran, and Saudi Arabia.

1   **Lebanon remains unique for its freedoms.** It is the only land in the Middle East where people can legally change their religion. Believers from most other Arab countries can come here more freely for Christian training at good evangelical Bible schools. Pray for protection of this religious freedom.

2   **Lebanon must recover** after 70 years of tragic communal wars and foreign interventions. Wars and conflicts have displaced over 80% of the population. All lost loved ones, and many lost homes and jobs. Relative political stability now allows the people a chance to rebuild. Pray that the Holy Spirit brings forgiveness and healing where hatred and bitterness took root. Evangelicals worked together to reach out in love to refugees from the 2006 crisis (in the south). Pray for such cooperation to continue and to grow.

③ The Christian population decreased from 62% in 1970 to 32% in 2010. Many Christians left to seek work and safety, including foreign missionaries and national leaders. The Orthodox and Catholic Churches struggle with spiritual deadness, but renewal movements in some Orthodox churches offer hope. Smaller Protestant churches struggle with divisions, and with losses from emigration. Pray for many Christians, especially leaders, to remain in Lebanon as salt and light. Pray for new believers from non-Christian backgrounds to grow in number and missions vision. Pray that many Lebanese come to faith in Jesus.

④ Lebanon is a long-time centre for Christian ministries to the whole Middle East. The Bible Society distributes Bibles throughout the region. Many respected Christian schools and orphanages now have good influence in society. Pray for effective ministry to young people of all faiths— they are the future of Lebanon, and many feel restless. Foreign Christian workers can show the love of Christ through work in reconstruction, drug rehabilitation, ministries of compassion, church development, and more. Pray that Lebanese believers may regain a vision for others and for other lands.

⑤ There is wonderful openness in Lebanon to spiritual things, and the number of new believers from other backgrounds continues to grow. But it is costly to follow Christ, despite official freedoms. Pray for the unreached. Shi'a Muslims live in the south, and Sunni Muslims live mostly in the northeast and key cities. The Druze practise a secret religion that came out of Islam, but several hundred now worship Christ through a multi-agency partnership that serves them. Pray for these secret believers. The Palestinians have a tragic story, and many still live in refugee camps with extreme poverty. Some Palestinians are Christian, but most are Muslim and unreached. Pray that Christians take every opportunity to minister to the poor and disadvantaged, and show the love of Jesus.

Malaysia
Asia

Pop 27.9 million. **Capital** Kuala Lumpur (1.5 mill).
Christians 2.6 mill. *Evangelical Christians* 1.2 mill.
Largest Religion Muslim.
Fastest Growing Religion Non-religious.

Largest Ethnic Groups Bumiputeras (58.4%, 141 indigenous Malay and tribal peoples), Chinese (31%, 12 peoples, influential in business and trade), South Asian (9.4%, mainly urban or poor estate workers), Southeast Asian (0.8%, 10 peoples).

Official Language Malay (Bahsa Malay). **All Languages** 145.

Economy Based on exports of products made from natural resources (palm oil, rubber, petroleum, others)

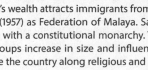

and of manufactured hi-tech goods. The Chinese and Indian populations dominated the economy since before independence (1957), but government initiatives since 1971 seek to uplift the economic status of the Malay and indigenous populations. Malaysia's wealth attracts immigrants from poorer Asian countries.

Politics Independent from Britain (1957) as Federation of Malaya. Sabah and Sarawak joined in 1963 to form Malaysia, a federation of 13 states with a constitutional monarchy. The ruling party continues in power after 2013 elections, but opposition groups increase in size and influence (Chinese, liberal, and Islamist parties). Political Islam could sharply divide the country along religious and ethnic lines.

1 **Malaysian society faces a troubled future.** The ruling party followed policies that helped a small group of Malays become wealthy, but greatly increased the gap between rich and poor Malays (the majority ethnic group). At the same time, minorities feel frustrated with the discrimination and government corruption. Pray for the leaders, who must seek to hold the country together in ways that satisfy both moderate and conservative Muslims, as well as minorities.

2 **Islam grows** in both numbers and influence. The constitution guarantees religious freedom for all faiths, but laws and actions threaten this. Over 100 radical Islamist groups push for rule by *shari'a* law for all of Malaysia. State laws prohibit evangelism of Muslims in 10 of 13 states, and conversion from Islam to another faith is illegal in all but one state. Pray for wisdom and courage for all Muslims who choose to follow Christ. Laws and society isolate Malays from the gospel. Pray for them to encounter Jesus!

3 **Church growth is steady,** and churches now engage more in society and politics. Christians cooperate more than ever before, even across denominational and racial lines. Malaysia has a good number of Bible colleges, seminaries, and church-training programmes, but many smaller churches still have no trained pastor. The government forces Malaysians to use Malay as a common language, but restricts its use for Christian literature and church services. It fears that Christian use of Malay will cause Malays to become Christian. One main issue is the ban of the word *Allah* (God) that is used in Christian Bibles and literature. Pray for all faith communities to have freedom to use the entire language. Expatriate Christian workers have declined in numbers due to visa restrictions, but various ministries depend on their input. Praise God that the mission vision of the Malaysian Church continues to increase (over 30 active agencies).

PENINSULAR MALAYSIA (PM)

1 **PM is only 3% Christian.** 80% of Malaysia's population live here, but only 25% of its Christians. Praise God that Christianity now grows among all non-Muslim ethnic groups. Pray for a deep work of the Holy Spirit to allow believers to preserve and build up the Church, despite the pressures from Islam and non-Christian family members.

2 **Pray for the less evangelized.** The Malaysian Church has the resources and cultural knowledge to reach them, but it also needs the courage and commitment.

- *The Malays* are one of the world's largest unreached groups. Some now worship in house groups and multi-ethnic churches, but no public congregation of ethnic Malays exists.

- *The Chinese* have a significant Christian minority (mostly among the urban, English-speaking Chinese). Only half the 450 Chinese villages have a church, and few of those who speak Hainanese, Hakka, or Teochew are Christian.

- *The Orang Asli of Peninsular Malaysia (PM)* are original inhabitants of the Malaysian peninsula. The Malay-dominated government considers them Muslim, but most practise animism. 8 of the 19 groups have no churches or believers.

- *Indian Malaysians* make up a high number of the country's poor. They include many Tamil Christians, but also other less-reached minorities, especially Punjabis and Telugus.

- *Drug addicts* need effective Christian ministry. Addiction is a major problem, especially among Malay youth. They generally face rejection from family, and often turn to crime.

Sabah

1 **Sabah is the nation's poorest state,** with 26% below the poverty line. This beautiful region suffers from racial prejudice, corruption, crime, drug trafficking, and piracy. The government gets significant income from Sabah's natural resources, but it fails to invest it wisely in ways that help the local people.

2 **Peoples who need prayer.** Praise God for rapid church growth among the Chinese, Kadazan-Dusan, Tagal, and Murut peoples! Pray for local Christians to engage and evangelize their society, as expatriate mission and ministry is difficult here.

- *The Muslim peoples of Sabah* are almost untouched by the gospel. Pray for specific outreach to Filipino-related peoples (mostly refugees), Indonesians (mostly illegal immigrants), and local Malay and Muslim tribal peoples.

- *Indigenous (Bumiputera) groups* have had large people movements to Christ, but the Church has neglected them. Few languages have the New Testament. Tribal peoples suffer the greatest levels of poverty, unemployment, and lack of education.

Sarawak

1 **Sarawak enjoys spiritual blessing,** with 70 years of God at work! The majority of Iban and nearly half the Chinese are Christian. But the Church faces many trials. Materialism in urban areas pulls people away from faith, and pressure from Muslims is strong in rural areas. Ministry and discipleship are extremely difficult due to the remote location, and due to the traditional animist beliefs of the Iban people (former headhunters). Pray for churches to overcome their trials! Ask God to call more pastors and Christian workers to this needy but responsive province.

2 **Pray for Christians to assist the poor, and to reach out in love** to other peoples around them who suffer even greater needs. Most indigenous groups remain poor, especially in rural areas. The government takes advantage of their situation, and the churches often overlook them. Many have little opportunity for education, employment, or healthcare.

Maldives
Asia

Pop 314,000. **Capital** Malé (126,000). [Population figures generally do not include non-Maldivians.]
Christians Around 500. *Evangelical Christians* <250.
Largest Religion Muslim.
Fastest Growing Religion Muslim.

Largest Ethnic Groups Indigenous (80%, Maldivians of South Asian Dravidian origin), Foreign (20%, Indian, Sri Lankan, Pakistani, Bangladeshi, and some Westerners, almost all in temporary employment).
Official Language Dhivehi (of Sanskrit origin). **All Languages** 2.

Economy Based on tourism and fishing. Lack of fertile soil and fresh water, and the dense population mean

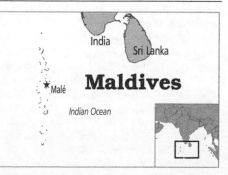

most people live at subsistence level. Rising sea levels threaten the ecosystem, and could destroy much land and completely cover many islands.

Politics 1,200 coral islands in 20 groups, with only 202 inhabited. The nominal British protectorate was terminated in 1965. Ruled by one president from 1978 to 2008. Very poor human rights record. Demonstrations and international pressure led to a multi-party democracy in the 2008 presidential elections. 3 presidents since 2008. Some limited freedoms now, but not for religion.

1 **Tourists see the Maldives as an island paradise, but a darker reality hides below the surface.** Powerful social and official forces limit freedom of expression and belief. The Maldives has one of the highest divorce rates in the world. Crime rates and gang activity both continue to rise. Child abuse and teenage drug abuse (among up to 70% of teens) indicate deep problems. Islam is the only recognized religion, and the government forbids open practice of all other religions. But beyond Islamic beliefs, many people follow occult practices called *fanditha*. Pray for the light of the gospel to shine among Maldivians. Pray against strongholds of pride, fear, and selfish pursuit of physical pleasures.

2 **The Maldivians remain among the least evangelized** on earth. The government has never allowed mission work or Christian literature. It denies Christianity exists here (but arrests those who believe!). Maldivians interpret Western culture, media, and tourists as "Christians", and therefore see Christians as immoral. Political opponents now use the word *Christian* to insult one another. Pray for this nation to know the true nature of Jesus.

3 **Persecution of believers is strong.** Any Maldivian who practises Christianity can expect social exclusion, harsh treatment, prison, and even torture. Pray for those who believe. Pray for their protection, their courage in the face of great trials, and for opportunity to share their faith. Many Maldivians travel as sailors or students, or to seek medical care abroad. Some live in other lands (India, Sri Lanka, Malaysia). Pray for witness to them!

4 **Workers translated the Gospels** in 1811, but the work was lost or destroyed! Today the only portions of Scripture in Dhivehi are the Gospel of Luke and Acts. Pray for ways people can freely access the Word in their heart language. Christian video and audio messages in Dhivehi exist on the Internet for those able to find their way past the government's filters.

Mongolia

Asia

Pop 2.7 million. **Capital** Ulaanbaatar/Ulan Bator (966,000).
Christians 46,000. *Evangelical Christians* 33,000.
Largest Religion Buddhist.
Fastest Growing Religion Christian.
Largest Ethnic Groups Mongolian (90.9%, 7 distinct dialects), Kazakh (5.3%), Chinese (1.5%), Tuvan (1.2% in far west).
Official Language Khalkha Mongolian. **All Languages** 15.

Economy A pastoral and agricultural economy. Mining important for foreign exchange. Severe winters brought great losses to livestock, which left many poor and forced thousands to move to the cities for work. Thousands more seek work abroad.

Politics Unified as a nation in 1206 under Genghis Khan, and expanded to create the greatest land empire ever known (from China and Korea to Central Europe). Under foreign domination from 1368 to 1911. Marxist government from 1921 until a multiparty democracy was established in 1990. Corruption and poverty are major challenges.

Christianity in Mongolia is a reality for the first time in modern history! Perhaps only 4 Mongolian believers existed in 1989, but by 2010 over 40,000 believers worshipped in hundreds of churches and groups around the country! The Church is less than one generation old, but it already sends missionaries to unreached areas, runs national ministries, and develops its own Mongolian-style worship music.

2 **The difficult economic situation** deeply affects every area of life (employment, education, children's well-being, others). A few became rich in the new market economy, but many struggle in deep poverty. Economic difficulties led to increased social problems such as crime, alcoholism, prostitution, and homelessness in the cities. Most mission agencies work in health, relief, education, or literature programmes. These opportunities demonstrate Christ's compassionate love.

3 **Mongolia's traditional religions** (Lamaistic Buddhism, shamanism) became popular again after Communism ended (1990). Traditional superstitions and even occult practices have a strong hold on most people's lives. Young Mongolians often consult shamans for health, finance, and relationship issues. Pray for complete freedom and changed lives through the Lord Jesus.

4 **Discipleship and church leadership.** Most Christian ministry is based in Ulaanbaatar, so rural churches especially have little support or teaching. A TEE programme that serves the faraway congregations may be the Mongolian Church's greatest need! Blue Sky Aviation (Mission Aviation Fellowship) helps address the needs for evangelism, training, and humanitarian work throughout the vast rural countryside.

5 **The less evangelized.** Pray for foreign workers to truly learn and adapt to Mongolian culture, and for all believers to work in unity.

- *Nomads* find their traditional life difficult to maintain. Pray for ministries that demonstrate the gospel to them, and a church model that suits their mobile lifestyle.

- *Kazakhs* are a majority in the far west. A few are Christian, but most are Muslim. Muslim missionaries seek to bring them back to Islam.

- *Among the ethnic minorities,* the Chinese and Russian communities have a few believers, but little outreach goes to the Kalmyk, Tuvan, and Evenki peoples.

Myanmar

Asia

Pop 50.5 million. **Capital** Naypyidaw (1 mill).
Christians 4.5 mill. *Evangelical Christians* 2.5 mill.
Largest Religion Buddhist.
Fastest Growing Religions Christian, Chinese religions.

Largest Ethnic Groups Very diverse, with 8 major national races and (officially) 135 sub-groups and tribes. Many more smaller tribes and language groups exist. Burmese/Bama (62.8%), Karen (9.4%, 24 peoples), Shan (8.5%), Mon-Khmer (4.5%), Kuki-Chin (2.5%, 39 peoples), Miri-Kachin (2.4%), Chinese (2%), Rohingya (1.9%, South Asian), Palaung (1.4%).
Official Language Burmese. **All Languages** 116.

Economy Rich in natural resources (teak forests, fertile soil, gems and minerals, oil/gas deposits), but most people live in poverty due to mismanagement by the former military junta, and corruption. Political isolation and lasting damage from cyclone Nargis (2008) intensify the challenges. Tourism and current reforms now bring economic growth.

Politics Independent since 1948, after rule as part of India under the British Empire, then occupied by Japan during WWII. Controlled by military junta until 2010, when elections began a transition to a civilian democracy. Some increase of freedoms came in recent years. Armed separatist movements operate in several regions, and violent clashes occur between some ethnic/religious groups.

---

1 **Myanmar's military junta (1962-2011) was ruthless.** Their policies brought poverty to a land rich in resources. They reacted violently to protests, put their opponents in prison, and implemented forced labour. A policy of violence against certain minorities led to destroyed villages, rape, torture, displaced populations, and international condemnation. Myanmar was deeply broken as a result, with divisions along political, religious, and especially ethnic lines. Pray for what seems impossible except through Christ: ethnic harmony, effective national government, and true peace.

2 **The military regime tried to destroy Christianity,** yet faith continues to spread. They destroyed over 3,000 Christian villages from 2000 to 2010, and expelled foreign Christian workers in 1966. This persecution and isolation helped believers develop a faith that endures hardship. The Church of Myanmar shows us an example of how God can use even terrible suffering to accomplish His purposes for His people.

3 **Christianity** arrived in the early 19th century. Now, generations later, the Church is a mix of those who follow Christianity by tradition only, and those in the midst of spiritual revival and renewal. The country's desperate situation creates opportunities to demonstrate Christ's compassion. Myanmar has one of the region's worst AIDS crises, and drug use is widespread. At least 750,000 children live "at risk". A number of nationals already serve the Lord cross-culturally. Pray for willingness to serve in the rural villages and not just the cities.

4 **Most Christians belong to minority groups** that have engaged in military actions against the central government. Pray this may not cause bitterness, hatred of other peoples, compromise of their faith, or the decrease of missions vision. In the past, Christians had many causes for division, but God raised up prayer movements that unified some believers across denominational and ethnic boundaries. The new generation of leaders more often joins to stand as one Church in the nation. Pray for reconciliation and unity among believers.

5 **Buddhism has a strong hold** on the Burmese majority, as well as over the Shan, the Rakhine, and the Mon peoples. Most children receive education in Buddhist monasteries. Burmese Buddhism mixes in occult beliefs, superstition, and fear of the spirits. The Church must learn to understand the Buddhist mindset, and must also minister in spiritual power, in order to see a breakthrough among the majority. Reportedly, thousands of Buddhist monks have quietly become believers, and many study the gospel and listen to Christian radio.

6 **The least-evangelized peoples.** Pray for genuine love across deep ethnic divides, and for good training, so that the indigenous Church is well-equipped to evangelize the nation!

- *The Bama (Burmese)* peoples, who are only 0.1% Christian. Pray for followers of Christ among this strongly Buddhist people. Mistrust and prejudice exist between this politically dominant group and the tribal believers.
- *The Shan,* related to the Thai. Only 0.9% are Christian. Despite being Buddhist, they suffered greatly in the wars with the military regime.

- **The Chinese** (over 1 million). Only about 2.5% are Christian. Many Chinese hold significant influence in Myanmar, but the more recent and massive influx causes some resentment.

- **The Rohingya.** This Muslim people is one of the most neglected and unwanted peoples on earth. The government denies them citizenship, and they face numerous restrictions on their basic rights. Many fled to Bangladesh or other countries. Few are Christian, and little outreach exists to them. Violence between Buddhists and the Muslim Rohingya broke out in 2013.

- **The 9 Hindu peoples.** Workers planted churches among them in 1928, but they remain only around 1% Christian.

- **Refugees and displaced peoples.** Over 2 million Burmese live in Thailand, and more in Malaysia, Singapore, and Western nations. Another 1 million have lost their homes in Myanmar, mostly in Christian areas. Many remain without the gospel, and far from home.

Nepal   *Asia*

Pop 29.9 million. **Capital** Kathmandu (1 mill).
Christians 851,000. *Evangelical Christians* 838,000.
Largest Religion Hindu.
Fastest Growing Religion Christian.

Largest Ethnic Groups Up to 100 ethnic groups, made up of over 300 peoples, sub-groups, and castes. Caste is often as important as ethnicity in this strongly Hindu culture. South Asian (78%, 285 peoples/castes, mainly in south and east), Tibetan-Himalayan (21.5%, 38 peoples, mainly in north and west).
Official Language Nepali. **All Languages** 127.

Economy One of the world's poorest countries (around one-third live below the poverty line). 90% of population work in subsistence farming. Development hindered by geographical isolation, difficult land, poor infrastructures, environmental damage, natural disasters, and political instability. Potential for hydroelectric power and tourism (Nepal contains 8 of the 10 highest mountain peaks in the world).
Politics The ancient monarchy ended in 2008, when Nepal became a multi-party constitutional republic. Colonial powers never ruled Nepal. It was politically isolated until 1951. Civil unrest by Maoist rebels greatly disrupted the 1990s and 2000s, and a Maoist-dominated government took office in 2008. Civil war ended, but political instability continues, and politicians cannot agree on a new constitution.

---

1 **A new Nepal began in 2008,** when the absolute power of the Hindu monarchy finally ended after years of Maoist rebel fighting and then pro-democracy protests. This answers the prayers of most Christians in Nepal! New freedoms and opportunities for Christian ministry are now possible. But deep divisions still affect society (between religious groups, political parties), and the government faces severe economic and social problems. 13,000 died in the civil war, and many endured human rights abuses. Without justice, many people will continue to see violence as an acceptable means to achieve political gain. Pray for wisdom, courage, and grace for all Nepal's leaders.

2 **The Nepali Church grew through many trials.** The first church started in 1952 with 29 Christians. It grew to 200,000 believers by 1990, and persecution was very strong. By 2010, 850,000 followers of Christ gathered in nearly 10,000 groups! Now all 75 districts have at least 1 church. Growth came through prayer and the willingness to suffer for the gospel. Praise God for the Nepali believers' courage to evangelize, even though they risk fines or prison. The law guarantees freedom of religion, but non-Hindus cannot spread their faith. Opponents of the gospel claim that Christianity is a foreign religion, but the large majority of Nepali Christians worship and fellowship in indigenous structures and networks.

3 **The next generation of Nepali Christians** must build on this good foundation. Pray that the first generation of Christians will hand over leadership well to the second generation. For years, no formal training was available. Now over 15 Bible colleges and seminaries exist, and some churches and agencies offer training courses. But the fast-growing Church urgently needs more leadership training. How can a Church so poor release enough pastors to serve the flock? Some look for foreign donors. Pray that leaders learn to be tentmakers, and that congregations learn to support their pastors. Pray for perseverance for the believers, and that no laws or threats will keep them from sharing the gospel!

4 **Social needs remain a huge challenge** in this beautiful but troubled land. Despite much progress, Nepal's poverty, political struggles, geography, and caste system leave many people suffering and oppressed. Pray that the Church takes this opportunity to engage with the needs in Nepali society.

- *Around 2.6 million children work as child labourers.* 70% of them work more than 9 hours a day. Until Nepal gets children out of the workplace and into school, development for the future is impossible.

- *Up to 300,000 Nepali girls work in the sex trade* in India, the Middle East, and elsewhere. Traffickers target poor and lower-caste girls. Nepali Christians reach and rescue some of these girls in Nepal and in Mumbai.

- *Millions suffer from preventable diseases.* Lack of basic sanitation causes over 80% of diseases. 30,000 child deaths each year result from malnutrition. 90% of trafficked girls who return are HIV-infected, and AIDS has rapidly spread.

- *The impact of the caste system* continues to leave many oppressed, especially Dalits. Discrimination based on caste is illegal, but still very common.

5 **Holistic ministry powerfully demonstrates the love of Christ** in practical and spiritual ways. Foreign agencies work in hospitals, leprosy treatment, agriculture, education, and with society's most vulnerable. Nepali Christian NGOs also work to address high unemployment, illiteracy, environmental problems, and dependence on foreign aid. Praise God for greater unity among Christians, and for greater cooperation between Christianity and other faiths. Christian Efforts for Peace, Justice, and Reconciliation formed in 2003, and later joined a peace-building process with representatives of all other faiths. Pray for all Christians to include social transformation as a key part of evangelism.

6 **Pray for the less reached.** Around 55% of the population are unevangelized, and 309 peoples/castes remain unreached. William Carey (the well-known British missionary to India) translated the New Testament into Nepali in 1821. But only 8 of Nepal's 80 languages have a complete Bible translation.

- *The high-caste Hindus* (more than 30% of the population). They respond more to the gospel in Nepal than in India, but Hinduism keeps most in bondage. Few openly proclaim Christ as Lord.

- *The Awadhi and Bhojpuri speakers* on the Indian border.

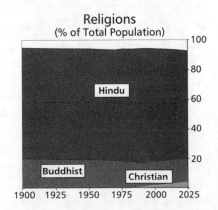

Religions
(% of Total Population)

Hindu

Buddhist   Christian

1900 1925 1950 1975 2000 2025

- *The mountain peoples,* who are almost entirely Tibetan-related Buddhists. The famous Sherpa of the Everest region do not have a single Church, and have only around 50 believers.
- *The increased number of Muslims,* mostly Bengali, Kashmiri, or Urdu-speaking farmers or labourers.

Oman

Asia

Pop 2.9 million. **Capital** Muscat (650,000).
Christians 80,000. *Evangelical Christians* 24,000.
Largest Religion Muslim.
Fastest Growing Religion Hindu.

Largest Ethnic Groups Approximately 25% of the population are expatriate, and make up the majority of the workforce. Omani (42.7%), Gulf Arab (15.1%), South Asian (14.3%), Baloch (13.4%), Persian (2.6%), Dhofari Arab (2.5%), Mahra Arab (1.8%), Filipino (1.8%), Egyptian Arab (1.5%).
Official Language Arabic. **All Languages** 21.
Economy Based primarily on oil production, with some agriculture, fishing, and light industry. Tourism is increasing. Oil wealth has been distributed wisely for the improvement of living standards.
Politics A monarchy, with no political parties permitted. But a high degree of personal freedom and political stability for the region. A Consultative Assembly is elected by the people.

---

1 **Praise God that Oman** enjoys an open and modern society compared to others in the region. All residents may practise their faith, and the government gave land to build places of worship! Wealth from the oil industry allowed a greater level of education and economic balance. Pray now for spiritual openness to the gospel among all peoples of Oman.

2 **The entire Muslim majority** remains a challenge. Evangelism of Muslims is illegal, and the few Omanis who find Christ face pressure to turn away. There are no known churches for the semi-nomadic Mahra or Jibbali peoples, the Baluch of the eastern coasts, the rural population, or the Swahili speakers.

3 **Christians grow in number,** with a steady stream of converts particularly among foreign workers. But Omanis also come to faith in Christ. There are four centres where Christians from over 30 denominations hold services in different languages. The Bible Society distributes Scriptures from these centres. Pray for other means of witness. 4 broadcasters provide over 100 hours of Christian radio each week in Arabic, English, and several Asian languages. The Internet and mobile phones spread the gospel in cautious but effective ways. Pray for Christians to live godly lives that demonstrate Christ to their foreign and Omani neighbours.

4 **The door remains open for Christian professionals** to share the gospel through words, actions, and lifestyles that honour Jesus. Samuel Zwemer, a famous missionary to Muslims, began work in Oman in 1890, and the Reformed Church in America carried on his good witness especially within the healthcare industry. Other Christians work in education and business. Pray that more workers may be willing to serve here.

Pakistan

Asia

Pop 184.8 million. **Capital** Islamabad (856,000).
Christians 4.5 mill. *Evangelical Christians* 1.1 mill.
Largest Religion Muslim.
Fastest Growing Religions Muslim, Hindu.

Largest Ethnic Groups Pakistan's ethnic groups must be understood in the context of ethnicity, language, and caste (a more complex arrangement than in most nations). Group names can be misleading if assumed as only related to geography or language. South Asian peoples: Urdu Muslim (30.5%, 103 groups), Jat (16%, 3 groups), Sindhi (12.8%, 32 groups), Punjabi (7.6%, 65 groups), Bengali (6.8%), Rajasthani (3.7%), Kashmiri (1.3%), Brahui (1.2%), Other South Asian people clusters (2.1%); Indo-Iranian (18.1%, includes Pashtun and Baloch). Many Afghan refugees and immigrants (Pashtun) not documented with these figures.

Official Language English (official government language). Urdu is the national language. Its use is spreading.
All Languages 77.

Economy Based on agriculture, light industry, and services. Shortages of electricity and gas disrupt normal life and reduce industry effectiveness. Much of the population lives in poverty, especially in rural areas. High military and security spending, and the fight against radical Islamist groups, burden the economy. Rapid population growth, limited land and water, and weak infrastructure all must be addressed. Floods, earthquakes, and landslides further damage development.

Politics Muslim politicians sought a separate state, which led to partition of British-ruled India at independence (1947). Pakistan's history includes 4 conflicts with India, the loss of East Pakistan (which became Bangladesh), the effects of decades of war in nearby Afghanistan, and almost constant political turmoil and corruption. The tension between modern secular voters and Islamist forces creates internal problems. Tensions with India, Afghanistan, and the West create external problems.

---

1 **Pakistan's government normally alternates** between inefficient, corrupt political parties and authoritarian military dictatorships. Power and wealth are concentrated in too few hands. This hinders economic and social development. The country faces pressure from Islamist forces (in the west, Afghanistan, the Punjab), and from troubles with India over the Kashmir region. Pray that the Lord would free Pakistan from spirits of lawlessness and violence that harm the nation. Pray for government that will move the nation forward.

2 **Fundamentalist Islam** (driven by the Taliban) impacts the whole nation, even though only a minority support it. It causes violence against religious minorities. Social and economic progress is difficult for non-Muslims (and non-Sunni Muslims). Women who live under fundamentalist Muslim values have very few freedoms or rights. Education is minimal, and domestic abuse is widespread. Pray that the true nature of this type of Islam might become clear for all to see, so that it might lose its power.

3 **Religious minorities face discrimination and persecution** in many forms. Christians, Hindus, and minority Muslim groups (Shi'a, Ahmaddiya) suffer the most. The famous "blasphemy law" allows the death penalty on anyone who insults Mohammed, and life in prison for anyone who damages a Quran. Extremists use this law to falsely accuse innocent people. They stir up religious frenzy so the crowd enforces the punishment. Enemies of Christ vandalize or destroy churches. They beat, murder, abduct, rape, or force conversion on Christians and other minorities. Even amidst such persecution, Pakistani Christians love their nation and want it to prosper. Pray that believers might always be ready to share about Jesus, and to repay violence with love.

4 **The Church continues to grow,** despite many obstacles. Poverty, illiteracy, and lack of teaching opened the door to corruption, immorality, and low spiritual standards among Christians. Some Christians live devoted lives, committed to God, but the majority have a weak, immature faith. Common problems in churches include leadership struggles, greed, court cases, substance abuse, and divisions. Ask God to raise up humble, committed spiritual leaders with passion to serve the Church. Pray for more students in Bible and leadership training, wise and godly leaders, and adequate financial resources for Christian work.

5 **Outreach by Pakistani Christians** needs major change. The Pakistani Church comes mostly from the lowest classes of society (largely Hindu Dalits of the Punjab and Hindu tribal peoples of the Sindh). Huge cultural boundaries separate the Muslim majority and the Christian minority. Most churches do little to reach Muslims or even Hindus. Christians have legal freedom to share the gospel, but fear and a negative attitude to Muslims hold many back. Praise God for the few that reach out.

6 **A small number of Muslims come to faith in Jesus,** even though they can face severe punishment or even death. They hear the gospel through media (literature, radio, TV), through dreams and visions, or from Pakistani Christians. Pakistani churches (Hindu background) struggle to include these Muslim-background believers. Many revert back to Islam, become atheists, or practise their faith privately. Networks of Muslim-background believers now exist to offer spiritual support and discipleship. Ask God to raise up fellowships and leaders among them, and for godly disciples to reach out to other Muslims.

7 **Pray for ministry to these specific groups:**

- *Young people.* Two-thirds of rural youth deal with poverty and the old practices of child labour, bonded labour, or forced marriages (families may use children to repay debts). They lack opportunities for education. Most never hear the gospel. Many urban youth battle drug addiction. Militant groups find recruits among those who feel hopeless and discouraged about the future.
- *The Pakistani diaspora.* Around 7 million now live in the Middle East, North America, Britain, and Australia. Very few follow Christ, and Christians have done little to reach them.
- *Afghan refugees* (up to 1.8 million). Christian groups have reached out to them with aid and assistance, and Karachi and Islamabad both have a number of Afghan believers!
- *The Ahmadiyya.* Other Muslims view them as heretics, and persecute them heavily. Few Ahmadiyya have ever come to Christ, and no groups focus on outreach to them.
- *The Seraiki-speaking peoples.* These 200 largely rural peoples of the Punjab and Sindh regions have almost no Christian workers or resources.

8 **Christian missions** began in Pakistan in 1833. This increased around independence (1947). After 9/11, a large number of missionaries left Pakistan and never returned. Pray especially for labourers among Muslims in the east and south of the country. Many opportunities to serve exist in medical, educational, and training ministries within legally recognized organizations, but serving in Pakistan is hard. Only 7 of Pakistan's 70 languages have a New Testament or Bible. Translation teams work on 16 languages. Ask God to place a burden for Pakistan on many people's hearts!

The Regions of Pakistan

Pakistan has over 350 unevangelized peoples and castes. Many of these have no churches, no believers, no missionaries, and no Christian witness. Pray for each of these specific regions, that Jesus may be known more widely, more deeply, and more quickly!

1 **The peoples of the far north** (Gilgit-Baltistan). Only a few Christians and fellowships exist among these mostly Muslim peoples (27 groups).

2 **Azad Kashmir**. Massive earthquakes (2005, 2007) destroyed many lives and homes. Christian groups brought aid and relief, with positive response among Muslims here.

3 **Khyber-Pakhtunkhwa and FATA** (Federally Administered Tribal Areas) are the mountainous regions that border Afghanistan. Militant Islam and the Taliban are strong here. Most Taliban come from among

the Pashtun, who also control the drug and weapon trades in Pakistan and Afghanistan. Some claim that the Pashtun heartland is one of the most spiritually oppressive places on earth. Only two Pushtu-speaking fellowships exist.

4 **Balochistan** is poor and underdeveloped, the living conditions are harsh, and access for expatriates is very difficult. 75% of the world's 10 million Baloch live in Pakistan, and they are difficult to reach.

5 **Punjab** is home to the majority of Pakistan's Christians, but this region still has a higher number of unreached individuals per Christian worker than any place in the world! Pakistan's most culturally influential city (Lahore) is in this region. It is 95% Muslim.

6 **Sindh.** Most Hindu tribal groups live here, and there is a new, indigenous church among believers from a Hindu background. Some Muslim-background believers live here as well. Karachi is Pakistan's largest and most ethnically diverse city, and is the business and economic centre. It is the easiest place for foreigners to work. The Mohajirs (Urdu-speaking peoples who are native to India) make up nearly half of Karachi's population. Only 1 fellowship and 1 church-planting team try to reach this population of up to 10 million.

Palestine

Pop 4.4 million. **Capital** Jerusalem (claimed); Ramallah (27,000, administrative).
Christians 71,000. *Evangelical Christians* 4,100.
Largest Religion Muslim.
Fastest Growing Religion Muslim.
Largest Ethnic Groups Arabs (92.3%, almost all Palestinian Arabs, with small numbers of other Arab peoples), Jews (6.3%).
Official Language Arabic. **All Languages** 6.

Economy Israel's control of access points cripples industry, and caused foreign investment to fall by 95%. Restricted travel and access to water/power supplies further intensify this problem. Unemployment is around 30%. Palestine's administration so far offers few economic solutions.
Politics Two separate parts, the West Bank and Gaza Strip. The Palestine Authority controls the main towns and scattered areas. Jewish settler areas and Israeli military authorities control the remainder. The loss of most of their land (1948) and further conquest by Israel (1967) dominate Palestinian history and identity. International efforts to settle bitter confrontations between Israelis and Palestinians have only a small chance for success. Internal struggles also exist between Hamas (ruling the West Bank) and Fatah (ruling Gaza), and Hezbollah's influence adds further complications and conflict.

Pray for God's purposes to be fulfilled in these areas:

- *A just settlement of the land issue,* and the future of both the Jewish settlements in Palestine and the Palestinians in Israel itself. Both sides feel strong claims to the land. Both Israelis and Palestinians claim Jerusalem as their exclusive capital.

- *Improved living conditions.* Estimates suggest that 70% of Gaza live in deep poverty, and 80% depend on external aid. Only 28% of Gaza have regular access to clean water.

- *A legitimate and effective leadership* to govern Palestine. Political groups Fatah and the PLO (Palestinian Liberation Organization) both have low approval ratings. Together with the heavy-handed treatment by Israel, this leaves many open to recruitment by radical and violent Islamic groups. Pray for every Palestinian family to hear and see the gospel of Jesus Christ.

Pray not only for the peace of Jerusalem, but also that both sides meet the Prince of Peace. It is through Him alone that any meaningful reconciliation will come.

Palestinian Christians find themselves attacked or betrayed from all sides, even though they trace their roots to pre-Islamic times. Israel sees them as Arab Palestinians. Extremist Muslims see them as Western collaborators. The global Church generally ignores or abandons them. Large numbers leave to find a better life elsewhere. Pray that those who remain might continue to stay strong in their Christian faith, and in their commitment to demonstrate the gospel in difficult conditions. Reconciliation work between Arab Christians and Messianic Jews will be a long road, but a worthy investment. Pray that God will protect them.

61% of all Palestinians live abroad as exiles, especially in Jordan and Lebanon. Most Palestinians in exile live in refugee camps, in poverty and uncertainty. The situation has not changed much for generations. Pray for a solution that offers justice and righteousness to these often unwanted people. Pray for Christians to show love and concern for them.

Philippines

Pop 93.6 million. **Capital** Manila (Manila/Quezon City 11.6 mill).
Christians 86.4 mill. *Evangelical Christians* 11.6 mill.
Largest Religion Christian.
Fastest Growing Religion Non-religious.
Largest Ethnic Groups Filipinos (98.1%, Tribal peoples 9.6%, Muslim majority peoples 5%), Chinese (1.7%, mostly urban, involved in commerce and industry).
Official Language Filipino (based on Tagalog), English.
All Languages 181.
Economy Based on agriculture and industry. Poverty and unemployment made worse by high population

growth, widespread corruption, social and political unrest, and natural disasters. Progress held back by high crime rates and low foreign investment. Many Filipinos that work abroad send home remittances as a vital source of income.
Politics A Spanish colony (1565-1898), which led to the large Catholic majority and many Spanish customs. Governed by the USA until independence (1946). American-style republic that functions more like a one-party republic. No government has successfully addressed the need for land reform, for limits on the military, or for limits on the power of the wealthy elite. The Muslim minority in Mindanao seeks an independent Islamic state in the south.

---

1 **The Philippines has not yet achieved its economic and political potential.** The nation has natural resources, democratic roots, and a well-educated population. But governments routinely fail to address serious economic and social issues that limit development. Half the population live in poverty. Tropical storms, floods, and landslides destroy lives and homes, especially in slums. Most farmers do not own land. High levels of corruption are scandalous, especially in Asia's most Christianized nation! Pray for the Fellowship of Christians in Government, which promotes biblical standards among Christian public servants.

2 **Metro Manila** is a mega-city of 11 million people, with the Greater Manila area up to 20 million. It faces enormous challenges, but God is greatly at work here. Modern ministry to the urban poor began in Manila. Many are open to the gospel, but most evangelical churches are in wealthier areas. Nearly 50% of slums and squatter communities have no evangelical church. At the same time, Manila is home to the country's wealthy elite. Pray that the gospel will impact them also, as they hold much power and the potential to transform Manila and the whole nation.

3 **The Roman Catholic Church** retains great influence, but needs to change as the country's religious diversity increases. Some Catholics want to preserve the Church's role in politics and society, and a few work to oppose Protestant or Independent movements. Recent surveys show that 15-30% of Catholics identify themselves as charismatic, and several new movements within Catholicism have committed evangelicals among them. Pray for God's grace on these lively communities. For many Catholics, witchcraft or animism actually holds more influence over their lives than Christianity. They need the power of the true gospel.

4 **Almost all evangelical denominations continue to grow,** especially the indigenous Pentecostal groups. Church planting slowed down after strong growth in the 1980s and 1990s, but many large congregations emerged, together with a diversity of Christian ministries. Praise God for increased spiritual unity among evangelicals. Several groups work to strengthen fellowship and collaboration between churches. Few countries have more extensive Christian television coverage, and the Filipino Church makes impressive use of the Internet (online communities, podcast sermons, Bible studies, webstreaming TV). Of the Philippines' 42,000 *barangays* (its smallest government unit), 23,000 still have no evangelical church. Pray for new passion and commitment to church planting.

5 **The Filipino Church is a significant missionary-sending Church.** The Philippines already supports over 3,000 cross-cultural workers, coordinated through the Philippine Missions Association (PMA). Their goal is 5,000 (also 2,000 mobilizers and 500,000 mission intercessors!). They also train and encourage the Filipino evangelicals who work overseas (over 500,000) to be Kingdom ambassadors. Meanwhile, over 2,000 Filipino Catholic missionaries serve in other lands. Shortwave broadcasts go out from the Philippines to less accessible Asian areas (China, Siberia, Indochina, Myanmar, others).

6 **Evangelicals of this generation face new challenges.** Pray for the spiritual health of the Church. Pray for the Bible and other Christian resources to make a deep and lasting impact on lives (54 translation projects underway, 14 languages still have translation needs).

- *Many sects and cults* mix Christian ideas with false teachings. Most have highly controlling and manipulative leadership. Ask God to expose all lies, and pray for effective ministry to the millions caught within these groups.
- *Church and denominational splits* are frequent among the over 2,000 registered denominations, often because of broken fellowship among believers.
- *Extreme poverty* (especially in rural areas) can lead to additional problems. Some depend on foreign funds and sponsorships. Others adopt prosperity theology. Pray that Christian organizations and Filipino churches with better resources might find sustainable ways to assist the poor.
- *Leadership development* is a priority. Praise God for many Filipino leaders with national and international influence! Yet even the more than 100 seminaries and Bible colleges and numerous training courses cannot keep up with the rapid church growth. Rural congregations especially suffer, as trained graduates have less desire to serve there.
- *Expatriate missionaries* see their role change as the Filipino Church matures. Praise God for all He has done! Pray for wisdom for expatriate Christians to serve in the most helpful ways. Pray for fruitful partnerships between expats and nationals.

7 **The major export of the Philippines is people!** Filipinos are hard working, and many are highly skilled, but too few work opportunities exist at home. Over 8.1 million live abroad. Many work as nurses, engineers, domestic servants, nannies, menial workers, and seamen (the 245,000 Filipino seamen are the largest group from any nation). Many go to difficult and "closed" countries to witness for Christ, and some suffer much for their faith. Pray that Christians from the Philippines may be lights to the whole world.

8 **Pray for the less-reached peoples and regions.** The Church made great progress in reaching isolated tribal peoples all over the islands. Of the 17 that remain unreached, most are Muslim. Pray for the Church to grow in its concern for and outreach to Muslims, ethnic minorities, and vulnerable peoples.

- *Mindanao has a good number of evangelicals,* but growth has slowed down. Violence between government forces and Muslim rebels, and ethnic resentment among some groups block the spread of the gospel. Pray for peace in Mindanao, and for a fair solution that ends the cycle of military presence, violence, kidnappings, and suffering.

- *The Sulu Islands* (between Mindanao and Borneo) are home to the Muslim Tausug, Sama, Sinama, and Yakan peoples. A significant breakthrough came among the Sama Bajau Sea Gypsies who moved to urban areas! They now take the gospel back to their home areas.

- *Paluwan* (a long, isolated island) receives many new Tagalog and Muslim immigrants as it rapidly develops. Praise God that some of the indigenous peoples responded to the gospel! Pray for spiritual fruit to come among the Muslim Molbog, Batak, Palawano, and Sama Mapun.

- *Luzon* has some regions with few Christian peoples (the Bicol, the north and northeast coastal mountains). Church planting there is difficult.

- *Visayas* is a needy region of the country. Christianity is widespread, but many do not actively practise their faith. Widespread poverty leaves many people without hope.

- *The nearly 1 million Chinese* are only 2-3% evangelical Christian, although many are Catholic. Some of the Philippines' oldest Protestant churches are Chinese. Pray especially for new outreach to the younger generation of Chinese-Filipinos, and to the newly arrived mainland Chinese.

- *Vulnerable and at-risk groups* need special ministry. Over half the population are under age 20. 24% miss their education because they must work to help their family, or they have no local school. Up to 100,000 children and 400,000 women are currently involved in the sex trade, with many of them trafficked to other countries.

Qatar

Asia

Pop 1.5 million. **Capital** Doha (457,000).
Christians 89,000. *Evangelical Christians* 15,000.
Largest Religion Muslim.
Fastest Growing Religion Hindu.
Largest Ethnic Groups Arab (58.3%, Qatari, Palestinian, Lebanese, Syrian, others), Persian (16.1%), South Asian (10.9%, Indian, Pakistani, Sri Lankan; some sources claim up to 35% in reality), Bantu (7.7%), Filipino (4.4%). The expatriate community is about 65% of the population, and difficult to count with many residents undocumented, and only in the country for a short term.
Official Language Arabic. **All Languages** 6.

Economy Based on oil and gas products (85% of exports). Some of world's largest gas reserves. Most Qataris live in great wealth, but Asian migrants form an economic lower class. Influential TV broadcaster Al-Jazeera based in Doha.
Politics Part of the Turkish-Ottoman Empire until 1918. Under British protection until independence in 1971. The current Emir overthrew his father in a bloodless coup (1995), and his foreign and domestic policies reflect an open and progressive attitude. His son then took over peacefully in 2013. Qatar won World Cup bid (2022), and faces international pressure to reform widespread inhumane treatment of migrant workers.

1 **Almost every Qatari follows Islam** whether Arab, Persian, or Bantu (former slaves). Pray that Qataris at home and abroad would hear about Jesus, and for the birth of a Qatari Church. Expatriate workers come from many nations. Pray for Christians to take employment opportunities (from manual labour to executive positions) to increase the presence of God's Kingdom in Qatar.

② **Regulations and financial hardship limit Christians' ability to meet together,** and to share the gospel. Praise God that authorities recently offered land on which to build the first churches in Qatar since Islam's arrival! Plans exist for a Catholic facility, then Anglican and Protestant buildings. Pray for space where large Asian fellowships and other congregations committed to outreach and evangelism might meet together for worship.

③ **Pray for the many groups of believers** among Filipinos, Westerners, Lebanese, Indians, Pakistanis, and others. Pray that they might bear fruitful witness among both their own communities and other non-Christians. Pray also that gospel radio, TV, and Christian websites might reach into the homes and hearts of all who live in Qatar.

Saudi Arabia
Asia

Pop 26.2 million. **Capital** Riyadh (4.8 mill).
Christians 1.4 mill. *Evangelical Christians* 89,000. (Figures are estimates.)
Largest Religion Muslim.
Fastest Growing Religion Christian.
Largest Ethnic Groups Saudi Arab (73%), Foreign Arab (7.4%, including Egyptian, Yemeni, Palestinian, Lebanese), Indian (5.2%), Filipino (3.7%), Bangladeshi (3.7%), Pakistani (3.3%), African (1.5%, Somali, Arab-African, Nigerian).
Official Language Arabic. **All Languages** 20.

Economy Enormous oil wealth produces 75-90% of government revenue. It provides the foundation of the economy and infrastructure, and a means to export Islam globally. The economy relies heavily on foreign labourers. Unemployment is high (20-40%), as Saudis disdain certain types of labour.
Politics An absolute monarchy controlled by the large royal family. An advisory council is elected by eligible Saudis (females eligible for vote and inclusion since 2011). An Islamic state committed to its role of "custodian of Islam" and its holiest sites.

① **Saudi Arabia is the birthplace and stronghold of Islam.** From Mecca, Islam holds influence over billions, and touches many cultures worldwide. Billions of oil dollars go towards promotion of Islam around the world every year. A spiritual breakthrough for Jesus Christ here would transform Islam and all who follow it! All Muslims must pray toward Mecca 5 times daily, and over 2 million Muslims make the pilgrimage (*Hajj*) to Mecca every year. Pray that many who seek God might encounter the living Christ.

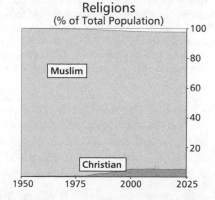

Religions
(% of Total Population)

Muslim

Christian

1950   1975   2000   2025

② **Saudi Arabia's record on religious freedom and human rights** is probably the world's worst. People of faiths other than Islam can live in Saudi Arabia, but they cannot practise their religion openly or even gather privately. Restrictions limit women in driving, voting, work, and their presence outside the home. Authorities watch Christian expatriates all the time, and those caught meeting even in homes can face beatings, prison, expulsion, or even execution. Pray for strength, wisdom, and courage for the community of foreign believers. Pray also for a witness to Christ among all foreign workers, that many might come to Jesus while in this land.

3 **The nation faces enormous stresses.** National leaders feel severe pressure both from those who want greater freedom, and from those who want stricter Islamic rule. Despite strict Islamic laws, alcohol and drug abuse, sexual immorality, and HIV/AIDS are hidden but real problems. Expatriates can make good money from work here, but the social restrictions, the often cruel work environments, racial prejudice, and the lack of personal or religious freedom, all make life very difficult.

4 **Saudis who come to faith in Christ** face the death penalty if discovered. Still, more and more continue to seek and find Jesus! Every Saudi city now has believers. Pray for them to persevere, and even to multiply in number. Saudi students, businessmen, and tourists visit the West and other more open Arab states, where Christians could reach them more easily. The government bans Christian literature, video materials, and Bibles, although many listen secretly to Christian radio. Pray that believers could meet together in safety, and could gain access to God's Word. Pray for a miracle: the legalization of Christianity for Saudi Arabs.

Singapore
Asia

Pop 4.8 million. **Capital** Singapore (4.8 mill).
Christians 776,000. *Evangelical Christians* 377,000.
Largest Religion Buddhist.
Fastest Growing Religion Non-religious.
Largest Ethnic Groups 95 racial groups live in the country and speak many languages. Chinese (74.2%), Malay (13.6%), Indian/South Asian (9.2%), Other (3.2%, includes Thai, British, Eurasian, and many Asian ethnicities).
Official Languages Mandarin (Chinese), English, Malay, Tamil Indian. English is primary language for education.
All Languages 31.
Economy One of the world's most efficient trading and financial centres. Among the world's wealthiest countries, with a high standard of living. Dependent on exports and on employment of foreign nationals for industry.
Politics British rule (1824-1959). Autonomous, then part of Malaysian Federation (1963-1965). Independent as a parliamentary democracy in 1965. The strong government has provided excellent growth and stability. Because of this, most people accept its limitation of certain freedoms.

1 **The Church in Singapore grew steadily** from 1970 to 2010, especially evangelical groups. Some independent and charismatic churches now attract over 20,000 in weekly attendance! Mission schools and effective campus ministries draw many of Singapore's educated people to faith. As a result, many believers have influence in society, as well as good opportunity as missionaries to work in professional roles around the world.

2 **Singaporean society** is built on dedicated labour, discipline, and national self-reliance. This leads to stability, good governance, and a culture that resists corruption. But it also places high value on performance and wealth. Pray that the strengths of Singapore would not become the idols that it worships. Many young Christians become inactive in their faith once they marry and get caught up with the "5 Cs" (career, cash, car, club, and condo). People struggle to cope with the focus on material wealth, and current social concerns include broken marriages, family violence, elderly who are poor, depression, issues of sexuality, drug abuse, and gambling addiction.

Many regard Singapore as the "Antioch of Asia", because its stability, location, and strong Christian population all make it a good centre for regional and global Christian mission. As many as half of all congregations send missionaries directly to the field. Many others serve with international organizations, some of which have headquarters or bases in Singapore. A number of institutions offer excellent Bible and leadership training programmes for pastors, missionaries, and theologians. Pray that Singapore will be a blessing to the least-evangelized nations and peoples around it, and a servant leader that helps newer missions movements from other Asian nations.

Singapore's 1.25 million foreigners come from over 100 nations. The majority work in lower-paid jobs, and many come from unevangelized lands. The Church itself is often sophisticated and successful, which can lead to spiritual pride and ministry far removed from the needy. Pray for humility, and for more ministry to the needy through the local churches.

- *The Malays* (over 500,000) almost all follow Islam, but now a small group of believers grows among them.

- *The Indian population* (nearly 400,000) are mostly Tamil (over 50% Hindu and 25% Muslim). Lively churches exist among Hindu-background groups, but Indian Muslim groups receive little attention.

- *The Mainland Chinese* (over 200,000) come to Singapore as professionals, students, or migrant workers. Some are Christian, but the majority remain unevangelized.

- *Migrant workers* include large numbers of Indonesians, Filipinos, Burmese, Bangladeshis, Thais, Sri Lankans, and Vietnamese. Ministry exists for all these groups. Pray for more believers, and for the integration of many cultures into local churches and home groups.

Sri Lanka

Asia

Pop 20.4 million. **Capital** Colombo (683,000, administrative), Sri Jayewardenepura Kotte (123,000, legislative).
Christians 1.7 mill. *Evangelical Christians* 243,000.
Largest Religion Buddhist.
Fastest Growing Religion Muslim.

Largest Ethnic Groups Sinhala (75.9%, one of the few Buddhist people clusters with castes), Tamil (14.3%, numbers reduced through war and emigration), Sri Lankan Moor (8.3%, of Arab-Tamil descent), Other South Asian (1.5%, Sri Lankan Malay of Indonesian descent, others).
Official Languages Sinhala and Tamil, with English as the link language. **All Languages** 7.

Economy Based on textiles, tea, tourism, and money sent home from those who work abroad (especially the Gulf region). The civil war slowed what could have been a healthy economy. Much infrastructure is damaged, and many people are unemployed and displaced.
Politics Independent since 1948 as a parliamentary democracy after 450 years of colonial administration (by Portuguese, Dutch, British). Discrimination against ethnic and religious minorities since 1956 finally resulted in civil war between the Sinhala and Tamil communities (on and off from 1983 to 2009). Despite an end to hostilities, Sri Lanka lacks a political solution to this social issue.

1 **The end of civil war was an answer to prayer.** Government forces defeated the "Tamil Tigers" in 2009, but with much violence. Sri Lanka suffered greatly in the past generation from the long civil war, the excessively bloody end to the conflict, and the 2004 tsunami. Over 100,000 people lost their lives, and over 900,000 (mostly Tamils) fled the country. More than 1 million people left their homes. Many Tamils feel deep resentment. Corruption and ethnic prejudice remain common. Pray that this new era might bring a time of safety, stability, justice for all ethnic and religious groups, and freedom for the gospel.

2 **Sri Lanka once was known for its tolerance and non-violence.** For centuries it was a Buddhist kingdom that welcomed refugees from India (Hindu, Muslim, Christian). But Buddhist extremism has grown in this multi-religious, multi-ethnic country. Many reacted to the Tamil violence, to Muslim growth, or to inappropriate methods of Christian evangelism. Persecution against Christians comes in waves, and at least 250 churches were destroyed or damaged in recent years. Beneath the layers of Buddhism and Hinduism the ancient spirits, gods, and demons still hold power.

3 **Traditional mainline Churches decline, but evangelical movements grow.** The Sri Lankan Church produces many global Christian leaders, thinkers, and writers, despite its small size. But the Church is divided between Tamil and Sinhalese, between Catholic and Protestant, between mainline and evangelical groups, even between older and newer Pentecostals. These divisions offer a poor testimony for Christ. Pray for national Christian organizations that work for unity. The gospel is the best way to bring reconciliation to bitterly divided ethnic communities.

4 **The churches prioritize evangelism and church growth.** This wins converts, but does not always lead to discipleship and maturity. The Church largely failed to establish Christian practice in authentic Sri Lankan forms, and this keeps it from greater growth. Some people see Western support for Tamil churches as foreign support for terrorism. Pray that Christians might be without fault in the way they conduct ministry, both in financial matters and in their attitudes towards others. Mission by expatriates has mostly ended because of visa restrictions. Tentmaking ministry provides a way to contribute to Kingdom work and to the needs of society. Praise God for a recent formation of the first interdenominational mission agency from Sri Lanka, with a focus on South and Western Asia.

5 **Those who suffer need compassionate ministry.** Injured and disabled Tamil fighters need to find a new place in society, and injured and disabled government soldiers need rehabilitation and new jobs. Orphans and widows need compassionate care, and those who fled their homes need a chance to return and rebuild. Malnutrition, abortion (especially of females), abuse, and child prostitution all affect children. Up to 700,000 Sri Lankan women work abroad, and endure the pain of leaving their children in order to provide for their family.

6 **Most Christians live in the urban areas of Colombo and Jaffna, and on the northwest coast.** Pray for recent efforts to spread the Christian witness into every administrative division of Sri Lanka. The Buddhist and Hindu communities have new Christians among them, and need ministers who will serve in these humble, challenging rural environments. Pray especially for:

- *The Lanka Tamil community,* who have lived over 1,000 years in Jaffna and on the east coast. Pray for their churches to be forces that evangelize Sri Lanka, rather than forces that push for divisions based on ethnic identity.

- *The estate Tamils,* who descend from 19th- and 20th-century migrant workers. They are poor, and other groups look down on them. Some have turned to Christ.

- *The 25,000 villages* without a church. Many have no Christian witness. The war-torn areas of the north and east have particularly great need.

- *The unreached peoples.* The Moors (Muslim traders, officials, or farmers), the Malays (Muslims, who mix their faith with other religions), and the "Kaffirs" (descended from African slaves brought by the Portuguese) need the gospel. The educated Buddhists, the coastal fishing communities, and the Tamil and Sinhala militants, all need specific outreach. Several tribal groups (including Sri Lanka's original inhabitants, the Veddah) remain unreached.

Syria

Asia

Pop 22.5 million. **Capital** Damascus (2.6 mill).
Christians 1.4 mill. *Evangelical Christians* 24,000.
Largest Religion Muslim.
Fastest Growing Religion Christian.

Largest Ethnic Groups Syrian Arab (67%), Alawi (7.9%), Bedouin (7.1%), Kurd (6.7%), Palestinian (3.1%), Druze (2.2%). As many as 1.8 million Iraqi refugees fled to Syria in the 2000s. Around 2 million Syrians (along with most of the Iraqis) fled their own country during the Syrian civil war. The figures do not account for these movements.
Official Language Arabic. **All Languages** 22.

Economy Agriculture, oil, and tourism provided income before the war. Even the nominal economic progress of the last decade was halted by civil war. Widespread damage to infrastructure, cities, and homes will now require extensive rebuilding.
Politics An ancient civilization. Damascus is known as the oldest continuously inhabited city in the world. In the modern era, Syria gained independence from France in 1946. Continuous upheavals followed until a 1970 coup Led afterwards by military leaders from the Alawite minority group. Political opposition is limited. 2011 protests met with violent government response, and by 2012 escalated into civil war with no clear end in sight.

1 **The anti-regime protests of 2011 led to a bloody civil war.** Over 120,000 died, more than 2 million fled as refugees to nearby countries, and the strife continues. Government forces bombed city neighbourhoods and carried out mass killings. Opposition forces reacted with their own bombings and violence. Use of chemical weapons resulted in strong international condemnation. Pray for an end to the violence, and for solutions that will allow Syrians a chance to rebuild their lives and their nation.

2 **Syrian Christian minorities** enjoyed freedom and stability in the past. The Orthodox and Catholic Churches existed here before Islam, and still have many godly members. Protestant numbers are small, but churches did grow. The government allowed foreign Christian workers to minister among Christians under the national Church. But the civil war has almost completely destroyed the Christian presence in some areas. Some radical Muslim groups want to erase Christianity from Syria, and in some places they intimidate, persecute, and even murder Christians. Massive numbers of Christians have left the country.

3 **God used the faith and devotion of the early Church in Antioch (in Syria)** in His mission to the Gentiles (Acts 13). Before the war, most modern Syrian cities had an evangelical presence. Pray that all believers might grow in godliness, and reach out to those around them. Pray for a future where skilled Christians with humble hearts can have a large role in efforts to rebuild the country, and in efforts to reach the Arab world. Pray for a return of Syrian evangelicals to their homeland.

 Unreached peoples to pray for:
- *The Sunni Arab majority.* Most have never heard the gospel.
- *The Alawite minority* (an offshoot of Islam), who have influence in the army and politics.
- *The Druze* (south). A few believers now exist in this group, a secretive offshoot of Islam that was difficult to contact.
- *The Kurds* (north and northwest). Some are Orthodox Christian, but most are Sunni Muslim. They respond more openly to the gospel than most Arabs.
- *The millions of Syrian refugees.* When refugees from Iraq fled to Syria to escape war, some were open to the gospel message. Pray that Syrians abroad might respond to the gospel in the same way.

Tajikistan

Asia

Pop 7.1 million. **Capital** Dushanbe (716,000).
Christians 74,000. *Evangelical Christians* 7,000 (most are ethnic Slavs or Germans, and expatriates).
Largest Religion Muslim.
Fastest Growing Religion Muslim.

Largest Ethnic Groups The majority of the non-indigenous population left in the 1990s due to civil war. Tajik (65.9%), Uzbek (22.8%), Russian (2.1%), Shughni (1.4%), Kyrgyz (1.4%), Tatar (1.4%).
Official Language Tajik. **All Languages** 33.

Economy Mineral and hydro-electric potential. The poorest former-USSR state. Soviet collapse and the civil war that followed severely damaged the economy. Criminal networks prosper while most live in poverty. Dependent on external aid for development.
Politics The northeastern edge of the Persian Empire for much of its history. Russian colonial rule from the mid-19th century. Civil war lasted from Soviet collapse until 1997. A republic with an elected president and parliament, though elections not agreed internationally to be free and fair.

---

1 **The civil war** left an unforgettable mark on the nation. 83% of the population still live below the poverty line. Prisoners, the elderly, widows, and orphans face the greatest risks. The country needs relief-and-development work, as well as education and business training. Pray for sensitive Christian ministry that can address the great social and spiritual needs. Ask God to call more long-term personnel, especially from among Iranian believers who have an ethnic relationship with the Tajiks.

2 **The Christian population** massively declined as people fled the country during the civil war (1990s). Most Christians were (and still are) Russian Orthodox. Praise God for the birth of the Tajik Church. Only about a thousand now follow Christ, but the numbers continue to grow! Multi-ethnic congregations exist in a few cities, but the majority rural population remain unreached. The government prohibits or restricts religious teaching, publishing, and evangelism. Pray for Christians to find ways to teach and minister, even under the harsh restrictions.

Islam is the religion of 94% of the population, but most people also practise folk superstitions and Zoroastrian beliefs (ancient Iranian religion). Because Tajikistan is close to Iran and Afghanistan, some more radical Muslims cross the borders and promote extremist teachings. Pray that their goals might be thwarted, and that many Muslims will have opportunities to discover Christ.

 Pray for indigenous peoples with little opportunity to hear the gospel. Pray for God to use the Christian radio and satellite TV programmes in Farsi, Russian, and a few other languages.

- *Tajiks* (13 million across Central Asia). For almost 1,000 years, no outreach to them existed. In addition to the 1,000 Tajik believers in Tajikistan, Tajik believers also live in Afghanistan, Pakistan, and Uzbekistan. Pray for godly Tajik churches, and for job opportunities for believers. Many Christians move away to find work, which drains the church leadership.

- *Uzbeks* (around 1.7 million). A number of Uzbek believers live in Tajikistan, but there are almost no Uzbek churches to reach out to their own people.

- *The mountain peoples* (east). The 6 unreached Ismaili Muslim peoples have never been reached.

Thailand

Asia

Pop 68.1 million. **Capital** Bangkok (Bangkok/Thonburi greater area: 7 mill).
Christians 750,000. *Evangelical Christians* 307,000.
Largest Religion Buddhist.
Fastest Growing Religion Christian.
Largest Ethnic Groups Thai (78.4%, 4 main peoples), East Asian (10.8%, mostly Thai-speaking Chinese), Malay (6.1%, 8 peoples, mostly in the far south), Tibeto-Burman (1.2%, 17 peoples), Mon-Khmer (1.2%, 25 peoples), Tai (0.9%, 16 peoples). [These numbers do not account for over 1 million Burmese migrants (from many ethnicities), nor the high number of Cambodian migrants.]
Official Language Thai. **All Languages** 85.

Economy A strong economy based on agriculture, industry, and related exports. World's largest exporter of rice. Tourism is a major aspect of the economy. Sadly, the sex trade and drug trafficking also generate enormous wealth.
Politics A kingdom since the 13th century. In the modern constitutional monarchy, the popular king plays a strong role in society. The powerful army dominated politics and commerce for 60 years. Recent governments have been civilian and democratically elected. Corruption is widespread, and rivalry between the two main parties has often left the country paralyzed. A military coup in 2014 leaves long-term political future unresolved. Thailand also has disputes with Cambodia and with nearby Myanmar.

 Thailand was traditionally a stable country in a troubled region. Now a power struggle between political parties, the military, and the royal family creates ongoing violence and instability. Violent activity among Muslims in the south at times brings further upheaval. Widespread corruption in business, politics, the military, and the police allows dishonest people to make themselves rich by oppressing others. Thailand means "Land of the Free", because it remained free when Western powers colonized the countries around it. Yet the land remains captive to Buddhism, traditional culture, spirit worship, and even occult practices. Pray for spiritual breakthrough, so that the Thai might truly be free in the Lord Jesus.

2 **Thai Christians remain around 1% of the population,** even after 400 years of missionary work. Most of Thailand's churches are small (30-50 members). More than 6,000 of Thailand's 7,415 subdistricts have no church! Nearly half of Protestants come from tribal groups (less than 5% of Thailand's population), and not ethnic Thais. A lack of Thai leadership in the churches is one reason for slow church growth. Praise God that national leaders now have a bold goal to reach every one of Thailand's 80,000 villages and neighbourhoods with the gospel! Pray for their plans: a national prayer network, leadership development, extensive research, community development ministry, all in addition to evangelism. Many church and mission leaders feel Thailand is ready for a breakthrough of church growth.

3 **Foreign expressions of Christianity dominated the churches** for a long time. In a recent survey of non-Christian Thai, 89% said they could not understand the Christian message. Pray for Thai Christians to develop music, art, architecture, and styles of worship and leadership that will make sense within Thai culture, all under the Holy Spirit's guidance. Thai culture is tolerant and relaxed, and this can pull people away from the need for holy living. Pray for believers to develop lifestyles of prayer, Scripture reading, witness, and ministry.

4 **The extensive sex trade** (focused in Bangkok, Pattaya, Phuket, Hat Yai) is deeply integrated into Thai society. Millions of people gain from this "industry". Some estimate that up to 2.8 million people engage in sex work, and possibly 10% of all tourist money is spent on it. Pray for:

- *The women involved* (and the much smaller numbers of men). Some desperate families sell girls into the sex trade for money. Other women enter because they hope for a better income or a rich foreign boyfriend/husband. Leaving the trade becomes almost impossible. Risk of abuse and disease is high. Everyone involved needs the redemption and unconditional love that Christ offers.

- *Those who gain.* Pray for moral conviction to fall on the corrupt police and officials, the traffickers, the Chinese-Thai mafia, the owners of businesses where it occurs, and relatives who sell girls into sexual slavery. The Thai men who pay for sex far outnumber the hundreds of thousands of foreign sex tourists. Pray for the freedom these men need from this vile practice.

- *The agencies that minister* to those caught in the trade. Some provide care for prostitutes, or assistance for those who want out. Other groups work against sex trafficking.

5 **Missions have plenty of freedom** for ministry. Long-term and short-term workers can fill roles in evangelism, church planting, Bible teaching, English teaching, and compassionate ministry to the most vulnerable parts of society. 29 languages still lack Scriptures, and 10 of those need translation programmes. Pray for effective partnership between foreign missionaries and Thai believers, as expatriates hand over leadership to indigenous workers.

6 **Particular groups for prayer:**

- *The most vulnerable.* Over 1 million may serve as child labourers, and tens of thousands of children live on the streets. Thailand's HIV/AIDS infection rate is Asia's highest by far (officially around 700,000 people suffer, but actual figures could be double). 1.2 million refugees come from Myanmar alone and can easily be exploited.

- *Buddhist monks* (300,000). Some true seekers exist among this group, who hold positions of high regard in their society.

- *Muslims* (5.3 million). This is the only major Muslim population in Southeast Asia open for evangelism. Yet after years of hard work, only a few small communities of believers exist among them.

- **Tribal peoples** have come to Christ in significant numbers! Pray for the remaining unreached tribes in the east. Opium poppies are a profitable cash crop for most northern tribes, even though the narcotics trade leads to instability and violence.

- **The Chinese-Thai community** has influence and wealth that could be a great force for evangelism! Currently strong links exist in the areas of prostitution, gambling, and drugs. Chinese-Thai Christians are a minority in the Church, especially in leadership.

Timor Leste   *Asia*

Pop 1.2 million. **Capital** Dili (174,000).
Christians 1 mill. *Evangelical Christians* 27,000.
Largest Religion Christian.
Fastest Growing Religion Christian.
Largest Ethnic Groups Timorese (95.9%, Largest peoples: Mambai, Tetum, Makasai, Tokode, others), Indonesian/ Javanese (3.5%).
Official Languages Portuguese (understood by 13.5%), Tetum and its dialects (understood by 91%). Bahasa Indonesia also common (understood by 43%). **All Languages** 19.
Economy Damaged by years of neglect, then destroyed in vengeance after the vote for Independence in 1999.

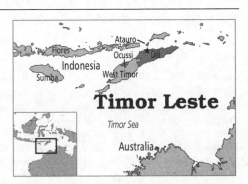

The new nation will take decades to rebuild. Most of the population live in poverty. Oil and gas deposits, shared with Australia, are a potential future revenue source.
Politics Portuguese rule (1511–1974). Followed by civil war, then Indonesian invasion which directly caused 100,000 deaths over the 25-year occupation. International pressure led to independence (1999), then armed militia (with military support) looted and destroyed 75% of the country's infrastructure and economy before the UN intervened. Finally independent in 2002, Timor now faces internal strife and violent outbreaks among factions. The 2012 elections brought a new president and prime minister to power, and the UN peacekeeping mission ended.

---

1 **Timor appears caught in a downward spiral** of poverty, poor health, and illiteracy. The poor suffer most from the violence and destruction brought by various groups. Every aspect of life needs transformation. Education, job creation, healthcare, and leadership training all need major investments. The Indonesian military and the Timorese militia left a legacy of hatred and trauma that will take decades to heal. Many children and young people especially have lost everything, including parents. Large numbers roam the streets, or join dangerous gangs. Pray for peace for Timor, and for reconciliation among the many divided factions.

2 **Most Timorese are Christian,** but many do not understand the gospel. The Catholic Church grew rapidly as a symbol of national resistance to Muslim Indonesians. But traditional Spiritism remains strong, mixed with Christianity. Protestant churches came more recently, and growth is slower. Indonesian immigrants planted the Reformed Church and many Timorese joined, but Timorese view Protestants with suspicion since they originate from Indonesia. Pray for

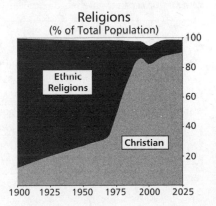

Religions
(% of Total Population)

Ethnic Religions

Christian

1900 1925 1950 1975 2000 2025

all Christians to renounce any associations with spirit worship. A New Testament exists in the Tetum language, but 13 other languages have no Scripture at all.

3 **None of the 19 indigenous people groups is well evangelized.** Pray for pioneer church planters. Pray for evangelical churches to grow in every people and in every area. Holistic ministry is the best option for Timor because people have many physical and emotional needs. Government emphasis on development opens the door for professionals in education and the legal profession. Christian Vision (UK/Brazil) and Transformation Alliance (Singapore) both seek to impact every village with practical and spiritual assistance. Many NGOs assist with Timor's needs, but the unstable situation causes constant disruptions and evacuations. Pray for healthy partnerships between expatriate workers and Timorese church leaders.

Turkey   *Asia*

Pop 75.7 million. **Capital** Ankara (3.9 mill).
Christians 163,000. *Evangelical Christians* 7,000. Most Christians in Turkey are not ethnically Turkish or Kurdish. Most of the evangelicals are ethnic Turks and Kurds from a Muslim background, plus some ethnic Assyrians, Armenians, and expatriate evangelicals who live in Turkey.
Largest Religion Muslim.
Fastest Growing Religion Non-religious.

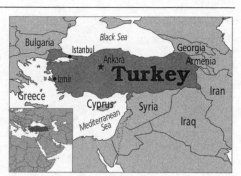

Largest Ethnic Groups Turkic peoples (71.8%, a Central Asian people that conquered and absorbed the indigenous peoples of the land from the 11th century onward), Iranian-Median (21.1%, mostly Kurds in east and southeast Anatolia), Eurasian peoples (2.8%), Arab (2.5%, near Syria).
Official Language Turkish. **All Languages** 45.

Economy A mix of traditional agriculture, industry and commerce, and tourism. Turkey has the world's 16th-largest economy, but also high inflation and unemployment. It is the richest, most developed of the 6 Turkic nations, but among the poorer nations in Europe. The east of the country is less developed. Turkey tried for years, unsuccessfully, to get into the EU.

Politics The Turkish Ottoman Empire once stretched across North Africa, Arabia, Western Asia, and Southeast Europe. Its final end (WWI) led to the formation of modern Turkey, and the famous leader Ataturk formed a republic in 1923. First a single party state, then a multi-party democracy with occasional military coups. The military still has strong influence. Turkey had conflict with Greece (over a divided Cyprus), and a long conflict with Kurdish separatists (lessened since 1999).

---

1 **Turkey is a nation torn in different directions.** It crosses 2 continents: 3% is Europe (Thrace), and 97% is Asia (Anatolia). It has economic links with Europe, cultural links with Central Asia, and sits near conflict areas such as Iraq/Syria, the Balkans, and the Caucasus. Turkey is a secular state, yet to be Turk is to be Muslim! The constitution, courts, and military are meant to uphold religious freedom, but even some secular Turks can be as anti-Christian (and anti-Western, anti-minority) as Islamists. Some of the population wish to join the EU and accept the required reforms, but others want a stronger role in the Middle East. Turkey's strategic location has made it important throughout history. It could serve as a powerful and stable mediator in a region of great conflict.

2 **For over 1,000 years, this region was a stronghold of Christianity.** Later it became a centre for the spread of Islam. The Christian population declined from 22% in 1900 to 0.21% in 2010. Few of today's 73 million Turkish Muslims have ever truly heard the gospel. The ancient Churches survived until the beginning of the 20th century, but massacres (Armenians), severe persecutions (Assyrians), and emigration (Greeks) removed most of them from the land. Pray for a reviving work of the Holy Spirit among the 130,000 Christians from these ancient confessions who still remain in Turkey.

3 **Give praise for the slow but steady growth** of Turkish evangelical Christianity. Turkish and Kurdish believers probably numbered around 10 in 1960, but rose to around 4,000 by 2010. Many hoped for or expected greater growth of the Church. But while small in number, it grew stronger and more mature. The growth of the 1990s and early 2000s slowed down when faced with spiritual, legal, and cultural opposition. Pray for the evangelism and church planting of the past generation to carry on!

4 **Ask God to break down the barriers of prejudice, mistrust, and dislike of Christianity.** Muslim Turkey had more than 1,000 years of bitter wars with "Christian" Europe. Some feel it would be an act of treason to become Christian. Many stay away from Christ because of family pressure, police intimidation, threats from Turkish nationalists, or threats from Muslim extremists. Some live as secret believers. The murder of a Catholic priest (2006), and the torture and murders of 1 expat and 2 Turkish Christians (2007), showed the intensity of opposition. The 2 Turks were the first converts from Islam to die as martyrs in the modern Turkish Church. Greater church growth will probably lead to greater opposition. Pray against a spirit of fear. Pray for local believers to persist in following Jesus, whatever the cost.

5 **Kurds (up to 15 million)** live throughout Turkey, and are the majority population in 16 of 81 provinces (east, southeast). The long conflict with the Turkish army left 30,000 people dead, thousands of Kurdish villages destroyed, and millions without homes. Legal reforms improved the situation for Kurds in Turkey. The government now recognizes their language, and allows Kurdish newspapers. Pray for an end to all conflict, and for a fair resolution of the issues. Some Kurds follow Christ. In mixed areas, they join Turkish fellowships. Pray also for a healthy Kurdish expression of the Church.

6 **Other unreached peoples and areas.** Two satellite TV channels potentially reach millions with the gospel. Christian websites in Turkish provide information for Muslim seekers and discipleship material for new believers. A Turkish Bible correspondence course, telephone hotlines, and online chat rooms, staffed by Turkish believers, receive many enquiries. Ask God for a growing fellowship of believers in each of the 81 provinces. Most provinces have none. Pray also for:

- *The ethnic Muslim minorities.* The largest are Azeri, Gagauz, Crimean Tatar, and Karakalpak. Many stay isolated in their own communities, and are difficult to reach.
- *The Alevi* (up to 25% of Turkey's population). They follow Islam, but have high regard for Jesus.
- *Refugees.* Over 620,000 Iranians remained in Turkey after they fled the 1979 Islamic revolution. African and Asian refugees use Turkey as a way to enter Europe. They face many hardships and have few rights, and need Christian ministry among them.
- *The Arab minority.* A number are Christian, but the majority are Muslim. Their numbers increased, as nearly 800,000 refugees from the Syrian civil war fled to Turkey.

Christian expatriates engage in teaching, study or business, or enter on tourist visas. Few have ever lived in eastern Anatolia, the Black Sea coast, or the interior provinces. These are some of the hardest places for Christians to minister. More than 50 agencies, with around 1,350 expatriates from over 20 countries, seek to bring blessing to the Turkish people. Pray for each worker to have a good testimony that glorifies Christ, and shows love and respect for the people of Turkey.

Turkmenistan
Asia

Pop 5.2 million. **Capital** Ashgabat (651,000).
Christians 95,000. *Evangelical Christians* 1,700.
Largest Religion Muslim.
Fastest Growing Religion Muslim.

Largest Ethnic Groups Turkmen (82.1%), Uzbek (9.4%), Russian (2.2%), Iranian-Median (2.2%). Ethnic minorities in decline as groups from the former USSR return to their homelands.
Official Language Turkmen. Uses Latin script since 1994.
All Languages 9.

Economy Famous for carpets, horses, camels, and desert, but oil and gas are major sources of wealth. Since 80% is desert, future water supply is a challenge. Rural areas especially poor.
Politics Nomadic, tribal past. United as a country (1881) under Russian Tsarist rule, then a Soviet Republic until independence (1992). The former Communist leader became a dictator, with control of the army, police, the justice system, the economy, and the press. His death (2006) opened the door for change, with some signs of movement towards a more open and less repressive system.

1 **The former dictator** (Niyazov) named himself "the father of all Turkmen", and people followed him as a kind of cult leader. He spent money on elaborate monuments to himself rather than on development for the people. His death brought hope for positive change, and Turkmen citizens may now travel abroad and within the country more easily. Pray that the new government will respect the human rights and religious freedom guaranteed by the constitution.

2 **Ethnic Turkmen Christians** are few, but after independence their number grew from 1 or 2 people to as many as 1,000! Most Christians are Russian, Ukrainian, or Armenian. The authorities expelled almost every foreign Christian, and they exiled, imprisoned, beat, or fined several national pastors. The persecution against any non-Orthodox Christian activity brought growth, greater unity, and a strong spirituality. The Church continues to grow despite the constant threats. Pray for believers to stand firm in their faith, and to win others to Christ.

3 **Expatriate Christians** concerned for Turkmenistan continue to pray from a distance, and to prepare for the country to open again. Pray that humanitarian organizations will have greater freedom to enter, and to bring both practical and spiritual blessing. Pray for translators to finish the Turkmen Old Testament, and to finalize work on the New Testament. Thank God for Christian broadcasts in Russian on satellite TV, and pray for Turkmen-language Christian TV broadcasts to begin soon.

4 **The diaspora.** Pray for the work of Christians (Turkmen and foreign) among the hundreds of thousands of Turkmen in Iraq and Afghanistan. Pray for similar work to begin among the almost completely unevangelized Turkmen in Iran, Uzbekistan, Syria, Russia, and Tajikistan.

United Arab Emirates

Pop 4.7 million. **Capital** Abu Dhabi (685,000).
Christians 402,000. *Evangelical Christians* 61,000.
Largest Religion Muslim.
Fastest Growing Religion Non-religious.

Largest Ethnic Groups All figures estimated. The massive presence of expatriate workers (often illegal) makes accurate figures difficult to obtain. The non-Arab population may be higher than reported. Arab (56%, Gulf Arabs are 24%), South Asian (23.2%, including Indian, Pakistani, Bangladeshi, Sri Lankan), Other groups (20.8%, including Filipino, Iranian, European, East Asian).

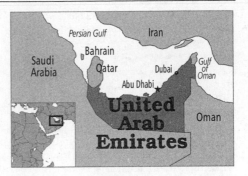

Official Language Arabic. **All Languages** 36.

Economy Unbelievable transformation in just one generation. Oil wealth drives the economy and massive spending on development, but projects rely heavily on migrant labour. Overinvestment (especially in Dubai) created massive debts.

Politics An independent confederation of monarchies since 1971. First steps towards a very limited democracy now underway. The Sheikh of Abu Dhabi is president of the Supreme Council, which rules the country. Federal laws apply to the whole country, and each emirate also has its own regulations.

---

1 **Oil wealth** transformed much of the United Arab Emirates (UAE) from a poor, rural region to a haven and playground for the world's ultra-rich. Now it branches out to business and finance, as well as tourism. While those at the top live with incredible wealth, millions of migrant labourers often work in terrible conditions for low pay. Injustice, human rights violations, and human trafficking are significant challenges.

2 **Rapid changes created a social and cultural crisis** in the UAE, and the younger generation must navigate it wisely. Will their Islamic heritage merely be replaced by selfish pursuit of material goods? Pray that new opportunities will create a spiritual hunger for the truth! Major faith groups mostly enjoy religious freedom. Praise God for this, and pray that the land and buildings allowed for Christians would become sites where God builds up the body and launches His people out to serve!

3 **Increased numbers of people came to faith in Jesus** from many backgrounds! This includes Arabs, South Asians, East Asians, and others. However, expatriates who evangelize or distribute Christian literature unwisely still face arrest, prison, or deportation. Pray that believers would demonstrate Christ in their words and deeds, with discernment and confidence. The Iranian, Pakistani/Afghan, Bengali, Somali, and Sudanese communities in the UAE all have few if any believers among them. The indigenous Arab population has limited access to the gospel. Pray that the humble witness of domestic labourers and expatriate professionals might lead many Gulf Arab employers to Jesus. Strategic prayer networks focused on the Gulf region play a crucial role in a future spiritual harvest.

Uzbekistan

Pop 27.8 million. **Capital** Tashkent (2.2 mill).
Christians 208,000. *Evangelical Christians* 85,000.
Largest Religion Muslim.
Fastest Growing Religion Muslim.

Largest Ethnic Groups Uzbek (78.4%, some are actually ethnic Tajik), Tajik (4.8%), Kazakh (4.1%), Tatar (3%), Russian (2.5%), Karakalpak (1.8%).
Official Language Uzbek. **All Languages** 39.

Economy Self-sufficient, with oil, natural gas, and mineral deposits. Also agriculture, as the world's 5th-largest cotton producer. Future water supply is a serious issue. But corruption leads to a stagnant economy, and most people struggle. Many young men seek work in Russia. A main transhipment nation for the drug trade from Afghanistan to Russia (into Europe).

Politics Samarkand was 14th-century capital of Tamerlane's vast Mongol/Turkic Empire. Russian colonial rule (1865-1917). Independent as a democratic republic in 1991. But the autocratic dictator holds control as firmly as in Communist times. Torture of dissidents and massacre of protestors (2005) brought international attention and condemnation. Close political ties to Russia.

 Uzbekistan is the strategic key for all of Central Asia, and tensions remain high between the post-Soviet regime and the Islamist movements (most radical in the Fergana Valley). Much of the population is tired of poverty, corruption, and failure to make economic progress, and Islamists attract jobless young men. Pray for genuine change, and leadership that governs for the sake of the people. Pray for the true peace only Jesus can give.

Most Christians come from minority groups, and large numbers have returned to their ancestral homelands since independence. Evangelical Christianity, especially Pentecostals/charismatics, grows among those who remain. Russians and Koreans have some freedom to evangelize their own people, but the government punishes any who attempt to reach Uzbeks or other Muslim peoples. Tashkent is the Islamic capital of Central Asia, in numbers and influence.

Uzbek believers continue to increase despite opposition from the government, the local Muslim leaders, and the community (family and neighbours). From possibly none a generation ago, more than 10,000 have probably now come to faith! The government expelled almost all expatriate Christians, and shut down most foreign agencies. This was a mixed blessing, as it forced the indigenous Church to unite, to mature, and to stand firm. Pray for godly Uzbek leaders, and for Bible training for this young Church.

Uzbekistan's government heavily persecutes the Church, especially Uzbek churches. Officials seize property, burn Bibles, expel Christian students, dismiss Christian employees, and arrest believers. Registration for churches is nearly impossible, so a well-networked union of house churches developed. Pray for Christians who face pressure to betray fellow believers to the authorities. Pray for those persecuted and in prison, that God may give them strength and boldness.

 The unreached. Almost every Muslim people group in Uzbekistan is less than 0.1% Christian. Pray specifically for:

- *Karakalpaks* (south of the Aral Sea). Most follow Sunni Islam, with strong Sufi (mystic) influence. Persecution is most intense in their area, but in the regional capital (Nukus) the Church grows quickly through underground house churches! Uzbeks in this region also come to Christ. Pray for completion of the Bible in Karakalpak.

- *The Tajiks.* They live as a majority in both Samarkand and Bukhara, with few believers among them. The government discriminates against them (they are an Iranian-Median people, rather than Turkic).

Vietnam

Asia

Pop 89 million. **Capital** Hanoi (2.8 mill).
Christians 8.4 mill. *Evangelical Christians* 1.6 mill.
Largest Religion Buddhist.
Fastest Growing Religion Christian.

Largest Ethnic Groups Vietnamese (84%, mostly coastal people with large cultural differences between northern and southern Vietnamese), Mon-Khmer (4.3%, 53 peoples), Zhuang (3%), Thai-Dai (1.9%), Hmong/Miao (1.5%, 8 peoples), Cham (1.1%, 9 peoples).
Official Language Vietnamese. **All Indigenous Languages** 106.

Economy Decades of war followed by Marxist economics. The loss of Soviet financial backing left the economy greatly weakened. Reforms since 1986 modernized the economy, and brought about a middle class. Large gap between urban wealth and rural poverty. World's 2nd-largest rice exporter.

Politics Independent from France in 1954, followed by 3 decades of war. North and South unified again under the Communist Party in 1975. The Party still has control over state policy and activity. Human rights violations continue, despite some improvement. Religious and ethnic minority groups face opposition. Economic growth and new wealth present new challenges to the Marxist ideals.

---

1 **Vietnam is one of the few Communist nations left in the world.** Its people suffer with continued oppression and increased social problems such as drug addiction, AIDS, prostitution, and exploitation of children. This land has known great violence, and much division and mistrust exist among its peoples. The deepest spiritual loyalty in Vietnam is to worship of ancestors, even more than to Communism, and even more than to the mixture of Buddhism, Taoism, and Confucianism traditionally practised by Vietnamese. Christians face hard questions as they try to handle this issue biblically. Pray that the light of the gospel will banish all darkness.

2 **Economic progress continues to open up the country.** Most of the population was born after the Vietnam War, and younger generations have more interest in wealth and the outside world than they do in Communist ideas or teachings. Many respond to the gospel. At the same time, the new openness gives opportunity for greed and pursuit of riches, as well as false religions. Pray that Christians might clearly proclaim the Truth, particularly among the masses of young professionals.

3 **A growing, witnessing Church** has emerged from years of persecution. Growth happens among Catholics and Protestants, new congregations and old ones, registered and unregistered churches, and different people groups. Many in the Vietnamese diaspora also became believers. Praise God for this! Pray for the 3 main groups where the Church grows:

- *Among the mountain tribal peoples* of central and southern Vietnam, despite cruel persecution by the government.

- *Among the Hmong* and other minority peoples of northern Vietnam. Christians grew from no believers in 1988 to estimates of up to 400,000 in 2010! The radio broadcasting work of FEBC (Far East Broadcasting Company) contributes greatly to this movement.
- *Among the ethnic Vietnamese (Kinh),* though on a smaller scale. A Christmas gathering in Ho Chi Minh City (2009) attracted 40,000 people.

4 **All open Protestant missionary work** ended in 1975. Before that, the Christian & Missionary Alliance worked for 64 years. Other agencies came in the 1950s, and by 1974 over 280 missionaries worked in South Vietnam. Those years of sowing the gospel now reap a good harvest! Current economic development offers opportunity for Christians in business, English teaching, and aid projects. Pray for Vietnam to become fully open to Christian workers, and for many to respond.

5 **Suffering and persecution** dominate the story of Christianity in Vietnam, together with faith and perseverance. Some improvement came since 2005, but government opposition and persecution continues to affect both Catholics and Protestants. Pray for the hundreds of Christians that endure harsh conditions in prison. Registration of churches remains a difficult and divisive issue for the Church. Registered churches must deal with strict regulations, while unregistered churches often face police interference (breaking up meetings and detaining leaders). Pray for a solution to this issue that best unifies and builds the Church of Vietnam.

6 **The Church urgently needs leadership development and theological training.** The rapid growth of evangelicals is wonderful, and now we must pray for creative, sustainable, and effective ways to develop a new generation of Christian leaders. Many pastors already carry responsibility for multiple congregations, and lack the time and money for full-time training. Both academic and informal training programmes face government restrictions, as well as other challenges. Beyond theology, believers need training in leadership areas such as management, finance, accounting, and vocational skills.

7 **Pray for the less reached.** Many ethnic minorities lack the Word of God in their language, but praise God the government recently allowed printing of the Bible in 4 minority languages (as well as Vietnamese)!

- *The northern Vietnamese.* This region had a longer Communist presence, and remains less evangelized than southern Vietnam. But God is at work, and a Church now grows in the north!
- *The Muslim Cham and Buddhist Khmer* of the Mekong Delta. Greater response to the gospel has come to these peoples in Cambodia, but only a few follow Christ in Vietnam.
- *The northern minority peoples.* Most follow Buddhism or tribal religions. Christian radio is a vital ministry, but only some have programmes in their language.
- *Followers of the Cao Dai and Hoa Hao religions.* Pray that Christians might learn more about these groups' unique beliefs and cultures, and reach them with the gospel.
- *Communist party members,* government officials, and military personnel. These people are pillars to Vietnamese society, with few Christians among them.

Yemen

Pop 24.3 million. **Capital** Sana'a (2.3 mill).
Christians 19,000. *Evangelical Christians* 4,300.
Largest Religion Muslim.
Fastest Growing Religion Muslim.

Largest Ethnic Groups Arab (97%, in over 1,700 clans and tribes), Immigrant and refugee communities (2.6%, Somali, Ethiopian).
Official Language Arabic. **All Languages** 14.

Economy Poorest country in the Arab world. Foreign earnings come from oil and from remittances (from Yemenis who work in Saudi and the West). High unemployment. Oil and water supplies continue to decrease, a huge challenge for a country with rapid population growth.

Politics A history of wars and conquests. The north was part of Ottoman Empire until 1918, then an isolated state until 1962. Aden (the south) was ruled by Britain until independence (1967). The 2 countries united in 1990, with the north dominant. A presidential government with some democracy, but the political situation remains fragile with pressures from inside and outside the country.

---

1 **Yemenis find life in Christ** through radio, Bible distribution, careful witness, and dreams and visions from the Lord! Believers meet secretly and only in small groups. They often face dangerous opposition. Praise God for these followers of Jesus. Pray for them as they learn how to honour their culture and family while faithfully serving the Lord.

2 **Yemen suffered in recent decades** from 3 civil wars, tribal conflicts, and war in nearby countries. Tensions grow between the Shi'a and Sunni Muslim communities. Tribal identity remains strong, while government authority is weak. Rivalries between tribes escalate through kidnapping, crime, and deliberate destruction of property. Yemen was once famous for frankincense, myrrh, and coffee. Now the mild drug *qat* dominates agriculture. Workers waste around 20 million hours per day chewing *qat*, which hurts the economy as well as social and family life. Pray for new ways to care for Yemen's economy and its people.

3 **Christianity was once strong here,** but was almost completely erased by the 7th-century Muslim conquest. Traditional stories say that Shem founded the city of Sana'a, and the Queen of Sheba who sought wisdom from King Solomon reigned in Yemen. Most Christians in Yemen are refugees from Ethiopia or expatriate workers from the West, South and East Asia, and other Arab lands. Opportunities to serve God exist in business, education, health, and development programmes. Pray for more believers who will live and serve in this difficult land, with sacrifice and love.

4 **Yemen remains one of the world's least-evangelized countries.** Pray for:
- *The northern tribes,* which include the people of Sana'a (capital) and the peoples of the northern mountains and northeastern deserts. A number live as nomads.
- *The southern Yemenis,* the key cities being Aden, Taiz, and Ibb.
- *The Mahri* (fishermen), who live along the border of Oman, and remain isolated from society and modern life.
- *The Socotra islanders,* who were Christian until the 17th century. Today, no known Christians live on these Indian Ocean islands.

- ***Yemeni women.*** Their life is difficult, with limited opportunities for education or activities outside the home. How will they hear about Jesus, and learn to live for Him?
- ***Residents and refugees from Somalia*** (possibly over 500,000). A few follow Christ, but most remain unevangelized.

QUOTES ON MISSION

The history of missions is the history of answered prayer.
Samuel Zwemer

If Jesus be God and died for me, then no sacrifice can be too great for me to make for him.
C. T. Studd

The Spirit of Christ is the Spirit of Missions, and the nearer we get to Him the more intensely missionary we must become.
Henry Martyn

He is no fool who gives what he cannot keep to gain what he cannot lose.
Jim Eliot

All God's giants are weak men who did great things for God because they reckoned that God was with them.
Hudson Taylor

If a commission by an earthly king is considered an honour, how can a commission by a Heavenly King be considered a sacrifice?
David Livingstone

If God has called you to be a missionary, don't stoop to be a king.
Jordan Groom

As long as there are millions destitute of the Word of God and knowledge of Jesus Christ, it will be impossible for me to devote time and energy to those who have both.
J. L. Ewen

The Great Commission is not an option to be considered; it is a command to be obeyed.
Hudson Taylor

The weakness of much current mission work is that we betray the sense that what is yet to be done is greater than what Christ has already done. The world's gravest need is less than Christ's great victory.
P. T. Forsyth

Expect great things from God. Attempt great things for God.
William Carey

Do not pray for easy lives; pray to be stronger men. Do not pray for tasks equal to your powers; pray for powers equal to your tasks. Then, the doing of your work shall be no miracle, but you shall be a miracle.
Bishop Phillips Brooks

I have but one passion – it is He, it is He alone. The world is the field, and the field is the world; and henceforth that country shall be my home where I can be most used in winning souls for Christ.
Count Nikolaus Ludwig Von Zinzendorf

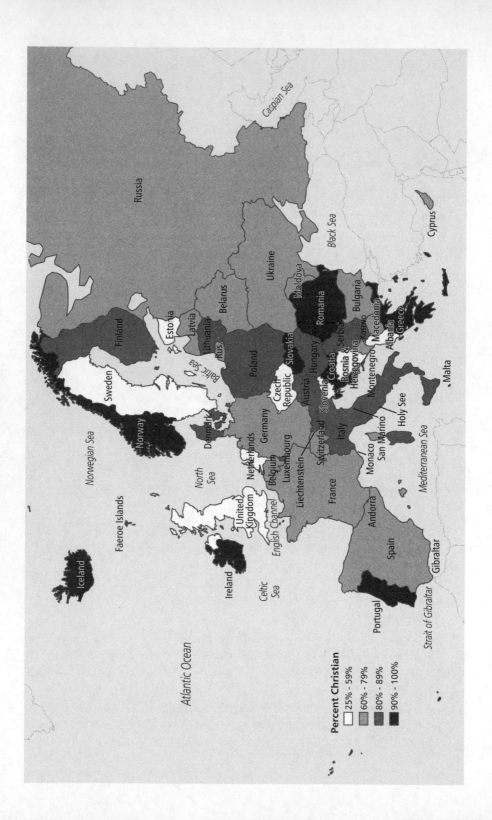

Percent Christian

- [ ] 25% - 59%
- [ ] 60% - 79%
- [ ] 80% - 89%
- [ ] 90% - 100%

EUROPE

Pop 732.8 million.
Christians 522 mill. *Evangelical Christians* 18.3 mill.
Largest Religion Christian.
Fastest Growing Religion Islam.

Indigenous Languages 269 (3.9% of the world's total).
Languages with Scriptures 63 Bibles, 31 New Testaments,
61 Old or New Testament portions. 73 languages have
translation needs.

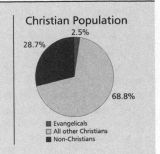

Christian Population

2.5%
28.7%
68.8%

- Evangelicals
- All other Christians
- Non-Christians

The countries of Europe and the entire Russian Federation (including Siberia, which is technically in Asia) make up 17% of the earth's surface, and have 10.6% of the world's population. In 1900, that proportion was 25%. Europe has 61 cities of over 1 million people, 2 of which are over 10 million.

As Europe becomes less religious and more secular, a non-religious worldview or a mixed spirituality dominates many people's belief systems. Christians decline in number, and the rate of decline increases each year. Many that are considered Christian do not actually practise their faith, and probably less than 10% of Europeans regularly attend church.

Europe's ethnic diversity and long history of conflicts shaped much of the political framework of the nations of today. As Europe attempts to be multi-cultural, liberal, and open, it loses much of its life and energy, and its economic situation becomes more difficult. An ageing population, low birth rates among Europeans, and high immigration rates all mean that Europe's future will be very different from its past. Europe desperately needs a revival. The Church must watch and pray!

Albania

Pop 3.2 million. **Capital** Tirana (444,000).

Christians 966,000. *Evangelical Christians* 14,000.
Largest Religion Muslim.
Fastest Growing Religion Muslim.

Largest Ethnic Groups Albanian (91.2%, Tosk in south, Gheg in north, and Aromanian/Vlach), Greek (3.2%), Romani/Gypsy (more than 2.7%), Serb (1.2%), Macedonian (1.1%).
Official Language Albanian. **All Languages** 7.

Economy One of Europe's 2 poorest nations. Some improvement, but poor infrastructure, corruption, and high emigration rates hinder growth.

Politics Communist regime from 1944 to 1991, with a ban on all religions. Multiparty elections held since then, and religious freedom since 1998. Kosovo's independence is an important issue for Albania.

1. **Thank God for His work in this land!** For a long time it was closed to the gospel, but evangelicals grew from nearly zero to several thousand in just a few years. The Albanian Evangelical Alliance (VUSH) now represents and connects more than 160 congregations. The Church has indigenous leadership, nationwide networks, a vision for discipleship and evangelism, and it sends out workers to other lands! And all this came about during a politically and economically unstable time. Many believe that years of devoted prayer for Albania opened the way for ministry here.

2. **Albania faces a long road to recovery** from the destructive effects of atheism and Communism. The chaos and corruption of the 1990s and 2000s showed that to build a healthy and productive society, people must rebuild economically, but also morally and spiritually. Pray that believers might positively impact Albania's government and business culture with biblical ethics.

3. **The religious context remains unclear,** and reliable sources for statistics are difficult to find. Many people claim a religion, but do not practise their faith. Pray that religious tensions in the wider region will not grow here among the 3 main groups (Muslim, Orthodox, Catholic). Islam is the largest religion of Albania (possibly up to 70%). Many Muslims follow a superstitious, folk version of Islam. Pray for Albanian Muslims to encounter the living Christ.

4. **The evangelical Church** needs the most prayer for leadership training. When a Church grows so quickly from nothing in just 2 decades, no biblical leadership models exist to copy, and most believers know very little about the Bible. Orthodox, Catholics, and Protestants worked together to re-translate the New Testament into modern Albanian, and then began work on the Old Testament. Pray for its completion, and for widespread use of the Scriptures!

5. **Missions and ministry.** Almost all mission agencies and national ministries combine practical assistance with sharing the gospel. Many ministries assist the poor and suffering, and provide employment for Christians. Pray for this love in action to profoundly change Albania. Foreign evangelical mission agencies can serve the Albanian Church through training, resource development, and holistic mission. Fewer workers serve here now than in the 1990s, but Albania still needs more. Pray for the Albania Encouragement Project, which networks over 60 agencies that cover every type of ministry.

6

The least-reached minorities:

- *The Bektashi* (a Sufi dervish movement of 600,000) follow beliefs influenced by folk religion and the occult. They worship with a fast-spinning dance. The Sunni Muslims (the majority in Albania) do not accept them. Some became evangelical believers.
- *The Vlach* follow Orthodox Christianity by culture. Society looks down on this group.
- *The Gorani, Golloborda, and Cham* follow Islam by culture. They live in isolation, but some short-term teams began to reach out to them.

Austria

Europe

Pop 8.4 million. **Capital** Vienna (1.7 mill).

Christians 6.9 mill. *Evangelical Christians* 41,000.
Largest Religion Christian.
Fastest Growing Religion Non-religious.
Largest Ethnic Groups Austrian (84.4%), Swiss German (3.4%), German (3.2%), Balkan (3.1%, Bosniak, Croat, Slovene, other), Other European (1.7%).
Official Language German. **All Languages** 20.

Economy Strong tourist, commercial, agricultural, and industrial sectors. Many trade links with Central European economies, especially Germany. Over 10% of the workforce are foreign.
Politics The heart of the Austro-Hungarian Empire until 1918. A multiparty democratic republic and a member of the EU. A neutral buffer state between East and West from 1955 to 1990.

1 Austria is a country of beautiful culture, music, art, and scenery, but it mostly feels spiritually empty. Many believe in God (84%, which is high for Europe), but few know Jesus personally. Large numbers leave the Catholic Church every year, despite the longstanding Catholic culture. Sex scandals among the clergy and the church tax (1% of taxable income) both contribute to this. People do not tend to seek God outside the Catholic Church, so we must pray fervently for the renewal movement in the Catholic Church to grow.

2 The Lutheran and Reformed Churches also decline. The tradition and formal style do not attract young people. Many do not practise their faith, even though some Bible-believing pastors and lay leaders seek to deepen spiritual life of church members. Pray for the Spirit of God to move, and to make these churches a force for the evangelization of Austria.

3 Almost all church growth occurs within evangelical/charismatic churches. Pentecostal churches almost doubled from 2000 to 2010. Prayer movements grew among teenagers and led to an Austrian Prayer Congress of over 1,000 that now meets bi-annually! Even so, evangelicals are only 0.5% of the population. Pray for God to multiply congregations that honour and proclaim the Lord Jesus Christ.

4 Less-reached sections of the population. Austria needs more full-time workers. It is possible that more Austrians serve God outside of Austria than inside it! Foreign workers planted most of the country's evangelical churches. Pray for the Lord of the harvest to send more workers, both Austrians and foreign missionaries, to this needy field! Pray especially for:

- *Rural areas.* People who live away from cities have less chance to hear the gospel. Most do not have an evangelical group among them.

- *Cults and sects.* Aggressive activities of New Age movements, Eastern religions, Jehovah's Witnesses, Mormons, and others have gained thousands of followers. The Dalai Lama conducted a rite where he released 722 spirits to make Austria the bridgehead of Buddhism for Western Europe. Pray for God to cancel these efforts, and to release the people caught up in false beliefs.

- *Foreign migrants and refugees.* Pray especially for the 6 ethnic groups of the former Yugoslavia, some of the least-reached peoples of Europe. Pray also for Muslim Turks, Afghans, Kurds, and Pakistanis, who often face prejudice from society.

Belarus   *Europe*

Pop 9.6 million. **Capital** Minsk (1.9 mill).
Christians 6.8 mill. **Evangelical Christians** 123,000.
Largest Religion Christian.
Fastest Growing Religion Christian.
Largest Ethnic Groups Belarusian (77.6%), Russian (13.2%), Polish (4.2%), Ukrainian (2.9%), All other peoples (2.1%, 22 groups mostly from the former USSR).
Official Languages Belarusian, Russian (more widely used).
All Languages 11.
Economy 80% of industry still controlled by the state. Heavily dependent on trade with Russia. Still affected by economic and health consequences of the 1986 Chernobyl nuclear disaster.

Politics Often called "Europe's last dictatorship". A republic in name, but still dominated by Russia and the Communist past.

1 **Belarus gained independence,** but it continues to operate more like a Communist-era authoritarian regime. Elections do not reflect democracy, and Russia's influence is widespread. A democratic revolution seems unlikely, but many do oppose the current regime and seek increased freedoms. Pray for hope, justice, and a brighter future for the people of Belarus.

2 **The Orthodox and Catholic Churches** have special status as historic Slavic religious groups, but even these face limitations from government. Russian Orthodoxy is very much a part of traditional Slavic identity, but many see the Church as primarily a place for baptizing, for weddings, and for burials. Pray for renewal and reformation within these ancient Christian confessions, which could potentially affect millions of people. All other religious movements face pressure from government officials. These include other Catholics, Protestants, and cults or foreign religions, as well as Orthodox expressions that do not submit to the state-approved Moscow authority structure.

3 **The believing Church grows** in numbers, maturity, and confidence, despite opposition and persecution! The state prohibits congregations of more than 20 people, the use of homes to meet for worship, new religious schools, ministry outside of the congregation's home town, and importing or distribution of literature it does not first approve. The struggle to rent or buy property for worship creates the biggest problem for evangelicals. Pray for believers to overcome these difficulties with patient faith. Pray for those in government who persecute God's Church, that they might discover the truth of the gospel and the love of Christ. Foreign religious workers often struggle to get or renew visas to serve in Belarus. Pray for divine openings and opportunities for those God calls to Belarus.

The less evangelized:
- *Jews.* Up to 70,000 live in Belarus, with one Messianic Jewish group in Minsk. The majority must still be reached.

- *Muslims.* Tatars settled here since the 15th century, and smaller groups immigrate from across the former USSR. Very few Muslims ever encounter the good news.

Belgium
Europe

Pop 10.7 million. **Capital** Brussels (1.9 mill).

Christians 6.7 mill. *Evangelical Christians* 133,000.
Largest Religion Christian.
Fastest Growing Religion Muslim.

Largest Ethnic Groups Flemish (54.4%, mostly in north and west), Walloon (31.1%, mainly in south and east), Other European (7.7%), Arabic-speaking (2.7%, mostly North African), Turk (0.5%). Also large numbers of Sub-Saharan Africans and Latin Americans.
Official Languages Flemish, French, German. **All Languages** 29.

Economy A strong economy with a highly skilled workforce. Headquarters of the EU, NATO, and other international organizations.
Politics Became a nation in 1830 as constitutional monarchy. Deeply divided by language regions, and politically unstable from many failed attempts at a national coalition government.

1 **Belgium is a deeply divided nation.** For 2,000 years its land has stretched across the cultural divide between the Latin/Romance world and the Germanic world. The Walloon (south) and Flemish (north) peoples speak different languages, and this affects the economy, politics, religious life, and worldviews of both communities. New immigrant communities increase the complexity. Some fear the country could break apart. Pray that national leaders have wisdom to address this complicated challenge. Pray that the Church might demonstrate unity, and be used to bring about true reconciliation and peace.

2 **Secular views spread quickly.** Atheists and non-religious now number 31% of society. While almost half of the population consider themselves Catholic, only 7% attend mass. Mainline Protestant Churches also lose members. For many centuries up until 1960 the Catholic Church discouraged use of the Bible. But in 2006, after the release of a new Bible translation, French and Flemish Bible Societies worked together to share the history and stories of the Bible around the nation. Pray that the Word of God might take root deeply in Belgian society. Drug use, sexual immorality, occult and New Age activities all increase.

3 **Belgian evangelicals** number only 1.2% of the population, but faith is stronger than ever. Pentecostal churches grew the most, but other churches in both Flanders and Wallonia also grew through intentional church-planting efforts. About half of all evangelicals in Belgium are foreigners and include immigrants who found Christ in Belgium. Many churches identify themselves as "international churches" rather than "immigrant churches", which shows their multicultural character and interest to reach both Belgians and other Europeans!

(4) **Unity and cooperation among the many Protestant and evangelical groups** increased significantly in the last decades. Since 2003, a national body represents denominations to the government, which gives them legal recognition and a unified voice in society. Newer prayer movements now draw young people together to pray and talk about God through websites, online chats, and local meetings. Pray for success of creative outreach ideas like floating Bible exhibits on river barges, ministry to sailors whose ships dock at Belgian ports, and Christian centres for marriage and family counselling, or for women in crisis.

(5) **Belgium is one of Europe's most spiritually needy countries.** Pray especially for:
- *Smaller towns and villages* in the Flemish-speaking areas and the French-speaking Ardennes region. These have the greatest need for gospel outreach.
- *The capital city of Brussels.* Over 45 nationalities of 1,000 people or more live here. Brussels has both poor neighbourhoods and communities of wealthy young professionals. Overlooked foreign immigrants live alongside powerful European politicians. Pray for church and mission programmes that reach out to the diverse groups in Brussels's society.
- *Muslims* (North Africans, Turks, Kurds), the 2nd-largest religious population with over 380 mosques. Most live in poorer areas. Pray for more workers to join the outreach.
- *The Eastern European population,* which grows rapidly (Polish, Russians, Bulgarians, Kosovars, Romanians, others). Only the Romanians have a significant number of evangelical congregations. The Polish and Kosovars have none, with little or no outreach to them.

Bosnia (Bosnia-Herzegovina) *Europe*

Pop 3.8 million. **Capital** Sarajevo (396,000).
Christians 1.5 mill. *Evangelical Christians* 2,200.
Largest Religion Muslim.
Fastest Growing Religion Muslim.
Largest Ethnic Groups Bosniak (48.4%), Serb (29.3%), Croat (16.6%), Romani (2.2%). Massive population shifts from 1991 to 2002, from civil war and resettlement.
Official Language Bosnian. **All languages** 8.
Economy Devastated by war in the 1990s, which displaced up to half the population. Foreign aid is important. Infrastructure damaged by war still needs rebuilt. Floods in 2014 devastated the water supply and population.

Politics Separated from Serbia in AD 960. Many Bosnians later became Muslim during the 500-year Turkish occupation. Croat and Bosniak Nazi collaborators murdered hundreds of thousands of Serbs during WWII. When Yugoslavia broke up (1992), the minority Serbs fought against the Croat-Muslim attempt at independence. This 3-sided war (Serbians, Croatians, Bosnians) caused great damage, loss of life, displacement of millions of people, and war crimes. The war ended in 1995 with no winner, and left the nation sharply divided between the Serb Republic and the Croat-Muslim Federation. Now an independent state under international administration, with a balanced but limited central government.

(1) **Bosnia has a tragic history of violence.** The hatred among ethnic groups burdens Bosnia, and appears impossible to resolve. Recovery from the most recent conflict (1992-1995) continues even now. Many have not returned to their original homes. Roads and buildings can be rebuilt, but deep community wounds remain. Only God can bring true reconciliation and unity. Bosnia also struggles with poverty. Organized crime thrives, and it must be stopped for the country to progress. Young people feel discouraged, and more than 60% want to leave the country. Pray for a new generation of Bosnians to stay and lead their nation into a bright future!

2 **Religious communities divide deeply along ethnic lines.** The Orthodox Church was dominated by Serbian nationalism, and the Catholic Church by Croat nationalism. Bosnians largely follow Islam, and it grows more militant under the influence of Middle Eastern groups. All groups view Protestant and Independent Christian groups with suspicion. Pray for the Spirit to move with power among all churches, and for all Christians to recognize that their citizenship lies first in Heaven.

3 **The number of evangelicals increased significantly,** from 3 congregations in 1991 to about 35 in 2010. But it remains tiny overall (around 2,000). Evangelicals are the only group that has unified people from across different ethnic groups. Pray for believers and their witness in this divided land! Bosnia has not been a spiritually receptive place, and we must pray that hearts might open to the gospel. The Church needs expatriate Christians to assist in leadership development, aid, rehabilitation, outreach, and church planting.

4 **The less reached.** Christians use creative ways to share Christ's love such as the Alpha Course, home construction and repair, German-language classes, coffee bars, sports and camps, and most importantly prayer and intercession!

- *Bosniak Muslims* are possibly the least-evangelized people group in Europe, and Islamic mission activities may make them harder to reach. The number who follow Jesus has grown to around 500.
- *The Orthodox Serbs* endured Islamic rule for 500 years. Pray that the faith for which they suffered so long might come alive and transform this often bitter and disappointed people!
- *The Romani* (mostly Muslim) are one of the poorest and most hated people groups, but they respond well to the gospel.
- *The Muslim Turks* have little to no work among them.

Bulgaria *Europe*

Pop 7.5 million. **Capital** Sofia (1.2 mill).
Christians 6 mill. *Evangelical Christians* 146,000.
Largest Religion Christian.
Fastest Growing Religion Non-religious.
Largest Ethnic Groups Bulgarian (82%), Turks (8.2%), Gypsy groups (4.7%), Macedonian (2.7%).
Official Languages Bulgarian. **All languages** 16.
Economy Reforms after Communism helped the economy, but high unemployment and corruption hinder progress.
Politics A nation since 5th century, but rarely independent. Multiparty democracy since 1990. Entered EU in 2007.

1 **Bulgaria suffered under Communist rule** from 1947 to 1989, and troubles remain. Corruption, crime networks, and poverty affect many lives. More abortions occur than live births, and divorce is common. The population continues to age as its overall size declines. Pray for the Church to demonstrate God's love in this country where racial tensions are strong and hope is rare.

2 **The Orthodox Church** needs renewal and new life. A bitter split under Communist rule weakened the Church and continues to have an impact, even at a local level. Pray for the Holy Spirit to reconcile relationships, and to bring the spiritual richness of Orthodoxy fully alive.

3 **God transformed harsh spiritual repression** in the 1980s into more openness today. Praise Him that evangelicals grew in number and matured through these challenges! Churches relate better to one another now, but need more progress. The Evangelical Alliance (BEA) brings churches together to act and speak with a common voice, and to evangelize the country. Sofia has many churches, but needs more. 2,500 villages still need an evangelical church. Pray that the Church remembers the spiritual needs of rural areas. Ask God to bless this countrywide vision.

4 **Residential and informal training courses** prepare church leaders to serve well. However, missionaries sent by Mormons, Jehovah's Witnesses, "prosperity gospel" teachers, and Eastern cults reach many. Pray for believers to recognize false doctrine with the help of wise leadership and Bible knowledge.

5 **Cross-cultural missions from and to Bulgaria.** Bulgarians serve in Asia, Africa, and Europe, and go with short-term teams to nearby countries. Pray for greater global vision in Bulgarian churches. Foreign missions sometimes find Bulgaria difficult, but missionaries and tentmakers who learn the culture and language can help train leaders and join with nationals to reach the unreached minorities. Pray for more foreign workers. Pray for practical funding methods for all Christian workers, and for wise use of resources.

6 **Ethnic minorities suffered** under the Bulgarian majority in days past, and discrimination continues. True unity among believers of different ethnic and denominational backgrounds can give a powerful testimony. Pray for each of these people groups.

- *The Rumelian Turks* have barely 150 evangelical believers among them.
- *The Millet* (an oppressed, Turkish-speaking Gypsy minority) experienced a people movement to Christ in the 1990s. 15,000 came to faith, many by dreams, visions, and healings. But now less than 8,000 follow Christ. Pray for Turkish-speaking Christians to disciple these oppressed Gypsy believers.
- *Bulgarian-speaking Muslims* in the south face rejection from both Christian Bulgarians and Turkish-speaking Muslims. Only a few congregations exist. They need specific outreach that values their identity.

Croatia

Pop 4.4 million. **Capital** Zagreb (687,000).

Christians 4.1 mill. *Evangelical Christians* 19,000.
Largest Religion Christian.
Fastest Growing Religion Non-religious.

Largest Ethnic Groups Croat (87.5%), Serb (4.5%), Romani (2.3%), Bosnian (0.5%), Hungarian (0.4%), Albanian (0.3%), Slovene (0.3%), Friulian (0.2%).
Official Language Croatian (related to Serbian, but written in Latin rather than Cyrillic script). **All Languages** 22.

Economy Still recovering from decades of Communist mismanagement and the war with Serbia. High unemployment and low wages, but some development, especially through tourism.

Politics Hatred between the Croats and Serbs has dominated regional politics for centuries, and was one cause of the Balkan wars (1990s). Croatia continues its transition to a liberal democracy. A member of the EU since 2013.

 The deep impact of historic and recent hatred among Croat, Serb, and Bosnian may hurt the nation for generations to come. Pray for true reconciliation, and for God to break these religious and ethnic bondages through the power of Christ! The Catholic Church holds much influence in society, and some Catholic leaders work towards reconciliation. Many people still suffer psychological and emotional trauma from the conflicts, and churches could have a great impact in this area where few others currently work.

Evangelicals are one of the few groups to successfully unite people from different ethnic backgrounds. Praise God for the Bosnians, Croats, and Serbs that came to Christ and now fellowship together! When churches and missions cared for those who suffered during the war, the gospel gained respect. Pray that evangelicals continue to demonstrate the love of God that overcomes divisions. As the Church recognizes that prayer holds the power to transform the nation, new prayer movements emerge around the country.

The less reached:

- *The Croatian majority.* Novi Zagreb is a region of the capital with a large population and no evangelical church. Believers must also move into the Istrian Peninsula, the Dalmatian Coast, and Zagorje (north) to witness for Christ.
- *The Romani* do not get attention from evangelicals, but they respond well to the gospel, especially the young people.

Cyprus

Some statistics below apply to the whole island, and some for each of the 2 entities (see below).

Pop 880,000. **Capital** Lefkosia (Nicosia) 243,000.

Christians 637,000. *Evangelical Christians* 6,600.
Largest Religion Christian.
Fastest Growing Religion Non-religious.
Official Language Greek. **All Languages** 4.

The country is divided as a result of Turkey's 1974 invasion and occupation of the north. The Greek and Turk populations are separated: The north calls itself the Turkish Republic of Northern Cyprus (TRNC) and the south claims the whole island as the Republic of Cyprus (ROC). The ROC is internationally recognized as the legal government of the whole island (only Turkey recognizes the TRNC).

Republic of Cyprus

Capital (divided) Lefkosia (Nicosia) 219,000.
Largest Religion Christian.

Largest Ethnic Groups Greek Cypriot (91.8%), Arab (3.4%), British/American (1.6%).
Official Languages Greek, Turkish. English widely used.

Economy Crippled by Turkey's seizure of the north, and by a third of the population made refugees as a result. Recovery and development of light industry and tourism, but badly affected by 2012 recession. One-sixth of the world's merchant ships are registered in Cyprus.
Politics Ruled by 11 foreign empires over 3 millennia. Independent from Britain in 1960, then partitioned in 1974 after Turkish invasion. Efforts to reach a settlement remain unsuccessful. Cyprus joined the EU in 2004, but membership is suspended for the north.

 The 50-year conflict between the 2 communities has lasted too long. The majority seem to favour reunification, but the inflexibility of some hinders overall progress. Pray that forgiveness might replace the old complaints and bitterness. Pray that unhelpful interference from foreign powers might end, and that Cypriots might move forward into a unified future! Financial crisis in 2012 led to anxiety and insecurity for many. Pray that Cypriots will find confidence in Christ.

 The Orthodox Church remains a centre of Greek Cypriot culture and identity. But it is mostly the older generation and rural people who attend church. Pray for the Holy Spirit to draw religious Cypriots into a relationship with Christ. The Orthodox Church distributes New Testaments in schools. Pray for this work to bear fruit among students.

 A large population of foreign workers lives on Cyprus, from Asia, Africa, the Middle East, and Eastern Europe, as well as UN peacekeepers and 3,000 British military personnel and their families. Evangelicals have grown rapidly among English-speaking, Russian, Filipino, Sri Lankan, and Iranian communities. Few evangelical churches exist among Greek Cypriots, and very few ministries focus on the island's majority people. Pray for effective outreach to all these groups in Cyprus's multicultural society.

4 **Cyprus provides a major base for Christian organizations** that serve the Middle Eastern states. Most expatriate workers serve in these offices rather than in local outreach. The creative and influential Christian satellite TV ministry SAT-7, whose broadcasts impact the whole region, has its base here.

Turkish Republic of Northern Cyprus

Capital (divided) Lefkosia (Nicosia) 49,000.
Largest Religion Muslim.
Largest Ethnic Groups Turkish Cypriot/Turkish (98.6%).
Official Language Turkish.
Economy Lower standard of living than south due to political and economic isolation. Heavily dependent on Turkish subsidies and trade. High unemployment.
Politics A democratic government since 1974 partition. Declared independence in 1983, but only recognized by Turkey.

1 **Almost the entire population are Muslim,** though many have a more secular outlook. Pray that the history of ethnic and cultural prejudice against Christianity would not prevent spiritual openness. Pray that whatever changes come in politics and economics bring new chances to encounter the gospel!

Czech Republic *Europe*

Pop 10.4 million. **Capital** Prague (1.2 mill).
Christians 2.7 mill. *Evangelical Christians* 73,000.
Largest Religion Non-religious.
Fastest Growing Religion Non-religious.
Largest Ethnic Groups Czech (93.2%), Romani (estimated 2.9%), Slovak (1.9%), Polish (0.5%).
Official Language Czech. **All Languages** 20.
Economy One of the most developed economies in central Europe. Strong tradition of industry and manufacturing, with growth in tourism.
Politics A bloodless "Velvet Revolution" against Communist rule (1989). Rapid move towards democratic rule followed as did the "velvet divorce" from Slovakia (1993). A multiparty presidential democracy, and EU member from 2004.

1 **Over 70% of the population consider themselves non-religious,** although many use horoscopes and mix together different spiritual ideas. The successful transition to a market economy was a positive change for the country, but it put economic stress on the most vulnerable people. Crime, sexual immorality, substance abuse, depression, and suicide all have notably higher rates today than they did during Communist times. Ask God to lift the spiritual heaviness from over the Czech Republic. Social changes create new opportunities for ministry. The ageing population and new immigrants (especially Russian speakers, East and Southeast Asians) need loving outreach.

2 **The Catholic Church** lost both size and influence, and now plays only a minor role in society. The openness of the 1990s was a window of opportunity to present society with a faith full of life, but the Church failed to fully embrace it. As a result, many view the Church as an institution for traditionalism, and Christianity as a "religion for grannies". The future looks uncertain, as both church members and clergy are often quite old.

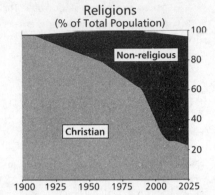

Religions
(% of Total Population)

3 **Czech Protestants must reclaim their heritage and demonstrate new life!** Churches now have freedom after centuries of suffering, but they face spiritual decline. The strong legacy of reformers like John Hus and the Moravians has lost its influence. Pray for evangelicals in both the traditional Protestant denominations and the smaller, younger groups (Baptists, Pentecostals, others). Pray for loving outreach and evangelism to bring new growth. For many years, little training of leaders was allowed. Praise God that now the nation has several Protestant theological training facilities.

4 **New expressions of Christianity emerged** that connect well with the younger generation. The more Western-style approach with large meetings and events does not have the same appeal as grassroots, discipleship-oriented communities (small congregations, house churches, cell groups). In 2009 workers completed a new Czech Bible translation in everyday modern language (called Bible21), and it was a bestseller that year. Pray for fulfilment of the vision to see 1 million copies distributed in years to come!

Denmark *Europe*

Pop 5.5 million. **Capital** Copenhagen (1.2 mill).
Christians 4.7 mill. *Evangelical Christians* 193,000.
Largest Religion Christian.
Fastest Growing Religion Muslim.
Largest Ethnic Groups Danish (91.2%), Middle Eastern and Asian (4.4%), Foreign European (3.3%), Faroese (0.9%, Danish citizens), Greenlander (0.1%, Danish citizens), African (0.1%).
Official Language Danish. **All Languages** 13.
Economy A strong economy with a large service sector. Social security system requires high taxes.
Politics Stable parliamentary democracy with a constitutional monarchy. A member of the EU.

1 **Denmark retains a core of Christian traditions and values** in its social laws and values. And Danes began to show more openness to spiritual things in recent years. But over half the population is agnostic or atheist by some reports. And many people's spiritual search does not lead them to Christian faith and the Church. Pray that more Danes will rediscover the faith that shaped so much of the nation's history and society.

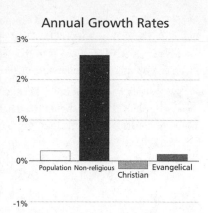

Annual Growth Rates

2 **Many evangelical congregations do not grow,** and some even decline. 80% of the population remain members of the Lutheran Church, but most Danes see it as a place of ritual and tradition rather than a place of life and community. Free Churches contribute greatly to the spiritual life of Denmark, but even with new ministries and new churches planted, a shortage of pastors holds back the work. Pray for God to provide capable, godly leaders. Pray for fresh winds of the Holy Spirit to blow through every congregation.

3 **Pray for immigrants to Denmark:**
- *Christian immigrants.* Guest workers and refugees may be a significant force for spiritual and mission renewal in Denmark. Over 150 new churches of migrants emerged across the last few years. Pray that Danish Christians will receive this new missionary gift!
- *Unevangelized immigrants.* Tens of thousands of Turks, Arabs, Pakistanis, Iranians, and Chinese recently came to Denmark. Many may be open to the gospel, but have never heard it.
- *Islamic relations.* This nation struggles with matters of free speech, religious tension, and inter-community relations with Muslim immigrants. Pray for Danes and others to display the unconditional love of Christ to Muslims in Denmark.

Estonia
Europe

Pop 1.3 million. **Capital** Tallinn (399,000).
Christians 607,000. *Evangelical Christians* 66,000.
Largest Religion Non-religious.
Fastest Growing Religion Non-religious.
Largest Ethnic Groups Estonian (68.6%), Russian (25.7%), Ukrainian (2.1%), Belarusian (1.2%), Finnish (0.8%).
Official Language Estonian. Russian remains common. **All Languages** 18.
Economy One of the most successful post-Soviet economies. Foreign investment and sustained economic growth followed the movement towards a capitalist free market society and EU membership.

Politics Long dominated by surrounding nations. Independent 1918-1940. The Soviets invaded in 1940, then deported and murdered many Estonians. Resentment towards Russia remains strong. Independent as a multiparty democracy by 1991. A member of the EU and NATO since 2004.

1 **Estonia found political and economic success** after the time of Soviet domination (1940-1988). Poverty remains a problem, and greed for material possessions grows as the economy grows. Estonia faces a crisis of values as the people become more and more secular in their attitudes. Pray for a wise and upright government to model righteousness and biblical values.

2 **Estonia has a Protestant heritage, but genuine faith is rare.** Estonians now have religious freedom and many hold Christian beliefs, but few truly commit to follow Jesus. Mormons send more missionaries to Estonia than any Christian agency, and Christian sects grow and gain influence here. Some Estonians show interest in the old pagan religions. Pray for good Christian education and discipleship to prepare believers for Christian life and witness. Pray for a new vision for evangelism, and for revival to reawaken all the churches!

3 **Ministry to minorities.** The large Russian population needs specific outreach, and we must pray for reconciliation between Russians and Estonians. Unity in the Church would be a powerful witness for Christ! Pray that Christ's faithful followers in every denomination would demonstrate His love for one another. Pray also for believers to share the gospel with the Tatar Muslims, Jews, and other minority groups in Estonia.

Faeroe Islands
Europe

Pop 50,000. **Capital** Torshavn (20,000).
Christians 45,000. *Evangelical Christians* 14,000.
Largest Religion Christian.
Fastest Growing Religion Non-religious.
Largest Ethnic Groups Faeroese (97%), Danish (2.6%).
Official Languages Faeroese, Danish.
Economy Based largely on fishing industry (along with fish farming). Undersea oil reserves may provide opportunity to diversify economy.
Politics A self-governing region of Denmark with a parliamentary democracy. As it is not part of the EU, trade is governed by special treaties.

1 **Many Islanders hope for a more independent future.** Pray that God would give political leaders wisdom to oversee increased autonomy from Denmark. Pray also that God would give courage to make strong decisions about the shrinking fishing industry and the potential oil industry, as both will affect society and the environment.

2 **The Faeroese need revival,** and local Christian leaders agree that the Holy Spirit has started to move in new ways on these islands! 29% of the population are evangelical. The Faeroe Islands send a large number of missionaries for their small population size (100, in more than 20 countries!). Faeroese have good Christian resources (Bible translations, Christian radio and TV, a Christian magazine, and 2 bookstores). Pray for the Spirit to continue to impact the Church in the Faeroe Islands, and for wisdom as Christians engage the secular attitudes that grow within society.

Finland

Pop 5.3 million. **Capital** Helsinki (1.1 mill).

Christians 4.5 mill. *Evangelical Christians* 649,000.
Largest Religion Christian.
Fastest Growing Religion Non-religious.

Largest Ethnic Groups Finns (97.6%, with 5.5% Swedish-speakers), Other European groups (0.9%), Saami (0.05%, 3 groups).
Official Languages Finnish, Swedish, Saami, sign language.
All Languages 23.

Economy A strong economy, primarily from high-tech and exports. Some unemployment, especially among minorities.

Politics Ruled by Sweden (700 years), then by Russia (100 years). Independent since 1917. A stable multiparty democracy, and a member of the EU.

---

1 **Finland has a largely secular society,** even though Christians number 84% of the population. 90% look with favour on the Church's social work, but only 8% consistently attend any kind of religious service. The last revival came in the 1960s. Strong belief in the power of human reason, and rejection of supernatural things, now dominates the society. An ultra-modern country like Finland probably needs both reformation in the existing Church and also new expressions of faith. Pray for a spiritual breakthrough that will cause people to seek the Lord.

2 **The Lutheran Church has a stronger evangelical tradition than most state churches,** but still only 12% of Lutherans are considered evangelical. Independent and grassroots movements grow within the national Church, and this is where the most committed Lutherans find fellowship. Pray for continued freedom to function within the Lutheran Church and for opportunities to influence Finland's spiritual life. The Free Churches, both Pentecostal and non-Pentecostal, are small but spiritually alive. They currently do not grow, but they keep their members at a time when other churches lose them. Pray for cooperation in evangelism and missions, both among these groups and between the Free Churches and Lutherans.

3 **Finland's strong Christian tradition and location on the map** give it a strategic role to reach the many peoples of the former Soviet Union, especially the Finno-Ugric peoples (distant ethnic cousins) in Russia's interior. Finns have a strong history of sending missionaries, but as the Church declines and changes, this will be hard to maintain. Pray for more workers and supporters.

4 **Pray for these social groups with particular needs:**
- *Unreached immigrant minorities.* Very few churches actively reach out to unreached immigrant groups. The number of foreign university students grows, and many come from other faiths. Pray that foreigners in Finland might have the chance to encounter Jesus in a real and attractive way.
- *Indigenous minorities.* The Saami people of Lapland are Europe's last truly nomadic people group. Pray for them to develop a culturally relevant expression of Christian faith.
- *Men's ministry.* Finland has a deeply private culture, and this makes discipleship with men difficult. Pray for ministries that call Finns into relationships of mentoring and accountability.

France

Pop 62.6 million. **Capital** Paris (10.5 mill).

Christians 38.3 mill. *Evangelical Christians* 603,000. (Some studies identify a smaller number of evangelicals, but differences in definitions and counting methods can account for the variation.)
Largest Religion Christian.
Fastest Growing Religion Muslim.

Largest Ethnic Groups French (69.5%), Other European (8.9%, excludes French and Germanic groups shown separately), North African/Middle Eastern (9.2%), Germanic (5.1%), African/Caribbean (4%, representing every Francophone nation, most West and Central African ethnic groups, and French Caribbean ethnicities), Asian (2%).

Official Language French. (French is the first language of 136 million people worldwide.) **All Languages** 62.

Economy The 6th-largest economy in the world; based on agriculture and industry. The world's number one tourist destination, with a strong service industry. Good public service (healthcare), infrastructure, and skilled professional workforce, but the complicated administration policies and many strikes put pressure on the system.

Politics A democratic republic. A core member of the EU that works to balance its role in global politics with internal challenges. Unrest in some immigrant/minority communities turns violent at times.

---

1 **France stands at a political and economic crossroads.** The economy needs radical reforms to prosper in the globalized world. The population has aged to the point that the current retirement age and pension system cannot support it. The large immigrant community continues to grow and challenges the traditional understanding of French identity. The majority feel content as individuals, but they do not have much confidence in the future of the Republic, with so many points of tension in their society. Young people especially feel the crisis, and often long for meaning and purpose.

2 **Major spiritual strongholds** keep people from the gospel. Religious history in France includes violent religious wars (16th century), the persecution of Protestants (16th–17th centuries), and the French Revolution (1789-1801). By the end of the Age of Enlightenment (18th century), many French embraced a godless and human-focused view of life and the world. Other religious movements and philosophies (including New Age and witchcraft) later began to fill this spiritual hole. Less than 10% own a Bible, and 80% have never handled one.

3 **France's Catholics and Protestants** rapidly decreased in number while atheism grew. The Catholic Church lost much of its influence in society, and perhaps as few as 51% of French still call themselves Catholic. This decline led to change and a growth in humility. Pray that French Catholicism might experience new life. Many Catholic parishes now use the Alpha Course. During the Reformation, society accepted Protestants, and some estimate that up to 25% of the population followed Protestant teaching. But persecution and 200 years of secular philosophy reduced this number to only 1.9% (2010). Many Protestants do not actively practise their faith, but evangelical believers remain within most Reformed and Lutheran congregations. Pray that the faith and commitment of the martyrs' legacy might return to these churches.

4 **Evangelical Christians** are few, but grew from 180,000 (1960) to 600,000 (2010)! They meet in 2,500 fellowships, across many denominations and confessions, and more fellowships form every year. Evangelicals tend to be younger in age than the average age of France's population, and demonstrate high levels of commitment. Most French people still associate the evangelical message with immigrant groups and American right-wing politics, which can lead to difficulty with local authorities. New churches face 2 immediate challenges: to hire a pastor, and to find a building in order to gain better status in the community. Pray for God to provide resources and solutions.

5 **Praise God for greater unity among evangelicals** after a history of division. The National Council of French Evangelicals (CNEF) formed in 2001, and grew to represent most of the church unions as a voice for evangelical Protestants in France. Unity with other Protestants and Catholics also increased. Minority churches grow quickly (especially African, Antillean, Gypsy), and bring new passion and expression to the evangelical movement. Pray for deeper unity between the various immigrant churches and French indigenous congregations. French evangelicals have sent out around 400 missionaries, about half to other lands. Pray for churches to gain a vision for world evangelization. The French and foreign students who graduate from Bible schools and seminaries have great potential to bless the whole Francophone world!

6 **Many sectors of French society remain unreached.** Nearly 50 million French people have no link with a Christian church. Of the 37,000 *communes* (municipalities), around 35,000 have no evangelical church! The CNEF picked up the vision started by France Mission to plant one church for every 10,000 people. France remains difficult ground for the gospel. Foreign workers often struggle to adapt to French culture, and to share the gospel effectively in this context. Dropout rates are high. Both French and foreign mission agencies must work in evangelism and church planting. Pray for the grace, endurance, and faith to establish the 4,200 churches needed to reach the goal.

7 **Pray for the less-reached minorities:**
• *The French Jewish community* is the 3rd-largest in the world (between 580,000 and 700,000), but less than 20 Christian workers minister among them. Messianic Jews (Jews who follow Christ) number around 600. About 77% of French Jews never attend a synagogue service.

• *North Africans* are almost entirely Muslim, and few have ever heard the gospel. Hostility between them and the French majority increased across recent decades. Pray for believers to break down barriers through friendship.

• *Black Africans* come in large numbers from Francophone Africa as students, refugees, and to seek work. Some come from Central Africa and bring their vibrant Christian faith! Others come from unreached West African people groups, and little outreach exists to them there or here.

• *Indo-Chinese refugees* came in the 1970s and 1980s from France's former colonies. They still live mostly isolated from French society. Over 82 Asian evangelical churches now exist (Chinese, Korean, Hmong, Vietnamese, others), but too few pastors and full-time workers serve this large population.

8 **Saint Pierre and Miquelon** is an overseas territorial collectivity of France (off the eastern shore of Canada). The population (just over 6,000) are French, mostly of Breton and Basque origin. Most are Catholic, and no formal Protestant or evangelical presence remains on the islands. Pray for the people to find hope in a living relationship with Christ!

9 **Islam** grows largely through immigration and higher birth rates, but some estimate around 150,000 French have converted to Islam (most through marriages). Deep divisions exist within French Islam, primarily between secular Muslims and those who follow fundamentalist teachings. The French Republic was founded on secular ideas and the desire to integrate society, but a large percentage of Muslims struggle to integrate. They live in larger cities, gathered in low-cost housing areas, with higher than average crime rates and unemployment. Fear and misunderstanding keep Christians from reaching out, with only around 100 full-time Christian workers among this large population. Believers from Muslim backgrounds have good fellowship with other evangelicals, and it presents a good testimony to both Muslims and atheists!

Germany

Europe

Pop 82.1 million. **Capital** Berlin (3.4 mill).

Christians 52.7 mill. *Evangelical Christians* 1.7 mill.

Largest Religion Christian.

Fastest Growing Religion Muslim.

Largest Ethnic Groups Germanic (88.3%), Turk (3%), Slavic (2.6%, 12 groups). Recent studies indicate up to 19% of people who live in Germany come from a "migration background".

Official Language German. (Over 95 million German speakers live around the world.) **All Languages** 69.

Economy Dramatic recovery post-WWII to become one of the world's strongest economies. One of world's largest industrial producers. Unemployment high (especially in the east), but remains Europe's strongest economy.

Politics The collapse of Hitler's Reich (1945) was followed by 45 years of division between the democratic Federal Republic (FRG) and the Socialist "Democratic" Republic (GDR). The collapse of Communism led to a rapid reunification of the 2 states in 1990. Now a strong, stable democracy. A core member of the EU, with a central role in European affairs.

---

1 **The decline of Christianity in Germany** continues into the 21st century. West Germany was 97% Christian in 1960, but Germany is now 63% Christian, and that percentage decreases every year. Church attendance for all denominations is low, and many churches have shut down. Christians divide between Protestants and Catholics, liberals and conservatives, and conservative evangelicals and Pentecostal/charismatic groups. However, we can thank God that this decline has drawn some believers together in new ways. Prayer movements formed and spread, and churches now work together across some cities or regions for evangelism, outreach, and mission.

2 **Germany's wealth, influence, and location** in the EU and Europe could be of great value for the Kingdom of God. This would require strong, courageous leadership based on Christian values, but the spiritual health of Germany is currently in decay. Destructive criticism of the Bible in the 19th century weakened the Church, and opened the way for pagan Nazi rule in the 20th century. New Age, the occult, Satanism, and new forms of the old pagan religions all gain followers. Horrible crimes and murders recently increased, along with depression and suicide rates. Pray for God to raise up leaders who will love righteousness and strong moral values, even when they face temptation to compromise.

3   **The German Church needs another deep and lasting reformation,** like the one Martin Luther started 500 years ago. Most people do not see the Church as relevant to society or their lives, and hostility towards Christians increases. Many Lutheran clergy do not even still believe in life after death. Born-again ministers in the EKD (a federation of 23 Lutheran, Reformed, and United Protestant groups) can find it difficult to openly minister in their own churches! The Free Churches have more evangelical believers in them, but they are only 1% of Germany's population. Most active Christians are over age 50, and only about 2% of the nation's young people look to Jesus as their saviour. Pray for a return to genuine faith in the Bible.

4   **German evangelical groups** continue to grow and offset the decline in the mainline churches. 1,000 new church plants started in the last 15 years, but Germany needs many more. The Evangelical Alliance networks the 1.2 million evangelicals in all denominations for prayer, theological reflection, projects, social actions, evangelism, and mission. Ethnic German immigrants from Central Asia and Eastern Europe brought in over 4,000 Mennonite and Baptist congregations that have a missions mindset, but often remain culturally isolated from other evangelicals. Lively and evangelistic immigrant churches among African, Asian, and Latino populations could have greater impact beyond their own language and ethnic groups.

5   **New expressions of spirituality** demonstrate a vibrant spiritual life beyond the organized religion in decline! House churches, youth movements, multicultural congregations, new worship styles, and Christian media/publications all appeal to unbelievers who are put off by traditional religious structures but who have spiritual questions. The German language has more theological publications than any language after English. Excellent websites for believers and those who seek to learn more about Christ reach many adults and children.

6   **The total number of Protestant missionaries grew notably** in the last 30 years, due to the growth of evangelical missions. Pray for the Association of Evangelical Missions (AEM), with 90 member organizations that represent 3,700 missionaries. The Association of Pentecostal and Charismatic Missions has 43 agencies with 400 missionaries. German churches and mission agencies must spread the light to the areas of greatest need, especially in the east (where 65% of the population are agnostic or atheist), and in some areas of Western Germany (the northern plains, Bavaria, the Eifel area, others).

7   **Millions of immigrants, guest workers, students, and refugees** came to Germany since 1989. Many arrive illegally, and some have connections to international criminal networks. Some are vibrant Christians, but most do not know the gospel. German society and government struggle to react well to this inflow of people, and some have reacted with violence or bitterness towards immigrants, especially in the east. Pray for:

- *More churches among many foreign peoples* (Asian, African, Latin American, European). German Christians must seize this open window to share the gospel! Pray also for immigrant churches to reach out cross-culturally to their host country and to other migrant neighbours.
- *International students* (250,000, the world's 3rd-highest total after the USA and UK).
- *Muslims* (3.6 million, from over 40 nations). They often live in neighbourhoods with their own people, and do not integrate into German society. 4,000-5,000 come to faith in Christ each year, but 1,000 or more ethnic Germans convert to Islam each year.

- *Least-reached people groups.* Pray for outreach to the 2.5 million Turks and up to 1 million Kurds. Pray also for the Iranians (100,000), North African Arabs and Berbers (300,000), and Bosnian Muslims (285,000). Jews suffered severely in the Holocaust (from 564,000 Jews in 1925 to 27,000 in 1945), but many have come to Germany as immigrants. Of the now 200,000, perhaps around 2,000 have come to faith in Messiah Jesus.

Greece
Europe

Pop 11.2 million. **Capital** Athens (3.3 mill).

Christians 10.2 mill. *Evangelical Christians* 41,000.
Largest Religion Christian.
Fastest Growing Religion Non-religious.

Largest Ethnic Groups Greek (85.9%, descendants of the ancient Greeks whose civilization so changed the world), Albanian (4%), 'Slavomacedonian' (1.8%), Turkish- and Bulgarian-speaking minorities (1.4%), Gypsy/Romani (0.8%). Large undocumented immigrant movement means all numbers are estimates.
Official Language Greek. **All Languages** 24.

Economy Greece faces impossible debts, increase in public unrest, and no easy solution. Economy shrank by almost 1/4 from 2008 to 2013. Problems affect Greece and the entire EU. Tourism, agriculture, and industry all important. Greece has the largest fleet of merchant ships in the EU.
Politics Independence (1827) after 4 centuries of Turkish rule. After civil war, two military dictatorships, and tensions with Turkey, Greece is now a republic with a parliamentary democracy. Large-scale immigration from the Balkans and Middle East/Asia changes the ethnic and religious populations.

 1 **Greece's economic and social problems** cause much uncertainty and disruption. The economic meltdown, and the protests and riots that followed, shook the country's foundations. Pray this difficult time will drive the nation to cry out to God.

2 **The evangelization of Europe started in Greece** (Acts 16:10), but Christianity today is mostly a cultural tradition. Less than 3% of the population regularly attend church, and evangelicals represent less than half of 1 percent. The "Macedonian call" to evangelize remains valid today! Even though EU membership opened the doors to many Europeans, too few long-term workers serve here. Pray for more workers, and for more fruit from their labour. Pray also that national churches might develop in the areas of prayer, outreach, and church planting.

3 **The Orthodox Church** provided a strong cultural identity for Greeks during centuries of foreign occupation. Sadly many Greeks now see other expressions of Christianity as a threat. Most Greeks have not heard the gospel message, and resist any witness from outside the Orthodox Church. Some within Orthodoxy have called for a re-evangelization of the Greeks, and even Protestants agree that Greeks will most likely find new life in Christ through a renewed and reformed Orthodox Church. Pray for the archbishop, bishops, and priests to be led by the Word of God and the Holy Spirit, and to lead the people into a life-changing encounter with the living God! Pray that Protestants and Greek Orthodox will put aside distrust, and will work together for God's Kingdom.

4 **Few ethnic Greeks are evangelical** in their faith. They need courage to witness in a society where the majority claim to be Christian, yet most do not have a living faith and relationship with Jesus. Pray they might find ways to communicate the need for salvation, but with respect to the legacy and heritage of Orthodoxy. Only a few Greeks serve cross-culturally, but missions interest grows among the younger generation. The country's position near the Arab, Turkic, Balkan, and Slavic worlds makes it highly strategic.

 Pray for the many Greeks who have never clearly heard the gospel:

- *The 150 Greek islands* mostly lack evangelical congregations, and the few believers feel spiritually isolated. Hellenic Ministries uses its yacht in short-term outreaches to evangelize these communities.

- *Albanians* (at least 500,000) are the largest ethnic minority. Many entered Greece illegally. Some got involved in criminal activities, and too many end up in jail. Pray for Greeks and others to reach out to them in Christian love.

- *Minority communities* increase as new immigrants and asylum seekers reach Greece each year by the thousands. Immigrant churches grow the fastest in Greece, especially among Russians, Romanians, Filipinos, Africans, Afghans, Iraqis, and Pakistanis. Many immigrants encountered Jesus through compassionate outreach combined with evangelism. Pray for more churches to get involved!

- *The 200,000 drug addicts and the 10,000 prostitutes* (mostly foreign born and trafficked into Greece) need to know God's love. Ministry among them bears some fruit.

Holy See (Vatican City State) *Europe*

Pop 785.
Christians 785. Perhaps less than 50 evangelical Christians.
Economy Financed by contributions from Roman Catholic dioceses around the world, from tourism, from sales of mementos, coins, and stamps, and from interest earned on its large investments and real estate portfolio.
Politics The Pope is the head of state, as well as leader of the world's Catholics. He is advised and elected by the College of Cardinals.

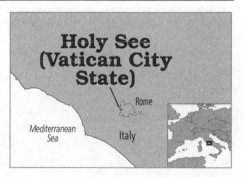

 The Vatican leadership plays a large role in the faith and lives of Roman Catholics. It also influences the wider world. The Pope is one of the world's most powerful people. The fresh and humble approach of Pope Francis's leadership (from 2013) has begun to change people's perception of Catholicism, and even of Christianity overall. Pray for God's grace for this man, and for the Holy Spirit to guide him.

 The Catholic Church faces upheaval and change in the 21st century. Catholicism now has over a billion followers, in hundreds of cultures, with a wide variety of expression in theology and worship. Many doctrines and positions divide this diverse body, such as celibacy for the priesthood, the role of women, homosexuality, the use of birth control, and others. Both historical and modern-day scandals grieve and burden the Church. In all these things, pray for the gospel of Jesus to be at the heart of all Catholic faith and practice.

Pray for spiritual renewal. Catholics inherit a rich religious tradition, but hundreds of millions do not have an active faith of their own. Praise God for the charismatic movement in Catholicism that remains lively and strong across many countries (many Catholic missionaries are charismatic). But it is not yet evenly spread throughout the world. Catholics worldwide engage in countless good works, especially in health care and education for the poor. Beyond theological and cultural diversity, the experience of life in Jesus matters most. Pray for all Catholics to know this reality!

Hungary

Europe

Pop 10 million. **Capital** Budapest (1.7 mill).

Christians 8.8 mill. *Evangelical Christians* 282,000.
Largest Religion Christian.
Fastest Growing Religion Non-religious.

Largest Ethnic Groups Magyar/Hungarian (86.8%), Romani/Gypsy (7.7%), Slavic (1.8%, 9 peoples), German (1.2%), Jews (1%), Romanian (1%).
Official Language Hungarian. **All Languages** 17.

Economy Traditionally rich agricultural land. Successful transition from a socialist to market economy, but the older generation still struggle to adjust. Economic reforms are still required.

Politics Hungary lost 60% of its land area when the Austro-Hungarian Empire broke apart (1918), and left large Hungarian minorities in nearby lands. Soviets imposed Communism after WWII until 1991. After an uprising (1956), the Soviets inflicted terrible revenge (80,000 killed, wounded, or sent away, and 200,000 fled to the West). Hungary was the first ex-Communist state to establish multiparty democracy (1990), though most of the leaders remained the same as under Communism. Member of NATO and the EU.

In 2000, Hungary celebrated 1,000 years since its conversion to Christianity. However, Hungarian people have now mostly lost contact with the gospel. They seek answers to life's problems in material possessions, personal pleasures, alcohol, and false religions. Occult activity and Eastern mysticism, pagan witchcraft, ancient Magyar shamanism, Tibetan Buddhism, or a mix of these various spiritual ideas all increased in recent years. Ask God to expose all false teaching and empty philosophies, and to reveal Christ as the truth in this historically Christian nation.

The Church does not affect society, politics, ethics, education, or the economy as it should, even though Christianity is present and active. Many people feel disappointed, and are sceptical of the government and economy. An open door to share the gospel came during the 1990s (after Communism), but the Church did not respond well enough to the opportunity before it closed. Today it is again more difficult to witness openly. Revival came to the Church in 1939, and in 1946-1950. Pray for a new revival that gives birth to a new spirit of witness and active service!

The small evangelical movement grows in size, maturity, diversity, and in confidence. Vibrant charismatic and renewal movements are active inside the major denominations (including Catholic and Reformed). Independent churches also grew, and many new ministries sprang up around the nation. Hungarians have a vision to see an evangelical church planted in every city, town, and village in Hungary! Pray for unity, trust, and cooperation among all the churches, and for the Holy Spirit to bring revival and renewal to all expressions of God's family in Hungary.

4 Hungary is a hub in Central Europe for theological education. Several Christian universities provide education, as well as other colleges and institutes and distance TEE programmes. Pray for the younger generation to commit itself to the work of the Lord, and for the Lord to provide for those who take on full-time training. The Hungarian missions movement remains in its early stages, but a Missions Expo in recent years attracted 20,000 people!

5 The less reached:

- *The Jews.* Before the Holocaust, there were 800,000. Now there are 90,000, which is still Eastern Europe's largest concentration of Jews outside Russia. Pray for reconciliation between Christians and Jews.

- *The Romani (Gypsy) community,* which is the largest minority community in Hungary, and the most disadvantaged. Spiritual breakthrough came to Romani groups in Spain, France, and Romania, but not as much yet to Hungary. Several agencies minister to their social and spiritual needs, and ethnic Hungarians have begun to show the love of Christ to this needy people in both spiritual and practical ways.

- *The homeless* (up to 30,000), mostly in Budapest. Pray for believers to establish Christian ministries and facilities to care for them and demonstrate the gospel in real ways.

- *The many immigrant peoples,* including mostly Slavic peoples, Chinese, and others. Most have a better chance to encounter Christ in Hungary than in their own nations.

Iceland   *Europe*

Pop 329,000. **Capital** Reykjavik (202,000).

Christians 298,000. *Evangelical Christians* 12,600.
Largest Religion Christian.
Fastest Growing Religion Non-religious.

Largest Ethnic Groups Icelandic (91.7%). The other 8.3% are mostly European (Danish, Swedish, Polish, others), with some from other continents.
Official Language Icelandic. **All Languages** 2.

Economy One of the world's highest living standards. Traditionally based on fishing and agriculture, but now also tourism, hydroelectric and geothermal energy, and aluminium smelting projects. Massive financial crisis and banking collapse (2008-2009), with impressive recovery since 2011.

Politics The world's oldest parliament (established in 930). Under Norwegian and Danish rule for 6 centuries. Now a parliamentary republic and a member of NATO, but not part of the EU.

1 Challenges threaten to change traditional Icelandic life. Divisions come over land, where some want to conserve the environment and others want to make money from its resources. Immigration brings other faiths and cultures into a traditionally guarded society. Pray for wisdom for leaders who deal with these new challenges.

2 Most Icelanders are Christian by tradition, but many people do not actively follow Christ. Some isolated areas have almost no active Christianity at all. Ask the Lord to break into the society, and to bring revival that touches every person and every aspect of life in Iceland. Pray for new life in the congregations and the leadership. The Lutherans already have a good number of young trainees.

Evalengical believers grew to almost 4% of the population. Lutheran Free Churches, Pentecostals, and charismatic churches show unity and cooperate well. Several congregations use the Alpha Course and see results. But the Lutheran and Free Churches lose members, and have low attendance at services. Pray that faithful followers of Jesus will multiply. Pray that the living faith of evangelicals might open the hearts of many to the good news.

Ireland
Europe

Pop 4.6 million. **Capital** Dublin (1.1 mill).

Christians 4.2 mill. *Evangelical Christians* 71,000.
Largest Religion Christian.
Fastest Growing Religion Non-religious.

Largest Ethnic Groups Irish (88.2%), British (3%), Polish (2.3%). Increasing numbers of immigrant groups (Eastern European, Latino, Asian, African, other).
Official Languages Irish, English. 40% speak Irish, but less than 4% use it as a first language. **All Languages** 5.

Economy Hi-tech industry and services are now more important than dairy farming and tourism. EU membership since 1973. Good economic growth dropped sharply since the 2008-2009 financial crisis.

Politics Under British rule for 700 years. Partitioned in 1921 between the 26 Catholic (Celtic) counties and the 6 mostly Protestant (Scots Anglo-Saxon) counties in Northern Ireland. The south gained independence in 1922, and became a parliamentary republic in 1949.

Ireland transformed dramatically in the last 20 years. EU membership and foreign investment helped the economy, and increased contact with Europe and the world. But this new wealth only benefitted some, and many people struggle economically. Cooperation with Northern Ireland (from the late 1990s) led to greater peace, an answer to prayer! The political future of Northern Ireland remains a sensitive issue, but healing, reconciliation, and forgiveness can occur. Pray that all Christians (Protestant and Catholic) might work together towards Kingdom goals.

Ireland's ancient Celtic Church strongly shaped society 1,500 years ago through its holistic spirituality. Sadly, centuries of suffering, oppression, violence, and bloodshed followed at the hands of the Vikings and the British. Pray that Irish society might be made whole. The Holy Spirit moved in the last decades and changed Ireland from strict Catholicism to a spiritually alive land, where new Christian fellowships form rapidly. Many are Pentecostal or charismatic, and a large number are multi-ethnic or immigrant congregations. These groups bring new life and passion to traditional denominations which were in decline, and many recognize the need to reach the unevangelized both in Ireland and throughout the world.

The Catholic Church was central to Irish identity for centuries, but cultural changes and sexual scandals (and their cover-ups) led to significant loss. More Irish are non-religious than ever before. However, a lively charismatic renewal movement now grows inside the Catholic Church. Pray for the Irish nation to rediscover its ancient heritage of deep faith in Christ. Pray also for true repentance and forgiveness over the sex scandals and cover-ups, and for purity in the Catholic Church.

4 **Evangelicals experience steady growth.** About 1/3 of evangelicals come from non-Irish ethnic groups, including more recent immigrants. Pray for the newly formed Evangelical Alliance to draw believers together across the many denominations and ethnic groups. Despite good growth, Ireland still has the lowest percentage of evangelicals of any English-speaking nation, and Muslim numbers grow faster than evangelicals. Some Christian leaders speak of "20/20 vision", a vision to see 20% of Ireland's population in a personal relationship with Christ by the year 2020. Pray to see this vision fulfilled!

5 **Christian ministries** help the unemployed find work, assist those who suffer with AIDS, and reach out to the urban poor. Pray that evangelicals might demonstrate the gospel by word and by deed in their communities. Missionaries now work in all 26 counties, but most focus on the Dublin area. Pray for patient, relational witness to Christ among the older generation, who are often rural and Irish speaking. Travellers (Gypsies) have been in Ireland for centuries, but little Christian work has reached out specifically to them. Many are poor, illiterate, and have lower life expectancy than any other group in Ireland.

Italy
Europe

Pop 60.1 million. **Capital** Rome (3.4 mill).
Christians 49.5 mill. *Evangelical Christians* 633,000.
Largest Religion Christian.
Fastest Growing Religion Muslim.

Largest Ethnic Groups Italian (93.4%, a wide variety of regional cultures with deep differences between north and south), European (3.8%, includes Albanian, French, Austrian, German, others).
Official Language Italian, but strong use of 9 regional languages related to Italian. **All Languages** 42.
Economy World's 7th largest economy. Highly industrialized, and known for quality manufactured

goods. Large contrast between the north (wealthy) and south (less modernized, high unemployment). Corruption, organized crime, and weak law enforcement limit growth.
Politics United as a single state in 1870. A republican democracy since 1946. Italy is known for its many changes of government (more than 60 since the end of WWII). A member of the EU.

---

1 **This great nation contributed much to the world** through its legal systems (Roman law), language (Latin), culture (Renaissance, art, music), and innovation (fashion, cars). But the country struggles with financial troubles and organized crime. Networks such as the Sicilian Mafia, Neapolitan *Camorra*, and now the powerful Calabrian *'Ndrangheta* influence local and federal governments, and every level of society. Pray for courageous people who will oppose this criminal system which hurts the Italian economy. Pray for Christians to live out Kingdom values when they face difficult decisions.

2 **Christianity once thrived in Italy,** but it soon became a formalized state religion. Today the majority of Italians are Roman Catholic by culture, but many distrust the Church. Some studies suggest as few as 3% faithfully practise Catholicism. The north is mostly secular, and the south has a mix of Catholic faith with folk superstitions. Those who do pray will more often pray to a saint than to Jesus. Satanism grows in some areas, and Turin acts as a global centre for its followers. Italians will more likely explore a New Age or pagan practice than explore the Bible. However, the Catholic

Church does take action in society. It offers compassion ministries, and takes a stand against secular philosophies. Ask God to remove the many barriers that keep people from understanding the gospel.

3 **The Protestant Reformation** that touched much of Europe had little impact in Italy, and the country has never had a widespread biblical revival. The world's oldest Protestant denomination (the Waldensian Church) began in northwest Italy. But today liberal theology dominates the Waldensian Church and some other Protestant groups. Protestant witness in Italy is weak, divided, and fragmented. The number of congregations increases more often by bitter church splits than by strategic church planting. Pray for revival that leads to fellowship and cooperative outreach!

4 **Signs of hope for the Church!** Several church networks (including the Evangelical Alliance) now work towards trust, respect, and even collaboration across the long-standing denominational divides. Traditional Pentecostal churches have more strength, particularly in the south, and charismatic churches grow quickly through active outreach. Brethren churches and others hold evangelistic events. Relational evangelism resulted in some new cell groups and house churches, and believers see this approach can be effective. New immigrant congregations among Eastern Europeans, Romanians, Africans, Asians, and Latinos encourage the Church in Italy with their lively and holistic outreach. They also open Italians' eyes to the needs of different people groups inside Italy and around the world.

5 **More than 70% of Italy's 8,101** *comuni* (communities that range from small villages to large cities) lack a Bible-believing congregation. Sardinia (a Mediterranean island) has 1.67 million people and its own language and culture, but only 30 evangelical churches and a few Christian workers serve here. The almost 1.9 million university students remain a needy mission field, as do around 500,000 drug addicts who have high rates of HIV infection and crime. Few Italians get involved in long-term career missions, whether in Italy or beyond. Pray that the various means of Bible-based training available would increase pastoral leadership across the nation, and in turn encourage the whole Church to new levels of maturity and mission!

6 **Pray for the unreached minorities.** Many immigrants risk their lives to cross the sea in overcrowded boats to reach Italy and illegally enter the EU. Organized criminal networks take advantage of their desperation, and it drains the resources of the Italian government. Some Italians respond with increased hatred towards immigrants. Pray for all legal and illegal immigrants who land in Italy, that they might discover spiritual freedom and riches in Jesus. Pray especially for the 1.5 million Muslims (70% North African).

Latvia

Europe

Pop 2.2 million. **Capital** Riga (707,000).

Christians 1.3 mill. *Evangelical Christians* 157,000.

Largest Religion Christian.

Fastest Growing Religion Christianity declines at a slower rate than other religious groups of significant size.

Largest Ethnic Groups Baltic (59.1%, Latvian and Lithuanian), Slavic (38.9%, Russian, Belarusian, Ukrainian, Polish), Other European (0.7%).

Official Language Latvian (Lettish). **All Languages** 13.

Economy The poorest EU nation, but with fastest-growing economy in EU in recent years. An industrialized and privatized market economy. Latvia lacks natural resources.

Politics Ruled by a succession of foreign powers since the Middle Ages: Germans, Danes, Poles, Swedes, and Russians. Independent briefly (1917-1940), then reconquered by Russians under Stalin, who murdered or deported one-fifth of population and forced Russians to resettle there. Independent from 1991 as a multiparty democracy. Joined NATO and the EU (2004).

1 **The Soviet Union's departure left a moral vacuum** filled by negative influences. Alcohol abuse, illegal drugs, the fast-growing sex trade, high abortion rates, the world's 4th-highest suicide rate, and corruption in government all revealed deeper problems. People often feel emotionally numb or even hopeless. Pray for society to face this challenge, and to build a nation known for hope and righteousness.

2 **Latvia has deep pagan roots,** and was one of the last European peoples to be Christianized. 60% belong to a Christian Church, but only a small minority practise their faith. Christian and pagan cults again spread and challenge Christianity. Pray for a new move of the Spirit in the historic Churches (most Christians are Lutheran, Catholic, or Orthodox).

3 **Praise God for the unity among churches!** Leaders of almost every denomination and Christian confession attend "prayer and worship summits". These meetings form the foundation for revival in Latvia. Pray that this unity might help reverse the moral decline in Latvia, and that church members will follow their leaders' example to worship and work together for the Kingdom.

Christian Blocs
(% of Christian Population)

- Other (0.6%)
- Orthodox (26%)
- Protestant (36%)
- Catholic (30%)
- Independent (7%)

4 **Missions vision.** The Latvian Evangelical Alliance has a vision (CP-21) to work with indigenous churches to plant new churches and reach every Latvian. Pray especially for more teams to evangelize in villages. Rural populations have fewer opportunities to encounter Christ. Pray for greater reconciliation and partnerships between Latvian Christians and ethnic Russians. Their painful history remains unresolved.

Lithuania

Europe

Pop 3.3 million. **Capital** Vilnius (541,000).

Christians 2.8 mill. *Evangelical Christians* 36,000.
Largest Religion Christian.
Fastest Growing Religion Non-religious.

Largest Ethnic Groups Lithuanian (83.5%), Polish (6.7%), Russian (6.3%), Belarusian (1.2%), Ukrainian (0.6%).
Official Language Lithuanian. **All Languages** 12.

Economy Based on industry and agriculture. Large numbers of emigrants to wealthier EU countries has negative effect on the economy.

Politics A powerful duchy that controlled much of West Russia, Belarus, and Ukraine in the 14th century. Later a joint state with Poland, then annexed by Russia (late 18th century). Independent in 1918, but again occupied by the Soviet Union (1940-1990). Independent as a parliamentary democracy from 1990. A member of the EU.

Freedom brought good progress. Doors for the gospel remain open! However, freedom also brought dangers like greed for material goods, selfish pleasure-seeking, and a belief that traditional morals have no value. Substance abuse, suicide, and trafficking of women for prostitution all damage the social foundations. Spiritual transformation must accompany economic growth. Lithuania was the last European nation to be Christianized. Pray that God will bring massive social change through His people!

Traditional Christianity. The Catholic Church plays an essential role in society, but only 1 in 6 Catholics attends church weekly. Pray that the Catholic Church increases fellowship with other Christian groups, and uses its influence to draw people to Christ. Franciscan, charismatic, and evangelical-style networks in the Catholic Church bring in younger leadership and fresh spirituality. Other traditional denominations also face challenges, and most struggle to keep members. Pray for new life among these groups (Lutheran, Reformed, Orthodox).

Pray for evangelical unity. Lithuania still does not have an Evangelical Alliance. Praise God that the more established evangelical groups (Baptists, Pentecostals, Adventists) survived through the Soviet era! Now they must adapt to meet spiritual needs of a new era. Newer Pentecostal and charismatic churches grew quickly in the last decade through active outreach and ministry. Pray for discipleship for the new believers. Cults and much false teaching entered the country when religious freedom came, and biblical foundations must be established.

Macedonia *Europe*

Pop 2 million. **Capital** Skopje (524,000).
Christians 1.3 mill. *Evangelical Christians* 4,300.
Largest Religion Christian.
Fastest Growing Religion Muslim.
Largest Ethnic Groups Ethnic populations are a sensitive political issue, so even with census data it is difficult to report accurately. Macedonian (61.6%), Albanian (25.2%), Romani (5.2%), Turk (3.9%), Serb (1.6%), Bosnian (0.9%).
Official Language Macedonian. **All languages** 10.
Economy One of the poorest regions of former Yugoslavia. Based on agriculture, as industry declines. High unemployment and emigration rates.
Politics A multiparty democracy. Tensions with nearby countries, but most historically with Greece over the name Republic of Macedonia (Greece has its own region called Macedonia). Greece uses its power to block Macedonia's entry to the EU and NATO.

Ethnic divisions dominate politics and society. The large Albanian population feels more connected with Albania and Kosovo than with other groups in Macedonia. Nearby Greece, Bulgaria, and Serbia each have plans for Macedonia. Economic struggles lead many to leave the country, or to migrate to cities. Many of the 2,000 villages have disappeared. Pray for wisdom for the government, and pray that divided communities might find ways to build their nation together.

The Macedonian Orthodox Church represents almost two-thirds of the population, but more than 1,000 churches remain largely empty and most Macedonians do not practise any faith. The

Church split away from the Serbian Orthodox Church, and conflict between them exists. The Macedonian Orthodox Church sometimes opposes new expressions of Christianity such as evangelicalism, but some dialogue happens between them. Pray for new life to touch this Church and all who belong to it.

3 **The evangelical church in Macedonia grows faster than in most of Europe!** It is small (fewer than 100 congregations), but they have ambitious goals for outreach. Many congregations deliberately move into unevangelized cities and neighbourhoods, and evangelicals minister across ethnic and national boundaries to share the gospel with their neighbours. This is remarkable in a very divided region! Pray that believers might work hard for true unity, and that Christian love for one another might attract many to Christ. Citywide worship events, pastors' prayer summits, and even websites focused on the issue of unity already address the challenge.

4 **Pray for the ethnic minorities,** each in need of ministry. Indigenous groups such as Macedonian Mission to the Balkans reach out to ethnic groups inside Macedonia as well as in neighbouring countries. Foreign missions find Macedonia to be one of Europe's most needy lands, responsive to the gospel but also difficult.

Malta
Europe

Pop 410,000. **Capital** Valetta (200,000).

Christians 397,000. *Evangelical Christians* 5,200.
Largest Religion Christian.
Fastest Growing Religion Muslim.

Largest Ethnic Groups Maltese (93%, descendants of Phoenicians, Greeks, Romans, Arabs, Normans, others), Other groups (7%, British, Italian, plus African and Asian immigrants).
Official Languages Maltese, English. **All Languages** 4.

Economy Based on tourism, light industry, shipping, I.T., and financial services.
Politics Independent from Britain in 1964. A parliamentary republic and member of the EU.

Mediterranean Sea — Italy — Sicily (Italy) — Tunisia — **Malta** Valetta

1 **Malta was the first European nation to embrace Christianity,** after the Apostle Paul was shipwrecked here. From 1000 BC onwards many powers seized this island, but the Maltese always kept their strong Christian identity. The majority regularly attend Catholic mass, and over 80% feel their religion is important. Malta remains the most religious nation in Europe. However, not many Maltese have a personal walk with the living Lord Jesus. Pray that the strong religious tradition will open the door into greater revelation of God in Jesus Christ.

2 **Evangelical witness.** Extensive use of the Alpha Course and JESUS film resulted in new believers, many of whom now worship within Catholic charismatic groups. Protestant evangelical witness did not exist until after independence (1964), but now around 500 evangelicals worship in 10-14 Protestant congregations and house churches. Many Maltese emigrated to other lands where some came to know the Lord. The Maltese diaspora outnumber the population on Malta, but some return home. Pray that those who return might include followers of Christ who witness to His gospel.

Pray for outreach opportunities. More than 2,000 immigrants try to reach Europe through Malta each year. Pray for Maltese to show compassion and Christian love. Pray also for someone to develop a special ministry to seafarers who pass through Malta on the many cruise and container ships.

Moldova

Europe

Pop 3.6 million. **Capital** Chisinau (656,000).

Christians 2.6 mill. *Evangelical Christians* 132,000.
Largest Religion Christian.
Fastest Growing Religion Non-religious.

Largest Ethnic Groups Moldavian (73.8%), Ukrainian (8.5%), Turkic (4%), Russian (6%), Romanian (2.2%), Bulgarian (1.9%).
Official Language Moldovan Romanian. **All Languages** 13.

Economy Potential from rich agricultural land. But among Europe's poorest nations due to political problems, lack of industry and trade, dependence on Russia, and effects of Communism that remain.

Politics Independent from the former Soviet Union in 1991. A republic with parliament. The country is divided on cultural and ethnic lines with some regions wanting to secede, gain autonomy, or join Russia.

---

1 **Moldova cannot move forward** until it solves several major issues. Transnistria functions almost as a separate state (with support from Russia), and makes the country unstable. It has become a centre for organized crime and smuggling. The depressed economy forces 1 out of every 4 people to seek work outside the country. Moldova has the largest proportion of women lured abroad into human trafficking rings. Many people struggle with alcohol and drug abuse. Pray for a government that wisely and effectively addresses these devastating challenges.

2 **Moldova remains open to the gospel,** and evangelical churches continue to grow and multiply! The gospel spreads more deeply into society as believers focus on evangelism and church planting. Still, poverty has forced many pastors and up to 20,000 evangelicals to leave Moldova in recent years. Pray that God might provide the Church's material needs such as jobs, buildings, discipleship materials, and training resources for leaders.

3 **The Orthodox Church** has strong political influence, and uses it against those it views as threats (unregistered Protestants, Muslims, and rival Orthodox groups). Traditional Orthodox villages especially oppose preaching and church planting, sometimes even with violence. But life grows in the Orthodox Church, particularly through the Agape ministry. Pray that the Holy Spirit would deepen the spiritual life of many from the Orthodox faith.

 The less reached:

- *The Gagauz* are Turkish, but Orthodox Christians. Some among them are evangelicals with a vision to reach Muslims in Moldova and Eurasia.
- *The Muslim minorities* face prejudice from the Orthodox majority, but the Gagauz and Moldovans share the gospel with them (mostly Turkic Muslims).
- *The Gypsy population* has very few evangelical Christians.

Montenegro

Pop 626,000. **Capital** Podgorica (144,000).

Christians 482,000. *Evangelical Christians* (around 280).
Largest Religion Christian.
Fastest Growing Religion Non-religious.

Largest Ethnic Groups Precise figures difficult to obtain, so estimated: Montenegrin (46.7%), Serb (34.6%), Bosniak (8.4%), Albanian (5.6%), Croat (1.2%), Slovak (1%), Romani (0.7%).

Official Language Montenegrin (Serbian, Bosnian, Albanian, Croatian also recognized as regional languages). **All languages** 6.

Economy Suffered from war and sanctions in the 1990s. Progress since adopting the Euro and opening to foreign investments. Tourism grows quickly along the beautiful coastline.

Politics First recognized as a state in 1077, but became part of the Kingdom of Yugoslavia in 1918. Retained ties to Serbia when Yugoslavia divided (1992), but gained independence in 2006. A multiparty parliamentary democracy.

---

1 **Independence brought optimism and hope.** Montenegro is a small country, but it has great potential. However, it must avoid the hatred among ethnic/religious communities that cripples most nations of the Balkan region. Pray for Montenegro to be a just, peaceful, and corruption-free nation which enjoys ethnic harmony! Pray that people will seek the truth of Christ in the midst of their newfound nationhood.

2 **The Orthodox Church** represents almost 75% of the population, but many do not practise their faith. The Montenegrin Orthodox Church seeks to establish itself in place of the Serbian Orthodox Church. Pray that instead of argument over rights and property, Orthodox leaders would demonstrate Christlike leadership to the people. Pray for the Holy Spirit to bring new spiritual life to the nation's Orthodox community.

3 **The evangelical community is tiny** (less than 300), but it grows! Pentecostals, Baptists, and Brethren have active churches. These few congregations have a vision to share the gospel. Pray for their faithful witness despite the opposition, for unity among denominations, and for fruitful ministry! Pray for good partnership among the local churches and the few foreign workers. Pray especially for loving outreach to the Bosniaks (almost all Muslim) and the Albanians (with no evangelical groups among them).

Netherlands

Pop 16.7 million. **Capital** Amsterdam (administrative, 1 mill), The Hague (government, 474,000).

Christians 7.8 mill. *Evangelical Christians* 717,000.
Largest Religion Non-religious.
Fastest Growing Religion Muslim.

Largest Ethnic Groups Dutch (78.2%), Frisian (5.1%), Groningers (3.7%), Asian (8.3%, Arab, Indonesian, Turkish, other), Caribbean peoples (2.1%, Suriname Creole, Antillean, other). Many other European nationalities.
Official Languages Dutch (Nederlands), Frisian. Many also speak English. **All Languages** 38.

Economy Strong industrial, agricultural, and trade economy. Member of the EU. Low unemployment, and a generous social security system supports a large number registered as unable to work.

Politics Independent from 1568 after Protestant-led revolt against Spain. Historically one of world's great commercial nations. Stable, democratic, constitutional monarchy.

---

1 **Christianity in the Netherlands** seems to have reached a low point. Its glorious history as a Christian nation includes ministry to refugees and Jews, and a long record of service in foreign missions. But secular society today turns its back on its Christian past. Less than 20% of the population now attend church regularly. The Netherlands leads the world in promotion of secular and New Age views or values. Few restrictions exist for drug use, deviant lifestyles, prostitution, euthanasia, and abortion. Half the nation's church buildings are now either destroyed or converted for other uses such as bars and mosques. Pray for revival that restores the nation spiritually.

2 **The Roman Catholic Church and historic Protestant Churches both declined** in the last century. Catholics dropped from 41% (1975) to about 20% in less than 40 years. Protestants went from 60% in 1900 to 18% in 2010. But praise God for the growth of charismatic and evangelical groups within Dutch Catholicism, and for the spread of Alpha Courses. Ask God to send spiritual renewal in the (Protestant) Calvinist and Free Church denominations. Pray for spiritual renewal to replace empty traditions, and for a recommitment to Scripture and biblical holiness. Pray also for a new generation of Christian leaders for all congregations.

3 **Signs of hope.** Even while evangelical numbers decline overall, Pentecostal Christians have a lively faith, and independent churches grow in number and strength. *(See chart "Evangelical Growth".)* The newer international churches and small congregations planted show the openness of some hearts to the gospel! Immigrant churches (700,000 immigrant Christians) bring diversity and new hope to the Netherlands. Pray that all churches will work in partnership for cross-cultural outreach to both the host nationality and other immigrant groups. Dutch missions no longer have their previous numbers or influence, but the rising immigrant population awakened some to the needs of the unevangelized world, and numbers of agencies and missionaries began to increase again.

4 **Most people have little meaningful contact with the gospel.** Open and relational outreach (such as the Alpha Course) effectively reaches people. Pray specifically for:

- *The secular, international cities.* Only 1-3% of Amsterdam attends church, and most of those are migrants. Other large cities face similar challenges. Pray for the outreach efforts of the small but lively churches.

- *Migrant ethnic minorities.* Some predict that 1/3 of the country will be immigrants by 2050. Some communities do not integrate into Dutch life and society, and social tensions rise. At the same time, these minorities are the least-evangelized peoples of the country. Pray for spiritually effective, intentional outreach to every culture.

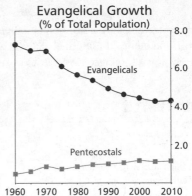

Evangelical Growth
(% of Total Population)

- *Muslims.* A steady but slow-growing number of Muslims now believe in Christ. Pray for this trickle to become a stream and then a flood! Now is an ideal time to reach out in friendship to Muslims with the love and power of Christ.

Norway

Europe

Pop 4.9 million. **Capital** Oslo (888,000).

Christians 4.4 mill. *Evangelical Christians* 410,000.
Largest Religion Christian.
Fastest Growing Religion Muslim.

Largest Ethnic Groups Norwegian (92%), Foreign-origin: European (7.4%), Asian (3.6%), African (0.6%), Sami (0.5%), Romani (0.1%, Gypsy).
Official Language Norwegian. **All Languages** 20.

Economy Strong, wealthy economy based on oil, mining, fishing, forest products, and hi-tech industries.
Politics A parliamentary monarchy. Independent from Sweden in 1905. Not an EU member, but participates in the European Economic Community (EEC).

1 Norway has a powerful spiritual heritage, and influence from prayer and revival movements across the last 200 years remains clear. The Lutheran Church is the most evangelical of all the state churches in Europe. Other denominations (Free Churches) also contribute to church life, and of these, Pentecostal and charismatic groups have the most members. But Norway faces the same battles as other European societies, where people believe that different religions or moral practices can be true for different people, or in different situations. Pray for a new revival, and for a deep commitment to biblical faith and practice. Pray for God to re-establish the roots of Norway's rich Christian past.

2 Norway needs new church-planting efforts. Missions that focus on foreign fields now also see the need at home. 90% of Norwegians are church members, but not all actively follow Christ. Only 4% attend church most Sundays. Between 1996 and 2005, workers planted more than 250 new congregations! Many immigrants are vibrant Christians who bring lively new congregations to Norway's cities. Most non-Christians live in and around Oslo. How can the Church disciple the large number of less-committed Christians to reach the increasing numbers of non-Christians in Norway?

3 **Norway has a strong mission-sending tradition,** and remains among the top sending nations. Many independent organizations both inside and outside the Lutheran Church grew out of "mission houses", or informal places believers gather for prayer, worship, and community. Pray for a new wave of younger missionaries to carry on the work at home and abroad.

Poland

Europe

Pop 38 million. **Capital** Warsaw (1.7 mill).

Christians 34 mill. *Evangelical Christians* 95,000.
Largest Religion Christian.
Fastest Growing Religion Non-religious.

Largest Ethnic Groups Polish (96.7%), Belarusian (0.15-1.6%), Ukrainian (0.1-2.1%), other Slavic and European peoples.
Official Language Polish. **All Languages** 20.

Economy Historically agricultural, but heavy industry added during Communist rule. Significant growth since 1990, but challenged by large number of young workers and skilled labourers who emigrate, and unemployment for those who remain.

Politics Gained a national identity in the 10th century. United with Lithuania in 1569. Divided and occupied by many nations since then. 1 in 4 people died during WWII. Communist rule from 1945, but overthrown in 1989. Now a multiparty democracy. EU member since 2004.

1 **Praise God for the stability, progress, and freedom** that allow believers to preach the good news! Many Poles dreamed of new wealth after independence from Communist rule. Sadly, unemployment and poverty still affect many, especially in rural areas. Even those who found riches did not find true satisfaction. Young people have more material possessions, but now struggle with violence, immorality, and meaninglessness in society. Pray the people might search first for God, above all other pursuits.

2 **The Catholic Church** served as a guardian of Polish culture and national pride for a long time, in the face of foreign domination. Nearly 86% of Poles are Catholic, and many feel committed to their faith. Poland remains one of the most religious states in Europe! The number of applications for the priesthood actually increases, and around 6,000 Polish priests serve around the world. However, regular attendance at mass has fallen from 58% in 1989 to 28% in 2008, and the influence of Christian faith on daily life continues to decrease. Pray for all Catholics to find renewal and spiritual life in the person of Jesus.

3 **Most Poles resist the gospel** because of their cultural commitment to Catholicism, or due to spiritual disinterest or confusion. The large Polish diaspora (millions) live and work in other places in Europe. Pray that many might encounter the gospel in a new way, and for host cultures to reach out to them. Jehovah's Witnesses are twice as numerous as evangelicals. Pagan, Wicca (witchcraft), and New Age groups all gain followers here. Many mix these practices with their Catholic beliefs. Polish Catholics believe Mary to be the spiritual queen of Poland and the intercessor between God and humans. Pray for her to be rightly honoured, but not worshipped. Pray for a demonstration of the power of Jesus, and for the defeat of all false teachings.

4 **Evangelicals remain a small minority.** More evangelicals live in Saudi Arabia than in Poland! 90% of municipalities have no evangelical congregation. Pray for the Holy Spirit to bring reconciliation, fellowship, and unity of vision in Jesus' name among all evangelical groups. Pray for well-trained, experienced pastors for the churches, as many who complete studies leave for other lands. Poles could be excellent missionaries, especially in the former Soviet Union. But the shortage of workers inside Poland and limited resources hinder missions. Pray for a healthy and large mission-sending movement from Poland!

Portugal
Europe

Pop 10.7 million. **Capital** Lisbon (2.8 mill).

Christians 10.1 mill. *Evangelical Christians* 319,000.
Largest Religion Christian.
Fastest Growing Religion Non-religious.

Largest Ethnic Groups Portuguese (91.3%), Indigenous minorities (1.1%, includes Romani, Galician, Mirandesa).
Official Language Portuguese. **All Languages** 9.

Economy Poor after years of dictatorship and colonial wars. Improved after entry into EU (1986), then declined since 2001. Tourism, manufacturing, and services support the economy.

Politics Independent kingdom from 1143. A republic in 1910. The 1974 revolution ended 48 years of dictatorship and instituted a parliamentary democracy. Granted all its African colonies independence in 1975. A member of the EU.

1 **Religious and political freedom** transformed Portugal after 1975. But the focus on individualism and material gain, and a rise in substance abuse, all challenge the nation. The Roman Catholic Church still has influence, but it needs renewal. In southern areas, less than 3% attend mass. Pray for the Holy Spirit to work so that many people encounter the Scriptures and the Saviour in a meaningful way.

2 **Evangelical growth** brings encouragement! In 2000, 69 counties had no evangelical congregation. Today, that number is only 44. But many denominations suffered painful splits. Pray for churches to focus on the core elements of the faith, and to extend grace to others in the minor differences. The Portuguese Evangelical Alliance (EA) set a goal to plant a church in every county by 2015. Pray for their success! Many congregations need full-time workers with spiritual maturity and theological training. The Portuguese Church has a unique role to play around the world because of the widespread use of the language. Pray for churches to increase their involvement in mission sending.

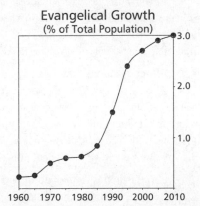

Evangelical Growth
(% of Total Population)

3 **Pray for the less-reached areas.** The 7 northern and northeastern provinces are strongly traditional Catholic, with few evangelical churches. The 4 provinces in the south are poorer, and less religious. Madeira Island (270,000) has fewer than 20 small evangelical churches, and the Azores

(250,000) has just 26. Pray also for outreach to ethnic minorities (from West Africa, Brazil, China, Macau, Ukraine, others). Many are unevangelized.

 Expatriate missions find Portugal a difficult field, but one with promise. Most new growth comes from immigrant communities rather than among Portuguese. Brazilians represent a large portion of expatriate missionaries and agencies. Pray for the work in evangelism, church planting, Bible training, and music. Sports are a useful form of outreach. The Internet is an area for evangelistic ministry that needs to be explored by skilled Christian workers.

Romania
Europe

Pop 21.2 million. **Capital** Bucharest (1.9 mill).

Christians 20.5 mill. *Evangelical Christians* 1.1 mill.
Largest Religion Christian.
Fastest Growing Religion Christianity declines at a slower rate than other religions.

Largest Ethnic Groups Romanian (86.5%, a Latin people descended from Romans), Hungarian (6.6%, most in Transylvania), Romani/Gypsy (3.8%, though actual figures may be higher), Slav (1.4%), Turkic (0.8%).
Official Language Romanian. **All Languages** 23.

Economy Rich in good agricultural land, minerals and oil. Grew more industrialized during Communism. Struggles with unemployment, and many emigrate to other European countries. Rural people increasingly abandon their farms.
Politics Independent from 1859 until Communist coup in 1947. Suffered under one of the Communist bloc's most oppressive and cruel regimes. Revolution (1989-1990) brought a parliamentary government. A member of the EU from 2007.

---

1 **A legacy of brokenness endures** from the days of Ceausescu's regime. Every kind of social evil came to fill the moral space left after Communism ended. People struggle with substance abuse, prostitution, human trafficking, and abuse of children. One of the world's highest abortion rates, with 3 abortions for every child born. Deep corruption led to economic instability and widespread unemployment. Pray for leadership that has wisdom to follow the right path, and integrity to establish right policies.

2 **Romania is one of the world's most Christian nations by percentage,** but it is difficult to see this in society. The atheistic worldview of Communism persists. Weak faith, hypocrisy, and slander of other denominations cause problems for all Christian groups. This does not glorify Christ, and does not build up the Church. Church members and even clergy mix faith with folk religious practices or the occult. Churches neglect many poor people. Pray for a breakthrough of love, holiness, discipleship, and prayer in all denominations.

3 **The Orthodox Church dominates society** (87% of the population affiliated), but many do not hold a personal faith. Some Orthodox priests oppose evangelical outreach, even with violence. Yet within this ancient Church is life and potential for great good. The Lord's Army is a powerful renewal movement within the Orthodox Church with 300,000 members and others who support it. Pray for renewal from within Romanian Orthodoxy, and for the Holy Spirit to awaken those whose faith is dead or asleep!

4 **Romania has Europe's 4th-largest evangelical population,** even with a decline in overall numbers. Some consider it one of the most spiritually receptive nations in Europe. Almost 6,000 evangelical congregations now exist, and believers plant over 100 new churches every year. A group of mission agencies partner to reach the 19 cities and 9,500 villages without an evangelical church. Pray for this vision to become a movement owned by the national Church, and able to plant churches in every city, town, and village.

5 **The Church faces many challenges.** It grows in size and maturity, but unity is a major problem. Almost no cooperative work or prayer exists. Ethnic divisions even inside the Church separate Hungarian and Romani minorities from fellowship with the Romanian majority. Young people and non-Christians struggle to relate to traditions that seem to serve no purpose. Generous but misguided foreign groups created an unhealthy dependence on outside money, which increased divisions in the Church. Most new churches lack a pastor, and many pastors lack training.

6 **Praise God for the 10 new indigenous mission agencies** begun since 2000. Romanians can easily access mission fields that Western missionaries cannot. Limited support and finance hinders the work, and we must pray for God to remove every barrier to a great mission-sending movement from Romania! The Romanian diaspora have planted many evangelical churches around Western Europe in countries where Romanians go to work. Pray that these churches might reach out beyond Romanians to the spiritually needy nations that host them!

Russia   *Europe*

Pop 140.4 million. **Capital** Moscow (10.5 mill).

Christians 93.9 mill. *Evangelical Christians* 1.6 mill.
Largest Religion Christian.
Fastest Growing Religion Muslim.

Largest Ethnic Groups Great diversity, but complex situation due to migration and efforts to make minorities more "Russian". Russian (80.5%), Ural-Siberian (6.8%, 37 peoples), Caucasus (3.8%, 34 peoples), Ukrainian (2.1%), Finno-Ugric (2%, 24 peoples), Armenian (0.8%), Belarusian (0.6%), Kazakh (0.5%, 3 peoples).
Official Language Russian; local languages in autonomous republics. **All Languages** 135.

Economy Vast natural resources (gas, oil, timber, minerals), and huge amounts of land for agriculture. The enormous size of the land, geographic isolation, and few seaports limit progress. Russia's oligarchs (wealthy billionaires) seized control of what were previously state-run industries, and most of the economy rests in the hands of a few powerful men. Despite a stronger economy in the last decade, the poor and unemployed number in the millions. Economic dependence on oil and gas exports, particularly to other European nations. Corruption, weak infrastructure, and population decline all present enormous challenges for Russia's future.

Politics The world's largest country (by area) stretches across 9 time zones. Became a country in the 8th century, with almost constant authoritarian rule by a person or a small group. Czarist Russia's collapse in 1917 was just before the Bolshevik Communist revolution. Russia dominated the USSR from its founding in 1922, and the Communist leadership took advantage of ordinary Russian people as well as the many ethnic groups and nearby states it seized or controlled. A multiparty federal democracy since the breakup of the Soviet Union (1990). Putin's appointment (1999) restored a strong central authority. Limited freedom of the press and media, unrest in the North Caucasus, and relations with the West and Asian superpowers are crucial but often strained. Upheaval in southern district could lead to civil war. Russian minorities in neighbouring countries are a source of tension.

1 **Russia has a long and proud history,** but remains a contradiction. Some see a bleak future, while others see a Russia on the rise. The older generation sometimes prefer the stability of life under the Communists. The younger generation see little hope offered by modern life. Russia has abundant natural resources and potential for greater output. Pray for balance of strong government with democratic accountability and respect of basic freedom. Russia tends towards authoritarian rule. Criminal networks remain highly influential at home and abroad. Pray they will be exposed and overthrown.

2 **Millions struggle against poverty and hopelessness.** Russia's population drops by over 500,000 each year, and its birth rate is among the world's lowest. At the same time, Russia's abortion rate is one of the world's highest. Statistics show more abortions than live births, and too many abortions also result in the death of the mother. Alcoholism, drug addiction, suicide, and family breakdown ruin many lives. Health care costs are too high for many to afford, and few have access to it. Russia has Europe's highest and fastest-rising rate of HIV/AIDS, which affects young people more than others. These struggles rob the country of its future.

3 **The Russian Orthodox Church (ROC)** survived Communism, and it remains the one major symbol of Russian identity. It sees itself as the preserver of a great Christian civilization handed down from Rome and Byzantium. It endured terrible persecution (along with other Christian groups) between 1920 and 1990 when up to 200,000 Christian leaders died as martyrs. Pray that all that is best about Orthodoxy's 1,000-year history will thrive and influence culture and society. Pray that the ROC will make peace with other Christian groups, and will stop any activity to suppress or harm them. Pray for the renewal movements within Russian Orthodoxy, and for fresh outreach to the Russian people. Russian Orthodoxy is culturally strong, but spiritually weak in the lives of most of its followers.

4 **The fall of the Iron Curtain opened Eastern Europe and Central Asia** to evangelism, church planting, rebirth of a Christian society, Bible translation work, and more. Churches more than doubled in number and in size, and the number of people who identify themselves as non-religious or atheist dropped by more than half from before 1991! Evangelicals tripled in number since 1991, and now have a recognized place within Russian religious culture. Their experience and maturity allow them to face with wisdom the agendas of both Western and Russian governments. But the days of fast growth (1990s) soon ended. Moscow and St Petersburg

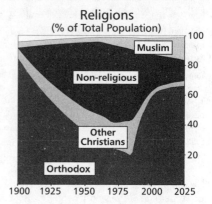

Religions
(% of Total Population)

have only 10% of Russia's population, but the largest amount of mission activity, ministry, and resources.

5 **Pray for a vision for outreach.** 90% of Russians still have no link to any church. Millions call themselves Russian Orthodox without actual belief in God. In 2009, 42 of Russia's 125 largest cities had no evangelical congregation. Many churches, especially newer groups, have big goals for evangelism and church planting. The New Testament Church of Perm, which meets in what was once Lenin's Palace of Culture, planted 300 daughter churches between 1991 and 2009, and planned to plant 100 more that year! Russian Baptists, along with the Slavic Gospel Association, aim to start one Bible-preaching church for each of Russia's 100,000 communities. Pray that this new spirit of faith will result in great fruit as believers proclaim and demonstrate the gospel locally, regionally, and nationally!

6 **Opportunities for open ministry and religious freedom** continue to decrease. The government passed complicated laws for registration of churches and organizations, and with regard to building codes. Laws require people to have education licences in order to teach the Bible, and at times stop academic and informal Bible training. All of this makes life difficult for evangelical groups. Some pressure comes from the ROC, which wants to keep its unique status and influence in Russia. Pray that all this prejudice will make the evangelicals stronger, and more dependent on God.

7 **Pray that foreign missionaries and agencies will humbly assist the national Church** to fulfil its own purpose. When the Soviet Union collapsed, a large surge of foreign Christian ministry entered Russia (1990s). Much of what happened was intended for good, but sadly was also insensitive and unhelpful. Some estimate over 1,500 missions and church-based agencies launched into ministry, with little coordination among them or with local believers. Since then, the government increases visa restrictions on foreign workers. It is now difficult, but not impossible, for foreign believers to stay long-term in Russia. Foreign believers can also have a strategic impact through short-term visits to teach, train, and help set up locally run ministries.

8 **Newer churches and younger people** especially now engage with many needs of society such as ministry to the poor, to widows and orphans, and with prisoners, drug addicts, and people with HIV/AIDS. This ministry earns evangelicals a better name with the government, and opens doors for collaboration with the Orthodox Church. Pray for the passion, the funds, and the people to be sufficient, so that these ministries may continue to have a powerful gospel impact in this way!

9 **The Church faces challenges** in unity and leadership. Apart from conflict with the ROC, evangelicals face tensions between Baptists and Pentecostals/charismatics, and between traditional Pentecostals and newer charismatics. While church networks join thousands of congregations, a national-level body to draw together all evangelicals within Russia does not yet fully exist. Pray for a spirit of unity and that Russian evangelicals would build each other up in love. The Russian Church has too few leaders, and those who serve face many challenges. Thousands of pastors and preachers have very little theological education, yet this is what congregations need most to help their young people from non-Christian backgrounds work through their Christian life and faith. Cell-based Bible study groups are one solution. Pray they will multiply. Hundreds of theological institutions have formed since 1991. Pray they will have high standards and be relevant to Russia's unique context. Pray for Russia's congregations and leadership to be truly biblical and truly Russian.

10 **Pray for a missions vision in the Russian Church,** and the ability to reach across the unique cultural and social barriers Russian missionaries face. For years Russian culture and language dominated, and Russia suppressed its ethnic minorities. Most Russian churches and even foreign missionaries focus on reaching Russians. Now nearly 20% of the population are non-Russian. Between them they speak 100 different languages. Ukrainians are more active than Russians in cross-cultural outreach in Russia. Pray for the Church to launch many more Russian sending agencies!

11 **Many peoples and social groups** need prayer. Over 78 ethnic minorities are unreached (over 13 million people). Moscow operates as the centre of the former Soviet world, and nearly every ethnicity from the former Soviet Union lives there. The Institute for Bible Translation (IBT) oversees around 100 translation projects into Russia's minority languages.

- **Muslims** number over 17 million, and are the majority of non-Russians across the Russian Federation. Their growth, and the decline of the ethnic-Russian population, could make them a majority by the end of the 21st century. Pray for openness to the gospel among Muslims, and for Christians to care about their salvation and reach out to them in love.

- **The Jews** once numbered over 2 million, but now are just 250,000. Emigration to Israel continues, but the European Russian cities have Jewish communities. Over 10,000 came to Christ, and a large number of Messianic Jews in Israel come from Russian or Ukrainian origin. Groups of Georgian, Tat, and Hill Jews in the Caucasus region remain unreached.

- **The Romani (Gypsy)** live scattered over European Russia, with many in the Ural Mountains. They live on the edges of society. God awakened some areas to the gospel, and churches were planted. About 5% of Russian Gypsies are evangelical.

- **The Chinese** number over 50,000 in Moscow alone, and over 1 million nationally (including temporary migrant workers in Siberia and the Russian Far East). Many Chinese come into eastern Russia, and some ethnic Russians view this as a potential threat, though they are essential to Russia's economy. Most are unevangelized. A small number of churches exist among them, but the wider Russian Church mostly neglects them.

- **16.5 million Russians live as ethnic minorities** in nearby countries. When the USSR collapsed, 15 new states formed and left Russians living within their borders. Their status and future are not secure, as their host populations often resent them. Nearly 20 million Russians returned to the Russian Federation in the last 25 years. Pray that many will be open to the gospel, and that they might receive a missions vision for the non-Christian peoples among whom they lived.

- **Followers of new religions** seem to gain more converts, even when faced with persecution. False teachings confuse spiritual truth, and they make the government and the ROC suspicious of all foreign groups. Scientology, Jehovah's Witnesses, the occult, shamanism, New Age, and others all gain followers. Pray that Christians may be trained and armed with the Word of God to combat these false beliefs.

Ethnic Minorities and Regions of the Russian Federation

The Russian Federation is a patchwork of republics, provinces, and other territories that vary in size, ethnicity, and religion. European Russian ethnicity and language long dominated the country. Minority groups face rejection by the very ones who colonized them through Russian imperialism and then Communism. However, without many minority group workers, the Russian economy would suffer greatly. And without massive-scale immigration in the future, Russia may become only a shadow of its former self.

Since the 1990s, Orthodox Christianity became associated with a "Russian" identity. In some areas Christianity seems part of the Russian oppression that brought the indigenous people great harm. How will Christians share the gospel in this context? Below we highlight some of Russia's minority ethnic groups. Please turn these facts into prayers for the salvation of many unreached across the Russian Federation, and for Christ to build his Church among all peoples.

THE NORTH CAUCASUS PEOPLES

1 **The North Caucasus region** is the poorest and least stable region in Russia. It has the highest unemployment, the highest birth rates, and widespread corruption. The region's 7 republics contain 50 to 60 ethnic groups of Caucasus, Turkic, and Iranian origin. The North Caucasus peoples are among the least reached on earth, and they live in Europe's least-evangelized region.

2 **Brutal wars between the Russian military and Chechen rebels** destabilized the whole region, and only ended in 2009. Local and foreign radical Islamic groups try to turn the complex conflict into a religious war. Pray that their plans may be defeated, and that the whole region might experience peace, progress, and religious freedom. Pray for wisdom, restraint, and moderation to replace radical extremes and hateful speech. Pray for a fair political situation, especially in Chechnya, Dagestan, Ingushetia, Abkhazia, and South Ossetia.

3 **Christian work in this region can be very dangerous.** However, the faithful work of Christians from the Russian Federation and beyond led to new groups of believers here. Most of the 50 or so groups have little Scripture in their languages or churches among their peoples. Pray for Bible translation in 25 languages of the area.

TATAR AND BASHKIR PEOPLES

1 **Tatarstan** has many minerals and good farmland, and a large degree of political and religious independence. The Tatar are Russia's largest Muslim people (5.5 million), and Europe's 2nd-largest. (More Tatars live outside Tatarstan than inside.) Only about 10% faithfully practise Islam, though it is a strong part of Tatar identity. Evangelical churches and groups increased among the Tatar, and may now total over 100 congregations! Most are Russian-speaking, but Tatar-speaking believers also grow in number. Persecution from the government, Muslims, and the Orthodox Church all draw evangelicals closer together in fellowship, even those who were historically divided by language and theology.

2 **Bashkortostan** is home of the Bashkort/Bashkir (18 million), a Turkic people related to the Tatar. They became Muslim in the 13th century, but the old paganism/folk religion remains strong and is mixed with their Islam. Pray for God to bind the powers that hold them. Evangelical congregations in Bashkortostan grew from 1 in 1991 to nearly 50 in 2010! Only a handful speak Bashkir.

PEOPLES WHO PRACTISE ANIMISM, SHAMANISM (OR TRADITIONAL RELIGIONS)

1 **The Udmurt** (560,000) mainly follow Orthodoxy, but some follow traditional pagan practices. Evangelical churches multiply rapidly among them, as they offer life to many who struggle with hopelessness, alcoholism, and other problems. Most congregations in Udmurtia include Russians, or a mix of Russians and Udmurts. Pray for opportunities for Udmurts to worship, pray, and learn about God in their own language and culture.

2 **The Mordvins** (700,000) still practise some of the traditional elements of beliefs they held before Russians forced them into Orthodoxy. Some are now evangelicals, but they have mostly mixed into Russian churches rather than having their own congregations. Pray for more Mordovian evangelical churches.

3 **The Mari people** (560,000) mostly follow their traditional animistic practices, although around one-third follow Christianity. The Mari attempt to revive their own culture and religion, but the government opposes these efforts. Estonians are ethnically related to the Mari, and teams of Estonian Christians minister among them with some results. Pray for the 40 or so small evangelical churches in their region.

4 **The Khanty, Mansi, and Nenet** are northern Finno-Ugric peoples whose future existence is in danger because of their nomadic lifestyle and their very small numbers. They retain most of their traditional animist beliefs under the surface of Russian Orthodoxy. Praise God that many Khantys recently became believers! The Nenets of the Arctic region have only a very small Christian minority. Pray for the Bible translation work that faces obstacles among them.

5 **The Altay people** (68,000) live mostly in the Altai Republic (where Russia, Mongolia, China, and Kazakhstan meet), a region highly important to shamanism, Buddhism, and even New Age religions. They practise shamanism, and spiritual opposition to the gospel is common here. Pray for the power and love of Jesus to break through to those who oppose the gospel. Evangelical numbers slowly grow, and a few churches have Altay pastors. Praise God for the Altay New Testament and a collection of Altay worship songs!

6 **The Khakass** (80,000 worldwide) practise animism/shamanism, and have close ties to nearby Tuvan and Altai peoples. Only 2 Khakass churches are known, with just over 100 believers. Pray that Christians might reach out to this small people group.

7 **The Sakha/Yakut people** (480,000) are Turkic, and were made Christian by the Orthodox Church. But they held on to their strong animist roots. 30 Sakha believers in 1987 grew to over 500 in 2010, and they actively evangelize their own people. Workers completed the New Testament in 2004, and they have produced Christian music in their unique Sakha style!

Buddhist Peoples

1   The Buryat (420,000) live north of Mongolia, mostly around Lake Baikal. They are the largest indigenous ethnic group in Siberia. Buddhists and Orthodox prevented a previous effort to evangelize this people who practise Buddhism and shamanism. Since 1990, a partnership of 26 agencies worked to reach the Buryat, and the number of people who join the Church increases.

2   The Tuvans (240,000) live northwest of Mongolia, and many know of them for their unique throat-singing traditions. They are 1 of only 2 Turkic peoples in the world to embrace Buddhism. They suffered severely under Communist rule, and have one of the highest rates of poverty, unemployment, and crime among Russia's ethnic groups. Spiritual warfare brought significant breakthrough among Tuvans. No known believers existed in 1990, but today a few thousand exist! Pray for discipleship for the new Tuvan believers.

3   The Kalmyk live northwest of the Caspian Sea, and are Europe's only Buddhist people (they practise a form of Tibetan Buddhism influenced by Mongolian shamanism). A handful of Christian churches with Kalmyk pastors exist among them. However, others label them as cultural traitors. East Asian missionaries often share a Buddhist background, and work effectively among these people.

Indigenous Peoples of the Russian Far East

1   The Chukchi, Evens (closely related to the Evenki of Siberia), Nanaⁱ, Koryak, Yupik, and others may each be small, but they have unique cultures and languages. Indigenous, Russian, Korean, and Western workers focus significant ministry on them.

Serbia   *Europe*

Pop 7.8 million. **Capital** Belgrade (1.1 mill).

Christians 6.2 mill. *Evangelical Christians* 46,000.
Largest Religion Christian.
Fastest Growing Religion Non-religious.

Largest Ethnic Groups Serb (82.9%), Hungarian (3.9%), Romani (2%), Bosnian (1.8%), Croat (0.9%), Montenegrin (0.9%), Albanian (0.8%), Slovak (0.8%), Romanian (0.5%).
Official Language Serbian. **All Languages** 21.

Economy Some slow growth this decade after years of war, UN trade sanctions, NATO military intervention, and disruption, and negative effects from 45 years under Communism. Devastated by floods in 2014.

Politics Serbia has rarely been independent since 1389. Ethnic nationalism in the region helped start WWI and provoke civil war/genocide in WWII. After Communism, the former Yugoslavia began to break apart and war commenced. Serbia fought Croatia and Bosnia. Treatment of Albanians in Kosovo brought NATO intervention (1999), then UN governance. Now a parliamentary democracy.

1   **Serbia sees itself as a defender of Europe and the Christian faith** against Muslim aggression. But much of the world sees Serbia as an aggressive, war-hungry nation guilty of horrible acts, and a promoter of hatred. Both views have some truth. Many Serbs hold bitterness about the centuries of domination by nearby peoples (Turks, Austrians, Germans, Croats, others). Pray for healing, and for a transformed Serbian identity. A mighty work of God is necessary!

2 The Balkan wars left a devastated economy, weak democracy, and poor relations with nearby countries and treatment of minority groups (including Kosovo). Resolutions must be found, but stubborn government and deep ethnic pride among the main faith groups (Orthodoxy, Islam, Catholicism) make political and religious structures a part of the problem. The tiny evangelical community is the only body that has multicultural fellowships. Pray God will use it to inspire change for good!

3 The Serbian Orthodox Church wants to regain great influence over national life. It suppressed other Orthodox Churches that serve ethnic minorities, and pushed for a law that restricts religious freedom. Pray for new life in this ancient Church, and for it to support religious freedom.

4 Evangelicals in Serbia face many difficulties. The recent religion law creates difficulty for all new religious groups, including many new evangelical groups. Protestants (110,000) have a long history among Hungarians and Slovak minorities, but little impact among Serbs and Albanians. Many do not live out their faith. Pray for revival. For groups where ethnic identity determines religious identity, evangelicals can appear to be traitors and part of a religious sect. But through all these challenges, newer churches do grow and minister Christ to others! Romani churches grow the fastest in Serbia, and reflect the culture of the Romani people well.

5 The war refugees (from the former Yugoslavia) need compassionate ministry. Millions became refugees or internally displaced, and few have returned to their homes. Many organizations, both foreign and indigenous, share Jesus' love through practical aid, and people do respond. Pray also for Serbs who now live in other lands. Many carry their troubles with them, and need effective outreach. Young people saw destruction of their parents' generation, and respond most to gospel outreach.

Kosovo *Europe*

Pop 2.1 million. **Capital** Pristina (183,000).
Christians estimated around 208,000.
Largest Religion Muslim.
Largest Ethnic Groups Albanian (88%), Serb (7-12% estimated), Bosniak (1.9%), Romani (1.7%), Turk (1%).
Major Languages Albanian, Serbian, English.
Economy One of Europe's weakest economies. Growth difficult amidst sanctions, poor policies and corruption, damage from conflict, and organized crime. About 50% of economy derived from foreign aid and remittances from Kosovars abroad.
Politics Officially a province of Serbia. Declared independence (2008), but not recognized by Serbia. Kosovo is a UN protectorate recognized by 107 UN nations. An ethnic Serb-majority area in northern Kosovo has some autonomy.

1 Kosovo's future is gloomy and uncertain. Ancient hatred between Serbs and ethnic Albanians led to the crisis of 1998-1999. Peace remains fragile, and a resolution appears very far off. Pray that community hatreds resolve into peace that lasts. Pray for an economy that grows to provide stability and good employment. Pray for God to stop the efforts of all who exploit Kosovars for personal gain.

2 Most Kosovar Albanians follow Islam, but some follow Christ. Money comes in (from Saudi Arabia, Iran) to build mosques, while hundreds of Christian sites were damaged or destroyed by angry mobs. Pray for an end to religious hatred! Pray that Muslims will see Jesus, to whom they are precious. Ministries find work in Kosovo difficult, but it does bear fruit, especially with children and youth. Pray that expatriate groups would keep the freedom to work in this majority Muslim land. Pray for more male workers, as many new believers are young men and teens.

 3 **Evangelicals grew from 80 in 1998 to over 2,000 today.** The 35 evangelical churches witness to their communities. Praise God that the country includes evangelicals as one of Kosovo's 5 faith communities, and for the formation of the Evangelical Movement of Kosovo (Evangelical Alliance).

Slovakia
Europe

Pop 5.4 million. **Capital** Bratislava (428,000).
Christians 5.1 mili. *Evangelical Christians* 67,000.
Largest Religion Christian.
Fastest Growing Religion Non-religious.
Largest Ethnic Groups Slovak (77.8%), Hungarian (10.7%), Romani/Gypsy (9.3%), Czech (1.1%), Ruthenian (0.3%), Ukrainian (0.3%).
Official Language Slovak. **All Languages** 13.
Economy One of the stronger economies in the EU. Many praised the post-Communist economic reforms. But wealth and employment opportunity not evenly distributed throughout the country.
Politics Part of Czechoslovakia until separation from the Czech Republic (1993). A multiparty republic. A member of the EU and NATO from 2004.

1 **Slovakia is a nation in the middle of great change.** Economic reform and EU membership solved some problems but created others. Increased wealth for some brought greed for material goods and a decline in moral standards. Depression and suicide rates are some of the highest in Europe. Pray for many to seek hope and truth, and to find them in Christ.

2 **Slovakia has a strong Christian heritage,** but the many Catholic, Lutheran, and Reformed Churches struggle with low attendance. Praise God for renewal movements, especially among Lutherans who focus on young people and small groups (Family Fellowships). Pray that the Holy Spirit would bring new life to the strong foundation of Christianity here.

3 **Evangelical denominations are few and small.** Previous church-planting efforts have slowed down, and the vision for the future needs to be renewed! To reach the whole country, believers must prioritize discipleship, evangelism, and church multiplication. Many desire to see churches in every city and town, but this will require thousands of new congregations planted. Pray for the accomplishment of this ambitious desire! Jehovah's Witnesses create a challenge for evangelicals, as more people attend their gatherings than Protestant evangelical services.

4 **Creative ministry ideas** introduce the gospel into the marketplace, into popular and youth culture, and into prisons and addiction centres. Pray that God will raise up a new generation of holy, faith-filled believers through these movements and outreach opportunities. Slovakia needs more foreign missionaries to evangelize, train leaders, and plant churches. The Apostolic Church now sends Slovak missionaries cross-culturally. Pray that mission agencies and local churches cooperate with joy and humility.

Slovenia

Pop 2 million. **Capital** Ljubljana (260,000).

Christians 1.1 mill. *Evangelical Christians* 1,800.
Largest Religion Christian.
Fastest Growing Religion Muslim.

Largest Ethnic Groups Slovene (90.2%), Serbo-Croatian (3%), German-Austrian (2.3%), Bosniak (1.5%), Italian (0.6%), Hungarian (0.5%).
Official Languages Slovene, Hungarian, Italian.
All Languages 10.

Economy Most wealthy of the former Yugoslav republics. Successful transition to a market economy. Good infrastructure, an educated workforce, and important location between Western Europe and the Balkans.

Politics Dominated for centuries by Austria. Independent from Yugoslav Federation in 1991. A parliamentary democracy with a coalition government. The 1st former-Communist country to hold presidency of the EU (2008).

1 **Catholic, Orthodox, and Lutheran Churches** lack spiritual life. New Age and Eastern religious beliefs, or a lack of any spiritual beliefs, all threaten the main Christian groups. Pray for God to awaken these churches, and help their members to grow in their faith in Christ.

2 **Slovenia has had a Protestant witness since the Reformation,** but still has very few evangelical churches and needs church-planting teams. The very small evangelical population is divided by ethnic group. Pray for unity, and for an Evangelical Alliance to unite the churches. Most congregations lack a full-time pastor, and need outside financial assistance. Pray for Slovene believers to evangelize their country, to support their pastors, and even to send missionaries!

3 **Churches need discipleship and evangelism resources.** The difficult language causes problems for the translation of books. Pray for more Slovene authors, and for the translation of quality materials. Pray for ideas to help Slovenians engage with the Bible! Primoz Trubar was a Protestant Reformer who wrote the first books in Slovene. Pray that his books help believers develop a right view of God. Believers have visions for Christian coffee shops, radio stations, and Slovene Christian websites. Pray for these dreams to become reality!

Spain

Pop 45.5 million. **Capital** Madrid (5.9 mill).

Christians 35.1 mill. *Evangelical Christians* 462,000.
Largest Religion Christian.
Fastest Growing Religion Muslim.

Largest Ethnic Groups Spanish (85.4%, includes Castilian, Catalan, Galician, others), Latin American (3.9%, Ecuadorean, Colombian, others), Basque (2.5%), Arab (1.9%), Gypsy/Romani (1.4%, known locally as Gitanos).
Official Language Catalán, Galician, Basque are official languages in their autonomous regions. Castilian (Spanish) is the only official language for the Spanish

territory. (Spanish is the world's 3rd-most widely used language, and the 1st language of over 340 mill people.)
All Languages 21.

Economy The world's greatest economic power in the 16th century, followed by 3 centuries of decline until Spain entered the EU (1986). Most income from tourism, industry, and agriculture. The global economic crisis of 2008 and crash of the housing market greatly slowed growth. By 2011, unemployment was among the highest in Europe (almost 23%). Small signs of growth since late 2013.

Politics Occupied by Muslim Moors for 700 years (ending 1492). Three centuries of Spanish empire followed by 2 centuries of instability, civil wars, and dictatorships. Now a constitutional monarchy with a multiparty democracy. Wide powers given to 17 autonomous communities and 2 cities, in order to preserve some national unity.

---

1 **Spain had an amazing transformation** after 1978. It abandoned a dictatorship for democratic rule, moved from poverty towards wealth, integrated into Europe, and increased religious freedom. But economic progress also brought greed for possessions and self-indulgent lifestyles. Sexual immorality, prostitution, and abortion now are common, and Spain has one of the lowest birth rates in the world. These problems combine with depression, debt, and disease to create future problems for society. Pray for Spain to wake up to the lies that have blinded it to the truth of the gospel.

2 **Spain is one of the world's heaviest users of cocaine, heroin, and marijuana.** Around 2 million take drugs, most of them young people. Over 100,000 addicts have found freedom through various rehabilitation ministries, and many have come to Christ. Ask God to grant love, power, and wisdom to all who work for the salvation of the Spanish people.

3 **Spain was considered one of the most Catholic countries,** but today less than 17% of Spanish people attend mass. The Catholic feasts or rituals no longer have spiritual meaning for most young people. In the 16th century (during the Inquisition), leaders tortured or killed thousands suspected of heresy, and forced hundreds of thousands of Jews, Muslims, and Protestants to either convert or leave. Pray for full repentance, and that the shame on Christianity may be lifted. Pray for renewal that breathes new life into the Catholic Church.

4 **Evangelical growth came with greater religious freedom,** mostly through immigration. Latin American, Romanian, and African believers came into Spain and brought their evangelical faith with them. Praise God for this truly diverse expression of Christianity that offers Spaniards new ways to experience belief in Jesus. Spain has never experienced a national revival, and the spiritual atmosphere seems very dry. Praise God for the "Filadelphia" movement among Spain's Romani, now the largest evangelical group in the country with more than 200,000 people involved!

5 **Pray for Christian workers** to serve in less-evangelized areas. Missionaries to Spain increased after 1978, and probably exceed 1,000 now. Latin American workers may plant as many as half of all new churches. Pray that new Bible translations in conversational Spanish, and in regional languages or dialects, will reach the various peoples of Spain. Pray especially for:

- *Unreached cities.* 345 cities and towns with over 5,000 people have no evangelical church, and many smaller towns or villages have no witness at all. Few churches can afford to pay a full-time pastor. Sometimes missionaries serve as pastors, though this limits their church-planting work. Pray for God to fill the seminaries and Bible schools with young Spanish leaders committed to both God's Word and God's work.

- *The Canary Islands* (7 islands off Africa's northwest coast). Evangelicals may be stronger here than in most of Spain. But Lanzarote, Fuerteventura, La Gomera, La Palma, and El Hierro need more ministry. Illegal immigrants from Morocco, Senegal, and other parts of Africa present an opportunity for Christian ministry.

- **Ceuta and Melilla** (70,000 people each). These cities on Morocco's north coast are half Muslim, half speaking Cherja (a Berber language). Pray for both cities to be bridges for the gospel to reach into North Africa!

- **The Basques.** No Euskera-speaking Protestant Church exists. The few Basque-speaking evangelicals find it difficult to worship or witness in their own language. The Basque people are ancient and proud. Pray for God to break down the centuries-old suspicions and fears towards outsiders.

- **Muslims** (perhaps more than 2 million). The Moors ruled much of Spain for 700 years, and Muslims long to win back what they lost. The majority immigrated from Morocco, but from other African nations also. Many mission agencies base themselves in South Spain to reach Muslims there and in North Africa, though few in Spain have come to Christ. Pray for God to open Muslim hearts, and for Spanish believers to reach out in love.

Sweden

Europe

Pop 9.3 million. **Capital** Stockholm (1.3 mill).
Christians 5.3 mill. *Evangelical Christians* 642,000.
Largest Religion Christian.
Fastest Growing Religion Muslim.
Largest Ethnic Groups Scandinavian (87.5%), Finno-Ugric (3.1%, includes Finnish, Saami), Slavic (2.6%). The remaining 5.3% represent a diverse mix of nearly 200 immigrant nationalities.
Official Language Swedish, with 5 official minority languages.
All Languages 30.
Economy Stable, highly developed economy. The wide-ranging social welfare system requires high taxation, but provides one of the world's best standards of living.
Politics Parliamentary government with a limited constitutional monarchy. EU member, but declined membership in NATO and the Eurozone.

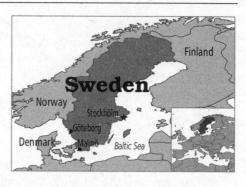

1. **Sweden faces widespread spiritual decline.** Nearly every religious group loses members, and only 23% of people still believe in a personal God. Sweden has a rich Christian history, with many 19th-century revivals, a strong Free Church movement, and a great commitment to missions. But numbers of Christian youth, and of missionaries sent from Sweden, declined drastically in the last 30 years. The Church of Sweden (Lutheran) is no longer the state church. Society places a high value on material comfort, personal pleasure, and individualism. Sweden desperately needs teachers and leaders who know the Bible, who know the culture, and who do not compromise with the majority mindset in society.

2. **Praise God for the unity among evangelicals.** God's Spirit remains at work! Because they are a minority, evangelical groups from different backgrounds work, pray, and worship together. Each year at Pentecost, around 20,000 from around the country gather together in Stockholm for "Jesus Manifestation". Evangelicals work together to plant churches, and to help those who struggle with alcoholism, sexual abuse, and unemployment.

③ Ministry challenges in Sweden:
- *The younger generation* know almost no biblical truth. But a new spiritual curiosity has begun to grow among them. Pray for effective youth-focused ministry!

- *The indigenous Saami peoples* (up to 25,000 in Sweden) live in Lapland (the north), and speak 4 languages. Pray for Bible translation, and for an authentic Saami expression of the Church.

- *European immigrants* arrive from Bosnia, Serbia, Poland, and Russia. Pray for genuine Christian witness that will address their spiritual needs. Orthodox Christianity grows quickly in Sweden as these groups increase in size.

- *Muslims* grew from only a few in 1960 to 330,000 in 2010. Most come from Iraq, Iran, Turkey, Bosnia, and Somalia. Very few workers minister to these groups, who sometimes live apart from society in their own neighbourhoods.

- *East and South Asian peoples* from nearly 35 nationalities can be difficult to discover and reach.

Switzerland

Europe

Pop 7.6 million. **Capital** Bern (347,000, administrative), Lausanne (122,000, judicial).
Christians 5.8 mill. *Evangelical Christians* 336,000.
Largest Religion Christian.
Fastest Growing Religion Non-religious.
Largest Ethnic Groups Swiss German (62.1%), Franco-Swiss (18.9%), Italian (5.4%, 3 groups), Serbo-Croat-Bosniak (4.9%).
Official Languages German, French, Italian, Romansh.
All Languages 26.
Economy Wealthy industrial state with a skilled, educated workforce. Highly dependent on trade. Tourism and banking also important. High living costs.
Politics Confederation founded in 1291, and federal state in 1848. A federal democratic government with a strong policy of non-involvement in world politics and strict neutrality. Joined the UN in 2002. Direct democracy practised here more than almost any other place on earth, with popular vote determining many important laws and policies.

① This exceptional nation now also struggles with the same social and spiritual issues of nearby lands. 80% of the population once participated in this direct democracy, but now voting turnout is down to 40%. Low birth rates and an older population put pressure on the pension system, and the nation requires high levels of immigration. Over 22% of the population are now foreign-born, and the mix of new ethnic and religious groups with traditional Swiss identity often causes problems. Pray for wisdom for leaders who must guide the country forward.

② The great reformers, Calvin and Zwingli, taught the truths of Scripture in this land, but few people today show interest in Christianity. People have wealth and material comfort, and less desire for religion. 60-80% of young people are open to explore God and religious matters, but they explore Eastern religions and the occult as much as Christianity. Pray that the Swiss may find the true way in Jesus Christ, and that the nation might be stirred again by the Holy Spirit.

Much of the Church declines in size and influence. The lack of clergy in the Catholic Church causes an enormous problem. Liberal theology weakens the faith of many Catholic and Reformed congregations. Praise God for some growth in the Free Churches, and for some signs of positive change in Reformed and Catholic Churches. Pray that God might use men and women of faith in State and Free Churches to bring renewal to the congregations, and revival to the nation!

Evangelicals have a renewed vision for the evangelization of Switzerland. Unity increases between traditional evangelical groups, charismatic groups, and the newer immigrant churches as they join together to proclaim Christ. Creative outreach comes through television, radio, Internet, newspapers, and conference events. The goal is to plant churches, but also to bring renewal and Christian testimony throughout society. Praise God that Swiss commitment to world evangelization also remains strong (nearly 1,700 long-term workers), even with its small number of evangelicals.

Switzerland has the highest proportion of foreign residents of any major state in Europe. Geneva is now 45% non-Swiss! Minority groups such as Latinos and Africans have over 200 congregations and contribute to outreach in Switzerland. Other groups are highly unevangelized. Muslims are up to 6% of the population, and almost 15% consider themselves non-religious. Pray for clear and loving outreach to these new communities.

Ukraine

Europe

Pop 45.4 million. **Capital** Kyiv/Kiev (2.8 mill).
Christians 35.9 mill. *Evangelical Christians* 1.7 mill.
Largest Religion Christian.
Fastest Growing Religion Muslim.
Largest Ethnic Groups Ukrainian (72.1%), Russian (13.2%), Polish (2.3%), Gypsy (1.5%), Turkic/Altaic (1%).
Official Language Ukrainian, but Russian spoken widely.
All languages 42.

Economy Great potential from mineral deposits and arable land. Some economic growth, but many live near the poverty line. Transition to a market economy crippled by excessive corruption, and by the wide

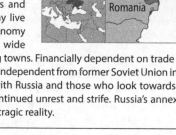

difference between growing cities and declining towns. Financially dependent on trade with Russia.
Politics Dominated and fought over for centuries. Independent from former Soviet Union in 1991. Deeply divided between those who want to re-establish ties with Russia and those who look towards the West/EU for the future. The failure to find a solution leads to continued unrest and strife. Russia's annexation of Crimea and violence in the eastern regions both reflect this tragic reality.

Thank God for the rich Christian heritage of Ukraine. Christianity in the Slavic world began in Kyiv 1,000 years ago. Churches here suffered greatly until independence (1991) and millions of Christians died, but the faithful perseverance of the Church now bears fruit. Today it impacts most of society. Evangelicals emerged from 130 years of persecution with larger numbers and stronger faith. Ukraine has a spiritual drive and vision present today that is different from generations before.

Communism fell 25 years ago, but its effects persist. The new market economy drove many into poverty while a few gained extreme wealth through corrupt means. These powerful oligarchs make money from Ukraine, but usually invest their riches outside the country. Ukraine's economic troubles increase the political tensions between East and West. When Communism ended, the empty space without values or morals led to a rapid increase of hopelessness, alcoholism, and the spread of HIV/AIDS. Many opportunities exist for holistic and compassionate ministries, and believers must not miss this open door!

3 **Ukraine's political story is troubled and its future uncertain.** The "Orange Revolution" (2005) demonstrated both the great potential of the people and the problems they face. Nonviolent protests resulted in new elections and greater freedoms, but in the end little changed. Corruption remains widespread, but so does the determination to defeat it. Political opponents argue and deal harshly with one another, and the divisions between East and West turned into violent clashes in early 2014. Meanwhile, forces in Russia manipulated the situation to exert greater power in the Crimea and eastern Ukraine. Both Russia and the West have their selfish agendas for Ukraine and its people. Finding the truth amidst all the propaganda is difficult. What is the Lord's purpose for this land? Pray for God to bring reconciliation to heal the deep divisions, and healing for the damage already done. Pray for justice for the whole society, especially the oppressed, and hope for the future.

4 **Ukraine forms a bridge** between East and West, and between Orthodox and Catholic. Just over half of Ukrainians belong to the Ukrainian Orthodox Church, but the divisions in society also exist in the Church (between loyalty to leaders in Kyiv or in Moscow). The Greek/Uniate Catholic Church uses Orthodox liturgy, but follows the leadership of the Pope. Other Orthodox, Catholic, and Protestant groups face internal strife. All Churches compete with one another for limited resources, for buildings, and for members. But those who love God and the Scriptures remain faithful! Pray that spiritual life and renewal will change relationships and overcome church politics. Those who call upon the Lord have a powerful redemptive role to play in how Ukraine's story unfolds.

5 **Evangelicals grew steadily,** even under persecution. Newer charismatic groups especially grew. Foreigners (notably Africans) started new congregations that then took on a Ukrainian identity. One house church movement focused on relational outreach, informal leadership, and on churches that reproduce both in Ukraine and in neighbouring countries. Pray for sensitive and gracious attitudes among all believers as Slavic roots, Western styles, African initiatives, and newer dynamic churches intermingle with each other and with traditional Christian denominations. Pray for the Holy Spirit to work through both the spiritual excitement of newer groups and the rich spiritual heritage of traditional ones.

6 **Pray for reconciliation and unity in the Church.** During the Communist era, all 3 confessions of the Church (Orthodox, Catholic, Protestant) split between those who collaborated with the Communists and those who resisted them. This left scars which need more healing. Partners from across all of the confessions work together with the Ukrainian Bible Society to promote biblical truth and moral values in society. Praise God that together they distribute hundreds of thousands of copies of Scripture every year!

7 **Ukraine is the "Antioch" of the Slavic world.** Indigenous Ukrainian mission agencies send out workers both into Ukraine and throughout the former Soviet Union. Pray for more workers, for God's provision, and for fruitful partnership with Western, Asian, and other mission agencies. Expatriate mission agencies faithfully served the persecuted Church before 1989. Long-term missionaries who will humbly learn the language and culture can still help, especially to teach the Bible, train leaders, and assist Ukrainians as they start their own ministries and missions.

Pray for these specific outreach challenges:

- *Children at risk.* Tens of thousands of children live on the street, and over 100,000 live in orphanages. Most become involved in drugs, crime, or prostitution unless help comes. The CoMission for Children at Risk unites dozens of ministries to reach them with the love of Christ.

- *Crimea.* Churches do not grow as well in this region. An ethnic Russian majority feels more linked to Russia than Ukraine. The indigenous Crimean Tatars (mostly Muslim) lived in exile in Siberia for decades, but more than 250,000 returned here to their traditional home. Christians reached out to them specifically, and some now follow Christ!

- *Foreign immigrants.* Many come from the Middle East and Asia to study. They struggle with loneliness and often face racial persecution. Many open their hearts to the gospel, and Ukrainian churches that reach out to them with love find a harvest!

United Kingdom   *Europe*

Pop 62.1 million. **Capital** London (8.6 mill).

Christians 37.1 mill. *Evangelical Christians* 5.5 mill.
Largest Religion Christian.
Fastest Growing Religion Non-religious.

Largest Ethnic Groups Anglo-Saxon/Celtic (85.2%), Asian (6.3%), European (3.3%), Middle Eastern/West Asian (1.9%), African Caribbean (1.4%, majority British-born), African (0.8%).

Official Language English. In Wales, both English and Welsh. English is the primary language of 400 million people globally, and the major language of international communication for over 1.4 billion. **All Languages** 15 indigenous; over 200 immigrant languages.

Economy The world's 1st industrialized economy, now primarily a service economy highly dependent on financial and business services. Decline after WWII reversed from the mid-1980s to late 2000s. One of the countries hardest hit by the 2008-2009 economic crisis, but still world's 5th-largest economy. Unemployment is becoming an issue. EU member.

Politics A parliamentary, constitutional monarchy. The United Kingdom (UK) formed in 1801 as a Union of Great Britain and Ireland. Southern Ireland seceded from the Union in 1921. The British Empire once covered one-fourth of the world, but has become 60 independent states (most are members of the British Commonwealth). The smaller constituent members of the UK (Scotland, Wales, Northern Ireland) have some degree of self-governance. The Isle of Man and Channel Islands are Crown Dependencies (not part of the UK, but geographically close, and reliant upon the UK for defence and foreign relations).

---

1 Britain's cultural, diplomatic, economic, and military influence shapes the world. It is head of the Commonwealth and a permanent member of the UN Security Council. London is one of the world's hub cities for finance, travel, politics, and culture. The UK has also contributed significantly to global Christianity for centuries, from Wycliffe and Tyndale until today with the Alpha Course, 24-7 Prayer, and many evangelical writers, theologians, and worship leaders. Pray for this power to be used for the sake of what is just and right.

2 Britain needs to discover a sense of purpose and direction for the 21st century. The sense of nationhood and core identity diminished after the British Empire ended. The Christian tradition once formed the foundation of society, but today minority religions, especially Islam, also receive significant attention and government support. Astrology, New Age, the occult, and old-world paganism (Druid/Wicca) all slowly become more popular. The "freedoms" of the 1960s had disastrous social consequences, and Britain has alarming levels of alcohol and drug abuse, sexually transmitted diseases, abortion, prostitution, gambling addiction, and personal debt. In almost every century of the last 800 years, revival came to Britain at least once. The last was in 1859-1869. Many Christians pray for another great spiritual awakening.

3 **Immigration is a reality of national life.** In London, over 50 nationalities have communities of over 10,000 people, and every nationality in the world is represented here! Many Brits struggle to welcome immigrants, and immigrants struggle to adjust to life in the UK. Some react negatively to these changes, but society must face the challenges of many cultures living together in peace. Immigration blesses the UK Church in 2 ways:

- *Widespread immigration from strongly Christian nations (such as Nigeria, Brazil, others) brings new church life and growth.* Around 1,500 Christian missionaries have come into the UK from the Americas, Africa, and Asia. The Church also grew from conversions among Africans, Chinese, Polish, "Travellers" (Romani/Gypsy), and even some among South Asians and other groups.

- *Many immigrants come from the world's least-evangelized nations, and now live on the doorstep of Christian churches!* Pray for God's people to open their doors, homes, and hearts to the peoples around them. Pray for local congregations to plant new churches, reach new peoples, and glorify Jesus by partnership with believers from many lands.

4 **The Church of England** faces a crisis. It is the mother Church for the world's 81.6 million Anglicans. Globally, deep divisions exist within the Anglican Church between evangelicals, liberals, and Anglo-Catholics. Differences arise over issues such as ordination of women, support for same-sex marriages, and others. In the UK, evangelicals now make up 34% of the UK's Anglicans, and the evangelical movement continues to impact the Church of England. (50% of evangelicals in the UK are Anglican.) Pray that church leadership might regain a prophetic role, and might speak in unity to this nation that has lost much of its moral and spiritual centre.

5 **Evangelical Christianity** no longer grows here. Without immigration of evangelicals into the UK (from Africa in particular), the numbers would decline. Many Christians no longer feel confident or certain about the truth and power of the gospel, about the uniqueness of Jesus, or about traditional forms of church life and evangelism. Britain made a unique contribution to world evangelization and the Protestant missions movement in the last 220 years. But as the Church grows weaker, interest in missions fades. Pray for God to restore vision and faith to His people, and confidence in His ability to change and use Britain again!

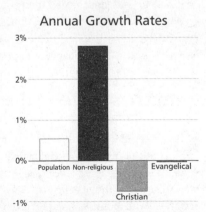

Annual Growth Rates

6 **Signs of hope** encourage the UK Church:

- *Many pastors and congregations experienced charismatic renewal* between the 1960s and 1990s, which led to new families of churches. The New Churches grew fast, and became significant spiritual forces in the nation, which brought more lively worship to many denominations.

- *The Alpha Course and Christianity Explored* both spread across the country to nearly every denomination, and around the world, as hugely effective outreach programmes.
- *London's churches* are often twice as large, more diverse, and more engaged in outreach and community projects than churches in other places in the UK.
- *New movements reach out to the younger generation* with different cultural approaches to prayer, worship, and ministry.

7 Specific ethnic minority groups that need prayer:
- *South Asians* (3 million, the largest minority group). About 4% of all South Asians are Christian. Some turned to Christ within Hindu and Sikh communities, but very few from Muslim groups.
- *Caribbean and African peoples.* 17% of this population attend church (3 times higher than the UK average). These churches used to be isolated from other evangelicals, but as churches became more multicultural this began to change. These ethnic groups struggle with poverty, education needs, and life in single-parent homes at higher rates than the general population.
- *Somalis in the UK* (100,000). One of the world's least-evangelized groups, but little outreach or ministry exists for them.
- *Middle Eastern and North African peoples.* Many wealthy Arabs come to the UK as tourists, businessmen, or students, and some come to faith. Several Christian fellowships exist for Arabs, and a few exist for Turks, Kurds, and Iranians. Yeminis, Moroccans, and Algerians all arrived more recently and remain largely unreached.
- *Chinese* (up to 500,000). Most now arrive from mainland China as students or for business. Many thousands enter illegally or as trafficked victims and may endure harsh conditions. About 5% of Chinese are Christian, with over 100 Chinese churches.

8 Muslims now number at least 2 million, and continue to grow through immigration and higher birth rates. The largest groups are of Pakistani origin, but numbers also come from Bangladesh, India, the Middle East, Somalia, and North Africa. London now serves as a hub for Islam, especially for extremist organizations. Radical Islam, terrorism, illegal immigration, and poor integration into UK society all create difficulties for the majority of Muslims who want to live quiet, peaceful lives. Pray that God would break down the barriers between Muslims and Christians, and provide opportunities to share the gospel.

Countries of the United Kingdom

1 England is the most secular of the 4 countries that make up the UK. Only 6% of people in England regularly attend church. Atheism as an intellectual and cultural force has grown strongly. England's inner cities change rapidly. Churches have closed, congregations died out, and Muslim mosques, Hindu temples or Sikh *gurdwaras* are common. Pray that God may raise up an army of workers with meaningful ways of meeting the many needs of those who live in poverty, and in areas full of drugs and crime. Pray that the Holy Spirit may break into lives and bring a sense of the reality of God and the truth of the gospel!

2 **Scotland** re-established its own parliament in 1998, and has a strong movement that seeks full independence within the EU. Scotland has a history of revivals, and of sending out well-known missionaries such as David Livingstone, Robert Moffatt, Mary Slessor, and Eric Liddell. Today many know Scotland more for its social problems. Nearly half of all children are born to unmarried parents. Alcohol and drug abuse remain high. Membership of the Church of Scotland (Presbyterian), the established Church, rapidly declines. Pray that the gospel might transform Scotland through the loving witness and ministry of believers across all denominations.

3 **Wales** has its own state assembly since 1998, but some dream of Welsh independence. It works hard to preserve its own language and culture (about 22% of the population speak Welsh). Wales has suffered deep economic decline. Many people left the area, and left the churches. This region is famous as the land of revivals and the land of song. But the last revival came in 1904, and the decline in church attendance since then is higher in Wales than in any other part of the UK. Some church growth came in recent years, especially when evangelical congregations both proclaim the gospel and demonstrate it through community involvement. Pray that revival may come again, and that the entire country will again sing the praises of Jesus!

4 **Northern Ireland** (Ulster) has its own assembly since 1998 (most recently reinstated in 2007). 3,000 people died in civil violence between the late 1960s and 1998 (the signing of the Good Friday peace agreement). Ulster remains a land divided between nationalists (historically Catholic), who want union with Ireland, and the majority Unionists (historically Protestant), who wish to remain part of the UK. Pray for reconciliation between these two communities, and for forgiveness of past crimes. Pray that Northern Ireland may become a testimony of the power of Christ to heal and restore a nation. Church attendance and missions vision are higher in Northern Ireland than anywhere else in the UK, but they also now decline. Pray that this generous spirit of giving money and personnel to world evangelization might continue!

Other European States

Europe's borders reflect its long history. A handful of small states mostly represent the leftover duchies and principalities from centuries past. Although their locations are spread around Western Europe, their small size and similar origins mean that the same dynamics shape their societies and economies. Included below are the countries that fit this profile with a population under 100,000. Luxembourg so closely fits the profile it has been added, despite its larger population. Countries with a population under 100,000 included separately are Holy See and Faeroe Islands.

Each of these nations works hard to preserve its identity in the presence of much bigger European neighbours. They tend to be conservative, wealthy with flexible tax laws, and more religious in their traditions than their practices. Even small numbers of migrants can significantly change the population of the country, and they usually have one large ethnic majority.

Christians find outreach and ministry quite difficult in these places due to the inward-focused, traditional nature of these small nations. The higher levels of wealth, comfort, and stability also leave most people without a strong felt need for God in their lives.

Pray for each of these lands, that God would do whatever it takes to break through into the lives of all who live there. Pray that every people could see that Jesus offers greater security, riches, and identity than any human society or tax shelter ever could!

1 **Andorra** (87,000) has been self-governing since 1278, as a monarchy under French and Spanish Co-Princes. It was once a refuge for smugglers, but today provides a wealthy tax haven. Andorra is Catholic by tradition (almost 90%), but in practice many consult astrologers or mediums for guidance and advice. Praise God for the few committed believers. Most are migrant workers, but some are indigenous Andorrans. Ask God to breathe new life into the Church of Andorra, and for the Holy Spirit to expose and remove the power of the occult.

2 **Gibraltar** (31,000) is a British overseas territory since its capture in 1704, but self-governing since 2007. Most of the population are Catholic, but other denominations have churches. Evangelicals/charismatics have small numbers, but grow. Significant numbers of Moroccans work here, as well as Jewish and Hindu communities. Gibraltar has a good position for outreach to the region (southern Spain and North Africa), as well as to locals, immigrants, and foreign tourists. Pray that local congregations will gain vision for outreach!

3 **Liechtenstein** (36,000) is a constitutional principality, and has some ties with Switzerland. The Prince's family have always been Catholic, as are the native citizens, though most do not actively practise their faith. The numbers of Muslims and non-religious people grow. British, Norwegian, and Swiss believers started the only evangelical fellowship in 1985. Some of the extended royal family have connections with the Catholic charismatic renewal movement, and profess personal faith in Christ.

4 **Luxembourg** (492,000) has the largest population of these small nations by far. Nearly half the population are expatriates. It is a parliamentary democracy with some ties to Belgium and the Netherlands.

- *Luxembourg's strong Catholic heritage remains.* The majority profess Catholicism, but only a small minority regularly attend mass or practise the faith. The growth of other faiths now challenges Christianity. Islam, Orthodoxy, Jehovah's Witnesses, and Eastern mysticism have transformed this small nation into a mix of religions. Protestant and Independent Christian groups add to the diversity. Pray for people to discover the power of the living Christ! Pray for completion of the Bible in the Lëtzebuergesch language, the heart language of many nationals.

- *Evangelicals are few in number,* and many are foreigners. In the 23 evangelical churches, believers worship in 9 different languages. Few churches have full-time pastors. Pray for unity among them to trust one another, and to pray and worship together at times. Government and society sometimes see evangelical groups as "cults", which makes it difficult to rent buildings and to openly evangelize. Pray that believers might see chances to share the gospel in creative ways, and to shape the nation with biblical principles.

5 **Monaco** (33,000) has a constitutional monarchy where the Prince shares power with the National Council. Monaco attracts the rich and famous, who come for its self-indulgent, luxurious lifestyle. Over 75% of the population are expatriates, with great wealth. The country has a Catholic tradition, but it is very difficult for people to find interest in spiritual things when surrounded by so much material wealth. Few evangelicals live here, so their influence is small. But praise God that for the first time a small group of Monégasque evangelical believers exists! Pray that committed believers from the Catholic, Anglican, French Reformed Churches, and the bilingual Monaco Christian Fellowship might impact the whole of society.

6 **San Marino** (32,000) has been an independent republic since AD 301, with ties to Italy. The Sammarinese are Catholic by tradition and culture, but few practise their faith. Some reject their religious heritage, and there are small groups of other faiths here. San Marino calls itself the "Ancient Land of Liberty", and people have freedom to worship. But evangelism hardly exists. Past outreach by evangelicals resulted in jail or expulsion from the country, so no churches or ministries currently evangelize here.

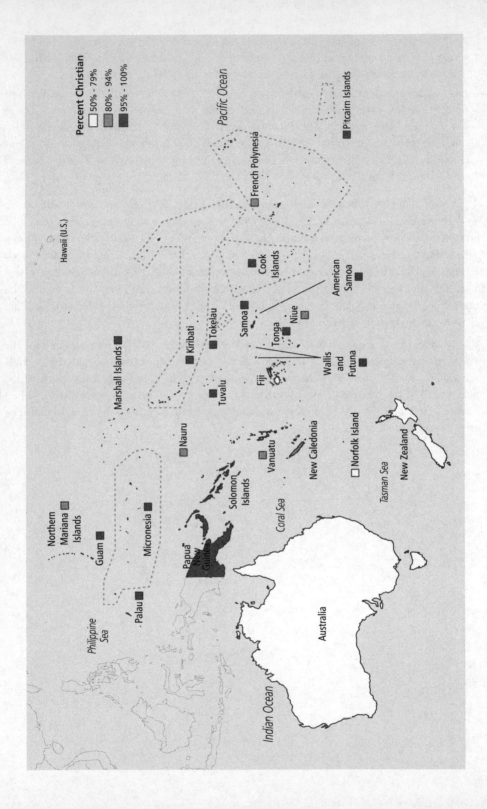

THE PACIFIC

Pop 35.8 million.
Christians 26.5 mill. *Evangelical Christians* 6.4 mill.
Largest Religion Christianity.
Fastest Growing Religion Buddhism.

All Languages 1,250 (18% of the world's total languages).
Languages with Scriptures 37 Bibles, 252 New Testaments, 185 Old or New Testament portions, 265 works in progress. 414 languages may still need Bible translation work.

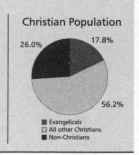

Christian Population

17.8%
26.0%
56.2%

■ Evangelicals
□ All other Christians
■ Non-Christians

The Pacific region consists of 25,000 islands scattered over 88 million square km of ocean (larger than the combined areas of Africa, Asia and Europe!). It comprises one continent (Australia), two large land masses (New Zealand and Papua New Guinea [PNG]), and 26 smaller island states and territories.

1,300 different people groups live in this region. Two-thirds of these groups live in Papua New Guinea! Australia and New Zealand dominate in terms of population. The majority are from European ethnic backgrounds. Without the Caucasian population, the region would be ethnically 77% Pacific Islanders and 20% Asians.

The Pacific Ocean region and its indigenous peoples are traditionally divided into three groups: Micronesia in the West, Melanesia in the South, and Polynesia in the East.

Australia

Pop 21.5 million. **Capital** Canberra (387,000).

Christians 14.9 mill. *Evangelical Christians* 3.1 mill.
Largest Religion Christian.
Fastest Growing Religion Buddhist.

Largest Ethnic Groups Anglo-Australian (67.9%, most with British or Irish roots), European (16.6%), Chinese (3.4%), Australian Aborigine (2.6%), Middle Eastern/West Asian (2.4%), Anglo–New Zealander (1.8%), Vietnamese (1.2%), Filipino (1%), Indian (1%).

Official Language English. 20% of population use English as a second language. **All languages** 207.

Economy Advanced market economy. Increasing links with East Asia. Recent droughts, bush fires, and flooding brought loss of life, and destroyed animals and food supplies.
Politics Federal parliamentary democracy since 1901. British monarch is the constitutional head of state.

---

1 **Modern changes in Australia bring strains and tensions to the nation.** Immigration created a multicultural country, especially in larger cities. Ethnic and religious minority groups grow quickly. 28% of Australians were born overseas! This diversity blesses the nation, but strains the attitudes of the people toward refugees, asylum seekers, and other immigrants who come. Australia provides stability and peacekeeping to other Pacific and Asian countries such as Timor, Bougainville, the Solomon Islands, and others. Thank God for the ability and will to save lives abroad. Pray that believers might engage their diverse society in a productive and meaningful way.

2 **Even if Australia's society succeeds, its land may fail.** Long years of drought, increased population size, and overuse of land and water all put the environment in danger, perhaps more than any other continent. The blessings of this nation, the society, and the land of Australia must be managed well. Pray for wisdom.

3 **The Church in Australia faces a mighty challenge.** The strong influence of Christianity declined as the country became more diverse in religions, and became more secular in its public life and laws. 70% of the population say they are Christian, but only 10% regularly attend church. Many Australians see the Church as intolerant and abusive of its power. More people prefer a personal spirituality based on individual preferences, and with no accountability. Almost all mainline churches declined or stayed the same in members, and evangelical growth slowed down. Pray for revival in the Church that will affect every area of Australian society.

4 **Evangelicals face social challenges with faith and prayerful action!** Those who recognized social changes began to adapt. Some ministries and congregations now reach out to the majority population with more focus and care. Some reach out across cultures to immigrant communities, including those from other faith backgrounds. Much work remains, but Australian Christianity shows signs of positive change. The greatest battle the Church faces may be debating with a secular public over issues of human origin, human sexuality, and the existence of God. Pray that evangelicals communicate the truth in love. Pray for a bold witness to the uniqueness of Jesus that reflects His humility and compassion.

5 **Less-reached peoples increase in number and diversity.** Australia has religious freedom, but many immigrants suffer persecution for following Christ or even exploring Christianity. Many people in working-class urban areas, and also those in isolated mining and farming communities, have no biblical witness. Pray for the local churches and mission agencies that seek to share Christ with the many different cultural communities of Australia. These minorities could impact their native lands for God if the Church reaches them with the gospel.

- *Over 500,000 Muslims, from at least 70 nationalities.* Most live in Sydney and Melbourne. Australia has over 100 active mosques and prayer centres.

- *Up to 500,000 people of Chinese ethnic background.* About 20% confess Christianity, and Australia's largest Presbyterian church is Chinese. Pray for the complete evangelization of the Buddhists and other non-Christian Chinese.

- *A quarter-million Vietnamese.* Many refugees settled since the Vietnam War. A minority follow Christ, but 2nd-generation Vietnamese struggle to find faith somewhere between two cultures.

- *The diverse peoples from the Balkans and Eastern Europe.* Most still use their native language: Croatian, Macedonian, Serbian, Bosnian, and Albanian. Also Polish, Russian, and Ukrainian. They come from some of Europe's least-evangelized countries, and few have evangelical believers among them.

- *Southern Europeans* (Italian, Greek, Maltese, Spanish). Melbourne is the 2nd-largest Greek-speaking city in the world. Some of these groups settled in Australia generations ago, and feel distant from their cultural roots and traditional churches. Pentecostals and Jehovah's Witnesses reach out the most to them.

6 **The 550,000 indigenous Aborigines** suffered indignity from their contact with Western culture and greed. They feel frustrated by the lack of control over their own lands and heritage. The Prime Minister improved reconciliation between white and black Australians in 1998 with an apology and an annual National "Sorry" Day. Recognition of land rights for first Australians remains a major political issue. At the same time, many missionaries showed love to the Aborigines across the years, and most Aborigines are Christian. But poverty, substance abuse, shallow faith, and the struggle to relate to Western Christian practices all limit spiritual growth. Pray for the Aboriginal Evangelical Fellowship. It coordinates Aboriginal Christians, and supports leadership development, training, and church planting among all Aboriginal communities.

7 **Ministry to students, young people, and children** needs priority attention. As Australia becomes more secular, the Church must reach out to the younger generation. Student ministries reach many, but need more help with over 600,000 students on 40 campuses. Pray for church volunteers who give religious instruction in secondary schools, and for believers who work as counsellors in primary schools. Pray for increased faith and support for each worker, to give wise advice to youth and students who face many personal and social issues.

8 **Norfolk Island, Christmas Island, and Cocos (Keeling) Island** – the 3 inhabited dependent territories of Australia. (Total population: 4,500. Christian population: 1,950. Christmas Island is 36% Buddhist and 25% Muslim, and Cocos Island is 71% Muslim.) Communities on these islands face the threat of violent weather. They depend on Australia for help, but their location is far away from immediate help. Australian churches struggle to reach out to these isolated peoples. Pray for God to move among the few churches there to renew and awaken believers. The Malays of Cocos Island and the Chinese of Christmas Island need outreach.

Fiji

Pop 854,000. **Capital** Suva (176,000).

Christians 556,000. *Evangelical Christians* 215,000.
Largest Religion Christian.
Fastest Growing Religion Christian.

Largest Ethnic Groups Fijian (52%), South Asian (36.7%, most descended from indentured labour brought in by British from 1879 to 1916), Vanuatan (6.4%), Caucasian (1.4%), Rotuman (1.2%, on Rotuman Island).
Official Language English; Hindustani and Bau Fijian commonly used. **All languages** 21.

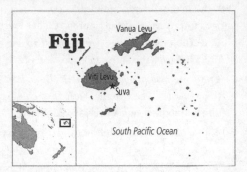

Economy Based largely on tourism and sugar. One of Pacific's most well-developed economies, and one of world's largest aid recipients per number of people. Indian community dominates most commercial activities, but are denied land rights, which leads business leaders to emigrate.
Politics British rule 1874-1970. Since independence in 1970, elected governments disrupted by periodic military coups condemned by the global community.

---

1 **British colonial greed left Fiji ethnically divided.** The British imported Indians as indentured labourers from 1870 onward. Fijians lived as a minority in their own country at times. Indians worked hard to build new lives in Fiji, but they cannot own land. They face resentment and racial prejudice. Poor treatment by the British and Fijians, both considered Christian, discredited the gospel for most Indians. Pray for a spirit of repentance and reconciliation, and a society known for freedom and equality.

2 **The Methodist Church was the primary Church in Fiji for 150 years.** The Church failed to overcome racism, and the coups led to church splits. Many left the Methodist Church for newer denominations with more spiritual life. Newer churches grew in number and influence in this decade, especially among Pentecostal groups. Evangelical and charismatic movements brought new life to Methodist, Anglican, and Catholic churches. Some see signs of revival in Fiji! God is at work to transform individuals, communities, and even the environment.

3 **Unity, leadership training, and mission vision.** The Association of Christian Churches of Fiji formed after the 2000 coup to bring unity and reconciliation. It represents mostly evangelical Protestant churches. The Fiji Council of Churches does similar work. Many denominations commit significant resources to training for mission and evangelism. Fiji once sent missionaries throughout the whole Pacific.

4 **The Indians of Fiji** form the largest non-Christian community in the Pacific. As few as 3% identify themselves as Christian. Hindus remain mostly unevangelized. Pray for appropriate outreach to the culture, and for the few Christian Indo-Fijians to reach their own people. Sikhs and Punjabis keep more of their culture and language, and there is little outreach to them. Gujaratis remain the least evangelized among all Fiji's South Asian peoples, with only a few believers and no specific outreach to them. The Muslim community keeps to itself, and overall resists the gospel. The few converts to Christ suffer from persecution, and from churches that fail to welcome them fully into community life. Many global Christians began to pray for them (the Pacific Islands' largest unreached people group), and local Christians now see signs of spiritual interest and response from the Muslim community!

New Zealand *The Pacific*

Pop 4.3 million. **Capital** Wellington (395,000).

Christians 2.3 mill. *Evangelical Christians* 784,000.
Largest Religion Christian.
Fastest Growing Religion Muslim.

Largest Ethnic Groups European (73.1%, majority from British roots, other Europeans increasing), Maori (13.4%), Samoan (3.0%), Chinese (2.8%), Indo-Pakistani (1.7%), Cook Islands (1.3%), Tongan (1.0%).
Official Languages English, Maori. Samoan widely spoken. **All languages** 22.

Economy Based heavily on tourism, export (agricultural and forest products), technology, and software-based innovation. High emigration rate: 16% of Kiwis live abroad. 2011 Christchurch earthquakes, with significant loss of life, impacted tourism and the housing market.

Politics Independent from Britain in 1907. Stable parliamentary democracy with British Monarch as official head of state. Considered among the least corrupt nations in the world.

---

1 **Other religions and spiritual options challenge Christianity in New Zealand.** 41% of the population claim to be non-religious, and basic unbelief threatens the Church. Only 14% attend church weekly, down from 40% in the past. New Age spirituality focuses on individualism and nature, and attracts many Kiwis (New Zealanders) who feel disappointed by the Church. But 24/7 prayer rooms and other recent prayer groups prove that God still moves in the Kiwi Church! Praise God for new growth in charismatic and Pentecostal groups, and new evangelical movements in mainline denominations. Pray that God will pour His Holy Spirit into the Church and draw back those who left.

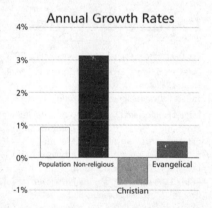

Annual Growth Rates

2 **Prosperity, stability, and freedom in New Zealand attract new immigrants.** Immigrants from other faith backgrounds bring an opportunity for Kiwis to share the gospel cross-culturally. Two-thirds of Asian immigrants live in Auckland, and are 20% of its population. More churches now reach out to immigrants with English-language classes and other practical helps. Some people find Jesus attractive, even when they feel uninterested in Christianity or organized religion. Pray for these groups:

- *Polynesians immigrate to NZ* to find work. Communities of Samoans, Tongans, and Islanders (from Cook, Tokelau, and Niue Islands) live in cities. Many come from Christian families, but younger generations do not all follow Christ.

- *Chinese immigrants* have a long history in NZ, but immigration increased recently. Chinese churches multiply and add new members! Pray for focus on discipleship and missions.

- *Indians* immigrate from Fiji, India, Malaysia, South Africa, and other places. Some are Christian, but they need Indian Christian leadership.

- *Other Asian groups* include refugees or migrants from Southeast Asia and Japan. Most are Buddhist, but a few Japanese churches exist. Koreans have many churches.
- *The Muslim community* is small, but grows quickly. Immigrants come from around the world and establish mosques. Little outreach comes to them from Christians.

3 **The Maori population grows and continues to revive its own culture.** The Treaty of Waitangi (1840) gave the British a right to settle in exchange for guarantees of Maori land and resources. The treaty was dishonoured over and over. This caused much pain for the Maoris, much legal debate, and also spiritual concern. Unemployment, domestic violence, youth gangs, and high crime rates challenged communities that felt removed from their culture. Religious sects such as *Ringatu* and *Ratana* attract Maori followers, as well as Mormon churches. Few attend evangelical churches. Pray that Maori may find their culture made alive by the gospel.

4 **New Zealand sends a larger proportion of church members as missionaries** than most other countries! Even so, Missions Interlink and many churches together have a goal to send 1 missionary for every 1,000 believers. This would mean 3,000 workers, twice as many as today. Pray for success!

Papua New Guinea

The Pacific

Pop 6.9 million. **Capital** Port Moresby (321,000).
Christians 6.6 mill. *Evangelical Christians* 1.8 mill.
Largest Religion Christian.
Fastest Growing Religion Ethnic religions.
Largest Ethnic Groups 1,000 peoples speaking around 830 languages. The world's most complex nation by ethnic groups and languages! Melanesian (98.2%, in numerous ethnic groups, with over half the groups less than 2,000 in population).
Official Languages English, Tok Pisin (Melanesian/English Creole), Motu. **All languages** 830.
Economy Cash crops (tea, coffee, copra) supplement traditional subsistence farming and fishing. Natural

resources exploited more recently. Dependent on trade and aid from Australia. High unemployment. 70% of the population live with very few resources.
Politics Independence in 1975. A parliamentary democracy and member of the British Commonwealth. The Germans controlled the north coast and island provinces (German New Guinea) until WWI and the British controlled the south (British New Guinea) until 1901. Both came under Australian rule (then called New Guinea and Papua) until independence. The costly war for independence on Bougainville (1988-1998) resulted in its autonomous rule.

1 **Papua New Guinea (PNG) faces crises.** Some groups and governments predict the state will fail. Widespread corruption limits progress, and foreign aid meant to help local workers rarely reaches them. Difficult geography makes natural resources hard to access, and greedy foreign companies seize control of them. Cities receive migrants who seek work, but cannot support them well. Violent crime increases, and HIV infections spread rapidly, mostly through sexual immorality. The vast ethnic diversity (1,000 groups) makes the country difficult to unite. Tribal fighting and revenge killings extend back thousands of years. Pray for peace that reaches beyond non-violence to bring true unity, and for national identity that rises above ethnic ties.

2 **More people practise witchcraft and sorcery again.** The culture of PNG recognizes the reality of the spirit world, but "witch hunts" have become more common. Those suspected of black magic face torture until they confess, and confession can lead to death. Recently, this also affects the lives of those who live with HIV/AIDS. Many see superstitious causes for the disease, rather than lifestyle and other medical causes. Pray for an end to occult activities and all related violence. When these problems exists in a nation 96% Christian, it points to a failure of the Church. It also reveals the challenge it faces and the opportunity for the gospel.

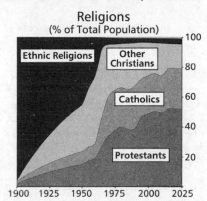

Religions
(% of Total Population)

3 **PNG experienced 130 years of great mission success.** It began at the coast, moved inland, reached to the Highlands, and to almost every people. In some places mass movements to Christ occurred, and over 95% of all peoples profess Christianity. Praise God for this living, active Church! Some people later turned back to ungodly traditions, to drunkenness or gambling, or to follow cults that mixed Christian teachings with old evil ways. Revivals have come to some places, but PNG needs more. Missionaries focus now on health, education, development, translation, Bible teaching, and other support work. The gospel must be more meaningful to New Guinean peoples so it can bring change to society.

4 **Churches and missions must prioritize leadership training** in the many small Bible schools, and the few theological colleges. Churches recognize the value of TEE, especially to reach rural pastors and church workers. Over 1,000 enrol each year. Pray for God to call more men and women to full-time Christian work. The difficult conditions of rural work discourage many, and higher-paying jobs tempt Christians with education away. This leaves the most isolated groups without good teaching or leadership. Isolation and illiteracy make radio a vital resource. It links people with the outside world and provides a way to learn.

5 **Praise God for great progress in Bible translation work.** About 210 languages have a New Testament, but only 12 have a complete Bible. Several foreign and indigenous groups participate in over 260 projects, and complete several New Testaments every year! But up to 400 different languages may still need translation teams. Pray for translators, and for ways to make the long task faster and more accurate. Pray for literacy training. The written, translated Word of God is little help if no one reads it.

6 **Aircraft and pilots of missionary organizations** provide a lifeline for churches and missions. Many areas of PNG can only be reached by air. Thick forests, high mountains, dense clouds, and dangerous weather make flight conditions among the worst in the world. When there are not enough flight staff, missions must reduce the number of flights. Pray for the flying staff of Mission Aviation Fellowship (36 foreign and 120 national workers, with 14 planes), for SIL/JAARS (6 planes and 2 helicopters), New Tribes Mission (3 planes and 1 helicopter), and all who service the aircraft and travel in them.

Bougainville. (Total population: 230,000. Almost all considered Christian.) Pray for long-term peace after decades of hatred between the PNG government and the Bougainville islanders. The need for forgiveness and reconciliation remains. About 20,000 islanders lost their lives in the fighting of the 1990s, and thousands more became refugees. The civil war in Bougainville destroyed much of the society, and few education or healthcare resources remain. Pray for the Church to work in partnership with the government to build a new Bougainville. Spiritual needs are even greater in Bougainville than PNG. Pray for revival of genuine faith in Christ. Many came to churches during the civil war, but fell away after the war ended.

Solomon Islands
The Pacific

Pop 536,000. **Capital** Honiara, on Guadalcanal Island (75,000).

Christians 513,000. *Evangelical Christians* 179,000.
Largest Religion Christian.
Fastest Growing Religion Local ethnic religions.

Largest Ethnic Groups Over 76 ethno-linguistic peoples. Melanesian (90.2%), Polynesian (4.2%), Euronesian (3.4%), Micronesian (1.2%), Han Chinese (0.7%).
Official Language English. Trade language: Solomons Pijin (spoken by more than half). **All Languages** 71 (up to 120 if dialects included).

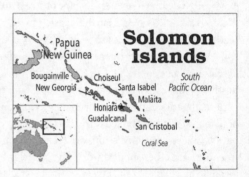

Economy Most people depend on agriculture and fishing. Undeveloped mineral resources. Upheaval and civil war (1998-2003) left many dead, 30,000 displaced, and harmed the economy.
Politics Independent from Britain in 1978 as parliamentary democracy that recognizes British monarchy. Ethnicity stronger than national identity and nationhood. Ethnic tensions led to upheaval and civil war, ending in 2003. Corruption a major problem.

 Ethnic diversity and a divided geography (6 major island groups) create a divided society. Tribes and political groups live together, but struggle to form a unified nation. Outside intervention brought peace in 2003 and disarmed the militias, but deep divisions remain. These language and culture barriers also inhibit Christian work. Each small ethnic group needs a different approach and language resources. Denominations divide along tribal lines. Pray that Christianity may take root in each group in a relevant way, and can overcome division. Pray for true forgiveness and reconciliation that come only through repentance. Without these, the nation can never truly progress.

 Revival came to the Solomon Islands in the past, to the South Sea Evangelical Churches (1935, 1970), and later to all denominations (1982). Today many Christians do not practise their faith. Churches compete against each other for members. Many islanders are attracted to false teachings of Christian-based cults or sects. Some continue in spirit worship. The Church needs a new revival!

Pray for training of pastors and leaders. Pray for several Bible schools and denominational seminaries. TEE programmes, especially ones developed in Fiji, and preaching seminars run by the Langham Partnership both show good growth and impact. Hundreds of trainees can in turn disciple whole congregations. The South Sea Evangelical Church sees new life within it as a result.

4 Local ministries grow as expatriate ministries decline. The Christian Care Centre (Anglicans), Haven in the Storm, and Bible Way Centre minister to women and young people affected by traumatic events. Prison ministry bears fruit, with high numbers enrolled in Bible correspondence courses! Only 3 languages have the whole Bible. Praise God for the Bible in Solomons Pijin (2008), the most widely used language. National believers now lead in translation work. Pray for fruit from the Global Recordings Network gospel messages in 88 languages and dialects. The nation's first Christian radio station, *Gud Nius Redio* (Pijin for Good News Radio), broadcasts from the capital.

The Pacific Islands

American Samoa, Cook Islands (includes the Cook Islands, Niue, Pitcairn Islands, Tokelau), French Poly-nesia, Guam, Kiribati, Micronesia (includes Federated States of Micronesia, Marshall Islands, Northern Marianas, Palau), Nauru, New Caledonia, Samoa, Tonga, Tuvalu, Vanuatu, Wallis and Futuna Islands. (Australia, Fiji, New Zealand, Papua New Guinea, and Solomon Islands are also written separately.)

Life on these small and isolated Pacific islands was never easy. Most of them could only support modest populations and simple lifestyles. People grew crops and fished to survive, and lived in healthy and traditional ways. The modern world changed that. Now, many islands sell the rights to fish in their waters to other countries. They grow cash crops instead of food crops. Alcohol and substance abuse became a big problem, and dietary and health issues increased. By the end of the 19th century, most of the Pacific region followed Christianity through the work of early Protestant missionaries. Great people movements brought whole peoples and islands to Christianity. The Church holds a strong legacy and faces a mighty challenge. These needs and the others listed below deserve our fervent prayers.

1 **Foreign intervention deeply disrupted traditional culture and values.** American and French military and naval presence, the increase of Asian immigrants, and the slow but unstoppable effects of a modern global economy and culture, all made a big impact. Outside influences now dom-inate local economies through island dependency on foreign aid, on American and East Asian fi-nancial investments, and on money sent home by Pacific Islanders who work abroad. A focus on gain in material possessions and progress now replaces the simpler island life and attitudes.

2 **The changes most affect the younger generation.** They feel detached from the older gen-eration, and distanced from their traditional ways and the family-like communities of the past. At the same time, youth struggle to find the kind of job and education opportunities they want as part of a 21st-century lifestyle. Many of them leave their homelands to work or study overseas. The ones who stay behind often feel bored or discouraged, and easily adopt dangerous habits like alcohol abuse. Pray for healthy, sustainable solutions that honour God in these difficult and complex challenges for island youth.

3 **Huge numbers of Pacific Islanders live in diaspora.** The population that lives overseas is larger than the population that lives at home for many of these islands. Most emigrate to look for work and for study. The money these workers send back home plays an important part in the local economies. But these overseas workers face new challenges such as loneliness, loss of their culture and their faith, and many new temptations. Pray for these diaspora workers, that Jesus would meet them in their places of need.

4 **Praise God for the glorious history of missions in the Pacific Islands!** Around 200 years ago, Protestant missionaries shared the gospel in this part of the world through bravery and sac-rifice. Some groups, like the Samoans and Tongans, even sent their own missionaries to other Pacific Islands! As a result of these efforts, the large majority of Pacific Islanders identify themselves as Christian. Praise God for the strong history and legacy of Christianity.

5 **The Pacific received and followed Christianity, but another side to this story exists.** Many are Christian in name only, and do not live the life of a follower of Jesus. Churches often fail to make disciples. Many islanders mix the older tribal superstitions and customs together with newer Christian teaching. Scripture translations exist for most island languages, but many people fail to read or use the Bible. Some people say that faith is so shallow today that the Pacific region needs to be re-evangelized.

6 **Churches and denominations grew with early mission activity,** but seem old and weak today. Each year the size of these groups often stays the same or declines. Some still hold social and even political influence, but very often their teachings no longer reflect Jesus or the Bible well. Newer Christian groups now grow, and they attract members away from existing ones. They include evangelicals and charismatic groups, but they also include Mormons and other cults. Pray for new life from the Holy Spirit to renew and revive these historic churches, and to restore them to their former glory and purity.

7 **Geography isolates the Pacific Islands, and populations remain small.** When one church grows, it means another church gets smaller. When a new denomination appears, it means a new competition for church members. As a result of this, Christian unity is very weak. Many divisions occur, even within denominations and churches. Splits happen too easily. The Church should be a place that shows the world how to live in peace and unity, not a place that lives with strife and rivalry. Pray that God would answer Jesus' prayer for His followers: that His followers would be one!

8 **Evangelicals grow in number on most islands,** in some places faster than others. This usually means that new denominations and congregations start, at the cost of the older ones. Signs of new spiritual life bring encouragement. Pray that God might guide believers in the right direction. Pray that these churches might make a positive impact on Pacific society in the spiritual realm, and also on communities, cultures, economics, and politics.

Appendix 1

GLOBAL FACTS AND FIGURES

This section of maps, charts, and lists communicates a host of issues significant to world evangelization. They are more than sets of data. They indicate the changes that occur in populations, missions, and church growth. They point to the rise and fall of societies. They visually and statistically express the task remaining for the fulfilment of the Great Commission. We hope this content will lead us to prayers of faith for the nations and peoples of the world.

Statistical Data by Country

On the following pages we include a reference table for a quick look at religious, Christian, economic, and population trends of every nation in the world. Countries are listed alphabetically. *Pray for the World* is a paraphrase of *Operation World*, 7th edition, with data from 2010. The first section of the chart includes 2010 population figures and all related Christian, religion, and peoples figures, as published in 2010. The second section of the chart includes 2015 population figures and updated figures for Urbanites (urban population), Population Under 15, Human Development Index Ranking, and Income/person. We added figures for Water Access and Internet Usage.

The data in this table helps us understand future challenges and unique opportunities for Christian ministry in various parts of the world. Consider the following:

- *Population growth occurs by immigration and childbirth.* The countries with the greatest growth experience both of these. Countries with the most pronounced decline usually face the challenges of both very low childbirth and significant emigration. They frequently have a low life expectancy as well.

- *Population growth can indicate success or failure of a society.* When measured over decades, it tells a much greater story than when measured over the course of only one year. Although a number of countries are smaller in population, the percent increase (or decrease) still communicates significant issues vital to the survival of those countries.

- *A connection exists between wealth, average population age, and fertility rates.* The world's wealthiest populations are almost without exception those with the lowest average number of children per family, and those with the highest median age. Longer periods in education, the delay in starting families, and smaller desired family sizes, all contribute to this. Meanwhile, poorer nations tend to have much higher fertility rates, a larger average family size, and younger populations (by virtue of having a greater proportion of children and shorter life spans).

- *Recent population growth has already resulted in migration* on a scale unprecedented in human history. As the population of poorer countries continues to increase, so will the number of people in competition for already-scarce resources, land, and employment. In wealthy countries, population growth is low or even in decline, with a growing proportion of society at retirement age. This creates a demand for younger workers from other lands.

- *As these trends continue, the levels of migration, legal and illegal, will only increase.* This reality will profoundly shape Christian ministry to poorer countries, which also tend to be the least evangelized. Ministry to migrant populations will continue as a growing area of need and opportunity.

COUNTRY	Pop 2010	Chr	Evang	Non-Chr	Unev	ALL	UP	Chr	Pop 2015	AGR	%Urban	Pop <15	HDI Rank	Income/ Person	Water	Internet Users
		(% total population)				(# of peoples)					(% total population)		(of 186)	(US dollars)		(of 100)
Afghanistan	29,117,489	<0.1	<0.1	100.0	78.5	76	71	4	32,006,788	2.4	23.8	44.9	175	$726	64.2	6
Albania	3,169,087	30.5	0.5	69.5	22.1	13	2	8	3,196,981	0.3	54.5	19.5	70	$5,344	95.7	60
Algeria	35,422,589	0.3	0.2	99.7	66.0	41	35	5	40,633,464	1.8	73.8	28.4	93	$5,767	83.9	17
American Samoa	68,505	95.1	21.3	4.9	0.6	10	1	9	55,538	0.0	94.1	–	–	–	100.0	–
Andorra	86,685	90.8	0.4	9.2	1.6	11	3	8	80,950	0.8	86.7	–	33	–	100.0	94
Angola	18,992,707	94.1	22.5	5.9	1.3	60	2	45	22,819,926	3.1	60.0	47.0	148	$6,255	54.3	19
Anguilla	15,465	90.0	17.2	10.0	0.7	6	0	5	14,614	1.2	100.0	–	–	–	–	1
Antigua and Barbuda	88,550	92.5	19.9	7.5	0.6	6	0	5	91,822	1.0	29.8	24.2	67	$14,726	97.9	63
Argentina	40,665,732	90.6	9.1	9.4	1.1	60	1	50	42,154,914	0.9	92.7	23.9	45	$8,926	98.7	60
Armenia	3,090,379	94.4	8.7	5.6	2.5	26	9	15	2,989,467	0.2	64.1	20.2	87	$3,517	99.8	46
Aruba	107,380	92.9	7.6	7.1	0.9	8	2	5	103,889	0.4	47.2	18.3	–	–	98.1	79
Australia	21,507,384	69.5	14.5	30.5	2.9	142	10	92	23,918,374	1.3	89.4	19.2	2	$62,337	100.0	83
Austria	8,387,491	82.6	0.5	17.4	3.0	47	7	36	8,557,761	0.4	67.9	14.4	18	$54,735	100.0	81
Azerbaijan	8,933,928	2.7	0.2	97.3	65.5	40	25	13	9,612,580	1.1	53.9	22.2	82	$9,279	80.2	59
Bahamas, The	345,736	94.7	35.9	5.4	0.6	10	1	9	387,549	1.4	84.5	20.9	49	$25,640	98.4	72
Bahrain	807,131	9.8	2.9	90.2	47.5	16	6	5	1,359,726	1.7	88.7	21.6	48	$28,168	100.0	90
Bangladesh	164,425,491	0.7	0.4	99.3	54.2	400	353	13	160,411,249	1.2	28.9	29.0	146	$1,100	84.8	7
Barbados	256,552	94.9	34.2	5.1	1.2	11	2	7	287,482	0.5	44.9	18.7	38	$15,810	99.8	75
Belarus	9,587,940	70.5	1.3	29.5	1.0	28	5	17	9,259,666	-0.5	75.5	15.8	50	$8,805	99.6	54
Belgium	10,697,588	62.7	1.2	37.3	2.9	38	10	21	11,183,411	0.4	97.5	17.2	17	$49,607	100.0	82
Belize	312,928	83.9	18.8	15.1	2.1	14	1	10	347,598	2.4	44.5	32.9	96	$4,764	99.3	32
Benin	9,211,741	39.9	8.3	60.1	25.5	69	13	17	10,879,828	2.7	45.6	42.2	166	$933	76.1	5
Bermuda	64,995	90.5	24.3	9.5	1.0	9	1	7	65,578	0.2	100.0	–	–	–	98.1	95
Bhutan	708,484	2.1	1.8	97.9	78.4	35	32	1	776,461	1.6	36.4	27.1	140	$2,827	98.1	30
Bolivia	10,030,832	91.0	16.2	9.0	0.7	43	1	33	11,024,522	1.6	67.2	34.1	108	$3,220	88.1	40
Bosnia	3,759,633	41.0	0.1	59.0	27.9	20	4	14	3,819,684	-0.1	48.8	14.7	81	$5,320	99.6	68
Botswana	1,977,569	65.6	8.1	34.4	5.4	51	1	27	2,056,370	0.9	62.3	33.0	119	$7,704	96.8	15
Brazil	195,423,252	91.4	26.3	8.6	0.6	289	58	116	203,657,210	0.8	84.9	23.1	85	$11,607	97.5	52
British Virgin Islands	23,276	84.9	27.3	15.1	0.8	7	0	5	28,800	1.1	41.5	–	–	–	–	–
Brunei	407,045	11.4	6.1	88.6	51.8	26	8	3	428,539	1.4	76.4	24.4	30	$39,886	–	65
Bulgaria	7,497,282	79.9	1.9	20.1	5.7	34	8	25	7,112,641	-0.8	73.7	14.0	57	$8,131	99.5	53
Burkina Faso	16,286,706	20.7	8.9	79.3	37.1	79	28	4	17,914,625	2.8	27.4	45.0	183	$857	81.7	4

COUNTRY	Pop 2010	Chr	Evang	Non-Chr	Unev	ALL	UP	Chr	Pop 2015	AGR	%Urban	Pop <15	HDI Rank	Income/Person	Water	Internet Users
		(% total population)				(# of peoples)					(% total population)		(of 186)	(US dollars)		(of 100)
Burundi	8,518,862	90.5	27.0	9.5	1.1	12	3	8	10,812,619	3.2	11.2	44.9	178	$344	75.3	1
Cabo Verde (Cape Verde)	512,582	94.6	6.6	5.4	0.5	7	0	7	508,315	0.8	63.4	28.2	132	$4,335	89.3	38
Cambodia	15,053,112	3.1	1.6	96.9	48.8	42	30	5	15,677,059	1.7	20.1	31.0	138	$1,177	71.3	6
Cameroon	19,958,351	53.8	9.0	46.2	17.9	290	16	205	23,393,129	2.5	52.7	42.5	150	$1,458	74.1	6
Canada	33,889,747	72.1	7.7	27.9	3.3	156	16	132	35,871,283	1.0	80.8	16.5	11	$51,594	99.8	86
Caribbean Netherlands[1]	n/a	–	–	–	–	–	–	–	20,000	2.4	94.1	14.7	–	–	–	–
Cayman Islands	56,628	77.1	21.3	22.9	2.3	11	1	9	59,967	1.5	100.0	–	–	–	95.6	74
Central African Republic	4,505,945	76.4	32.3	23.6	17.1	87	7	58	4,803,082	2.0	39.3	39.2	180	$395	68.2	4
Chad	11,506,130	38.5	10.1	61.5	50.2	141	72	39	13,605,625	3.0	21.9	47.9	184	$1,536	50.7	2
Chile	17,134,708	87.2	18.4	12.8	0.8	26	2	23	17,924,062	0.9	89.4	20.6	40	$15,736	98.8	67
China, Hong Kong	7,069,378	12.4	6.1	87.6	18.4	11	4	2	7,313,557	0.7	100.0	11.7	13	$42,748	–	74
China, Macau	547,591	5.4	1.7	94.7	26.3	12	4	6	584,420	1.8	100.0	12.5	–	–	–	66
China, PRC	1,330,584,783	7.9	5.7	92.1	35.5	516	427	19	1,401,587,000	0.6	51.9	18.2	101	$7,961	91.9	46
China, Taiwan	23,561,660	5.8	2.8	94.2	36.0	41	13	24	23,428,000	0.2	74.3	13.9	–	$22,743	–	–
Christmas Island	1,600	18.2	3.0	81.8	–	–	–	–	1,707	1.3	–	–	–	–	–	–
Cocos (Keeling) Islands	670	19.4	1.3	80.6	–	–	–	–	702	0.9	–	–	–	–	–	–
Colombia	46,300,196	94.4	7.5	5.6	0.8	92	4	61	49,529,208	1.3	75.6	27.0	91	$8,485	91.2	52
Comoros	691,351	0.9	0.2	99.1	66.8	12	8	3	770,058	2.4	28.1	41.7	169	$1,037	–	7
Congo, DR	67,827,495	92.2	18.7	7.9	1.3	239	4	222	71,246,355	2.7	34.8	44.5	186	$443	46.5	2
Congo, Republic of	3,758,678	89.7	15.9	10.3	1.2	77	3	71	4,671,142	2.6	64.1	42.5	142	$3,574	75.3	7
Cook Islands	19,933	96.2	12.6	3.8	0.4	9	0	9	20,833	0.5	74.5	–	–	–	96.6	–
Costa Rica	4,639,827	93.9	14.8	6.1	0.6	21	1	19	5,001,657	1.4	65.1	22.7	62	$11,352	96.6	46
Côte d'Ivoire	21,570,746	33.6	10.5	66.4	26.9	106	34	37	21,295,284	2.3	52.0	41.0	168	$1,413	80.2	3
Croatia	4,409,659	92.0	0.4	8.0	1.4	32	3	27	4,255,374	-0.4	58.1	14.6	47	$14,410	98.6	67
Cuba	11,204,351	56.5	8.8	43.5	0.9	14	2	10	11,248,783	-0.1	75.1	15.6	59	–	94.0	26
Curaçao[1]	n/a	–	–	–	–	–	–	–	164,463	2.2	94.1	19.1	–	–	–	–
Cyprus	879,723	72.4	0.8	27.6	11.8	19	3	14	1,164,695	1.1	70.7	16.6	31	$24,949	100.0	65
Czech Republic	10,410,786	25.9	0.7	74.1	0.9	39	5	30	10,777,060	0.4	73.4	15.4	28	$19,497	99.8	74
Denmark	5,481,283	85.3	3.5	14.7	2.8	32	8	21	5,661,723	0.4	87.1	17.3	15	$64,025	100.0	95
Djibouti	879,053	1.8	0.1	98.3	61.1	11	6	5	899,658	1.5	77.1	33.6	164	$1,789	92.1	10

COUNTRY	Pop 2010	Chr	Evang	Non-Chr	Unev	ALL	UP	Chr	Pop 2015	AGR	%Urban	Pop <15	HDI Rank	Income/ Person	Water	Internet Users
		(% total population)				(# of peoples)					(% total population)		(of 186)	(US dollars)		(of 100)
Dominica	66,515	91.8	16.8	8.3	0.6	11	0	8	72,680	0.4	67.2	–	72	$7,536	–	59
Dominican Republic	10,225,482	94.4	9.1	5.7	0.5	18	2	13	10,652,135	1.2	70.3	29.6	96	$6,032	80.9	46
Ecuador	13,774,909	94.5	8.5	5.6	1.0	31	2	20	16,225,691	1.6	68.0	29.3	89	$6,538	86.4	40
Egypt	84,474,427	12.8	3.9	87.2	32.2	39	23	8	84,705,681	1.6	43.6	30.9	112	$3,749	99.3	50
El Salvador	6,194,126	94.6	31.7	5.4	0.6	13	2	9	6,426,002	0.7	65.3	28.9	107	$4,164	90.1	23
Equatorial Guinea	693,385	90.0	4.4	10.0	1.5	22	2	20	799,372	2.8	39.6	38.5	136	$17,145	–	16
Eritrea	5,223,994	47.3	2.1	52.7	30.5	19	9	3	6,737,634	3.2	21.8	43.0	181	$544	–	1
Estonia	1,339,459	45.3	4.9	54.7	1.7	37	6	25	1,280,227	-0.3	69.5	16.1	33	$22,207	99.1	80
Ethiopia	84,975,606	60.7	19.6	39.3	17.5	116	20	30	98,942,102	2.6	17.2	41.4	173	$606	51.5	2
Faeroe Islands	50,152	90.6	28.8	9.4	0.5	5	0	5	49,496	0.0	42.0	–	–	–	–	90
Falkland Islands	3,038	65.2	10.8	34.8	0.7	5	0	5	3,058	0.3	76.0	–	–	–	–	–
Federated States of Micronesia	111,101	96.6	24.3	3.4	0.8	24	1	22	104,460	0.2	22.7	34.1	117	$3,341	89.0	28
Fiji	854,098	65.0	25.2	35.0	14.5	35	4	26	892,727	0.7	52.6	28.7	96	$4,931	96.3	37
Finland	5,345,826	83.8	12.1	16.3	1.0	35	7	24	5,460,592	0.3	83.8	16.5	21	$51,428	100.0	92
France	62,636,580	61.1	1.0	38.9	5.2	101	33	56	64,982,894	0.5	86.4	18.1	20	$47,030	100.0	82
French Guiana	231,313	91.2	4.5	8.8	2.0	25	1	17	261,729	2.5	77.1	31.5	–	–	–	–
French Polynesia	272,394	92.2	7.2	7.8	0.5	16	0	14	282,764	1.1	51.5	22.1	–	–	100.0	57
Gabon	1,501,266	79.4	12.7	20.7	2.2	49	4	43	1,751,199	2.4	86.5	38.3	106	$13,360	92.2	9
Gambia, The	1,750,732	4.5	0.8	95.5	61.2	32	14	7	1,970,081	3.2	57.9	45.7	165	$503	90.1	14
Georgia	4,219,191	78.7	1.6	21.3	6.2	36	13	21	4,304,540	-0.4	52.9	18.5	72	$3,949	98.7	43
Germany	82,056,775	64.3	2.1	35.8	2.9	82	19	55	82,562,004	-0.1	74.1	12.9	5	$50,384	100.0	84
Ghana	24,332,755	63.4	24.2	36.6	12.6	109	20	49	26,984,328	2.1	52.6	38.0	135	$1,509	87.2	12
Gibraltar	31,073	84.8	2.9	15.2	4.8	7	2	4	29,354	0.1	100.0	–	–	–	–	–
Greece	11,183,393	91.5	0.4	8.5	2.2	46	10	32	11,125,833	0.0	61.7	14.7	29	$23,787	99.8	60
Greenland	57,291	96.6	4.7	3.4	0.7	5	0	5	57,275	0.3	85.8	–	–	–	100.0	66
Grenada	104,342	93.7	19.6	6.3	0.5	7	0	7	106,694	0.4	39.5	26.5	63	$8,143	96.8	35
Guadeloupe	467,182	94.1	4.3	5.9	0.6	8	0	7	418,340	0.5	98.4	20.9	–	–	–	–
Guam	179,893	96.7	14.2	3.3	1.2	13	1	10	169,885	1.3	93.3	25.5	–	–	99.5	65
Guatemala	14,376,881	96.1	24.4	3.9	0.5	60	1	57	16,255,094	2.5	50.2	39.7	133	$3,816	93.8	20
Guinea	10,323,755	4.5	0.7	95.5	64.2	47	29	5	12,347,766	2.5	35.9	41.8	178	$638	74.8	2
Guinea-Bissau	1,647,380	10.9	1.6	89.1	57.6	32	14	4	1,787,793	2.4	44.6	41.0	176	$581	73.6	3
Guyana	761,442	52.7	19.8	47.3	18.5	22	2	15	807,611	0.5	28.4	34.5	118	$4,177	97.6	33

COUNTRY	Pop 2010	Chr	Evang	Non-Chr	Unev	ALL	UP	Chr	Pop 2015	AGR	%Urban	Pop <15	HDI Rank	Income/Person	Water	Internet Users
		(% total population)				(# of peoples)					(% total population)		(of 186)	(US dollars)		(of 100)
Haiti	10,188,175	95.1	16.0	4.9	0.5	9	1	6	10,603,731	1.4	54.8	34.2	161	$898	62.4	11
Holy See	785	100.0	2.5	0.0	0.0	2	0	2	800	0.0	100.0	–	–	–	–	–
Honduras	7,615,584	96.6	23.0	3.4	0.6	24	3	19	8,423,917	2.0	52.7	34.3	120	$2,422	89.6	18
Hungary	9,973,141	88.0	2.8	12.0	1.2	23	2	20	9,911,396	-0.2	69.9	14.8	37	$14,112	100.0	73
Iceland	329,279	90.6	3.8	9.4	0.6	11	1	10	336,728	1.1	93.8	20.6	13	$51,736	100.0	97
India	1,214,464,312	6.3	2.2	93.7	45.0	2533	2223	115	1,282,390,303	1.2	31.6	28.4	136	$1,702	92.6	15
Indonesia	232,516,771	15.9	5.6	84.2	41.6	783	200	367	255,708,785	1.2	51.5	28.1	121	$3,529	84.9	16
Iran	75,077,547	0.5	0.2	99.5	66.0	103	93	7	79,476,308	1.3	69.2	24.1	76	$5,306	95.9	31
Iraq	31,466,698	1.6	0.2	98.4	60.6	33	20	10	35,766,702	2.9	66.4	39.2	131	$7,079	85.4	9
Ireland	4,589,002	91.7	1.5	8.3	1.0	24	3	19	4,726,856	1.1	62.5	21.6	7	$50,019	99.9	78
Israel	7,285,033	2.0	0.4	98.0	52.4	53	40	8	7,919,528	1.3	91.9	28.0	16	$39,225	100.0	71
Italy	60,097,564	82.4	1.1	17.6	1.8	63	11	49	61,142,221	0.2	68.5	14.0	25	$37,577	100.0	58
Jamaica	2,729,909	82.9	28.0	17.1	1.0	11	1	8	2,813,276	0.5	52.1	26.0	85	$5,096	93.1	38
Japan	126,995,411	1.5	0.5	98.5	29.9	34	23	4	126,818,019	-0.1	91.9	12.9	10	$39,619	100.0	86
Jordan	6,472,392	2.2	0.3	97.8	56.9	21	14	5	7,689,760	3.5	83.0	33.4	100	$5,702	96.1	44
Kazakhstan	15,753,460	12.2	0.7	87.9	37.7	76	41	30	16,770,447	1.0	53.5	26.4	69	$13,227	93.1	54
Kenya	40,862,900	82.7	48.9	17.3	6.2	115	35	49	46,748,617	2.7	24.4	41.8	145	$1,266	61.7	39
Kiribati	99,547	98.5	7.2	1.5	0.5	7	0	6	105,555	1.5	44.0	30.9	121	$1,499	66.8	12
Korea, North	23,990,703	1.5	1.0	98.5	59.6	7	4	2	25,155,326	0.5	60.4	21.2	NR	–	98.1	–
Korea, South	48,500,717	31.0	16.8	69.0	1.5	11	0	5	49,750,234	0.5	83.5	14.2	12	$27,553	97.8	85
Kuwait	3,050,744	13.8	1.5	86.2	45.7	29	11	7	3,583,399	3.6	98.3	24.6	54	$45,342	99.0	75
Kyrgyzstan	5,550,239	5.3	0.7	94.7	55.3	47	27	16	5,707,529	1.4	35.4	30.9	125	$1,380	87.6	23
Laos	6,436,093	3.4	2.6	96.6	56.2	147	134	0	7,019,652	1.9	35.4	34.4	138	$1,699	71.5	13
Latvia	2,240,265	60.0	7.0	40.0	1.1	34	7	25	2,031,361	-0.6	67.7	15.5	44	$18,145	98.4	75
Lebanon	4,254,583	32.0	0.5	68.0	11.7	23	8	11	5,053,624	3.0	87.4	19.4	72	$10,424	100.0	71
Lesotho	2,084,182	89.3	12.1	10.7	0.7	13	1	11	2,120,116	1.1	28.3	35.6	158	$1,440	81.3	5
Liberia	4,101,767	41.4	14.6	58.6	27.8	40	4	24	4,503,439	2.6	48.5	42.3	174	$562	74.6	5
Libya	6,545,619	2.6	0.3	97.4	59.8	40	28	9	6,317,080	0.9	77.9	29.4	64	$13,294	–	17
Liechtenstein	36,190	79.2	0.5	20.8	3.9	8	1	7	37,461	0.7	14.3	–	24	–	–	94
Lithuania	3,255,324	85.4	1.1	14.6	0.8	24	7	16	2,998,969	-0.5	67.2	15.4	41	$18,143	95.9	68
Luxembourg	491,772	81.6	0.5	18.4	1.2	19	1	16	543,261	1.3	85.7	17.3	26	$120,525	100.0	94
Macedonia	2,043,360	65.5	0.2	34.5	10.5	25	6	17	2,109,251	0.1	59.4	16.4	78	$5,704	99.4	61
Madagascar	20,146,442	53.5	11.5	46.5	21.0	50	9	10	24,235,390	2.8	33.2	41.7	151	$526	49.6	2
Malawi	15,691,784	76.0	19.6	24.0	4.7	33	4	21	17,308,685	2.8	15.8	44.8	170	$240	85.0	5
Malaysia	27,913,990	9.4	4.3	90.6	44.1	182	56	33	30,651,176	1.6	73.5	25.3	64	$12,419	99.6	67

COUNTRY	Pop 2010	Chr (% total pop)	Evang (% total pop)	Non-Chr (% total pop)	Unev (% total pop)	ALL (# peoples)	UP (# peoples)	Chr (# peoples)	Pop 2015	AGR	%Urban (% total pop)	Pop <15 (% total pop)	HDI Rank (of 186)	Income/Person (US dollars)	Water	Internet Users (of 100)
Maldives	313,920	0.2	0.1	99.8	79.6	10	5	2	357,981	1.9	42.3	28.2	104	$8,220	98.6	44
Mali	13,323,104	2.6	0.7	97.4	62.6	62	37	2	16,258,587	3.0	35.6	47.5	182	$758	67.2	2
Malta	409,999	96.8	1.3	3.2	0.5	11	2	9	431,239	0.3	95.0	14.2	32	$25,792	100.0	69
Marshall Islands	63,398	97.1	44.5	2.9	0.5	7	1	5	52,993	0.2	72.2	--	NR	$3,352	94.5	12
Martinique	406,001	95.8	6.1	4.2	0.6	9	0	7	405,688	0.2	89.0	17.9	--	--	--	6
Mauritania	3,365,675	0.3	0.1	99.8	75.5	19	14	3	4,080,224	2.5	41.7	39.7	155	$1,197	49.6	6
Mauritius	1,294,569	32.7	10.1	67.3	27.5	17	5	4	1,253,581	0.4	41.8	18.9	80	$10,294	99.8	39
Mayotte	199,065	1.6	0.1	98.4	74.5	11	8	2	233,993	2.7	50.3	43.7	--	--	--	--
Mexico	110,645,154	95.0	8.3	5.0	0.6	317	14	303	125,235,587	1.2	78.4	27.4	61	$11,269	94.9	43
Moldova	3,575,574	73.4	3.7	26.6	1.4	31	8	21	3,436,828	-0.8	48.4	16.9	113	$2,456	96.5	49
Monaco	32,904	84.8	1.2	15.2	1.5	15	1	13	38,320	0.8	100.0	--	NR	--	100.0	91
Mongolia	2,701,117	1.7	1.2	98.3	59.9	20	17	1	2,923,050	1.5	69.5	27.7	108	$4,377	84.6	18
Montenegro	625,516	77.1	0.1	23.0	7.5	24	2	20	621,556	0.0	63.5	18.3	52	$7,929	98.0	57
Montserrat	5,962	95.3	23.4	4.7	0.5	6	0	5	5,176	0.9	14.8	--	--	--	--	--
Morocco	32,777,808	0.1	<0.1	99.9	69.6	30	24	5	34,559,157	1.4	57.4	27.9	130	$3,726	83.6	56
Mozambique	23,405,670	46.5	11.1	53.5	13.0	62	8	16	27,121,827	2.5	31.4	45.1	185	$711	49.2	5
Myanmar	50,495,672	9.0	5.0	91.0	41.1	142	51	43	54,164,262	0.8	33.2	24.2	149	$959	85.7	1
Namibia	2,212,037	91.4	12.2	8.6	3.8	35	2	25	2,392,370	1.9	39.0	35.0	128	$6,450	91.7	14
Nauru	10,254	91.5	12.1	8.5	3.6	9	0	8	10,122	0.2	100.0	--	NR	--	--	--
Nepal	29,852,682	2.9	2.8	97.1	59.5	351	325	6	28,440,629	1.2	17.3	33.0	157	$680	88.1	13
Netherlands	16,653,346	46.6	4.3	53.5	4.0	60	12	36	16,844,195	0.3	83.6	16.8	4	$51,910	100.0	94
New Caledonia	253,743	80.6	7.0	19.4	1.5	47	0	45	263,147	1.3	61.2	22.2	--	--	98.5	66
New Zealand	4,303,457	53.2	18.2	46.8	2.1	62	5	45	4,596,396	1.0	86.3	20.1	6	$44,958	100.0	83
Nicaragua	5,822,265	97.7	29.8	2.3	0.6	18	1	14	6,256,510	1.4	57.8	31.9	129	$2,023	85.0	16
Niger	15,891,482	0.3	0.1	99.7	62.6	37	28	4	19,268,380	3.9	18.1	50.1	186	$525	52.3	2
Nigeria	158,258,917	51.3	30.8	48.7	21.5	522	67	175	183,523,432	2.8	50.3	44.4	153	$1,895	64.0	38
Niue	1,438	94.9	8.0	5.1	0.6	5	0	3	1,273	-2.9	39.7	--	--	--	--	--
Norfolk Island	2,234	68.6	22.7	31.4	--				2,318	0.7	--	--	--	--	--	--
Northern Mariana Islands	88,409	85.2	12.7	14.8	1.2	12	0	10	55,070	0.4	91.9	--	--	--	97.5	--
Norway	4,855,315	91.1	8.4	8.9	2.6	56	14	36	5,142,842	1.0	79.7	18.6	1	$101,022	100.0	95
Oman	2,905,114	2.8	0.8	97.2	55.4	35	25	5	4,157,783	7.9	73.7	21.9	84	$24,561	93.0	66
Pakistan	184,753,300	2.5	0.6	97.6	57.1	389	374	7	188,144,040	1.7	36.5	32.8	146	$1,313	91.4	11
Palau	20,531	95.9	23.9	4.1	0.5	7	0	7	21,291	0.8	85.1	--	52	$15,267	--	--
Palestine	4,409,392	1.6	0.1	98.4	48.5	20	8	11	4,548,815	2.5	74.6	39.0	110	--	81.8	47

COUNTRY	Pop 2010	Chr	Evang	Non-Chr	Unev	ALL	UP	Chr	Pop 2015	AGR	%Urban	Pop <15	HDI Rank	Income/ Person	Water	Internet Users
		(% total population)				(# of peoples)					(% total population)		(of 186)	(US dollars)		(of 100)
Panama	3,508,475	90.5	19.3	9.5	0.9	32	1	23	3,987,866	1.6	75.9	27.6	59	$12,827	94.3	43
Papua New Guinea	6,888,387	95.8	25.7	4.2	1.4	879	3	747	7,631,819	2.1	12.5	37.2	156	$3,271	39.7	7
Paraguay	6,459,727	96.3	6.1	3.7	0.6	39	1	32	7,032,942	1.7	62.5	31.8	111	$4,516	93.8	37
Peru	29,496,120	95.5	11.6	4.6	0.7	104	5	69	31,161,167	1.3	77.6	28.0	77	$7,386	86.8	39
Philippines	93,616,853	92.3	12.4	7.8	6.3	186	19	58	101,802,706	1.7	49.1	33.4	114	$3,279	91.8	37
Pitcairn Islands	50	100.0	--	0.0	0.0	--	--	--	51	0.5	--	29.8	--	--	--	--
Poland	38,038,094	89.6	0.3	10.4	0.6	24	3	21	38,221,584	0.0	60.8	15.1	39	$15,012	--	63
Portugal	10,732,357	94.4	3.0	5.6	0.8	31	4	24	10,610,014	0.0	61.6	14.4	43	$22,687	99.8	62
Puerto Rico	3,998,010	95.3	25.2	4.7	0.6	15	1	12	3,680,058	-0.2	99.2	18.9	--	--	--	74
Qatar	1,508,322	5.9	1.0	94.1	50.1	23	7	6	2,350,549	5.9	98.9	13.6	36	$94,264	100.0	85
Réunion	837,094	87.0	5.9	13.0	3.2	16	4	10	895,099	1.2	95.1	24.7	--	--	--	50
Romania	21,190,154	97.0	5.4	3.0	0.4	29	6	22	21,579,201	-0.3	52.8	15.1	56	$10,185	97.0	61
Russia	140,366,561	66.9	1.2	33.1	7.9	163	77	57	142,098,141	-0.2	74.0	16.5	55	$14,769	97.0	61
Rwanda	10,277,212	89.1	26.9	10.9	1.3	13	3	9	12,428,005	2.7	19.4	41.5	167	$798	70.7	9
Saint Helena	4,406	94.7	8.8	5.3	0.6	3	0	3	4,124	-0.6	39.5	--	--	--	--	15
Samoa	178,943	96.6	18.0	3.4	0.5	8	0	8	193,228	0.8	19.6	37.3	96	$4,121	98.5	15
San Marino	31,537	88.8	<0.1	11.2	0.6	4	0	4	31,802	0.6	94.1	--	NR	--	--	51
Sao Tomé & Principe	165,397	87.5	4.2	12.5	0.5	7	0	7	202,781	2.6	63.4	41.4	144	$2,042	97.0	23
Saudi Arabia	26,245,969	5.4	0.3	94.6	60.1	41	24	7	29,897,741	1.8	82.5	28.3	57	$25,320	97.0	61
Senegal	12,860,717	6.4	0.2	93.6	58.2	57	27	7	14,967,446	2.9	42.8	43.3	154	$1,222	74.1	21
Serbia (includes Kosovo)	7,771,633	80.4	0.6	19.6	2.9	33	6	26	9,424,030	-0.5	56.7	15.9	64	$6,539	99.2	52
Seychelles	84,600	96.1	5.9	3.9	0.9	10	3	7	93,754	0.6	54.0	22.2	46	$16,503	96.3	50
Sierra Leone	5,835,664	13.2	3.9	86.9	43.8	31	12	5	6,318,575	1.9	39.6	40.9	177	$1,016	60.1	2
Singapore	4,836,691	16.0	7.8	84.0	25.7	51	21	10	5,618,866	2.0	100.0	15.3	18	$57,442	100.0	73
Slovakia	5,411,640	93.3	1.2	6.7	0.8	20	1	18	5,457,889	0.1	54.7	15.2	35	$19,999	100.0	78
Slovenia	2,024,912	54.2	0.1	45.8	1.5	19	1	17	2,079,085	0.2	49.8	14.5	21	$24,669	99.6	73
Solomon Islands	535,699	95.8	33.3	4.2	0.5	71	0	70	584,482	2.1	20.9	39.6	143	$2,240	80.5	8
Somalia	9,358,602	0.3	<0.1	99.7	65.9	22	17	5	11,122,711	2.9	38.2	46.7	NR	--	--	2
South Africa	50,492,408	75.2	21.1	24.8	2.2	62	5	41	53,491,333	0.8	62.4	29.3	121	$6,858	95.1	49
South Sudan²	n/a	77.2	36.3	22.8	14.2	78	3	25	12,152,321	4.0	18.2	41.5	NR	$1,043	56.5	--
Spain	45,450,497	77.1	1.0	22.9	1.6	53	6	42	47,199,069	0.4	77.6	15.5	23	$31,601	100.0	72
Sri Lanka	20,409,946	8.4	1.2	91.6	39.5	76	64	9	21,611,842	0.8	15.2	25.1	92	$3,658	93.8	22

COUNTRY	Pop 2010	Chr	Evang	Non-Chr	Unev	ALL	UP	Chr	Pop 2015	AGR	%Urban	Pop <15	HDI Rank	Income/ Person	Water	Internet Users
		(% total population)				(# of peoples)					(% total population)		(of 186)	(US dollars)		(of 100)
St Barthélemy	9,300	61.0	2.3	39.0	<0.1	--	--	--	10,309	2.0	37.0	--	--	$8,169	--	--
St Kitts & Nevis	52,368	93.0	21.8	7.0	0.6	5	0	4	55,376	1.1	32.0	--	72	$13,699	98.3	80
St Lucia	173,942	95.1	14.6	4.9	1.4	6	0	5	184,937	0.8	16.8	23.1	88	$8,169	93.8	35
St Maarten[1]	n/a	--	--	--	--	--	--	--	46,914	2.0	94.1	--	--	--	--	--
St Martin	38,250	83.9	2.5	16.2	<0.1	--	--	--	41,519	1.6	--	--	--	--	--	--
St Pierre & Miquelon	6,044	96.9	<0.1	3.1	0.5	3	0	3	6,049	0.0	91.2	--	--	--	--	--
St Vincent	109,284	90.1	39.1	9.9	1.3	11	0	9	109,374	0.0	49.7	24.5	83	$7,097	95.1	52
Sudan[2]	n/a	7.2	5.2	92.8	62.4	165	133	10	39,613,217	2.1	33.3	40.5	171	$1,818	55.5	23
Suriname	524,345	49.6	13.8	50.4	17.3	26	1	16	548,456	0.9	70.1	26.4	105	$10,293	95.2	37
Swaziland	1,201,904	84.7	25.1	15.3	1.0	12	1	10	1,285,519	1.5	21.2	37.3	141	$3,578	74.1	25
Sweden	9,293,026	57.2	6.9	42.8	2.4	63	8	49	9,693,883	0.7	85.4	17.3	7	$62,659	100.0	95
Switzerland	7,594,561	75.8	4.4	24.2	2.6	40	7	29	8,238,610	1.0	73.8	14.7	9	$88,746	100.0	87
Syria	22,505,091	6.3	0.1	93.7	45.7	34	16	13	22,264,996	0.7	56.5	34.5	116	n/a	90.1	26
Tajikistan	7,074,845	1.0	0.1	99.0	59.0	46	27	16	8,610,384	2.4	26.5	36.1	125	$1,163	71.7	16
Tanzania	45,039,573	54.1	17.9	45.9	16.3	160	33	72	52,290,796	3.0	27.2	44.7	152	$832	53.2	4
Thailand	68,139,238	1.1	0.5	98.9	44.8	113	75	7	67,400,746	0.3	34.4	17.5	103	$5,704	95.8	29
Timor Leste	1,171,163	87.4	2.3	12.6	6.5	23	0	18	1,172,668	1.7	28.7	44.8	134	$4,612	70.5	1
Togo	6,780,030	45.4	10.7	54.6	22.1	56	6	20	7,170,797	2.6	38.5	41.6	159	$754	60.0	5
Tokelau Islands	1,206	100.0	3.4	0.0	0.5	--	--	--	1,250	1.9	0.0	--	--	--	--	--
Tonga	104,260	95.8	15.5	4.2	0.5	10	0	9	106,379	0.4	23.5	36.8	95	$4,911	99.3	35
Trinidad & Tobago	1,343,725	65.6	20.2	34.4	8.8	15	2	12	1,346,697	0.3	14.0	20.8	67	$22,209	--	64
Tunisia	10,373,957	0.2	<0.1	99.8	65.9	23	15	7	11,235,248	1.1	66.5	23.2	94	$4,290	96.8	44
Turkey	75,705,147	0.2	<0.1	99.8	51.6	60	38	18	76,690,509	1.2	72.5	24.9	90	$10,504	99.7	46
Turkmenistan	5,176,502	1.8	<0.1	98.2	68.0	42	22	16	5,373,487	1.3	49.0	28.2	102	$9,217	71.1	10
Turks & Caicos	32,990	90.4	32.4	9.7	0.7	6	0	5	34,339	2.1	95.3	--	NR	$3,373	97.7	37
Tuvalu	9,970	97.7	17.8	2.3	0.5	6	0	6	9,916	0.2	51.0	--	--	--	98.0	--
Uganda	33,796,461	84.7	37.0	15.3	1.4	66	6	53	40,141,262	3.3	16.0	47.9	161	$692	74.8	16
Ukraine	45,433,415	79.0	3.8	21.0	2.2	66	22	36	44,646,131	-0.6	69.1	15.0	78	n/a	98.0	42
United Arab Emirates	4,707,307	8.6	1.3	91.5	44.1	43	26	7	9,577,128	2.5	84.7	16.1	41	$44,885	99.6	88
United Kingdom	62,129,818	59.7	8.8	40.3	3.0	104	28	64	64,094,856	0.6	79.7	17.6	26	$46,077	100.0	90
Uruguay	3,372,222	64.7	6.2	35.3	1.7	30	1	28	3,429,997	0.3	92.6	21.5	51	$17,750	99.5	58
US Virgin Islands	109,326	95.0	23.8	5.1	0.9	11	1	9	106,906	0.1	96.0	20.8	--	--	100.0	45
USA	317,641,087	77.6	28.9	22.4	1.7	363	59	254	325,127,634	0.8	82.6	19.4	3	$57,158	99.2	84

COUNTRY	Pop 2010	Chr	Evang	Non-Chr	Unev	ALL	UP	Chr	Pop 2015	AGR	%Urban	Pop <15	HDI Rank	Income/Person	Water	Internet Users
		(% total population)				(# of peoples)					(% total population)		(of 186)	(US dollars)		(of 100)
Uzbekistan	27,794,296	0.8	0.3	99.3	56.7	67	37	21	29,709,932	1.4	36.2	28.1	114	$2,174	87.3	38
Vanuatu	245,786	94.1	45.9	5.9	1.2	112	0	102	263,888	2.2	25.2	36.1	124	$3,221	90.7	11
Venezuela	29,043,555	84.5	10.8	15.5	1.0	65	2	44	31,292,702	1.5	93.7	27.9	71	$11,037	--	55
Vietnam	89,028,741	9.4	1.8	90.6	31.1	113	63	7	93,386,630	1.0	31.7	22.4	127	$2,234	95.0	44
Wallis & Futuna Islands	15,446	99.0	0.9	1.0	0.5	4	0	4	13,153	-0.6	0.0	--	--	--	--	--
Yemen	24,255,928	0.1	<0.1	99.9	65.4	28	17	7	25,535,086	2.3	32.9	39.1	160	$1,594	54.9	20
Zambia	13,257,269	87.0	25.7	13.0	2.3	82	5	51	15,519,604	3.2	39.6	46.3	163	$1,770	63.3	15
Zimbabwe	12,644,041	78.0	30.9	22.0	1.9	44	3	30	15,046,102	2.8	39.1	38.5	172	$1,077	79.9	19

NOTES:

[1] Formerly part of the Netherlands Antilles which dissolved in September 2010. From October 2010, Curaçao and Saint Maarten are autonomous countries in the Netherlands Kingdom, and the Caribbean Netherlands (Bonaire, Saint Eustatius, Saba) are special municipalities.

[2] The Republic of South Sudan gained independence from Sudan in 2011. Figures for Christian, Evangelical, and Non-Christian are estimates for 2015, based on the 2010 Operation World database.

SOURCES:

Population 2010 (Pop 2010). These figures are estimates taken from the 2008 UN population database. Operation World uses the medium population growth projections.

Christian (Chr), Evangelical (Evang), Non-Christian (Non-Chr). These figures are exact quotes of the Operation World database, with the exception of Sudan and South Sudan (which are derived from 2010 Operation World data). For further explanation, see p. 299.

Unevangelized (Unev). These figures come from the World Christian Database (2010).

All Peoples (ALL), Unreached Peoples (UP), Christian Peoples (Chr). These figures were taken from the Joshua Project database (2010).

Population 2015 (Pop 2015). These figures are estimates taken from the 2012 UN population database. Operation World uses the medium population growth projections.

Population Growth Rate (AGR). Represents average annual population growth from 2010 to 2015. These figures are estimates taken from the 2012 UN population database. Operation World uses the medium population growth projections.

Urbanites/Urban population (%Urban). These figures represent the percentage of the total population that lives in an urban context. They are taken from the UN Human Development Report (2013). For countries without UN data available, figures come from the World Christian Database.

Population Under 15 (Pop <15). These figures represent the percentage of the total population that is ages 0 to 14. They are estimates taken from the 2012 UN population database. Operation World uses the medium population growth projections.

Human Development Index Ranking (HDI). The HDI Rank is a composite of data that measures life expectancy at birth, literacy, education, and standard of living. We have figures for 186 countries, taken from the 2013 UN Human Development Report. Each country is ranked according to its assigned HDI. (Example: Albania 70. Albania ranks 70th out of 186 countries for human development.) NR designates an unranked country.

Income per Person (Income/Person). This represents the gross domestic product (GDP) for the country, in US dollars, divided by the total population. This does not represent the actual purchasing power within the country, which would reduce the disparities. These figures (GDP per capita) are taken from the International Monetary Fund database (2014).

Water Access (Water). These figures for 2013 are taken from the World Bank database. They represent the percentage of the total population that uses an "improved" drinking water source (piped water on premises, public taps or standpipes, tube wells or boreholes, protected dug wells, protected springs, and rainwater collection).

Internet Users. These 2013 figures are taken from the World Bank database. They represent the number of people (per 100 people) with access to the worldwide network.

Rank	Countries with the Highest % of Evangelicals (% Total Population)	% Evangelical
1	Kenya	48.92
2	Vanuatu	45.92
3	Marshall Islands	44.50
4	Saint Vincent	39.09
5	Uganda	37.01
6	Bahamas, The	35.92
7	Barbados	34.15
8	Solomon Islands	33.34
9	Turks & Caicos Islands	32.39
10	Central African Republic	32.25
11	El Salvador	31.65
12	Zimbabwe	30.93
13	Nigeria	30.84
14	Nicaragua	29.75
15	USA	28.89
16	Faeroe Islands	28.77
17	Jamaica	28.01
18	British Virgin Islands	27.30
19	Burundi	27.04
20	Rwanda	26.87

Rank	Countries with the Lowest % of Evangelicals (% Total Population)	% Evangelical
1	Turkey	0.01
2	Tunisia	0.01
3	San Marino	0.01
4	Morocco	0.01
5	Yemen	0.02
6	Afghanistan	0.03
7	Turkmenistan	0.03
8	Somalia	0.05
9	Montenegro	0.05
10	Saint Pierre & Miquelon	0.05
11	Bosnia	0.06
12	Mauritania	0.06
13	Maldives	0.07
14	Slovenia	0.09
15	Palestine	0.09
16	Tajikistan	0.10
17	Syria	0.11
18	Mayotte	0.12
19	Niger	0.14
20	Djibouti	0.14

Rank	Countries with the Fastest Growing Evangelical Population	Annual Growth*
1	Iran	19.6%
2	Afghanistan	16.7%
3	Gambia, The	8.9%
4	Cambodia	8.8%
5	Greenland	8.4%
6	Algeria	8.1%
7	Somalia	8.1%
8	Mongolia	7.9%
9	Kuwait	7.3%
10	Tajikistan	6.9%
11	Laos	6.8%
12	Mauritania	6.7%
13	São Tomé & Príncipe	6.5%
14	Sudan	6.4%
15	Suriname	6.3%
16	Guinea-Bissau	6.2%
17	Senegal	6.1%
18	Korea, North	6.0%
19	Colombia	6.0%
20	Andorra	5.9%

Rank	Countries with the Slowest Growing (or Fastest Declining) Evangelical Population	Annual Growth
1	Niue	-4.1%
2	Sweden	-0.6%
3	Georgia	-0.6%
4	Japan	-0.4%
5	Slovenia	-0.2%
6	Tokelau Islands	-0.1%
7	Falkland Islands	-0.1%
8	Finland	-0.1%
9	United Kingdom	0.0%
10	Cocos (Keeling) Islands	0.0%
11	Saint Pierre & Miquelon	0.0%
12	Palestine	0.0%
13	Denmark	0.2%
14	Swaziland	0.2%
15	Czech Republic	0.3%
16	US Virgin Islands	0.3%
17	Tonga	0.4%
18	Saint Helena	0.5%
19	Estonia	0.5%
20	New Zealand	0.5%

*For many of these countries, evangelical growth rates appear high because the evangelical population base is so small to begin with, borne out by the fact that many countries with the highest evangelical growth rates are also found in the list Countries with the Lowest % of Evangelicals (% Total Population).

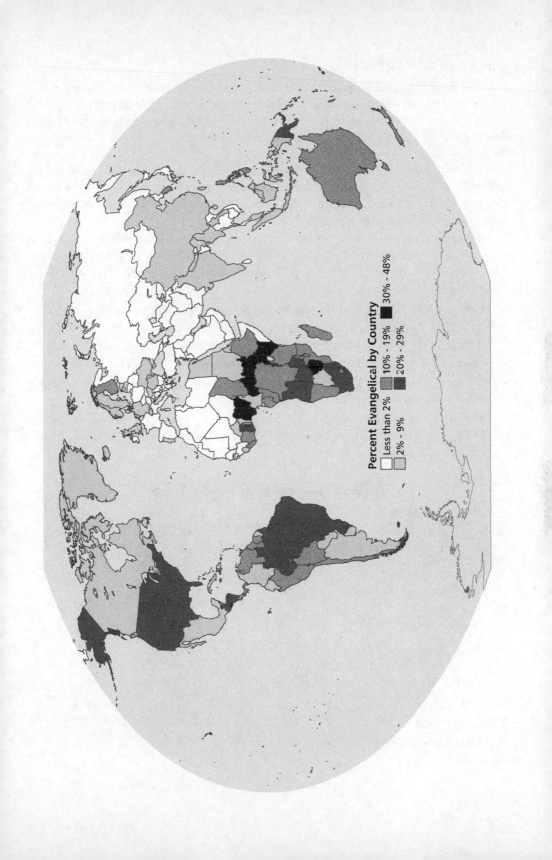

Percent Evangelical by Country

Less than 2%

2% - 9%

10% - 19%

20% - 29%

30% - 48%

UNREACHED PEOPLES

The maps on the facing page highlight the difference between a geopolitical concept of nation and the biblical concept of *ethne* (translated from Greek to English as "nation"). The complexity of countries is far greater than the simple border lines drawn on a map! In fact, many country boundaries were "drawn" by foreign imperial powers, with disregard for the geography of the land or relations among the peoples within it.

The bottom map indicates the scale of the task of evangelism, church planting, disciple making, and Bible translation. Each shaded area on the bottom map represents a unique people, with its own language, worldview, values, and culture. Note the particularly complex ethnic makeup in much of Africa, in South and Southeast Asia, and in Papua New Guinea.

No country is made up of only one people group. Some have thousands of diverse groups (India alone has 2,533). Some countries are divided among a handful of significant minorities. Other countries have one majority people that dominates the population (and usually the political and economic structures as well). Pray for:

- *Healthy relations among peoples.* Often rivalry, tension, and outright hostility characterize their interactions. These dynamics can date back centuries, and profoundly shape entire countries and regions. Yet the gospel has been shown to powerfully overcome such enmity once it has a foothold in cultures.

- *National leaders,* as they deal with the challenge of diversity, hopefully with wisdom and justice.

- *All those who seek to minister the gospel* and work to establish the Church across such cultural and ethno-linguistic boundaries.

- *Christians from different ethnic backgrounds* to be shining examples of the peace and reconciliation that comes only through Jesus. Pray that the Church will bring the gospel to every people group, neglecting none.

Countries with the Highest Number of Unreached Peoples (2014)					
Rank	Country	Unreached Peoples	Rank	Country	Unreached Peoples
1	India	2027	16	Vietnam	73
2	China	456	17	Chad	72
3	Pakistan	444	18	Myanmar (Burma)	52
4	Bangladesh	341	19	Canada	47
5	Nepal	330	20	Mali	47
6	Indonesia	227	21	Sri Lanka	43
7	Laos	138	22	Turkey	42
8	Sudan	133	23	France	41
9	Nigeria	112	24	Israel	41
10	United States	95	25	Ukraine	38
11	Russia	90	26	Kazakhstan	37
12	Malaysia	86	27	Uzbekistan	37
13	Iran	85	28	Cote d'Ivoire	36
14	Thailand	83	29	Algeria	35
15	Afghanistan	74	30	Philippines	33

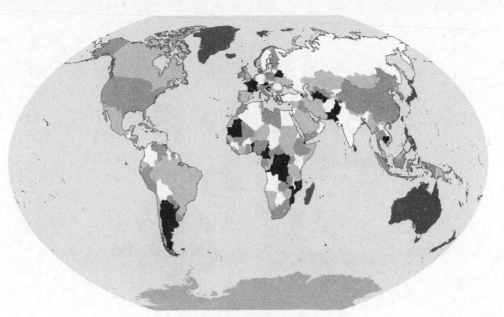

COUNTRY BOUNDARIES

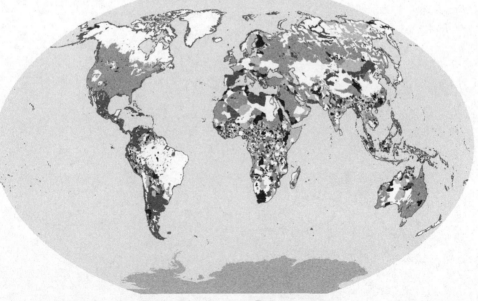

ETHNO-LINGUISTIC BOUNDARIES

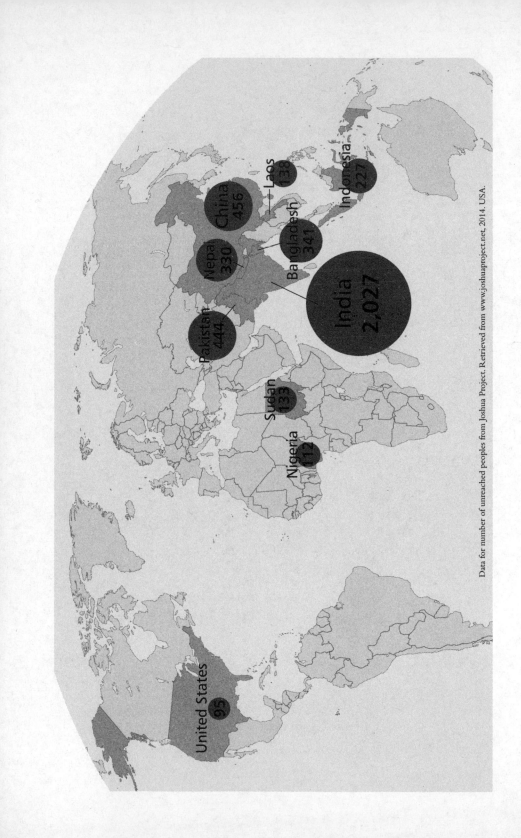

Data for number of unreached peoples from Joshua Project. Retrieved from www.joshuaproject.net. 2014. USA.

Largest Unreached People Clusters

Rank	People Cluster	Main Religions	Population (millions)	Peoples			Main Region
				All	UP	% Unreached	
1	Hindi	Hindu	434.46	586	529	90.3	S Asia
2	Bengali	Muslim	325.29	395	385	97.5	S Asia
3	Japanese	Buddhist	128.78	57	39	68.4	E Asia
4	Urdu Muslim	Muslim	103.87	358	358	100.0	S Asia
5	Jat	Muslim	68.84	166	164	98.8	S Asia
6	Rajasthan	Hindu	68.42	178	177	99.4	S Asia
7	Arab, Levant	Muslim	65.40	129	32	24.8	Middle East
8	Telugu	Hindu	61.55	164	147	89.6	S Asia
9	Marathi-Konkani	Hindu	59.77	140	129	92.1	S Asia
10	Arab, Maghreb	Muslim	59.41	35	34	97.1	N Africa
11	Turkic	Muslim	58.04	58	50	86.2	W Asia
12	Thai	Buddhist	55.08	33	31	93.9	SE Asia
13	Gujarati	Hindu	50.20	212	205	96.7	S Asia
14	Persian	Muslim	48.26	88	65	73.9	W Asia
15	Pashtun	Muslim	46.51	26	26	100.0	S Asia
16	Malayali	Hindu	36.10	115	82	71.3	S Asia
17	Sunda Betawi of Java	Muslim	35.63	3	2	66.7	SE Asia
18	Kannada	Hindu	34.91	164	160	97.6	S Asia
19	Punjabi	Muslim	33.70	241	230	95.4	S Asia
20	Hausa	Muslim	33.28	20	20	100.0	W Africa
21	Fulani / Fulbe	Muslim	32.64	50	49	98.0	W Africa
22	Burmese	Buddhist	32.46	26	24	92.3	SE Asia
23	Kurd	Muslim	29.86	53	53	100.0	W Asia
24	Arab, Arabian	Muslim	29.37	93	66	71.0	Middle East
25	Azerbaijani	Muslim	29.21	36	36	100.0	W Asia
26	Uzbek	Muslim	27.17	20	20	100.0	C Asia
27	Mon-Khmer	Buddhist	25.96	223	161	72.2	SE Asia
28	Malay	Muslim	24.82	82	44	53.7	SE Asia
29	Arab, Sudan	Muslim	23.46	44	43	97.7	N Africa
30	West China / Lolo	Ethnic religions	21.24	170	127	74.7	E Asia/SE Asia
31	Zhuang	Ethnic religions	18.92	29	26	89.7	E Asia/SE Asia
32	Chinese-Hui	Muslim	18.54	18	17	94.4	E Asia
33	Bedouin, Arabian	Muslim	17.37	15	15	100.0	Middle East
34	Oriya	Hindu	16.13	313	302	96.5	S Asia
35	Somali	Muslim	15.96	29	28	96.6	Horn of Africa
36	Gond	Hindu	15.88	11	8	72.7	S Asia
37	Uyghur	Muslim	15.61	24	24	100.0	E Asia/C Asia
38	Madura of Java	Muslim	14.90	5	4	80.0	SE Asia
39	Bhil	Hindu	14.65	8	8	100.0	S Asia
40	Jews	Ethnic religions	14.55	181	176	97.2	Middle East
41	Manchu	Non-Religious	13.42	4	4	100.0	E Asia
42	Other South Asian	Hindu	13.41	161	134	83.2	S Asia
43	Kazakh	Muslim	12.93	34	33	97.1	C Asia
44	Nepali-Pahari	Hindu	12.87	85	77	90.6	S Asia
45	Ural-Siberian	Muslim	11.67	104	57	54.8	E Europe
46	Caucasus	Muslim	11.32	157	122	77.7	W Asia/E Europe
47	Miao / Hmong	Ethnic religions	11.23	69	47	68.1	SE Asia
48	Arab, Yemeni	Muslim	11.18	16	16	100.0	Middle East
49	Mongolian	Buddhist	11.09	49	43	87.8	E Asia
50	Baloch	Muslim	10.44	22	22	100.0	S Asia

Appendix 2

EXPLANATION OF SOURCES, STATISTICS, AND ABBREVIATIONS

The purpose of this book is to inform and inspire God's people to prayer and action in order to change the world. Statistics are an essential element of this. The carefully researched figures provide the factual foundation for *Operation World*, and give strength and support to the prayer points that fill out the handbook.

The availability and accuracy of statistics (secular, religious, or Christian) varies widely across countries, denominations, and mission agencies. Some groups do not even keep statistics. The wide range of information quality, combined with the time it takes to complete research projects like *Operation World*, means that our statistics will never be 100% accurate. If you find any obvious error or mistake, please go to www.operationworld.org and send your suggestion or correction. We welcome input! The basis of this ministry is collaboration, and we rely heavily on thousands of contacts and correspondents scattered around the globe.

We pray these statistics present a balanced account of what God is doing in our world, and of the challenges we face as we follow the Great Commission. It is not an easy task! Apart from the Operation World ministry, only the World Christian Database/World Religions Database gathers data for all the religions, denominations, and churches in the world.

Statistical Sources

Below are explanations of how each category of statistics is handled for each region and country.

Pray for the World is a paraphrased (abridged) version of *Operation World*, 7th edition, published in 2010. Therefore, the figures given in *Pray for the World* are for 2010. The text information is valid for June 2014. We provided updates where major changes affected a country (such as the formation of South Sudan, the dissolution of the Netherlands Antilles, or some events of the "Arab Spring").

[Note: For a complete list of 2015 country population figures, see Appendix 1: Global Facts and Figures (p. 285). The statistical table of countries includes 2010 data for population, Christians, evangelicals, non-Christians, unevangelized, and people groups. It also includes 2015 data for urban populations, Human Development Ranking, literacy, population under 15, and income per person.]

GEOGRAPHY

Population These figures are exact quotes of estimates from the 2008 UN population database. Sometimes the UN figure disagrees with the national government figure. We have stayed with the UN figure for 2010 in these cases, to be consistent with the content in *Operation World*.

Capital These city population figures were generally taken from the World Christian Database in 2010. In the large majority of cases, they represent conurbations (a combination of the metropolitan area with the outlying urban areas). This reflects the population of the real-world urban sprawl, in contrast to population determined by the city boundary line on a map. However, the city proper population was used when it was more representative.

RELIGION

All religious, Christian, and evangelical statistics are exact quotes of the 2010 Operation World database, with the exception of Sudan and South Sudan (which are derived from 2010 Operation World data).

Christians The number applies to all self-identified Christians, regardless of denominational affiliation or level of commitment. See p. 304 for explanation of why we use a broad definition of "Christian", including some groups many believers may not regard as "Christian".

Evangelical Christians See p. 305 for an explanation of the concept. This figure is derived from Operation World Christian and denominational statistics. Operation World's understanding of "evangelical" differs slightly from some other notable Christian and religious data sources. These figures are the unique contribution of Operation World to the global body of knowledge with regard to the Christian faith.

Religions The largest religion is the religious group with the most adherents. The fastest-growing religion is the group with the highest average annual growth between 2005 and 2010. Groups that make up less than 1% of the total population are not included.

PEOPLES

Largest Ethnic Groups Ethnic diversity is shown in the manner we considered most helpful for the reader, for each country. Ethnic populations and percentages are derived mostly from the Joshua Project list, with occasional adjustments. People groupings are given as a percentage of the country's total population. Often additional notes or explanation follow in brackets. The groups included reflect the indigenous groupings, and/or the groups of a significant size. Not all groups within a country are listed. Refugees and temporary resident communities are sometimes listed, but not always included in national percentages. Each country situation is handled uniquely.

Official Languages are the languages known to be recognized as official by the country.

All Languages This figure counts languages with native speakers in that country. Figures are extracted from the Ethnologue database.

ECONOMY AND POLITICS

The brief comments are intended to be a most basic introduction, for the purpose of background summary. They are not intended to be full political assessments.

The Operation World Database and Information Sources

Pray for the World is based on the full text of *Operation World*, 7th edition. That work has around 1,000 pages and literally thousands of information sources and data points. It would be impossible to include a full bibliography in this book.

A few statistical sources were especially significant. Most of them offer consistent data for all countries in their area of focus. These included the United Nations, the World Bank, the International Monetary Fund, *Britannica Book of the Year*, the Human Development Report, the Ethnologue, the World Christian Database, and the Joshua Project database. We also referenced national census information where available.

Sources for the prayer points varied more widely. We had personal correspondence with over a thousand individuals, and sent/received nearly 100,000 emails, faxes, personal letters, and questionnaires to seek information, and to check accuracy of data and text. Internet searches provided a means to obtain vital information about most every country. It also allowed us to interact with people all over the world who provided information and advice on their areas of expertise.

The many statistics included in this work were compiled into a database of information that has been growing since 1984. That data is truly the backbone of *Pray for the World* and its big brother, *Operation World*. The Operation World database contains population, economic, social, religion, and Christian denominational and missionary statistics.

[Note: The full version of *Operation World* includes much more data in its pages, and the *Operation World* DVD has virtually all the data from the database, in tables and spreadsheets. We encourage you to check out the other Operation World resources at operationworld.org!]

Abbreviations and Acronyms

<	less than
>	greater than
$	US dollar
#	number
/	per with numbers (2%/year); and/or with text (his/her)
%	percentage
AD	in the year of our Lord *(anno Domini)*
AGR, Ann Gr	annual growth rate
BCC/s	Bible correspondence course/s
BIOT	British Indian Ocean Territory
C	Central
CAR	Central African Republic
E	East
eg	for example *(exempli gratia)*
et al	and others *(et alia)*
etc	and so forth *(et cetera)*
GDP	Gross Domestic Product (excluding imports and exports)
HDI	Human Development Index
HQ	headquarters
hrs/wk	hours per week
ie	that is *(id est)*

IMF	International Monetary Fund
Is	Islands
IT	information technology
km	kilometre
m, mill	million
misc	miscellaneous
MK/s	missionary kids (children raised in a missionary family)
N	North
NE	Northeast
NGO/s	non-governmental organization/s
NT	New Testament
NW	Northwest
NY	New York, New York (USA)
n/a	not applicable
OT	Old Testament
PNG	Papua New Guinea
pop	population
S	South
SE	Southeast
SIL	SIL International (was Summer Institute of Linguistics)
SS	South-south
SW	Southwest
sq km	square kilometre/s
TEE	Theological Education by Extension
TV	television
UK	United Kingdom of Great Britain and Northern Ireland
UN	United Nations
US, USA	United States of America
USSR	Union of Soviet Socialist Republics
W	West
WCD	World Christian Database
WWI, WWII	World War I, World War II
yrs	years

Appendix 3

DEFINITIONS

10/40 Window The area of the world between latitudes 10° and 40° north of the equator that covers North Africa, the Middle East, and Asia. This imaginary rectangle-shaped "window" contains most of the world's areas of greatest physical and spiritual need, most of the world's least-reached peoples, and most of the governments that actively oppose Christianity.

adherent A follower of a particular religion, church, or philosophy. This is a broad category that reflects how a person identifies themselves, rather than an indication of their practice and devotion. It refers to those people who would claim to have a religion, even if their adherence to it is only nominal.

affiliated Christians All who are considered as affiliated to organized churches. This includes both full members and participants in the church community who are not full members. It includes both adults and children. It is a broader category than church members.

Alpha Course Informal gatherings (often in homes, churches, cafés, and other locations) to introduce the gospel to non-Christians. The movement started in the UK, but spread to many countries in the last 20 years. It has been effective in most cultural contexts.

animism Belief that inanimate (non-living) objects are inhabited by spirits, which humans must please and keep from anger in order to keep harm away.

born-again believers Those who by grace, and through faith in the atoning work of Christ, have been given new life by the Holy Spirit. In common use, it often includes those who claim to have an evangelical conversion experience. However, only God knows the exact number of people who have truly been born again.

charismatics Those who testify to a renewing experience of the Holy Spirit, and who exercise the gifts of the Spirit (such as speaking in tongues, healing, prophecy, and miracles). The charismatic renewal, or "Second Wave" Pentecostalism, has generally remained within mainline denominations. A further "Third Wave" renewal movement occurred with many characteristics of the Second Wave, but with less open identification with formal Pentecostalism or the charismatic movement. Operation World counts Second and Third Wave charismatics as a single group. In our global survey of denominations, we assessed different percentages of affiliated charismatic Christians for each of the 37,500 denominations in the world from 1990 to 2010. The assessment largely excludes those no longer actively associated with charismatic renewal.

Christian Anyone who professes to be Christian. The term embraces all traditions and confessions of Christianity. It is not an indicator of the degree of commitment or of theological purity. Self-identification is the basic principle at work, and we accept the scriptural principles illustrated in Matthew 10:32 and Romans 10:9.

Church (uppercase C) A particular denomination, or the universal, invisible Church at a national or worldwide level.

church (lowercase c) A local fellowship of believers. This word is commonly used to mean a church building or church service, but here this usage has largely been avoided. The starting of churches is termed **church planting**.

cross-cultural missionaries Full-time Christian workers sent by their churches to work among peoples of a different culture. They may work either cross-culturally within their own nations or abroad.

denomination Any association or network of local congregations linked together, formally or informally, within any given country. Note that international denominations are counted multiple times according to the number of countries in which they have an established presence.

ethnic religions A generic term covering a range of informal religions based on ethnicity (ancestor worship, animism, fetishism, shamanism, spiritism, and so on).

ethnolinguistic people An ethnic or racial group speaking its own language. A people distinguished by its self-identity with traditions of common descent, history, customs, and language. It is the most common meaning of the terms **people** or **people group** in this book.

ethnoreligionist This is a collective term for adherents of faiths that are usually specifically confined to a particular ethnic group, rather than being open or universal. It encompasses (but is not limited to) animists, ancestor worshippers, polytheists, spirit worshippers, shamanists, folk religionists, pantheists, cargo cults, tribal messianic movements, and other such expressions of religious belief.

evangelicals All who emphasize and adhere to all four of the following:

- The Lord Jesus Christ as the sole source of salvation through faith in Him, as validated by His crucifixion and resurrection.
- Personal faith and conversion, with regeneration by the Holy Spirit.
- Recognition of the inspired Word of God as the ultimate basis and authority for faith and Christian living.
- Commitment to biblical lifestyle, witness, evangelism, and mission, that brings others to faith in Christ.

Evangelicals are largely Protestant, Independent, or Anglican, but some are Catholic or Orthodox. Evangelicals are counted by Operation World as:

- All affiliated Christians (church members, their children, other participants of the faith community) of denominations that are definitively evangelical in theology, as explained above.
- The proportion of affiliated Christians in other denominations (that are not wholly evangelical in theology) who would hold evangelical views.

This is a theological definition, and not an experiential one. It does not mean that all evangelicals defined above are actually "saved" or "born again". Only God truly knows the number of those born again! In some nations and many denominations, only a portion of evangelicals as defined here might have had a real conversion experience and a Christian walk. However, it does show how many people align themselves with churches where the gospel is proclaimed in this way.

evangelism The activity of Christians who spread the gospel.

evangelization The process of proclaiming and sharing the gospel, and then seeing the fruit of such activity (in both the spiritual and physical realms).

evangelized The state of having had the gospel shared in such a way that the hearer knows and understands the claims of Christ and the need to obey and follow Him. It does not necessarily mean that the hearer responds by believing. Possibly 1.7-1.9 billion people were in this category in 2010.

fetishes Inanimate (non-living) objects to which people attribute magical powers (amulet, charms, other objects), usually worn for protection or aggression. Mainly found in Africa and the Americas.

foreign missionaries Full-time Christian workers who serve in a country other than their own, sent and commissioned by a church or mission organization to spread the gospel.

Global North The countries in Europe and North America, as well as Australia and New Zealand. This is in contrast to the Global South.

Global South The countries of Latin America and the Caribbean, Africa, Asia, and most of the Pacific. This North/South division became more popular since the late 1990s, but means the same thing as the West/non-West division.

Great Commission The final series of commands of the Lord Jesus Christ before His ascension: instructing His followers to evangelize, baptize, disciple, and teach all the peoples of the world.

harvest force The entire body of Christians potentially or actively engaged in Great Commission activity.

least-reached people See definition of **unreached people**.

Majority World The countries of Latin America, Africa, and Asia. This term is preferred in *Operation World* over non-West and Global South.

marginal groups A general term used in this book to describe all semi-Christian or fringe groups, sects, and cults. These groups accept certain Christian features and parts of the Scriptures, together with extra revelations claimed to be divine. Most claim that they alone have the "truth". Readers may question why they are classified as Christian at all! However, we classify a person's religion according to how they identify themselves. All of these groups claim allegiance to Christ, even if their theological understanding of His person, deity, atoning work, or resurrection may be in error.

MegaBloc One of the 6 major groupings of Christian denominations used in *Operation World* and in this book: Protestant, Independent, Anglican, Catholic, Orthodox, Marginal.

missionary One who is sent with a message. This word comes from Latin and has the same basic meaning as the wider use of the term "apostle" in the New Testament. Christian missionaries are commissioned by a local church to evangelize, plant churches, and disciple peoples away from their home area, and often among people of a different race, culture, or language. Modern use varies widely, with strong regional preferences:

- The stricter North American usage – all who are sent to evangelize, plant churches, or minister outside their homelands.
- The wider European and Latin American usage – all who are sent to evangelize, plant churches, or minister cross-culturally, whether in other lands or in their homelands.
- The even broader African and Asian usage, which is closer to the biblical concept indicated above, and which includes all those sent to evangelize, plant churches, and minister away from their home areas, whether cross-culturally or not, and whether in their own countries or abroad.

Operation World generally seeks to bring together different perspectives, and divides missionaries into 3 categories: foreign, cross-cultural, and home/domestic. Most foreign missionaries are cross-cultural, though some work within expatriate communities of their own culture. (For more information, see appendix 3 in *Operation World*.)

non-Western world The countries of Latin America, Africa and Asia. Previously, it was common to use Third World or Two-Thirds World to describe these countries. Those terms are no longer used, since the collapse of the Communist Second World. Means the same as Global South and Majority World.

Pentecostals Those affiliated to denominations committed to a Pentecostal theology, usually including a post-conversion experience of a baptism in the Spirit, present practice of the gifts of the Spirit, and speaking in tongues.

people group A significantly large sociological grouping of individuals who see a common affinity in themselves. From the viewpoint of evangelization, this is "the largest possible group within which the gospel can be spread without encountering barriers of understanding or acceptance". The people group understanding used in this book is the **ethnolinguistic people group**, which defines a person's identity and primary loyalty according to their language and/or ethnicity. We generally use the term **people** rather than **people group** for this.

people movement A movement of a large number of non-Christians of a particular people group into faith in Jesus Christ. It usually involves whole families and communities coming to faith together.

reached/unreached A term widely used today to describe people groups and areas that have, or have not, responded to the preaching of the gospel. Strictly, it should be a measure of the *exposure* of a people group to the gospel, not a measure of the *response*. Use of the term has been continued in this book, even though the term and its use are faulty.

renewal When personal commitment to Christ among believers increases in the churches. Charismatic renewal in the historic denominations is one example. See definition of **charismatics** above.

revival The restoration of spiritual life and vitality to believers and churches that became cold, worldly, and ineffective. Often wrongly used of evangelistic campaigns, revival is an act of God (usually as an answer to prayer) that brings about a spiritual awakening and outpouring of the Holy Spirit on His people.

shamanism Traditional ethnic religious belief centred on the importance of witch doctors, healers, and/or soothsayers.

shari'a Islamic law based on the Qur'an and other Muslim traditional writings (*hadith*).

Shi'a Muslims The second-largest branch of Islam. Strong in Iran, Central Asia, and South Asia. They trace the line of succession in Islamic leadership back to Ali, the cousin of Mohammed.

short-term worker Missionary that serves for a period of 6 months to 2 years.

Sufi A practitioner of Sufism, which focuses on the hard to understand, ecstatic, mystical, and internal aspects of Islam.

Sunni Muslims Followers of the main branch of Islam.

syncretism The attempt to combine elements of different religious systems into a single body of belief and practice. Baha'i, for instance, combines Islamic, Christian, and other religious beliefs.

Some African Indigenous Churches have sought to combine elements of Christianity with pre-Christian traditional beliefs.

Traditional ethnic A generic term used to describe all the informal and ethnic religions in a country.

unaffiliated Christians Those who profess to be Christian, but are not associated with any formal congregation or church denomination.

unevangelized Those who have had no adequate opportunity to hear the gospel or respond to it.

Universalism The belief that ultimately all people will be redeemed, no matter what their belief and practice while alive.

unreached people An ethnolinguistic people, among whom there is no viable indigenous community of believing Christians with adequate numbers and resources to evangelize their own people, without outside (cross-cultural) assistance. At times, the terms **least-reached people**, hidden people or frontier people group are used.

Wahhabi A conservative, fundamentalist Muslim sect. Largely in Saudi Arabia, the Gulf States, and Central Asia.

Western World The countries of Europe, North America, Australia, and New Zealand.

OTHER RESOURCES FROM OPERATION WORLD

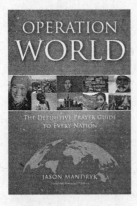

OPERATION WORLD

Operation World (OW) is widely regarded as the definitive volume of prayer information about the world. First published in 1964 and now in its seventh edition, OW is the recipient of the ECPA Gold Medallion Award for Excellence in Evangelical Christian Literature and was listed in *Christianity Today*'s Top 50 Books That Have Shaped Evangelicals.

INDIVIDUAL TITLES CURRENTLY AVAILABLE
Operation World (7th Edition)
Operation World (with CD) (7th Edition)
Operation World Personal CD (7th Edition)
Operation World Prayer Map (7th Edition)
Operation World Prayer Map (UV Coated) (7th Edition)
Operation World Professional DVD-ROM (7th Edition)

THE FUTURE OF THE GLOBAL CHURCH

In *The Future of the Global Church* Patrick Johnstone, author of six editions of the phenomenal prayer guide, *Operation World*, draws on his fifty years experience to present a breathtaking, full-color graphical and textual overview of the past, present and possible future of the church around the world.

WINDOW ON THE WORLD

The "*Operation World* for Kids," this A to Z collection of countries and people groups is a perfect beginner's guide to missional prayer for children. Short stories and attractive full-color design help kids relate to foreign lands and people in this age-appropriate prayer resource – ideal for families, churches and Christian schools.

THESE TITLES ARE AVAILABLE FROM IVPRESS.COM

For updates on future products, please visit operationworld.org.

Follow Operation World:

f Operation World

t @OperationWorld

DAILY PRAYER CALENDAR

DAILY PRAYER CALENDAR

DAILY PRAYER CALENDAR

DAILY PRAYER CALENDAR